DETECTIVES

Stories for Thinking, Solving, and Writing

Robert Eidelberg

AMSCO SCHOOL PUBLICATIONS, INC.
315 Hudson Street
New York, NY 10013

About the Author

A former journalist, Robert Eidelberg served for 19 years as the chair of the English department of William Cullen Bryant High School in New York City and a total of 32 years as a secondary school English teacher in the New York City public school system. Since retiring, Mr. Eidelberg has taught writing at Audrey Cohen College and the City University of New York, where he has also supervised student teachers in English education.

For Beba, my parents, and Frank.

Cover Photo: Alberto Rizzo/People Walking

When ordering this book, please specify:
either **R 673P** or DETECTIVES
STORIES FOR THINKING, SOLVING, AND WRITING

ISBN 1-56765-055-4
NYC Item 56765-055-3

Printed in the United States of America
1 2 3 4 5 6 7 8 9 10   03 02 01 00

CONTENTS

ACKNOWLEDGMENTS

"The Phantom Pistol" by Jack Adrian. Copyright © 1989 by Jack Adrian. Originally published in its present form in Felonius Assaults, edited by Bill Pronzini and Martin H. Greenberg (NY: Ivy Books, 1989). Reprinted by permission of the author.

"Out the Window" by Lawrence Block. Copyright © 1977 by Lawrence Block. First appeared in *Alfred Hitchcock's Mystery Magazine*. By permission of Knox Burger Associates Ltd. Literary Agency.

"The Man Who Read John Dickson Carr" by William Brittain. Copyright © 1965 by Davis Publications, Inc. First published in *Ellery Queen's Mystery Magazine*. Reprinted by permission of the author and Davis Publications, Inc.

"The Dead Sleep Lightly" by John Dickson Carr. Copyright © 1983 by Clarice Dickson Carr. Reprinted by permission of Harold Ober Associates, Inc.

"Candala" by George C. Chesbro. Copyright © 1988 George C. Chesbro. First appeared in *An Eye For Justice*. Reprinted by permission of the author.

"Witness for the Prosecution" by Agatha Christie. Copyright © 1924 by Agatha Christie Mallowan. First appeared in *Witness for the Prosecution and Other Stories*. Reprinted by permission of Penguin Putnam, Inc.

Extract from "Witness for the Prosecution." Copyright © 1954 by Agatha Christie. Copyright renewed 1992 by Agatha Christie Limited. Reprinted by permission of Harold Ober Associates, Inc.

"No One Likes to Be Played for a Sucker" by Michael Collins. Copyright © by Michael Collins. First appeared in *Ellery Queen's Mystery Magazine*. Reprinted by permission of the author.

"The Fat Man" from *Carnival* by Isak Dinesen. Copyright © 1977 by The University of Chicago. Reprinted by permission of the publisher.

"Death and Diamonds" by Susan Dunlap. Copyright © 1991 by Susan Dunlap. First published in *A Woman's Eye*, edited by Sara Paretsky. Published by Delacorte Press. Used by permission. All rights reserved.

"Sorry, Wrong Number" by Lucille Fletcher. Copyright © 1948 Lucille Fletcher. Reprinted by permission of William Morris Agency, Inc. on behalf of the author.

INTRODUCTION

All of the stories in this collection are mysteries. What is a mystery? We've all heard people say, usually in exasperation or frustration, "It's a mystery to me!" In effect, they are admitting that something they have experienced doesn't make sense in their mind. They are puzzled; they can't figure it out; they have difficulty coming up with an explanation or solution.

Inside ourselves, our mind makes assumptions about what our senses transmit to us as we see, hear, taste, touch, and smell the actuality of the physical world. When we think about what we have experienced and try to make sense of it, we are, in fact, asking "What does it mean?" And we want an answer that explains it to our satisfaction.

Mystery and detective stories, however, don't hand us answers, explanations or solutions. Instead, they invite and challenge us to seek them out in the intentionally obscured evidence that is presented to us. It is a process in which we observe and think, trying to put the pieces together, trying to make connections. For the meaning to become evident at last, we must combine careful *detection* (keeping a sharp lookout for clues) with *reflection* (thinking and reasoning logically about what we've observed).

Often, as we read mystery stories, we believe that we "haven't got a clue." The truth is that it's more likely that we didn't notice an important detail or that we were intentionally distracted (usually with false clues known as red herrings). The simple solution to the state of being "clueless" is to learn what to look for and how to look at it. In the stories and plays that follow, you will be asked to use your powers of observation and reasoning to discover what was evident all along. In other words, you will be required to detect and reflect, to notice and to think, to see and to realize. Good readers do this all the time with whatever they read. But it's important to know what else good readers do.

> Good readers read slowly and purposely enough to pay close attention to details.

> Good readers visualize in their minds what the words and sentences are trying to show and convey.

> Good readers make connections about what they are observing with what they know to be true.

> Good readers raise questions, examine assumptions, weigh possibilities, and draw conclusions well before the story is finished.

In fact, readers of mysteries may be some of the most skillful readers of all, making mysteries among the most pleasurable and popular genres available. Fans of detective stories, for example, never seem to get enough of them because they like to play detective themselves. Not only do they enjoy the challenge of demonstrating that they can outsmart the criminal, but they get immense pleasure from getting ahead of the story's detective and beating him or her to the solution.

Even when readers don't get ahead of the detective in the story and break the case themselves, many enjoy keeping up with the master sleuth as he or she goes through the intriguing step-by-step process of solving a tangled and seemingly impossible problem.

Not surprisingly, fans also get real pleasure from mystery stories so cleverly constructed that the reader is outsmarted by the detective and the author. When a complicated set of circumstances is unraveled and the solution is finally revealed, the reader extends congratulations to the triumphant detective and the author. Looking back over the story, the reader comes to see where he or she missed a clue, got distracted, or interpreted the evidence incorrectly. Even better, the reader feels he or she will be more observant and mindful next time, since the reader is honing his or her detection skills through practice, story after story.

Finally, it is satisfying to realize that in the end things do make sense, that there is a plausible explanation to questions the story raises. Not only does the truth come out, but ultimately things turn out all right. In this way, our moral sense that justice has been served is satisfied. Beyond that, to quote mystery writer Ross Macdonald, "The detective story offers some comfort against the dark, by showing that human reason may be a match for the anti-human forces in the world."

A Note to Students About This Text

In order for you to master the solutions to the stories in this text, you will be provided with several **Suspicions?** opportunities during your reading of each story. These questions, which appear at significant intervals within the stories themselves, are designed to assist you in tracking and analyzing clues as well as making connections and predictions so that you can begin to outsmart the detective.

At the conclusion of each story, questions and activities in the **How Clever?** section of the book will enable you to review just how capable you and the detective were in solving that particular mystery. You will explore how the solution was deduced and the ways in which observation and critical thinking assisted you in arriving at your conclusion.

Finally, in the **DetectWrite** section for each story, you will find a variety of structured writing activities to get you thinking and writing the way authors of detective stories think and write. These sections will lay the foundation for writing your own mystery or detective stories. In this way, you can use all that you have learned as a reader of detective stories to try to outwit those who go on to read the stories you write.

Part one

Amateur and Off-Duty Detectives

Kim's Game

M. D. Lake

"**N**ORA, ARE YOU SURE YOU WOULDN'T LIKE TO PLAY KIM'S Game with us?" Miss Bowers called to her from over by the great stone fireplace.

"I'm sure, thank you," Nora replied politely, glancing up and then dropping her nose back into her book. Outside, she could hear the rain falling on the sloping roof of the lodge. It had rained steadily ever since they arrived at camp.

She was at the far end of the room, curled up on a sofa, her feet tucked under her, as far away from the other girls as she could get. It wasn't that she didn't like them exactly; it was just that, after being cooped up with them for three days, they didn't interest her very much. None of them liked to read, and they all seemed to have seen the same television shows and movies. As a result, she couldn't understand half of what they were talking about or, if she could, why they got so excited about it.

"Nora's not very good at Kim's Game," she heard one of the girls say, in a high, clear voice that was meant to carry.

"She beat us all yesterday," another one pointed out.

"Twice. The first two times. Beginner's luck. She lost the third game and then she quit."

Nora smiled to herself. She'd never played Kim's Game, never even heard of it, until she got to summer camp and the counselors were forced to come up with indoor activities because of the cold weather and rain.

But after she'd won the first two games, she discovered it was too easy for her, and so she decided to have fun with the third game. She put down on her list things that weren't there—silly things, but the other girls didn't notice that—and left out obvious things that were—the teakettle, the butcher knife—and so, of course, she lost. Even then she didn't lose by much, because the other girls weren't very observant.

They didn't have to be, Nora supposed, in their lives. That thought went through her like a sharp knife and she realized she was suddenly close to tears. She straightened her back and put her feet firmly down on the floor and told herself she was glad she was so observant. It was a lot more important to notice things with your eyes than to cry with them.

She hadn't wanted to come to summer camp. She'd wanted to stay home, where she could keep an eye on her parents. She knew that something was wrong between them—worse than usual, a lot worse—and she thought that if she were there, she'd at least be able to figure out the meaning of all the little things she'd noticed and heard; her father's coming home late at night and going to work on the weekends, something he never used to do; his slurred, angry speech sometimes; the tears she'd seen in her mother's eyes; the abrupt changes of subject when she came into the room when her mother was entertaining friends; and the quarrels between her parents that got more and more frequent, when they thought she was in bed and asleep.

Usually they didn't insist that she do anything except homework and chores, but this year they'd insisted that she go to camp. She wondered what she'd find when she returned home. She wondered if both of her parents would still be living in the house and, if not, which one of them would be gone.

The main door of the lodge opened and a wet figure in a raincoat and hat came in. It was Miss Schaefer.

She hung her coat and hat on a peg and stepped into the room, looked around, and saw the girls standing in a circle over by the fireplace. They were staring with great concentration at objects scattered on a blanket, with Cathy Bowers standing behind them timing them with her watch.

Kim's Game! Lydia Schaefer had never liked it, thought it was stupid. She didn't have the kind of memory you need to be good at games like that, either.

She nodded to Cathy Bowers and crossed the room to the far corner, with its comfortable overstuffed chairs and a sofa and coffee table littered with books and old magazines. She sat down in one of the chairs and picked up a magazine. She took her reading glasses out of a case and put the case back in her shirt pocket. As she did, she noticed a girl on the sofa opposite her sitting up straight, her pointy nose buried in a book. She looked as though she'd been crying, or wanted to cry. Lydia Schaefer smiled and said, "I was always rotten at Kim's Game, too, when I was your age. Don't let it bother you."

Nora glanced up, as if surprised she was no longer alone. Her eyes met Miss Schaefer's without expression. She didn't like Miss Schaefer because she knew Miss Schaefer didn't like her—and not just her either: Miss Schaefer didn't like children period. Nora wondered why she was a camp counselor. Then she shrugged and decided it didn't matter. She had enough adults to try to figure out without adding another one to the list.

"What's your name?" Miss Schaefer persisted, somewhat uneasy under the child's stare. She also didn't like getting a shrug for a response. Hadn't she tried to console the child for being no good at a game?

"Nora." It wasn't just objects on a blanket Miss Schaefer wasn't able to remember.

"I'd probably be rotten at Kim's Game now, too," Miss Schaefer went on. "Oh, well, I'm sure you and I have inner lives that are much more interesting than theirs. Don't we?"

"I guess so," Nora said, wanting to get back to her book.

"It's probably why we wear glasses," Miss Schaefer went on, as if determined to make friends with Nora. "We don't need outer reality as much as other people, so our eyes—"

Before she could finish what Nora already knew was going to be a dumb sentence, a voice interrupted. "Could I see you in my office, Lydia?" Miss Schaefer turned quickly and looked over her shoulder, startled at the officious tone of voice. It was Ruth Terrill, the head counselor.

"Sure, Ruth," she said, trying to keep her voice normal. "Now?"

"Please," Ruth said.

Nora watched the two women disappear into the hallway. She'd known they hadn't liked each other for most of the three days she'd been at camp, but until that moment she hadn't known Miss Schaefer was afraid of Miss Terrill. She wondered why, then shrugged again. These adults, and the things going on between them, weren't her problem. Quickly she dipped her nose back into her book.

Over by the fireplace, the other girls were playing another round of Kim's Game. *You'd think they'd have just about every small object in the lodge memorized by now,* Nora thought.

She would have.

That night, when she first heard the voices, she thought she was at home and in her own bed, because they sounded the way her parents did when they thought she was asleep and wouldn't be able to hear them discussing whatever it was that was wrong between them that they were keeping from her. Then, seeing the log beams in the darkness above her and hearing the rain dripping from the eaves, she remembered where she was. She could hear the quiet sounds the girls around her made in their sleep and the sound of the wind in the forest outside. She hated the wind this summer, a sickly, menacing noise that never seemed to stop.

 Suspicions?

How good are you at Kim's Game? Nora tells us that by now she would have had "just about every small object in the lodge memorized." Which small objects do you remember?

The voices were those of the camp counselors in the main room of the lodge. Just as she did at home when her parents' voices woke her up, she slipped out of bed and went to listen. She tiptoed down the row of sleeping girls, then down the dark hall to the door to the main room. It wasn't closed all the way, which was why she'd been able to hear the voices.

Lydia Schaefer was describing how, just a little while ago, she'd been hurrying up to the lodge from her cabin. She'd heard sudden rustling in the forest next to the path, and then a man had grabbed her from behind. He had a knife, she said, and he threatened her with it, but she managed to tear herself away from him and run back to the lodge. She was still out of breath. Nora could hear that.

One of the other counselors asked Miss Schaefer why she hadn't shouted for help. She said she was too frightened at first and then, when she saw the lights of the lodge and knew the man wasn't going to catch up to her, she didn't want to scare the girls by making a lot of noise. The head counselor, Ruth Terrill, asked her if she could describe the man. It was so dark, Miss Schaefer answered, and it happened so fast that she didn't get a good look at him. But she thought he was tall—and he was wearing glasses, she was certain of that.

Miss Terrill said that she was going to call the sheriff, and they all agreed not to worry the girls with it.

That's what adults were always trying to do, Nora thought, as she tiptoed back down the hall to bed. *There's a rapist or even worse out in the forest, but they don't want to worry the girls with it! My mom and dad are breaking up, but they don't want me to know about it!*

Adults are a lot more childish than children in a lot of ways, she thought.

She was barely awake, trying to identify every creaking noise the old building made in the night, when she heard a car driving up the dirt road to the lodge. A car door shut quietly and, as she fell asleep, she could hear the voices again in the main room, a man's voice among them now. She dreamed of the forest and of a man waiting for her among the trees.

The next morning, Nora looked up from her book and saw through the big front window, a police car pull up in front of the lodge and a large man in a brown uniform climb out. Miss Terrill and Miss Schaefer must have been watching for him too, for they met him before he could come inside. They stood on the wide porch, out of the rain, talking in voices too low for Nora to hear.

She wondered if it was the same man who'd come when Miss Terrill called the police the night before. *The other girls probably wouldn't have paid any attention to him even if he'd come in,* Nora thought. *They were all sitting at the dining-room table, writing letters home, probably complaining about the lack of television and shopping malls and anything fun to do.* Nora wasn't going to give her parents the satisfaction of complaining about anything. Besides, she didn't know which of them would be there to read whatever she wrote.

The weather was clearing up and they were supposed to go horseback riding the next day. Maybe, on account of the man in the forest, they'd stay indoors. She hoped so.

After all the other girls were asleep that night, she lay in bed and thought about the man in the forest with the knife. She had a good imagination and could see the knife blade and the lenses of his glasses glittering in the moonlight as he watched the lodge from the darkness, watched and waited for somebody to come down the path alone. What would Miss Terrill do, she wondered, if he tried to come into the lodge, tried to kidnap one of the girls? Miss Terrill always slept in the lodge with them. The other counselors had small cabins of their own, two to a cabin except for Miss Schaefer, who had a cabin all to herself, farthest down the path. Apparently none of the other counselors wanted to share a cabin with Miss Schaefer, or else she didn't like any of them. Nora was glad she didn't have to sleep in one of those cabins, alone in the forest with the darkness and the sick wind in the pines that never stopped—and the man in the trees.

Then she heard a noise—it sounded like the start of a shout—coming from the lodge's main room, and then the sound of something falling. She sat up and strained to hear more, but there wasn't anything more—only the quiet breathing of the sleeping girls in the room with her, and the wind. She stared at the door to the main room, waited for it to open and for a tall man wearing glasses to come through, but nothing happened.

Maybe she'd been asleep and dreaming. Maybe it had been her imagination. But she couldn't stand it, here any more than at home. She had to know.

She slipped out of bed and crept silently down the dark hall on her bare feet. She opened the door a crack, very slowly, and peered into the room. At first she thought it was empty except for the moonlight, but then she saw something on the floor by the fireplace, a huddled figure. She forgot the man in the forest with the knife. She forgot to be scared. She went across the room to see who it was.

It was Miss Terrill. She was lying on her back, staring up at the ceiling, the wooden handle of a knife protruding from her throat.

Nora stared for a long moment, seeing everything there was to see—Miss Terrill's brown leather bag on the floor by her hand and the things that had spilled from it, some of them in the slowly spreading blood and some where the blood didn't reach.

A sound, a flicker of movement, made her look up. Miss Schaefer was coming through the front door.

"What are you doing out of bed, child? You get—Ruth!" She rushed over to Miss Terrill and knelt by her, saw what Nora had seen, and scrambled back to her feet.

"Did you see what happened?" she asked.

"No. I just heard something, so I—"

"You can't stay here," Miss Schaefer said. "Come with me." She took Nora by the hand and, instead of taking her back to the dormitory, almost dragged her across the room and down the hall to the kitchen.

"What's your name again?"

"Nora."

"Oh, yes, Nora," Miss Schaefer said. "The little girl who likes to read. You stay here until I come back. You'll be all right. Whoever did that to poor Ruth is gone now." She pushed Nora down onto a chair. "I'm going to call the police. Don't go back to the dorm—you might wake the other girls, and we don't want to scare them, do we? Promise?"

Nora promised and Miss Schaefer turned and went quickly down the hall.

Nora didn't like it in the kitchen. The clock on the wall made an ominous humming noise, like the wind outside. It was almost one A.M. There were knives on the drying board by the sink that the cook used to cut meat and vegetables, sharp and glittery in the moonlight pouring through the window, with handles like the one on the knife in Miss Terrill's throat. The man from the forest might have been here, might be here now, hiding in the pantry or the closet or in the darkness over by the stove.

A sudden noise behind her made her jump up and spin around, but nothing moved in the kitchen's shadows. It was probably a mouse. Nora didn't like that thought either, because she wasn't wearing shoes.

She didn't care what she'd promised Miss Schaefer. She ran back to the main room. She meant to cross the door to the fireplace, run to the room where the telephone was and Miss Schaefer, but when she got to Miss Terrill's body, she couldn't help it—she stopped to look again.

What she saw this time terrified her.

"I told you to stay in the kitchen," Miss Schaefer said, so close that Nora jumped and almost screamed. Her voice was soft and cold with anger—the worst kind—and she took Nora in her hard grip.

"I got scared," Nora said, trying not to tremble. They were alone with the body, the two of them, and the hallway door was closed. The other children slept soundly; the other counselors were far away.

"Scared? Of what?"

Then Nora blurted out, so suddenly it surprised her, "Of *him!*"

"Who?" In spite of herself, Miss Schaefer straightened up and looked quickly around the room.

"A man," Nora said. "He was looking at me through the kitchen window!"

"What did he look like?" Miss Schaefer sounded as surprised as Nora.

"He was big," Nora told her. "Tall—and he had dark hair. Miss Schaefer, what if he comes back?"

"I locked the door," Miss Schaefer said. "He can't get in now, nobody can." And then she asked, "How could you see him through the window, Nora? It's dark outside."

"Because," Nora said, and hesitated, trying desperately to think of an explanation, feeling Miss Schaefer's cold eyes on her and remembering the knives in the kitchen that glittered in the moonlight. "Because the *moon* was so bright, I could see it glittering in his glasses!"

Miss Schaefer thought about that for a moment and then she exhaled and relaxed her grip on Nora's arm. She almost smiled. "I called the police," she said. "They'll be here soon. I don't think you have anything to be afraid of now."

Nora didn't think so either.

 Suspicions?

1. Which additional small objects do you remember being mentioned since you first tried to see how good you were at Kim's Game?

2. What aspects of the story or people in it strike you as suspicious? Why?

3. Why does Miss Schaefer think that Nora doesn't have "anything to be afraid of now"? Why do you think Nora agrees?

The police arrived, and the sheriff, the man she'd seen talking to Miss Terrill and Miss Schaefer that morning. The other counselors came too, staring down in horror at Ruth Terrill. One of them took Nora by the arm and led her over to the couch by the front windows, away from the body. She said that wasn't anything for a girl her age to see, but since she'd found the body, she'd have to talk to the policemen. Nora almost laughed at how dumb that sounded. She could see the heads of some of the other girls, crowded in the entryway to the dorm, their eyes big. A counselor was standing in front of them to keep them from seeing too much.

Miss Schaefer explained to the other counselors that she'd been afraid to go outside and down the path to tell them what had happened—not with a killer on the loose—and of course she hadn't wanted to leave Nora and the rest of the children alone either. After all, he'd attacked her too, out there in the forest, but she'd been lucky—luckier than Ruth Terrill— she'd managed to get away from him.

The sheriff asked her why she'd come up to the lodge in the first place. She told him she'd left her book there, the one she wanted to read in bed before going to sleep. "I had my flashlight," she said, "and I ran all the way." Then she called over to Nora, as if anxious to turn attention away from herself. "Tell the sheriff about the man you saw at the window in the kitchen, Nora."

"I didn't see anybody," Nora answered. "But I saw something else— over by Miss Terrill's body."

"What did you see?" the sheriff asked. "Come over here and tell me."

"No. You go over by Miss Terrill's body."

"Go—" The sheriff hesitated, gave her a puzzled look, and then he did as she asked. Something in her voice made him do that.

"What's this all about?" Miss Schaefer wanted to know. "You told me, Nora—"

Nora didn't pay any attention to her, only looked to make sure one of the policemen was standing between her and Miss Schaefer. "You just tell me if I'm right about the things scattered around Miss Terrill," she called to the sheriff.

"Nora," Miss Schaefer said and tried hard to laugh, "we're not playing Kim's Game now."

"What's Kim's Game?" the sheriff asked.

"It's a game we play sometimes," Nora told him, "when we have to be indoors on account of the weather. Miss Bowers gives us about fifteen seconds to look at a lot of things she's put on a blanket on the floor and then we have to go to another part of the room and write down everything we remember. Whoever remembers the most things wins."

"Nora's just like me, sheriff," Miss Schaefer said. "She's not very good at it." Her laugh had the same sickly sound as the wind had in the forest, but the forest was quiet now.

Nora looked back at the sheriff and said, "There's a pen and a little tube of sun cream and a pocketknife with a red handle. There's a change purse too. It's brown."

"That's right," the sheriff said, glancing across the room at her. She was staring straight ahead, with her eyes wide open. The sheriff had a daughter too, but when she tried hard to remember things, she screwed her eyes tight shut.

"There're some keys on a ring," Nora went on, "in the middle of the blood, and there's a box of Band-Aids and a comb next to them. There's money too. Two quarters and some dimes—three dimes, I think."

"Is that all?" the sheriff asked.

"That's all there is *now*," Nora said. "But when I found Miss Terrill, there was a glasses case, and the glasses were still in it. It was blue and red—plaid—and part of it was in the blood. You can still see where it was, if you look—I could, anyway, when I came back in here, after Miss Schaefer took me to the kitchen and left me there alone. There's a kind of notch in the blood where the glasses case was. The blood must have run up against it and then had to go around."

The sheriff looked and said, "The notch is still there, Nora, in the blood. Do you know where the case is now?"

"No," she said.

"Do you know who has a glasses case like that?"

"Yes," she said, in a very small voice, but forcing herself to look at Miss Schaefer.

"You have a plaid glasses case, Lydia," Miss Bowers said to Miss Schaefer.

Miss Schaefer ran out of the lodge, but she didn't get far. Maybe she didn't try very hard; maybe she didn't want to be alone in the forest.

Suspicions?

1. We know that Nora lied to Miss Schaefer about seeing a man outside the kitchen window. How do we know that now Miss Schaefer realizes it? Why do you think Nora lied?

2. What significance, if any, do you find in the objects Nora states she remembers seeing? What significance, if any, do you find in Nora's comment that "That's all there is *now*"? What are the implications of the vocally emphasized "now"?

3. Who killed Miss Terrill—and how do you think Nora figured it out?

"I should have cut your little throat when I had the chance," she said to Nora when one of the policemen brought her back into the lodge. She was smiling when she said it, but it wasn't the nicest smile Nora had ever seen.

The glasses case had fallen out of Miss Schaefer's jacket pocket as she killed Miss Terrill. She didn't notice it was gone until she started down the path to her cabin, but when she came back to get it, Nora was there. After she took Nora to the kitchen, she went back and got the case, wiped off the blood, and then put it back in her pocket before she called the sheriff.

Why had she killed Miss Terrill? Nora never found out, and she didn't care anyway. It had to do with something that happened between the two women a long time ago—probably before Nora was even born—the kind of thing adults fight over, not really caring who gets hurt. It was the kind of thing kids aren't supposed to know about, so Nora only got bits and pieces of the story.

When they heard about the murder, some of the parents drove up the mountain and took their daughters home. For a while there was a regular parade of cars arriving and departing with little girls. Some of the cars had one parent in them, and some had both.

The sun was shining and Nora was getting ready to go horseback riding with the girls who were left when Miss Bowers came out and told her that her mother was on the phone and wanted to know if she wanted to go home.

Her horse had huge eyes, like brown marbles, with curiosity in them. Nora wondered what it would be like to ride a horse like that.

"Tell Mom I'm fine," she said to Miss Bowers, "and that I'm having a good time. Tell her to say hello to Dad for me too, and give him a big kiss if she can."

The man in charge of the horses showed the girls how to mount them, and when they were all ready, they rode into the forest together.

 How Clever?

1. What character traits does Nora have that make her very good at playing Kim's Game?

2. Where and how did Nora function in the story as an amateur detective, using detection and reflection to solve the murder of Miss Terrill?

3. Find the earliest mention in the story of a knife similar to the murder weapon. Find the earliest mention of Miss Schafer's glasses. How does the author cause the reader to take notice of these two small objects?

4. Miss Schaefer tells Nora that she "was always rotten at Kim's Game" when she was Nora's age and that she would "probably be rotten at Kim's Game now, too." How does Miss Schaefer prove she is rotten at Kim's Game in the course of the plot of the story?

5. Why did Nora insist that the sheriff go over to Miss Terrill's body, and why did she make sure that one of the policemen was standing between her and Miss Schaefer?

6. The author mentions that when Nora first saw Miss Terrill's body, she noticed that some of the objects that had spilled out of Miss Terrill's brown leather bag were in the slowly spreading blood and some of them were where the blood did not reach. Why is this an important detail to take note of—for both Nora and the reader?

7. When Nora looks at Miss Terrill's body for the second time, we are told that "What she saw this time terrified her." What was it that Nora saw this time—and why would it terrify her?

DETECTWRITE: Characterization

As you have discovered, Nora, a teenager at summer camp, has what it takes to be a good detective: she's observant, she has a good memory, and she makes connections among the things she notices in order to come to justifiable conclusions.

It's not too soon for you to begin to think about a detective you might create for a mystery story of your own.

He or she can be young or old or anywhere in between; from the city, the suburbs, the country or a small town; from anywhere in the world or from the world of fantasy or science fiction; from our time, from the past or from the imagined future; a police officer, a plainclothes detective, a private investigator; a full-time or part-time sleuth, for example, a student or, like Saxon in the story "The Pig Man" in this collection, a part-time actor.

But whoever and whatever your detective is, he or she must possess the combined abilities of detection and reflection if he or she is to be a success as a solver of mysteries.

Ask yourself now where your detective might have gotten his or her detection ability from. Nora seems to have gotten hers, with practice, from the necessity of understanding the changing relationship between her father and her mother.

Write a paragraph in which you explain either why it is that your detective is so observant, how he or she got that way, or how he or she practices observation skills in a profession, job, hobby, or activity separate from being a professional or amateur detective.

DETECTWRITE: Plot

1. Review the language the author uses to call attention to two key objects in the story: the butcher knife that Nora intentionally forgets when she plays Kim's Game for the third time and the first mention of Miss Schaefer's reading glasses.

   Choose a common small object that could play a critical role in a detective story you might write. Write a brief paragraph that includes enough description of that object so that the reader is made aware of it and might remember it without giving away the ultimate importance of the object in the plot of your story.

2. Review the sequence of events in the unfolding of the plot of "Kim's Game." Think of the entire story as a building with a stone foundation set deep into the ground. Above the foundation are several floors or stories that are supported by the foundation. In a paragraph, describe what you consider to be the foundation of "Kim's Game."

DETECTWRITE: Setting

In "Kim's Game," an ordinary location—a summer camp—becomes the setting for a not-so-everyday occurrence—a murder. Think of a fairly ordinary location that you are familiar with and that you could capture in your writing with a few carefully chosen details. Consider how the place you've selected might serve as the setting for a murder in a detective story you would write.

The Pig Man

Les Roberts

I MAKE HALF MY LIVING INVOLVED WITH PEOPLE YOU'D never ask to dinner. Punks, wise guys, skels, grifters, junkies, hookers, and the bigger, dirtier fish who feed off them. It can get sticky sometimes. Nevertheless, I don't consider myself a violent person. I cross the street to avoid confrontation, and when I do find myself hip-deep in hard guys and loaded guns, I keep kicking myself for not paying more attention to my second career, which is acting. It's why I came to Los Angeles in the first place, and while no one in their right mind would call show business a kindlier, gentler profession than being a private investigator, it's considerably less dangerous.

My agent had packed me off to Minnesota for a picture, which sounded okay until they had an early snow and fell behind schedule, and I wound up doing seven weeks in a town so bereft of anything to do that the locals think it's big time when they drive over to Duluth on a Saturday night and have supper at Denny's. Tends to lull one into a feeling of safety and security to spend so much time in a place where the most heinous crime they've ever heard of is crossing against the municipality's single red light.

So when I came home to Los Angeles I was ready for some excitement. I wasn't prepared for terror and sudden death.

Since my plane arrived in L.A. at nearly midnight on a Sunday, I hired a limo to ferry me from the airport to my rented house on one of the canals in Venice. Anyone who thinks you can't drive from LAX to Venice must be thinking of the city in Italy; we have one in Los Angeles, too, just a few blocks from the ocean, built as a tourist attraction near the turn of the century and now home to a colorful collection of yuppies, druggies, elderly home owners who've been there thirty years, and a counterculture stunning in its infinite variety. If you don't believe me, check out Ocean Front Walk some Sunday afternoon, where third runners-up in a Michael Jackson look-alike contest and turbaned evangelists and one-man bands on roller skates zoom past Small World Books and the endless line of stalls and shops selling sunglasses and T-shirts.

The limo was an indulgence I couldn't afford but felt I'd earned. The backseat, the well-stocked bar, and the wraparound sound system made me feel like a Sybarite. I like that word—like a warring tribe of ancient Judea. "And Samson rose up and slew the Sybarites . . ." Of course, Samson had not slain the Sybarites at all; they'd simply moved to Los Angeles, bought a BMW, and subscribed to *Daily Variety*.

I had invited my adopted son, Marvel, to join me in the wilds of Minnesota, but he'd turned his big brown eyes on me and said, "You got to be kidding!" So he went to stay with my best friend and my assistant, Jo Zeidler, and her husband Marsh. Jo spoils him and Marsh talks basketball to him more intelligently than I can, so Marvel didn't complain about the living arrangements.

I paid off the limo driver after we'd struggled into the bungalow together with seven weeks' worth of luggage, tipping him less lavishly than I'd planned when he observed that I must be carrying the baggage for the entire Yugoslavian army. Nobody likes a smart-ass.

It was good to get home after so long, to be surrounded by my own books and paintings and furniture. And my plants. Since my lifestyle doesn't allow for pets, I'm a plant freak. I have more than fifty in varicolored pots all over the living room and about eight in my bedroom, including a ficus I'd nursed back from near-extinction and moved from my last residence in Pacific Palisades. My house sometimes resembles the set of a Tarzan movie. My next-door neighbor, Stewart Channock, had graciously consented to come in and care for the greenery while I was gone, as well as pick up and forward my mail and start my car every few days so the battery wouldn't expire.

I refuse to eat airplane food, so after dumping my bags I checked the refrigerator. Not much after seven weeks of absence—a bottle of Chardonnay, a six-pack of Guinness Stout with one missing, and a forgotten wedge of cheese that had outlived its usefulness. Nothing you could make a meal out of. What I really wanted was the kind of fancy omelette Spenser always cooks before he makes love to Susan Silverman on the living room floor—but I was out of both eggs and Susan.

Sighing, I changed into a sweatshirt and jeans and went out to my car, which by prearrangement I park across the street in the lot of an apartment building. My destination was an all-night market four blocks away. Even in the dark I could see that someone had scrawled WASH ME in the dust on the trunk, not an unreasonable request after the car had sat out in the elements for seven weeks.

I was pleased that the engine started and made a mental note to buy Stewart a bottle of scotch for his trouble. I switched on the headlights. The windshield was smeared with an overlay of greasy California grit, in which someone had written with a wet finger: CIA. Damn kids, I thought as I Windexed the glass with a paper towel. It's not a bad area I live in, it just isn't a great one, but then unless you're in Beverly Hills or Bel Air, there are no great neighborhoods in Los Angeles.

The next morning I called my various children, friends, and lovers to announce my return, made plans to pick up Marvel that evening, walked to the corner for a *Times*, and read it out on my balcony with a mug of coffee at my side. Los Angeles doesn't have much going for it anymore except its weather; being able to read the paper outside in October is one of the few pleasures we have left.

I went into the small den I'd constructed from a storage room on the second floor of the house and booted up my computer. I'd ascertained from Jo that there was nothing pressing at the office and had decided to take a day for myself before getting back into the swing of things. I sat there reading the scrolling screen. Travel fatigue made it tough, trying to get my head back into reviewing some of my old cases, including a few that I hadn't yet closed, but it beat the hell out of wearing a tie, fighting the freeways, punching a time clock, and putting up with crap from a boss. We self-employed people have the best life imaginable—if we can make a living.

By three o'clock I was in high gear. Overdue bills were paid, overdue letters written, and I was feeling almost back to normal. Until something hit my window with a thump.

I work beside a sliding glass door with a peaceful view of the canal, replete with noisy ducks, an occasional rowboat or paddleboat, and every so often an empty Slurpee cup or a used condom floating by. The window overlooking the street is across the room, and when the sound made me glance over there, something wet was running down the glass. I heard a voice, raspy with hatred, scream, "CIA *pig!*"

I ran to the window in time to see a battered brown Dodge van roaring around the corner as if the hounds of Hell were snapping at its tail pipe. On the sidewalk just below my window a can of Budweiser beer was still rolling.

I remembered the writing on my windshield I'd dismissed as a kid's prank, and a strange burning started in my stomach like yesterday's bratwurst sandwich. I didn't realize it then, but it was the icy heat of fear.

At six o'clock I went over to the cinder-block house next door with which mine shared a common front yard. Stewart Channock answered my knock holding a drink, wearing the dress shirt and tie in which he worked all day as a financial consultant, whatever that was. I didn't really know Stewart well; we were more neighbors than friends. We said hello in the parking lot, shared a gardener, and he'd kindly offered to water my plants while I was gone.

"Welcome home," he said. "When'd you get back?"

"Last night, late."

"Come on in. Drink?"

"I need one," I said.

He went into the kitchen and poured me more than a jigger of scotch. I swallowed it down as though I was thirsty.

"Hope I didn't kill your plants—I even talked to them. About football."

"You did a great job, Stewart. I appreciate it. Uh—when was the last time you started my car?"

He frowned, thinking. "Wednesday, I guess. Did the battery die?"

"No, no. Was anything—written on the windshield?"

"Written on the . . . ? No, why?"

I told him what I'd found, and about the beer can incident that afternoon and the brown Dodge van.

He laughed.

"It's not funny," I said.

"Sure it is. Listen, the people walking the streets in this town are Looney Tunes. You start letting them get to you, you might as well go back to Wisconsin to stay."

"Minnesota. But what if this guy thinks I really am with the CIA and wants to kill me?"

"Then he could have done it, and not left his calling card. Come on, this isn't one of your movies."

Right there you could tell Stewart wasn't in show business. Actors call them pictures, directors call them films, and distributors and theater owners call them shows. No one in the business ever uses the word "movie."

"So you think I should ignore it?"

"What's your other option? Go tell the cops someone threw a beer can at you and wrote on your car, but you don't know who he is? What do you think, they're going to stake out the street and wait for him to do it again?"

I nibbled at my drink, feeling more than a little foolish. He was right, of course; I was overreacting. Seven weeks in the North Woods with nothing to do but watch haircuts, eating Velveeta cheese which was a small town hotel's idea of gourmet food, and living out of a suitcase takes its toll, and I was undoubtedly stretched thin.

"All right, Stewart, I'll forget it," I said, getting up. "And thanks again for the caretaking."

I went back to my own house, picking up the beer can and putting it in the big bag I take to a recycling center every few weeks. At least I'd made two and a half cents on the deal.

Jo and Marsh had invited me for dinner, and it was good to see them again. It was even better seeing Marvel. In the four years he'd been living with me I'd watched him grow from a scared, skinny adolescent who could barely read and write into a handsome, athletic, and witty young man who was beginning his senior year in high school. Considering the adoption had been unplanned and almost out of necessity rather than any desire on my part to share my life with a strange black kid, it had worked out well. He'd become part of who I am, a part I hadn't known existed, and I'd evidently done a damn good job raising him, because he was turning into a real champ.

I spent the evening recounting war stories from the trenches in Duluth, and we didn't get back home until nearly eleven, late for a school night. Marvel went to sleep and I sat up and watched Johnny and then Dave, a habit I'd fallen into on location when there wasn't anything else to do.

The next morning I was refreshed and raring to go, but my feeling of well-being evaporated like a raindrop in Death Valley when I went out to get my car and drive it to my office in Hollywood and saw someone had spray-painted CIA in red letters on the sidewalk, with an arrow pointing to my door.

I've lived in big cities all my life, Chicago before L.A., and I've steadfastly refused to become one of those urban paranoiacs who triple-lock their doors, scan the street for possible muggers, and sleep with a .44 Magnum under their pillows which will undoubtedly discharge someday and blow off an ear. But this CIA business had me worried.

Trying to keep my mind on my work at the office was a bear. I kept worrying what might be happening at the house while I wasn't there. I decided to go home early.

I'd stopped at the store on my way home and picked up the very basics a gourmet cook like me needs to simply survive a few days—butter, garlic, tomato sauce and tomato paste, several different wedges of cheese that were not Velveeta, and milk. After changing into comfortable sweats and a pair of deck shoes with too many holes in them to wear out-side, I went up to my den and sat down at my desk, reading while I ate the linguine with the sauce I'd made from scratch.

Then I heard the raspy shout from the street again. "CIA *pig!*"

This time I got to the window in time to see him. The Pig Man. He was over six feet tall, in his early forties with a droopy mustache, slim and ropy with a slight potbelly, long dirty-blond hair flowing almost to his shoulders from a balding crown, in blue jeans and a turquoise muscle shirt, and just climbing into the Dodge van parked halfway down the street. The set of his shoulders was tense and rigid. As far as I knew, I'd never set eyes on him before.

He sat in the van for a moment. From my vantage point I could only see him from the neck down, his fists clenched on the steering wheel. Finally he banged them on the dashboard before starting the motor and peeling away from the curb, leaving a strip of rubber. It was profoundly disturbing. God knows there are enough people ticked off at me for good reason without having to worry about some deluded stranger.

I dumped the remainder of my lunch into the garbage disposal and poured myself a Laphroaig, neat. I never drink during the day, but I was wound as tight as a three-dollar watch. Anybody bizarre enough to throw a beer can at my window and spray-paint my sidewalk was capa-ble of worse.

Just past three the phone rang. My agent, asking me how it had gone in Minnesota and was I interested in reading for a new series on the Fox network. I was and I wasn't. Getting tied down to a six-days-a-week job didn't appeal to me, but the kind of money they pay you for a series did. I was standing in the middle of the room with the phone cradled against my shoulder, pulling yellow leaves off my schefflera plant, when I glanced out the window and saw the brown van come around the corner again and park across the street.

"I'll call you back," I said. I hung up and went to the window, being careful to stay well out of sight. The Pig Man got out, cast a look of loathing toward my house, and went into the building across the street. I waited for about two minutes, then grabbed a pencil and notepad and went downstairs to copy the number on his license plate.

I peered into the front seat of the paneled van, half expecting to see a claymore mine or a flamethrower or a box of hand grenades. All that was in evidence, however, was a crumpled Styrofoam box from Burger King and a few cans of Budweiser, one empty. That was hardly damning evi-dence; there must be at least a million people in greater Los Angeles who drink Bud.

I came back inside, half expecting a bullet to smash into my back. There were twelve apartments in the building across the street, and I wondered which one he was visiting, whether its window faced mine. I usually leave my drapes open all the time so the plants can get light, but now I pulled them shut. I was as safe in my own home as I was ever going to be, and the security felt woefully inadequate.

Marvel came home and we chatted for a few minutes—it was World Series time and to my horror he was rooting for Oakland. But he had homework to do and repaired to his room, his stereo making the whole house tremble. I tried to read, but I couldn't concentrate. Instead I paced and chain-smoked, every so often sneaking a peek through the closed drapes to see if the Dodge van was still there.

It was.

Somewhere around dinnertime I heard Stewart Channock going into his house. Some human companionship would have been welcome, and I had the urge to walk next door and have a drink with him, but he would have thought it peculiar; we didn't have that close a relationship. We had nothing in common. I don't understand people who move numbers around all day long, and I was sure he was equally mystified by those who chase around after insurance cheats, embezzlers, skips, children kidnapped by divorced parents, and occasionally, people who kill.

I decided I didn't want to be in the house anymore that evening. My paranoia was going to turn me into a candidate for the rubber room if I stayed there much longer. I waited for Marvel to finish his studying and we went out to a Japanese restaurant for sushi and saki. As usual, Marvel talked up a storm, and it took my mind off my troubles.

We got home at ten o'clock, and I noted with relief that the brown van was gone. But in the living room the drapes across the window were blowing. Marvel went over to investigate, and his shoes crunched on long, wicked shards of broken glass that hadn't been there when we left.

"Marvel, stay back!" I said.

He froze, looking at me with eyes that were just this side of frightened. I went past him and pulled the drapes aside.

The window had been shattered, and lying on the carpet amid the debris was a big rock. If I had been sitting by the window with the drapes open, reading, I would have been decapitated. The skin on the back of my neck tingled unpleasantly.

Enough was enough.

The next morning, slightly cranky from a hangover and from the onerous task of cleaning up the glass from my carpet, I was at the front desk of the

Culver City division of the Los Angeles Police Department, talking to the desk officer, whose silver name tag said he was L. Tedescu.

I put the rock on the desk in front of him. "My name is Saxon," I said, and told him my address. "This came through my living room window last night."

He looked at it without emotion. "See who did it?"

"I wasn't home at the time."

L. Tedescu's eyebrows—or eyebrow, rather, he only had one that went clear across his forehead—lifted.

"I'm being harassed," I went on, and told him about the man in the brown Dodge van. "From his age and the way he looked, the way he was dressed, I'd guess he was probably a Vietnam veteran with a grudge against the CIA."

"*Are* you with the CIA, Mr. Saxon?"

A real rocket scientist, L. Tedescu. I felt the essence of a headache starting behind my eyes. If I didn't get at least three aspirin down my throat in the next few minutes it was going to be a bitch kitty. "First off, if I were with the CIA I wouldn't tell you. Secondly, I'd take care of it myself."

"Don't even think about taking the law into your own hands, sir," he said pompously. "You'll be the one in trouble."

"If I was going to do that I wouldn't have come here for help. I have the guy's license number." I pushed the number from my notepad across the glass-topped counter. L. Tedescu looked at it as if he could divine the mysteries of the ages from it. Then he handed it back to me. "There's not much we can do about this."

"Why not?"

"He hasn't committed any crime."

 Suspicions?

1. You have reached the mid-point in the story. Think about the four means of transportation mentioned so far by the narrator of the story. Which of these vehicles would probably not have been included in the story if the main character had not been out of town on an acting assignment? Explain why. Which of these four vehicles would probably have been included in the story, regardless of the main character's location? What details about them and their involvement in the development of the story might have been different if the main character had not been out of town for seven weeks? Explain.

2. Consider the above clues and brainstorm as many possible connections as you can between all the means of transportation mentioned in the story. Then, draw some tentative conclusions about why "the Pig Man" considers the main character to be a "CIA pig."

"Throwing a rock through a window isn't a crime?"

"You didn't see it. You don't know it's the same man."

"Who else could it be?"

He looked at me, his face a mask of apathy. "You'd know that better than I would, sir."

"Well, what about screaming outside my window? It scares the crap out of me."

"That may be, but it's not a crime."

"Disturbing the peace?"

He shook his head. "We'd have to arrest everyone who raised his voice. Now, if he calls you on the phone and makes threats, that's a crime. But if he does it in person it isn't, and we can't take any official action."

For a bit I was too stunned to reply. The best I could come up with was "That's the dumbest thing I ever heard."

L. Tedescu's eyes turned to slits. "It's the law."

The rock sat incongruously on the desk between us. "He spray-painted the sidewalk. He wrote CIA on the city sidewalk. Defacing public property?"

"Yes it is, and he probably did it. But you didn't see him." He put his hand on the rock and moved it a few inches toward me. "Look, Mr. Saxon—right now, not five hundred yards from where we're standing, someone's probably selling illegal drugs to eight-year-olds. Armed robberies happen at gas stations and convenience marts four or five times a night in this division. People getting behind the wheel of a two-thousand-pound car when they're too drunk or stoned even to walk, driving up on a sidewalk and killing a kid. Rape. Spouse abuse. Child abuse. And I won't even mention the hookers and drug dealers and the knife fights in the bars."

"I understand all that . . ."

"I'm glad you do. Los Angeles just doesn't have nearly enough cops—even if what you know this guy to be doing was illegal, it'd be pretty low on our priority scale." He ran his fingers through his mouse-brown hair. "If he does anything else, if you catch him at it, let us know, all right? Otherwise . . ." He turned both hands palms up to show me he was powerless. "I can't even write up a report."

I glared at him for a moment, clenching my teeth to bite back all the angry, frustrated things I wanted to scream. Then I spun on my heel and stalked toward the glass doors. My righteous indignation was like a steel rod up the middle of me.

"Mr. Saxon?"

I stopped and turned back eagerly, hoping he'd change his mind and write up a report, that the police, whose motto in Los Angeles is "To

Protect and Serve," would hunt down the Pig Man in the brown van so I could go on with my life and my work and not be spooked by every zephyr that stirred a tree or every stray cat prowling in a Dumpster for its dinner. "Yes, officer?"

He held his hand out to me, and it wasn't until I got all the way back to the desk that I saw what the offering was.

"Did you want your rock?"

It's only a short walk from the police station to the sheriff's office in the Culver City municipal center. Last year's tragic murder of a young actress made it more difficult to get someone's name and address from their automobile license plate, but nothing's impossible if you have a friend in a high place. At least I hoped she was still a friend.

Female law enforcement officers don't often look like Angie Dickinson or Stepfanie Kramer, but Sergeant Sharyl Capps came pretty close, with a headful of honey-blonde hair, green eyes, and an overbite that could drive a person crazy. We'd met when I was researching my first novel some years ago and had enjoyed a nine-week fling that ended, as most such relationships do, with a gradual distancing that eventually turned to nothing at all. She was almost as tall as I, with several medals and commendations in her service record. I wasn't sure how I would be received, but she smiled when I walked into her office—it wasn't the broadest, most welcoming smile I'd ever seen, but it was a smile nonetheless—and shook my hand in a manner that was a little too businesslike, considering.

"It's been a while," she said. The ironic lilt in her voice just made her more appealing.

"I guess it has. I've been busy."

"I know. I've seen some of your movies and TV stuff. I guess you're doing all right. Are you still a P.I. too?"

"Whenever anyone asks me. Sharyl, I've got a problem."

"I know." I suppose I deserved the dig. When I'd been with her I was commitment-phobic, and I guess she was still a little miffed. I winced. Then I told her about my adventures of the last few days. Her face remained passive but the amusement in her eyes annoyed the hell out of me. "You're a big tough private eye," she said. "Why don't you take care of it yourself?"

"Take the needle out, Sharyl—this is serious."

"Well, the police told you right. There's not a damn thing they can do." She shrugged. "Nothing I can do, either."

I held out the paper with the license number. "You can run this for me."

She looked at it without touching it. "I'd get my butt in a sling," she said.

I thought about remarking that it would look good even in a sling, but wisely desisted. "I'm not going gunning for him." I said. "Just on television."

"Then what's the point?"

"I'd like to know who my enemy is, at least."

She started to shake her head when I said, "Sharyl, you wouldn't want my murder on your conscience, would you?"

She regarded me narrowly. "Not unless I got to do it myself," she said. She took the paper from me, pointing to a chair opposite her desk. "Park it. I'll be back in a minute."

She left me sitting there with nothing to do. Unlike dentists and lawyers, deputy sheriffs don't have back-dated magazines in their offices to browse through while you wait. I did notice a framed photograph on her desk, a smiling Sharyl and a big beefy muscle-hunk, both on bicycles down by Venice Beach, looking the way Southern Californians in love are supposed to.

In twenty minutes she was back.

"Who's your friend?" I said, pointing at the photo.

"He's my partner. Name's Frank Trone."

"Was that taken one day out on bicycle patrol?"

"None of your business. Look, Saxon, I've already violated procedure here. You want this stuff or not?" She waved some computer printouts at me.

I sighed. Sometimes it seems as though life is one long series of what ifs and might have beens. "Sure," I said.

"The van is registered to one Harlan Panec," she said, handing me one of the printouts. Harlan Panec lived over in North Hollywood, in the San Fernando Valley. Not a high-rent district.

"I never heard of him."

"You sure?"

"Sharyl, if you'd ever met a guy named Harlan Panec, wouldn't you remember?"

"Just for the hell of it, I put him through the computer to see if he had a sheet," she said. "He's a naughty boy. Forty-three years old, dishonorable discharge from the army in '73, misdemeanor possession of marijuana, assault, drunk and disorderly, and several citations for speeding."

I jotted the address down in my notebook.

Sharyl frowned. "Stay away from this guy, Saxon."

I tried to be casual. "Why? He's not exactly a master criminal."

"Because." Her laser gaze reduced me to a small dust pyramid. "You're not nearly as tough as you think you are."

I called a glazier to fix the window, but of course he couldn't come for three days, so I made do with natural air-conditioning and prayed for no rain. The brown van didn't appear the rest of that day, or if it did, the Pig Man didn't indulge his penchant for screaming under windows like

Brando in *A Streetcar Named Desire*, but the curiosity that was eating a hole in my gut, the twin of the one caused by fear, got to me by the next morning.

I had to see Harlan Panec, tell him he was mistaken, that he had me mixed up with somebody else, so I could get on with my life without waiting for another rock to come through my window—or worse.

The street address Sharyl Capps had given me was just off Lankershim Boulevard near Vanowen Street, a neighborhood of small industrial buildings and a few houses that were tiny, old, and dilapidated. Not many of the residents spoke English as their first language, and when I pulled my car around the corner at about eleven o'clock they were all out on the street in the sunshine, watching the black-and-white squad cars and the city ambulance, talking in Spanish or Korean or Farsi in the hushed tones reserved for the presence of death.

 Suspicions?

1. How do you know from the conversation Saxon had with desk officer L. Tedescu that Saxon is not with the CIA? Since Panec has Saxon "mixed up with somebody else," how might this case of mistaken identity have happened? Review the story for clues.

2. Make a prediction about the conclusion of the story, and explain why you predicted what you did.

I pulled over to the curb and watched with them. There must have been twenty uniformed policemen running around on the barren front lawn of the house where Harlan Panec lived. The brown van was parked in the weed-choked driveway, and behind it an ancient Volkswagen Bug. On the sagging porch a woman of about forty, in baggy jeans and a tie-dyed shirt that was a holdover from the Woodstock years, was crying and screaming while a policewoman who didn't look like Angie Dickinson tried to talk to her. There were reddish-brown stains on the hysterical woman's hands and arms. It was hard to tell because emotion distorted her features, but she looked vaguely familiar to me. It took me a few minutes to remember where I'd seen her—going in and out of the apartment building across the street from me.

I got out of the car and stood near the curb as a team of paramedics wheeled a gurney out of the house and lifted it carefully down the steps. I couldn't identify its passenger because he was wrapped in a plastic bag from top to toe, but I knew in my heart it was the Pig Man I'd seen beneath my window.

"What happened?" I said to an Asian woman nearby as they loaded the body into the ambulance. She glanced at me fearfully and moved away. I wandered down the sidewalk and repeated my question to a short, muscular black man in a tank top.

"The woman come over this morning," he said, "an' found him." He rolled his eyes and drew his finger across his throat, making a hideous sound with his mouth. "They got him in the bed."

Suspicions?

"They got him in the bed." Who do you think cut Harlen Panec's throat and what was the motive?

I shoved my hands into my pockets. That way no one would see them shaking.

When I got home at about one in the afternoon I poured myself a Laphroaig and downed it in two swallows. It was too good—and expensive—to gulp down like that, but sometimes need overcomes nicety. Thus fortified, I crossed the front yard, nearly tripping over a duck, and rapped on Stewart Channock's door. I'd seen his car in its space across the street, so I knew he was home. I'd known he would be anyway.

"Yes?" he said, his voice muffled.

"It's me, Stewart. We have to talk."

"I'm a little busy right now." I heard him move away. I banged on the door again, harder this time, with more authority.

"Not now," he said through the door.

"CIA pig!" I yelled. There was a pause—a loud one—and then he opened up.

We just looked at each other. Then he sighed and moved aside. "Come on in," he said.

There were two suitcases on the floor near the sofa. "Taking a trip, Stewart?"

"What do you want?"

"You know what I want. Except for a real dumb cop and a real smart lady sheriff, you were the only one who knew about the guy who was hassling me and throwing rocks through my window. Now he's dead."

"That's got nothing to do with me."

"It's everything to do with you," I said. "The guy saw you getting out of my car last week after you'd gone over to start it up for me, right? He recognized you. He must have known you from Vietnam. I happen to know he was in the army in 1973 so it figures. Then he saw you come in here to water the plants, and he thought this was your house."

He shrugged.

"What was it, drugs? You were involved in covert CIA drug-smuggling in Asia and poor old Harlan Panec—that was his name—was in the wrong place at the wrong time and saw you."

"You have a vivid imagination, Saxon."

"A lot of guys who never got over Nam have vivid imaginations," I went on. "They came back home in the early seventies to a country that didn't give a damn, and have been fighting the war in their heads ever since, probably because they realized they'd been over there fighting for a government no better than the sleaziest drug peddler. Panec looked like he was one of them; he had that half-crazy, stretched-too-tight look. When he saw you again after all these years, the poor bastard snapped like a frayed rubber band. But he was too dumb to do anything except throw rocks and yell."

"You're talking crap you don't know anything about."

"Then pay no attention, let me ramble. Maybe you're still with the Agency, maybe not. But whatever you are doing it's probably illegal, so when I told you about the writing on my car, the brown van, the spray painting under my window, you realized you'd been blown. You waited for the van to show up again and you followed it to Panec's place in North Hollywood and cut his throat. Probably not the first guy you ever killed."

"You'll never prove any of this, you know."

"Maybe not."

"But you're going to try?"

"I have to," I said.

He pushed himself away from the door where he'd been leaning casually. "Let's head into the bathroom, shall we?"

I shook my head. "I don't have to go."

"Move it," he said, and there was a gun in his hand. It was a small gun that fit in his palm, the kind women might carry in their purses. At close range it wold kill as efficiently as a bazooka. I hesitated, and he said, "Don't be stupid. You know I'll use this if I have to."

"Those are noisy little devils," I said. "People will hear."

He moved toward me. "Do you want to take the chance?"

I didn't. I don't like having guns aimed at me. I should be used to it, but I'm not. On TV, of course, the private investigator would have slapped it out of his hand and overpowered him, but it had already been pointed out to me that I'm not as tough as I think I am.

I walked into the bedroom ahead of him. Another suitcase, half full, was open on the bed. He went over to the dresser, opened a drawer, and felt around inside. Then he pulled out a pair of silvery handcuffs.

"I never knew you were into kinky sex, Stewart."

"Shut up." He motioned with the gun and I went into the bathroom with him right behind me. He switched on the light, and the exhaust fan in the ceiling began humming noisily. There were cute little aqua and black mermaids on the shower curtain.

"Kneel down on the floor by the john. Do it!"

I did it. The porcelain tile was cold on my knees through my jeans. He took my hand and fastened one of the cuffs around my wrist. "Not too tight?" he said. He put the chain around the thick pipe running from the toilet into the wall, then braceleted my other hand and snapped the cuffs shut so I was kneeling over the closed toilet as though at prayer.

"There's no window," he said, "and the fan will muffle the noise, so don't bother yelling. Besides, no one else in the neighborhood will be home until evening."

"And by that time you're in another city with a whole new identity. Stewart, you're a slime."

"There's things you don't understand, so don't be so damned judgmental. If I was such a slime you'd be dead by now."

"You aren't going to shoot me?"

He considered it for more than a moment. Then he shook his head. "Finally you have to say 'enough' to killing." He went to the door. "You okay?"

"I'm real comfy," I said bitterly.

He looked at me for a minute. I suppose he was trying to decide whether he'd made a mistake, whether he should just shoot me in the head and be done with it. But my luck held.

"*Ciao*," he said, and left me there.

I couldn't hear much through the closed door, but I did hear him leave the house. He was an invisible man, marching through life carrying out his own twisted agenda, and if some other poor fool like Harlan Panec got in his way, he'd take care of it the same way and disappear again, vanishing into the mist like Brigadoon. It takes a special mind-set, I imagine, to live rootless without family or friends, worrying that someone was always in the shadows, watching. Not for nothing were guys like Stewart Channock known as "spooks."

I shifted around on the tile floor, trying to get comfortable, and flexed the fingers of my imprisoned hands. Between the toilet and the cabinet that housed the sink was a wooden magazine rack. From my vantage point I saw two *Newsweeks*, a *Forbes*, yesterday's *Wall Street Journal*, a crossword puzzle magazine, and a couple of paperback books—but I wasn't much in the mood for reading.

I knew what would happen when he got to his car—my making a simple phone call had ensured it—but in the completely closed room I could barely hear the gunshots from the parking lot, and I had no way of knowing who shot whom until Sharyl Capps and her partner/lover from the sheriff's office kicked in the door and told me.

How Clever?

1. Explain Panec's presence in Saxon's neighborhood and his motive for doing all the things he does to Saxon's car, sidewalk, and rented house.

2. Which three actions that one might do for an out-of-town neighbor are mentioned fairly early in the story? Which two of these three actions (which also serve as clues in the story) does Saxon specifically mention when he confronts Stewart Channock toward the end of the story? How do both these actions stem from Saxon's not wanting something he valued to die?

3. How did these two actions taken by Channock cause Panec to be completely mistaken about two things?

4. How is the third action, the one not referred to by Saxon, also a clue to what Panec is mistaken about?

5. Explain why there is no scene in the story during which Saxon and Panec come face to face.

6. What was Channock's motive for killing Panec and handcuffing Saxon to the toilet pipe?

DETECTWRITE: Characterization

1. Create a list of Saxon's character traits and personality features as stated or implied in the story. Compare and contrast private investigator/actor Saxon with other private investigators you know or have read about.

2. P.I. Saxon's being an actor as well as a private investigator serves the plot of this particular story because it is the means by which Saxon is separated from his car and his home for enough time for Panec to see Channock and assume that the car and home are his. Does Saxon's being an actor also serve characterization in this particular story, making Saxon more interesting or more capable as a P.I. in any way? Explain.

DETECTWRITE: Plot Details

1. Find the paragraph in which the three clues involving actions that one neighbor might do for another are planted in the story. Then describe how the author talks about these actions in such a way as to point them out to the reader and yet not direct so much attention to them that they are too obvious as clues.

2. Select one ordinary, everyday action that could play a critical role in a detective story you might write. Write a brief paragraph that includes enough mention of that action so that the reader is made aware of it and might remember it without giving away the ultimate importance of the action as a clue in the plot of your story.

   Then, in a separate paragraph, explain how the everyday action you have planted would turn out to be a clue in your projected story.

DETECTWRITE: Setting

1. List ways in which the southern California setting of "The Pig Man" helps to develop both the plot of the story and the characters of Saxon, Panec, and Channock.

2. Compare and contrast the California settings of "The Pig Man" and another story in this collection.

3. Based on your reading of "The Pig Man," explain how the presence or absence of certain props (a common short form for "properties," objects included in the setting of a story) can be used by the writer to develop the plot of a detective story.

The Fat Man

Isak Dinesen

ON ONE NOVEMBER EVENING A HORRIBLE CRIME WAS COM-
mitted in Oslo, the capital of Norway. A child was murdered in an
uninhabited house on the outskirts of the town.

The newspapers brought long and detailed accounts of the murder. In
the short, raw November days people stood in the street outside the
house and stared up at it. The victim had been a workman's child, resent-
ment of ancient wrongs stirred in the minds of the crowd.

The police had got but one single clue. A shopkeeper in the street told
them that as he was closing up his shop on the evening of the murder he
saw the murdered child walk by, her hand in the hand of a fat man.

The police had arrested some tramps and vagabonds and shady persons, but such people as a rule are not fat. So they looked elsewhere,
among tradesmen and clerks of the neighborhood. Fat men were stared at
in the streets. But the murderer had not been found.

In this same month of November a young student named Kristoffer
Lovunden in Oslo was cramming for his examination. He had come down
to the town from the north of Norway, where it is day half the year and
night the other half and where people are different from other
Norwegians. In a world of stone and concrete Kristoffer was sick with
longing for the hills and the salt sea.

His people up in Norland were poor and could have no idea of what it
cost to live in Oslo, he did not want to worry them for money. To be able to

finish his studies he had taken a job as bartender at the Grand Hotel, and worked there every night from eight o'clock till midnight. He was a good-looking boy with gentle and polite manners, conscientious in the performance of his duties, and he did well as a bartender. He was abstinent himself, but took a kind of scientific interest in the composition of other people's drinks.

In this way he managed to keep alive and to go on with his lessons. But he got too little sleep and too little time for ordinary human inter-course. He read no books outside his textbooks, and not even the newspapers, so that he did not know what was happening in the world around him. He was aware himself that this was not a healthy life, but the more he disliked it the harder he worked to get it over.

In the bar he was always tired, and he sometimes fell asleep standing up, with open eyes. The brilliant light and the noises made his head swim. But as he walked home from the Grand Hotel after midnight the cold air revived him so that he entered his small room wide awake. This he knew to be a dangerous hour. If now a thing caught his mind it would stick in it with unnatural vividness and keep him from sleep, and he would be no good for his books the next day. He had promised himself not to read at this time, and while he undressed to go to bed he closed his eyes.

All the same, one night his glance fell on a newspaper wrapped round a sausage that he had brought home with him. Here he read of the mur-der. The paper was two days old, people would have been talking about the crime around him all the time, but he had not heard what they said. The paper was torn, the ends of the lines were missing, he had to make them up from his own imagination. After that the thing would not leave him. The words "a fat man" set his mind running from one to another of the fat men he had ever known till at last it stopped at one of them.

There was an elegant fat gentleman who often visited the bar. Kristoffer knew him to be a writer, a poet of a particular, refined, half-mystical school. Kristoffer had read a few of his poems and had himself been fascinated by their queer, exquisite choice of words and symbols. They seemed to be filled with the colors of old precious stained glass. He often wrote about medieval legends and mysteries. This winter the theater was doing a play by him named *The Werewolf*, which was in parts macabre, according to its subject, but more remarkable still for its strange beauty and sweetness. The man's appearance too was striking. He was fat, with wavy dark hair, a large white face, a small red mouth, and curiously pale eyes. Kristoffer had been told that he had lived much abroad. It was the habit of this man to sit with his back to the bar, developing his exotic theories to a circle of young admirers. His name was Oswald Senjen.

Now the poet's picture took hold of the student. All night he seemed to see the big face close to his, with all kinds of expressions. He drank much cold water but was as hot as before. This fat man of the Grand Hotel, he thought, was the fat man of the newspaper.

It did not occur to him, in the morning, to play the part of a detective. If he went to the police they would send him away, since he had no facts whatever, no argument or reason even, to put before them. The fat man would have an alibi. He and his friends would laugh, they would think him mad or they would be indignant and complain to the manager of the hotel, and Kristoffer would lose his job.

So for three weeks the odd drama was played between the two actors only: the grave young bartender behind the bar and the smiling poet before it. The one was trying hard all the time to get out of it, the other knew nothing about it. Only once did the parties look each other in the face.

A few nights after Kristoffer had read about the murder, Oswald Senjen came into the bar with a friend. Kristoffer had no wish to spy upon them—it was against his own will that he moved to the side of the bar where they sat.

They were discussing fiction and reality. The friend held that to a poet the two must be one, and that therefore his existence must be mysteriously happy. The poet contradicted him. A poet's mission in life, he said, was to make others confound fiction with reality in order to render them, for an hour, mysteriously happy. But he himself must, more carefully than the crowd, hold the two apart. "Not as far as enjoyment of them is concerned," he added, "I enjoy fiction, I enjoy reality too. But I am happy because I have an unfailing instinct for distinguishing one from the other. I know fiction where I meet it. I know reality where I meet it."

This fragment of conversation stuck in Kristoffer's mind, he went over it many times. He himself had often before pondered on the idea of happiness and tried to find out whether such a thing really existed. He had asked himself if anybody was happy and, if so, who was happy. The two men at the bar had repeated the word more than once—they were probably happy. The fat man, who knew reality when he saw it, had said that he was happy.

Kristoffer remembered the shopkeeper's evidence. The face of the little girl Mattea, he had explained, when she passed him in the rainy street, had looked happy, as if, he said, she had been promised something, or was looking forward to something, and was skipping along toward it. Kristoffer thought: "And the man by her side?" Would his face have had an expression of happiness as well? Would he too have been looking forward to something? The shopkeeper had not had time to look the man in the face, he had seen only his back.

Night after night Kristoffer watched the fat man. At first he felt it to be a grim jest of fate that he must have this man with him wherever he went, while the man himself should hardly be aware of his existence. But after a time he began to believe that his unceasing observation had an effect on the observed, and that he was somehow changing under it. He grew fatter and whiter, his eyes grew paler. At moments he was as absent-minded as Kristoffer himself. His pleasing flow of speech would run slower, with sudden unneeded pauses, as if the skilled talker could not find his words.

If Oswald Senjen stayed in the bar till it closed, Kristoffer would slip out while he was being helped into his furred coat in the hall, and wait for him outside. Most often Oswald Senjen's large car would be there, and he would get into it and glide off. But twice he slowly walked along the street, and Kristoffer followed him. The boy felt himself to be a mean, wild figure in the town and the night, sneaking after a man who had done him no harm, and about whom he knew nothing, and he hated the figure who was dragging him after it. The first time it seemed to him that the fat man turned his head a little to one side and the other as if to make sure that there was nobody close behind him. But the second time he walked on looking straight ahead, and Kristoffer then wondered if that first slight nervous movement had not been a creation of his own imagination.

One evening in the bar the poet turned in his deep chair and looked at the bartender.

Toward the end of November Kristoffer suddenly remembered that his examination was to begin within a week. He was dismayed and seized with pangs of conscience, he thought of his future and of his people up in Norland. The deep fear within him grew stronger. He must shake off his obsession or he would be ruined by it.

At this time an unexpected thing happened. One evening Oswald Senjen got up to leave early, his friends tried to hold him back but he would not stay. "Nay," he said, "I want a rest. I want to rest." When he had gone, one of his friends said: "He was looking bad tonight. He is much changed. Surely he has got something the matter with him." One of the others answered: "It is that old matter from when he was out in China. But he ought to look after himself. Tonight one might think that he would not last till the end of the year."

As Kristoffer listened to these assertions from an outside and real world he felt a sudden, profound relief. To this world the man himself, at least, was a reality. People talked about him.

"It might be a good thing," he thought, "it might be a way out if I could talk about the whole matter to somebody else."

He did not choose a fellow student for his confidant. He could imagine the kind of discussion this would bring about and his mind shrank from it. He turned for help to a simple soul, a boy two or three years younger than himself, who washed up at the bar and who was named Hjalmar.

Hjalmar was born and bred in Oslo, he knew all that could be known about the town and very little about anything outside it. He and Kristoffer had always been on friendly terms, and Hjalmar enjoyed a short chat with Kristoffer in the scullery, after working hours, because he knew that Kristoffer would not interrupt him. Hjalmar was a revolutionary spirit, and would hold forth on the worthless rich customers of the bar, who rolled home in big cars with gorgeous women with red lips and nails, while underpaid sailors hauled tarred ropes, and tired laborers led their plowhorses to the stable. Kristoffer wished that he would not do so, for at such times his nostalgia for boats and tar, and for the smell of a sweaty horse, grew so strong that it became a physical pain. And the deadly horror that he felt at the idea of driving home with one of the women Hjalmar described proved to him that his nervous system was out of order.

As soon as Kristoffer mentioned the murder to Hjalmar he found that the scullery boy knew everything about it. Hjalmar had his pockets filled with newspaper cuttings, from which he read reports of the crime and of the arrests, and angry letters about the slowness of the police.

Kristoffer was uncertain how to explain his theory to Hjalmar. In the end he said: "Do you know, Hjalmar, I believe that the fat gentleman in the bar is the murderer." Hjalmar stared at him, his mouth open. The next moment he had caught the idea, and his eyes shone.

After a short while Hjalmar proposed that they should go to the police, or again to a private detective. It took Kristoffer some time to convince his friend, as he had convinced himself, that their case was too weak, and that people would think them mad.

Then Hjalmar, more eager even than before, decided that they must be detectives themselves.

To Kristoffer it was a strange experience, both steadying and alarming, to face his own nightmare in the sharp white light of the scullery, and to hear it discussed by another live person. He felt that he was holding on to the scullery boy like a drowning man to a swimmer; every moment he feared to drag his rescuer down with him, into the dark sea of madness.

The next evening Hjalmar told Kristoffer that they would find some scheme by which to surprise the murderer and make him give himself away.

Kristoffer listened to his various suggestions for some time, then smiled a little. He said: "Hjalmar, thou art even such a man . . ." He stopped. "Nay," he said, "you will not know this piece, Hjalmar. But let me go on a little, all the same—!

> I have heard
> that guilty creatures sitting at a play
> have by the very cunning of the scene
> been struck so to the soul that presently
> they have proclaim'd their malefactions.
> For murder, though it have no tongue, will speak.

"I understand that very well," said Hjalmar.

"Do you, Hjalmar?" asked Kristoffer. "Then I shall tell you one thing more:

> The play's the thing
> wherein we'll catch the conscience of the king.

"Where have you got that from?" asked Hjalmar.

"From a play called *Hamlet*," said Kristoffer.

"And how do you mean to go and do it?" asked Hjalmar again. Kristoffer was silent for some time.

"Look here, Hjalmar," he said at last, "you told me that you have got a sister."

"Yes," said Hjalmar, "I have got five of them."

"But you have got one sister of nine," said Kristoffer, "the same age as Mattea?"

"Yes," said Hjalmar.

"And she has got," Kristoffer went on, "a school mackintosh with a hood to it, like the one Mattea had on that night?"

"Yes," said Hjalmar.

Kristoffer began to tremble. There was something blasphemous in the comedy which they meant to act. He could not have gone on with it if he had not felt that somehow his reason hung upon it.

"Listen, Hjalmar," he said, "we will choose an evening when the man is in the bar. Then make your little sister put on her mackintosh, and make one of your big sisters bring her here. Tell her to walk straight from the door, through all the room, up to the bar, to me, and to give me something—a letter or what you

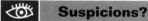

Suspicions?

Based on the two passages from Shakespeare's *Hamlet* and the questions Kristoffer asks Hjalmar, what scheme do you think Kristoffer will come up with to surprise the fat man and make him give himself away? Explain.

will. I shall give her a shilling for doing it, and she will take it from the counter when she has put the letter there. Then tell her to walk back again, through the room."

"Yes," said Hjalmar.

"If the manager complains," Kristoffer added after a while, "we will explain that it was all a misunderstanding."

"Yes," said Hjalmar.

"I myself," said Kristoffer, "must stay at the bar. I shall not see his face, for he generally sits with his back to me, talking to people. But you will leave the washing up for a short time, and go round and keep guard by the door. You will watch his face from there."

"There will be no need to watch his face," said Hjalmar, "he will scream or faint, or jump up and run away, you know."

"You must never tell your sister, Hjalmar," said Kristoffer, "why we made her come here."

"No, no," said Hjalmar

On the evening decided upon for the experiment, Hjalmar was silent, set on his purpose. But Kristoffer was in two minds. Once or twice he came near to giving up the whole thing. But if he did so, and even if he could make Hjalmar understand and forgive—what would become of himself afterwards?

Oswald Senjen was in his chair in his usual position, with his back to the bar. Kristoffer was behind the bar, Hjalmar was at the swinging door of the hall, to receive his sister.

Through the glass door Kristoffer saw the child arrive in the hall, accompanied by an elder sister with a red feather in her hat, for in these winter months people did not let children walk alone in the streets at night. At the same time he became aware of something in the room that he had not noticed before. "I can never, till tonight," he told himself, "have been quite awake in this place, or I should have noticed it." To each side of the glass door there was a tall looking-glass, in which he could see the faces turned away from him. In both of them he now saw Oswald Senjen's face.

The little girl in her mackintosh and hood had some difficulty opening the door, and was assisted by her brother. She walked straight up to

Suspicions?

Do you think the fat man did what Hjalmar expected him to do, namely, "scream, faint, or jump up and run away"? Why do you think he did or did not do those things?

What explanation do you think Kristoffer will have for why the fat man did not act in any of the ways Hjalmar predicted? What explanation would you have for Hjalmar?

the bar, neither fast nor slow, placed the letter on the counter, and collected her shilling. As she did so she lifted her small pale face in the hood slightly, and gave her brother's friend a little pert, gentle grin of acquittal—now that the matter was done with. Then she turned and walked back and out of the door, neither fast nor slow.

"Was it right?" she asked her brother who had been waiting for her by the door. Hjalmar nodded, but the child was puzzled at the expression of his face and looked at her big sister for an explanation. Hjalmar remained in the hall till he had seen the two girls disappear in the rainy street. Then the porter asked him what he was doing there, and he ran round to the back entrance and to his tub and glasses.

The next guest who ordered a drink at the bar looked at the bartender and said: "Hello, are you ill?" The bartender did not answer a word. He did not say a word either when, an hour later, as the bar closed, he joined his friend in the scullery.

"Well, Kristoffer," said Hjalmar, "he did not scream or faint, did he?"

"No," said Kristoffer.

Hjalmar waited a little. "If it is him," he said, "he is tough." Kristoffer stood quite still for a long time, looking at the glasses. At last he said: "Do you know why he did not scream or faint?"

"No," said Hjalmar, "why was it?"

Kristoffer said: "Because he saw the only thing he expected to see. The only thing he ever sees now. All the other men in the bar gave some sign of surprise at the sight of a little girl in a mackintosh walking in here. I watched the fat man's face in the mirror, and saw that he looked straight at her as she came in, and that his eyes followed her as she walked out, but that his face did not change at all."

"What?" said Hjalmar. After a few moments he repeated very low. "What?"

"Yes, it is so," said Kristoffer. "A little girl in a mackintosh is the only thing he sees wherever he looks. She has been with him here in the bar before. And in the streets. And in his own house. For three weeks."

There was a long silence.

"Are we to go to the police now, Kristoffer?" Hjalmar asked.

"We need not go to the police," said Kristoffer. "We need not do anything in the matter. You and I are too heavy, or too grown up, for that. Mattea does it as it ought to be done. It is her small light step that has followed close on his own all the time. She looks at him, just as your sister looked at me, an hour ago. He wanted rest, he said. She will get it for him before the end of the year."

How Clever?

1. How psychologically believable do you find Kristoffer's explanation as to why the fat man was the only man in the bar who did not give "some sign of surprise at the sight of a little girl in a mackintosh walking in here"? Explain your position.

2. What facts or evidence is there that the fat man in the bar, Oswald Senjen, is the same fat man who murdered the little girl in an uninhabited house on the outskirts of Oslo? What arguments could be made or reasons offered to the police that might lead to his arrest? Could Oswald Senjen be convicted in a court of law? Explain.

3. At the end of the story, why does Kristoffer believe that he and Hjalmar "need not go to the police"? What does Kristoffer mean when, in the final words of the story, he says to Hjalmar about the fat man: "He wanted rest. She will get it for him before the end of the year." Why do you agree or disagree with Kristoffer's belief?

4. In a conversation about fiction, reality, and happiness, the fat man, a poet, tells a friend in the bar that a poet's mission in life is to make others confound (confuse) fiction with reality in order to render them, for an hour, mysteriously happy. But the poet himself, more carefully than the crowd, must hold the two apart.

    "Not as far as enjoyment of them is concerned," continues the fat man. "I enjoy fiction, I enjoy reality too. But I am happy because I have an unfailing instinct for distinguishing one from the other. I know fiction where I meet it. I know reality where I meet it."

    This conversation, which Kristoffer has overheard, sticks in his mind. What connections can you make between what the poet said and what Kristoffer believes the poet has done to the little girl? Explain your thinking.

5. The first time Kristoffer follows the fat man outside the bar, "it seemed to him that the fat man turned his head a little to one side and the other as if to make sure that there was nobody close behind him." But, after following the fat man a second time, Kristoffer wonders whether the little turn of the fat man's head "had not been a creation of his own imagination," in effect, a work of fiction.

    Is it possible that Kristoffer's choice of this particular fat man as the murderer and his explanation for the fat man's failure to react to the Hjalmar's sister in the bar are also "a creation of his own imagination"? Is it probable? Explain why you feel the way you do.

6. Why did Kristoffer believe that "his unceasing observation had an effect on the observed, and that he was somehow changing under it"? Is this possible? Probable? Explain your thinking. What "sense" did Kristoffer make of the moment when "one evening in the bar the poet turned in his deep chair and looked at the bartender"? What "sense" do you make of it? Explain.

7. What "sense" did Kristoffer make of the fat man's leaving the bar early one night saying, "I want to rest"? What "sense" did one of the fat man's friends make of it? How do you explain these different meanings for the same action?

8. Did it make any difference to Kristoffer that he chose as his confidant not a fellow student but "a simple soul, a boy two or three years younger than himself" who, it turned out, knew everything about the case and "caught" Kristoffer's theory? Did it make any difference to the story? Explain.

9. The story's third-person narrator states that "the police had arrested some tramps and vagabonds and shady persons, but such people as a rule are not fat"? In your opinion, was this good detective work on the part of the police? Explain.

10. In "The Fat Man," the author has the student Kristoffer Lovunden function as an amateur detective. How do the following statements about Kristopher's nature make it possible, if not probable, that he would "play detective":

    As a bartender, "he was abstinent himself, but took a kind of scientific interest in the composition of other people's drinks,"

    "If now a thing caught his mind it would stick in it with unnatural vividness and keep him from sleep,"

    "The words 'a fat man' set his mind running from one to another of the fat men he had ever known till at last it stopped at one of them" and, "The poet's picture took hold of the student"?

11. How do the following statements about Kristoffer's nature make him an unlikely or unsuitable candidate for the role of amateur detective:

    "He got too little sleep and too little time for ordinary human intercourse,"

    "He read no books outside his textbooks, and not even newspapers, so that he did not know what was happening in the world around him,"

    "In the bar he was always tired, and he sometimes fell asleep standing up, with open eyes,"

    "The paper was torn, the ends of the lines were missing, he had to make them up from his own imagination," and,

    "The poet's picture took hold of the student"?

12. Regardless of his strengths and weaknesses when it comes to detection and reflection, in what specific ways did Kristoffer function in the story as an amateur detective?

DetectWrite: Characterization

1. What do you believe were the advantages and disadvantages of choosing a character like Kristoffer Lovunden as the amateur detective in this particular story?

2. Why do you suppose the character of the fat man is left fairly undeveloped by the author, and why do you suppose no motive for the crime is given?

DETECTWRITE: Characterization and Plot

1. Was it more Kristoffer's nature (characterization) or the situation he was in (plot) that got him caught up in the life of the fat man from the bar? Explain your thinking.

2. What function does the character Hjalmar serve in the plot of the story, and how was his character well suited to that function?

3. How logically acceptable (a plot consideration) to you are the actions of the characters in the story? How psychologically acceptable (a characterization consideration) are the characters in the story? Explain.

DETECTWRITE: Setting

How has the author used the general setting of Oslo, and the more specific settings of the bar and Kristoffer's room, to set a particular mood and create a specific atmosphere for the story? How has the author's style of writing reinforced that mood and atmosphere?

Trifles

Susan Glaspell

THE CHARACTERS

County Attorney
Mrs. Peters
Sheriff
Hale
Mrs. Hale

SCENE: The kitchen in the now abandoned farmhouse of John Wright, a gloomy kitchen, and left without having been put in order—the walls covered with a faded wallpaper. Down right is a door leading to the parlor. On the right wall above this door is a built-in kitchen cupboard with shelves in the upper portion and drawers below. In the rear wall at right, up two steps is a door opening onto stairs leading to the second floor. In the rear wall at left is a door to the shed and from there to the outside. Between these two doors is an old-fashioned black iron stove. Running along the left wall from the shed door is an old iron sink and sink shelf, in which is set a hand pump. Downstage of the sink is an uncurtained window. Near the window is an old wooden rocker. Center stage is an unpainted wooden kitchen table with straight chairs on either side. There is a small chair down right. Unwashed pans under the sink, a loaf of bread outside the breadbox, a dish towel on the table—other signs of incompleted work. At the rear the shed door opens and the Sheriff comes in followed by the County Attorney and Hale. The Sheriff and Hale are men in middle life, the County Attorney is a young man; all are much bundled up and go at once to the stove. They are followed by the two women—the Sheriff's wife, Mrs. Peters, first; she is a slight wiry woman, a thin nervous face. Mrs. Hale is larger and would ordinarily be called more comfortable looking, but she is disturbed now and looks fearfully about as she enters. The women have come in slowly, and stand close together near the door.

COUNTY ATTORNEY: *(At stove rubbing his hands)* This feels good. Come up to the fire, ladies.

MRS. PETERS: *(After taking a step forward)* I'm not—cold.

SHERRIFF: *(Unbuttoning his overcoat and stepping away from the stove to right of table as if to mark the beginning of official business)* Now, Mr. Hale, before we move things about, you explain to Mr. Henderson just what you saw when you came here yesterday morning.

COUNTY ATTORNEY: *(Crossing down to left of the table)* By the way, has anything been moved? Are things just as you left them yesterday?

SHERRIFF: *(Looking about)* It's just the same. When it dropped below zero last night I thought I'd better send Frank out this morning to make a fire for us— *(Sits right of center table)* no use getting pneumonia with a big case on, but I told him not to touch anything except the stove—and you know Frank.

COUNTY ATTORNEY: Somebody should have been left here yesterday.

SHERRIFF: Oh—yesterday. When I had to send Frank to Morris Center for that man who went crazy—I want you to know I had my hands full yesterday. I knew you could get back from Omaha by today and as long as I went over everything here myself—

COUNTY ATTORNEY: Well, Mr. Hale, tell just what happened when you came here yesterday morning.

HALE: *(Crossing down to above table)* Harry and I had started to town with a load of potatoes. We came along the road from my place and as I got here I said, "I'm going to see if I can't get John Wright to go in with me on a party telephone." I spoke to Wright about it once before and he put me off, saying folks talked too much anyway, and all he asked was peace and quiet—I guess you know about how much he talked himself; but I thought maybe if I went to the house and talked about it before his wife, though I said to Harry that I didn't know as what his wife wanted made much difference to John—

COUNTY ATTORNEY: Let's talk about that later, Mr. Hale. I do want to talk about that, but tell now just what happened when you got to the house.

HALE: I didn't hear or see anything; I knocked at the door, and still it was all quiet inside. I knew they must be up, it was past eight o'clock. So I knocked again, and I thought I heard somebody say, "Come in." I wasn't sure, I'm not sure yet, but I opened the door—this door *(Indicating the door by which the two women are still standing)* and there in that rocker— *(Pointing to it)* sat Mrs. Wright. *(They all look at the rocker down left.)*

COUNTY ATTORNEY: What—was she doing?

HALE: She was rockin' back and forth. She had her apron in her hand and was kind of—pleating it.

COUNTY ATTORNEY: And how did she—look?

HALE: Well, she looked queer.

COUNTY ATTORNEY: How do you mean—queer?

HALE: Well, as if she didn't know what she was going to do next. And kind of done up.

COUNTY ATTORNEY: *(Takes out notebook and pencil and sits left of center table)* How did she seem to feel about your coming?

HALE: Why, I don't think she minded—one way or other. She didn't pay much attention. I said, "How do, Mrs. Wright, it's cold, ain't it?" And she said, "Is it?"—and went on kind of pleating at her apron. Well, I was surprised; she didn't ask me to come up to the stove, or to set down, but just sat there, not even looking at me, so I said, "I want to see John." And then she—laughed. I guess you would call it a laugh. I thought of Harry and the team outside, so I said a little sharp: "Can't I see John?" "No," she says, kind o' dull like. "Ain't he home?" says I. "Yes," says she, "he's home." "Then why can't I see him?" I asked her, out of patience. "'Cause he's dead," says she. "Dead?" says I. She just nodded her head, not getting a bit excited, but rockin' back and forth. "Why—where is he?" says I, not knowing what to say. She just pointed upstairs—like that. *(Himself pointing to the room above)* I started for the stairs, with the idea of going up there. I walked from there to here—then I says, "Why, what did he die of?" "He died of a rope round his neck," says she, and just went on pleatin' at her apron. Well, I went out and called Harry. I thought I might—need help. We went upstairs and there he was lyin'—

COUNTY ATTORNEY: I think I'd rather have you go into that upstairs, where you can point it all out. Just go on now with the rest of the story.

HALE: Well, my first thought was to get that rope off. It looked . . . *(Stops, his face twitches)* . . . but Harry, he went up to him, and he said, "No, he's dead all right, and we'd better not touch anything." So we went back downstairs. She was still sitting that same way. "Has anybody been notified?" I asked. "No," says she, unconcerned. "Who did this, Mrs. Wright?" said Harry. He said it business-like—and she stopped pleatin' of her apron. "I don't know," she says. "You don't *know*?" says Harry. "No," says she. "Weren't you sleepin' in the bed with him?" says Harry. "Yes," says she, "but I was on the inside." "Somebody slipped a rope round his neck and strangled him and you didn't wake up?" says Harry. "I didn't wake up," she said after him. We must 'a' looked as if we didn't see how that could be, for after a minute she said, "I sleep sound." Harry was going to ask her more questions but I said maybe we ought to let her tell her story first to the coroner, or the sheriff, so Harry went fast as he could to Rivers' place, where there's a telephone.

COUNTY ATTORNEY: And what did Mrs. Wright do when she knew that you had gone for the coroner?

HALE: She moved from the rocker to that chair over there *(Pointing to a small chair in the down right corner)* and just sat there with her hands held together and looking down. I got a feeling that I ought to make some conversation, so I said I had come in to see if John wanted to put in a telephone, and at that she started to laugh, and then she stopped and looked at me—scared. *(The County Attorney, who has had his notebook out, makes a note.)* I dunno, maybe it wasn't scared. I wouldn't like to say it was. Soon Harry got back, and then Dr. Lloyd came, and you, Mr. Peters, and so I guess that's all I know that you don't.

COUNTY ATTORNEY: *(Rising and looking around)* I guess we'll go upstairs first—and then out to the barn and around there. *(To the Sheriff)* You're convinced that there was nothing important here—nothing that would point to any motive?

SHERIFF: Nothing here but kitchen things. *(The County Attorney, after again looking around the kitchen, opens the door of a cupboard closet in right wall. He brings a small chair from right—gets up on it and looks on a shelf. Pulls his hand away, sticky.)*

COUNTY ATTORNEY: Here's a nice mess. *(The women draw nearer up center.)*

MRS. PETERS: *(To the other woman)* Oh, her fruit; it did freeze. *(To the Lawyer)* She worried about that when it turned so cold. She said the fire'd go out and her jars would break.

SHERIFF: *(Rises)* Well, can you beat the women! Held for murder and worryin' about preserves.

COUNTY ATTORNEY: *(Getting down from chair)* I guess before we're through she may have something more serious than preserves to worry about. *(Crosses down right center)*

HALE: Well, women are used to worrying over trifles. *(The two women move a little closer together.)*

COUNTY ATTORNEY: *(With the gallantry of a young politician)* And yet, for all their worries, what would we do without the ladies? *(The women do not unbend. He goes below the center table to the sink, takes a dipperful of water from* *the pail and pouring it into a basin, washes his hands. While he is doing this the Sheriff and Hale cross to cupboard, which they inspect. The County Attorney starts to wipe his hands on the roller towel, turns it for a cleaner place.)* Dirty towels! *(Kicks his foot against the pans under the sink)* Not much of a house-keeper, would you say, ladies?

MRS. HALE: *(Stiffly)* There's a great deal of work to be done on a farm.

COUNTY ATTORNEY: To be sure. And yet *(With a little bow to her)* I know there are some Dickson County farmhouses which do not have such roller towels. *(He gives it a pull to expose its full length again.)*

MRS. HALE: Those towels get dirty awful quick. Men's hands aren't always as clean as they might be.

COUNTY ATTORNEY: Ah, loyal to your sex, I see. But you and Mrs. Wright were neighbors. I suppose you were friends, too.

MRS. HALE: *(Shaking her head)* I've not seen much of her of late years. I've not been in this house—it's more than a year.

COUNTY ATTORNEY: *(Crossing to women up center)* And why was that? You didn't like her?

MRS. HALE: I liked her all well enough. Farmers' wives have their hands full, Mr. Henderson. And then—

COUNTY ATTORNEY: Yes—?

MRS. HALE: *(Looking about)* It never seemed a very cheerful place.

COUNTY ATTORNEY: No—it's not cheerful. I shouldn't say she had the homemaking instinct.

MRS. HALE: Well, I don't know as Wright had, either.

COUNTY ATTORNEY: You mean that they didn't get on very well?

MRS. HALE: No, I don't mean anything. But I don't think a place'd be any cheerfuller for John Wright's being in it.

COUNTY ATTORNEY: I'd like to talk more of that a little later. I want to get the lay of things upstairs now. *(He goes past the women to up right where steps lead to a stair door.)*

SHERIFF: I suppose anything Mrs. Peters does'll be all right. She was to take in some clothes for her, you know, and a few little things. We left in such a hurry yesterday.

COUNTY ATTORNEY: Yes, but I would like to see what you take, Mrs. Peters, and keep an eye out for anything that might be of use to us.

MRS. PETERS: Yes, Mr. Henderson. *(The men leave by up right door to stairs. The women listen to the men's steps on the stairs, then look about the kitchen.)*

MRS. HALE: *(Crossing left to sink)* I'd hate to have men coming into my kitchen, snooping around and criticizing. *(She arranges the pans under sink which the Lawyer had shoved out of place.)*

MRS. PETERS: Of course it's no more than their duty. *(Crosses to cupboard up right)*

MRS. HALE: Duty's all right, but I guess that deputy sheriff that came out to make the fire might have got a little of this on. *(Gives the roller towel a pull)* Wish I'd thought of that sooner. Seems mean to talk about her for not having things slicked up when she had to come away in such a hurry. *(Crosses right to Mrs. Peters at cupboard)*

MRS. PETERS: *(Who has been looking through cupboard, lifts one end of a towel that covers a pan)* She had bread set. *(Stands still)*

MRS. HALE: *(Eyes fixed on a loaf of bread beside the breadbox, which is on a low shelf of the cupboard)* She was going to put this in there. *(Picks up loaf, then abruptly drops it. In a manner of returning to familiar things)* It's a shame about her fruit. I wonder if it's all gone. *(Gets up on the chair and looks)* I think there's some here that's all right, Mrs. Peters. Yes—here; *(Holding it toward the window)* this is cherries, too. *(Looking again)* I declare I believe that's the only one. *(Gets down, jar in her hand. Goes to the sink and wipes it off on the outside)* She'll feel awful bad after all her hard work in the hot weather. I remember the afternoon I put up my cherries last summer. *(She puts the jar on the big kitchen table, center of the room. With a sigh, is about to sit down in the rocking chair. Before she is seated realizes what chair it is; with a slow look at it, steps back. The chair which she has touched rocks back and forth. Mrs. Peters moves to center table and they both watch the chair rock for a moment or two.)*

MRS. PETERS: *(Shaking off the mood which the empty rocking chair has evoked. Now in a businesslike manner she speaks)* Well, I must get those things from the front room closet. *(She goes to the door at the right, but, after looking into the other room, steps back)* You coming with me, Mrs. Hale? You could help me carry them. *(They go in the other room; reappear, Mrs. Peters carrying a dress, petticoat and skirt, Mrs. Hale following with a pair of shoes.)* My, it's cold in there. *(She puts the clothes on the big table, and hurries to the stove.)*

MRS. HALE: *(Right of center table examining the skirt)* Wright was close. I think maybe that's why she kept so much to herself. She didn't even belong to the Ladies' Aid. I suppose she felt she couldn't do her part, and then you don't enjoy things when you feel shabby. I heard she used to wear pretty clothes and be lively, when she was Minnie Foster, one of the town girls singing in the choir. But that—oh, that was thirty years ago. This all you was to take in?

MRS. PETERS: She said she wanted an apron. Funny thing to want, for there isn't much to get you dirty in jail, goodness knows. But I suppose just to make her feel more natural. *(Crosses to cupboard)* She said they was in the top drawer in this cupboard. Yes, here. And then her little shawl that always hung behind the door. *(Opens stair door and looks)* Yes, here it is. *(Quickly shuts door leading upstairs)*

MRS. HALE: *(Abruptly moving toward her)* Mrs. Peters?

MRS. PETERS: Yes, Mrs. Hale? *(At up right door)*

MRS. HALE: Do you think she did it?

MRS. PETERS: *(In a frightened voice)* Oh, I don't know.

MRS. HALE: Well, I don't think she did. Asking for an apron and her little shawl. Worrying about her fruit.

MRS. PETERS: *(Starts to speak, glances up, where footsteps are heard in the room above. In a low voice)* Mr. Peters says it looks bad for her. Mr. Henderson is awful sarcastic in a speech and he'll make fun of her sayin' she didn't wake up.

MRS. HALE: Well, I guess John Wright didn't wake when they was slipping that rope under his neck.

MRS. PETERS: *(Crossing slowly to table and placing shawl and apron on table with other clothing)* No, it's strange. It must have been done awful crafty and still. They say it was such a—funny way to kill a man, rigging it all up like that.

MRS. HALE: *(Crossing to left of Mrs. Peters at table)* That's just what Mr. Hale said. There was a gun in the house. He says that's what he can't understand.

MRS. PETERS: Mr. Henderson said coming out that what was needed for the case was a motive; something to show anger, or—sudden feeling.

MRS. HALE: *(Who is standing by the table)* Well, I don't see any signs of anger around here. *(She puts her hand on the dish towel which lies on the table, stands looking down at table, one-half of which is clean, the other half messy.)* It's wiped to here. *(Makes a move as if to finish work, then turns and looks at loaf of bread outside the breadbox. Drops towel. In that voice of coming back to familiar things)* Wonder how they are finding things upstairs. *(Crossing below table to down right)* I hope she had it a little more red—up there. You know, it seems kind of sneaking. Locking her up in town and then coming out here and trying to get her own house to turn against her!

👁 **Suspicions?**

Mr. Henderson sees the motive in the death of Mr. Wright as arising out of "anger" or "sudden feeling"? How do you see it? Whom do you think killed Mr. Wright and what do you think the motive was? Explain your thinking.

MRS. PETERS: But, Mrs. Hale, the law is the law.

MRS. HALE: I s'pose 'tis. (*Unbuttoning her coat*) Better loosen up your things, Mrs. Peters. You won't feel them when you go out. (*Mrs. Peters takes off her fur tippet, goes to hang it on chair back left of table, stands looking at the work basket on floor near down left window.*)

MRS. PETERS: She was piecing a quilt. (*She brings the large sewing basket to the center and they look at the bright pieces, Mrs. Hale above the table and Mrs. Peters left of it.*)

MRS. HALE: It's a log cabin pattern. Pretty, isn't it? I wonder if she was goin' to quilt it or just knot it? (*Footsteps have been heard coming down the stairs. The Sheriff enters followed by Hale and the County Attorney.*)

SHERIFF: They wonder if she was going to quilt it or just knot it! (*The men laugh, the women look abashed.*)

COUNTY ATTORNEY: (*Rubbing his hands over the stove*) Frank's fire didn't do much up there, did it? Well, let's go out to the barn and get that cleared up. (*The men go outside by up left door.*)

MRS. HALE: (*Resentfully*) I don't know as there's anything so strange, our takin' up our time with little things while we're waiting for them to get the evidence. (*She sits in chair right of table smoothing out a block with decision.*) I don't see as it's anything to laugh about.

MRS. PETERS: (*Apologetically*) Of course they've got awful important things on their minds. (*Pulls up a chair and joins Mrs. Hale at the left of the table.*)

MRS. HALE: (*Examining another block*) Mrs. Peters, look at this one. Here, this is the one she was working on, and look at the sewing! All the rest of it has been so nice and even. And look at this! It's all over the place! Why, it looks as if she didn't know what she was about! (*After she has said this they look at each other, then start to glance back at the door. After an instant Mrs. Hale has pulled at a knot and ripped the sewing.*)

MRS. PETERS: Oh, what are you doing, Mrs. Hale?

MRS. HALE: (*Mildly*) Just pulling out a stitch or two that's not sewed very good. (*Threading a needle*) Bad sewing always made me fidgety.

MRS. PETERS: (*With a glance at door, nervously*) I don't think we ought to touch things.

MRS. HALE: I'll just finish up this end. (*Suddenly stopping and leaning forward*) Mrs. Peters?

MRS. PETERS: Yes, Mrs. Hale?

MRS. HALE: What do you suppose she was so nervous about?

MRS. PETERS: Oh—I don't know. I don't know as she was nervous. I sometimes sew awful queer when I'm just tired. (*Mrs. Hale starts to say something, looks at Mrs. Peters, then goes on sewing.)* Well, I must get these things wrapped up. They may be through sooner than we think. *(Putting apron and other things together)* I wonder where I can find a piece of paper, and string. *(Rises)*

MRS. HALE: In that cupboard, maybe.

MRS. PETERS: *(Crosses right looking in cupboard)* Why, here's a birdcage. *(Holds it up)* Did she have a bird, Mrs. Hale?

MRS. HALE: Why, I don't know whether she did or not—I've not been here for so long. There was a man around last year selling canaries cheap, but I don't know as she took one; maybe she did. She used to sing real pretty herself.

MRS. PETERS: *(Glancing around)* Seems funny to think of a bird here. But she must have had one, or why would she have a cage? I wonder what happened to it?

MRS. HALE: I s'pose maybe the cat got it.

MRS. PETERS: No, she didn't have a cat. She's got that feeling some people have about cats—being afraid of them. My cat got in her room and she was real upset and asked me to take it out.

MRS. HALE: My sister Bessie was like that. Queer, ain't it?

MRS. PETERS: *(Examining the cage)* Why, look at this door. It's broke. One hinge is pulled apart. *(Takes a step down to Mrs. Hale's right)*

MRS. HALE: *(Looking too)* Looks as if someone must have been rough with it.

MRS. PETERS: Why, yes. *(She brings the cage forward and puts it on the table.)*

MRS. HALE: *(Glancing toward up left door)* I wish if they're going to find any evidence they'd be about it. I don't like this place.

MRS. PETERS: But I'm awful glad you came with me, Mrs. Hale. It would be lonesome for me sitting here alone.

MRS. HALE: It would, wouldn't it? *(Dropping her sewing)* But I tell you what I do wish, Mrs. Peters. I wish I had come over sometimes when *she* was here. I— *(looking around the room)* —wish I had.

MRS. PETERS: But of course you were awful busy, Mrs. Hale—your house and your children.

MRS. HALE: *(Rises and crosses left)* I could've come. I stayed away because it weren't cheer-

 Suspicions?

In your opinion, what specific pieces of evidence have been found so far and by whom? How does this evidence strengthen or weaken your feelings about who killed Mr. Wright and why?

ful—and that's why I ought to have come. I— *(Looking out left window)* —I've never liked this place. Maybe because it's down in a hollow and you don't see the road. I dunno what it is, but it's a lonesome place and always was. I wish I had come over to see Minnie Foster sometimes. I can see now— *(Shakes her head)*

MRS. PETERS: *(Left of table and above it)* Well, you mustn't reproach your-self, Mrs. Hale. Somehow we just don't see how it is with other folks until—something turns up.

MRS. HALE: Not having children makes less work—but it makes a quiet house, and Wright out to work all day, and no company when he did come in. *(Turning from window)* Did you know John Wright, Mrs. Peters?

MRS. PETERS: Not to know him; I've seen him in town. They say he was a good man.

MRS. HALE: Yes—good; he didn't drink, and kept his word as well as most, I guess, and paid his debts. But he was a hard man, Mrs. Peters. Just to pass the time of day with him— *(Shivers)* Like a raw wind that gets to the bone. *(Pauses, her eye falling on the cage)* I should think she would 'a' wanted a bird. But what do you suppose went with it?

MRS. PETERS: I don't know, unless it got sick and died. *(She reaches over and swings the broken door, swings it again, both women watch it.)*

MRS. HALE: You weren't raised round here, were you? *(Mrs. Peters shakes her head.)* You didn't know—her?

MRS. PETERS: Not till they brought her yesterday.

MRS. HALE: She—come to think of it, she was kind of like a bird herself—real sweet and pretty, but kind of timid and—fluttery. How—she—did—change. *(Silence; then as if struck by a happy thought and relieved to get back to everyday things. Crosses right above Mrs. Peters to cupboard, replaces small chair used to stand on to its original place down right)* Tell you what, Mrs. Peters, why don't you take the quilt in with you? It might take up her mind.

MRS. PETERS: Why, I think that's a real nice idea, Mrs. Hale. There could-n't possibly be any objection to it, could there? Now, just what would I take? I wonder if her patches are in here—and her things. *(They look in the sewing basket.)*

MRS. HALE: *(Crosses to right of table)* Here's some red. I expect this has got sewing things in it. *(Brings out a fancy box)* What a pretty box. Looks like something somebody would give you. Maybe her scissors are in here. *(Opens box. Suddenly puts her hand to her nose)* Why— *(Mrs. Peters bends nearer, then turns her face away.)* There's something wrapped up in this piece of silk.

MRS. PETERS: Why, this isn't her scissors.

MRS. HALE: *(Lifting the silk)* Oh, Mrs. Peters—it's— *(Mrs. Peters bends closer.)*

MRS. PETERS: It's the bird.

MRS. HALE: But, Mrs. Peters—look at it! Its neck! Look at its neck! It's all—other side to.

MRS. PETERS: Somebody—wrung—its—neck. *(Their eyes meet. A look of growing comprehension, of horror. Steps are heard outside. Mrs. Hale slips box under quilt pieces, and sinks into her chair. Enter Sheriff and County Attorney. Mrs. Peters steps down left and stands looking out of window.)*

COUNTY ATTORNEY: *(As one turning from serious things to little pleasantries)* Well, ladies, have you decided whether she was going to quilt it or knot it? *(Crosses to center above table.)*

MRS. PETERS: We think she was going to—knot it. *(Sheriff crosses to right of stove, lifts stove lid and glances at fire, then stands warming hands at stove.)*

COUNTY ATTORNEY: Well, that's interesting. I'm sure. *(Seeing the birdcage)* Has the bird flown?

MRS. HALE: *(Putting more quilt pieces over the box)* We think the—cat got it.

COUNTY ATTORNEY: *(Preoccupied)* Is there a cat? *(Mrs. Hale glances in a quick covert way at Mrs. Peters.)*

MRS. PETERS: *(Turning from window, takes a step in)* Well, not *now.* They're superstitious, you know. They leave.

COUNTY ATTORNEY: *(To Sheriff Peters, continuing an interrupted conversation)* No sign at all of anyone having come from the outside. Their own rope. Now let's go up again and go over it piece by piece. *(They start upstairs)* It would have to have been someone who knew just the— *(Mrs. Peters sits down left of table. The two women sit there not looking at one another, but as if peering into something and at the same time holding back. When they talk now it is in the manner of feeling their way over strange ground, as if afraid of what they are saying, but as if they cannot help saying it.)*

MRS. HALE: *(Hesitatively and in hushed voice)* She liked the bird. She was going to bury it in that pretty box.

MRS. PETERS: *(In a whisper)* When I was a girl—my kitten—there was a boy took a hatchet, and before my eyes—and before I could get there— *(Covers her face an instant)* If they hadn't held me back I would have— *(Catches herself, looks upstairs where steps are heard, falters weakly)* —hurt him.

 Suspicions?

Whom do you think Mrs. Hale and Mrs. Peters have come to believe killed Mr. Wright? What do they feel the motive was? What evidence do they have to support their thinking? What do you expect the two women will do with their thoughts and feelings and the evidence they're based on? Why?

MRS. HALE: *(With a slow look around her)* I wonder how it would seem never to have had any children around. *(Pause)* No, Wright wouldn't like the bird—a thing that sang. She used to sing. He killed that, too.

MRS. PETERS: *(Moving uneasily)* We don't know who killed the bird.

MRS. HALE: I knew John Wright.

MRS. PETERS: It was an awful thing was done in this house that night, Mrs. Hale. Killing a man while he slept, slipping a rope around his neck that choked the life out of him.

MRS. HALE: His neck. Choked the life out of him. *(Her hand goes out and rests on the birdcage.)*

MRS. PETERS: *(With rising voice)* We don't know who killed him. We don't know.

MRS. HALE: *(Her own feeling not interrupted)* If there'd been years and years of nothing, then a bird to sing to you, it would be awful—still, after the bird was still.

MRS. PETERS: *(Something within her speaking)* I know what stillness is. when we homesteaded in Dakota, and my first baby died—after he was two years old, and me with no other then—

MRS. HALE: *(Moving)* How soon do you suppose they'll be through looking for the evidence?

MRS. PETERS: I know what stillness is. *(Pulling herself back)* The law has got to punish crime, Mrs. Hale.

MRS. HALE: *(Not as if answering that)* I wish you'd seen Minnie Foster when she wore a white dress with blue ribbons and stood up there in the choir and sang. *(A look around the room)* Oh, I wish I'd come over here once in a while! That was a crime! That was a crime! Who's going to punish that?

MRS. PETERS: *(Looking upstairs)* We mustn't—take on.

MRS. HALE: I might have known she needed help! I know how things can be—for women. I tell you, it's queer, Mrs. Peters. We live close together and we live far apart. We all go through the same things—it's all just a different kind of the same thing. *(Brushes her eyes, noticing the jar of fruit, reaches out for it)* If I was you I wouldn't tell her her fruit was gone. Tell her it *ain't*. Tell her it's all right. Take this in to prove it to her. She—may never know whether it was broke or not.

MRS. PETERS: *(Takes the jar, looks about for something to wrap it in; takes petticoat from the clothes brought from the other room, very nervously begins winding this around the jar. In a false voice)* My, it's a good thing the men couldn't hear us. Wouldn't they just laugh! Getting all stirred up over a little thing like a—dead canary. As if that could have anything to do with—with—wouldn't they laugh! *(The men are heard coming downstairs.)*

MRS. HALE: *(Under her breath)* Maybe they would—maybe they wouldn't.

COUNTY ATTORNEY: No, Peters, it's all perfectly clear except a reason for doing it. But you know juries when it comes to women. If there was some definite thing. *(Crosses slowly to above table. Sheriff crosses down right. Mrs. Hale and Mrs. Peters remain seated at either side of table.)* Something to show—something to make a story about—a thing that would connect up with this strange way of doing it— *(The women's eyes meet for an instant. Enter Hale from outer door.)*

HALE: *(Remaining up left by door)* Well, I've got the team around. Pretty cold out there.

COUNTY ATTORNEY: I'm going to stay awhile by myself. *(To the Sheriff)* You can send Frank out for me, can't you? I want to go over everything. I'm not satisfied that we can't do better.

SHERIFF: Do you want to see what Mrs. Peters is going to take in? *(The Lawyer picks up the apron, laughs.)*

COUNTY ATTORNEY: Oh, I guess they're not very dangerous things the ladies have picked out. *(Moves a few things about, disturbing the quilt pieces which cover the box. Steps back)* No, Mrs. Peters doesn't need supervising. For that matter a sheriff's wife is married to the law. Ever think of it that way, Mrs. Peters?

MRS. PETERS: Not—just that way.

SHERIFF: *(Chuckling)* Married to the law. *(Moves to down right door to the other room)* I just want you to come in here a minute, George. We ought to take a look at these windows.

COUNTY ATTORNEY: *(Scoffingly)* Oh, windows!

SHERIFF: We'll be right out, Mr. Hale. *(Hale goes outside. The Sheriff follows the County Attorney into the other room. Then Mrs. Hale rises, hands tight together, looking intensely at Mrs. Peters, whose eyes make a slow turn, finally meeting Mrs. Hale's. A moment Mrs. Hale holds her, then her own eyes point the way to where the box is concealed. Suddenly Mrs. Peters throws back quilt pieces and tries to put the box in the bag she is carrying. It is too big. She opens box, starts to take bird out, cannot touch it, goes to pieces, stands there helpless. Sound of a knob turning in the other room. Mrs. Hale snatches the box and puts it in the pocket of her big coat. Enter County Attorney and Sheriff, who remains down right.)*

COUNTY ATTORNEY: (*Crosses to up left door facetiously*) Well, Henry, at least we found out that she was not going to quilt it. She was going to—what is it you call it, ladies?

MRS. HALE: (*Standing center below table facing front, her hand against her pocket*) We call it—knot it, Mr. Henderson.

CURTAIN

 How Clever?

1. While the three men of the story search upstairs and in the barn (but hardly in the kitchen) for "important" things, things "that would point to any motive," the two women of the story find quite a few pieces of circumstantial evidence among "little things," "kitchen things." How did Mrs. Wright's own house "turn against her"?

2. In what ways does the play force us to look at what may be hidden in the things we take for granted and to realize that true observing means knowing both where to look and how to see? Give examples from the play of where this was true for both Mrs. Hale and Mrs. Peters.

3. In what ways was the victim, John Wright, "a good man"? In what ways was he "a hard man"?

4. Why does Mrs. Hale feel guilty about not visiting Mrs. Wright? How was Mrs. Wright like the bird whose neck her husband broke?

5. At the beginning of the play, Mr. Hale explains how he went to call on John Wright about getting him to go in with him on a party telephone. "I thought maybe if I went to the house and talked about it before his wife, though I said to Harry that I didn't know as what his wife wanted made much difference to John."

   How does this line of dialogue foreshadow a possible motive for the murder? How did Mrs. Hale and Mrs. Peters determine that the motive for the murder did in fact arise out of "something to show anger, or—sudden feeling"? Which "trifle" finally caused Mrs. Wright's mind to snap?

6. How did Mrs. Wright also have the opportunity and the means? Why did she use "such a—funny way to kill a man, rigging it all up like that," and not the gun that was in the house?

7. What different reasons can you provide for why the women of the story were able to function better as amateur detectives than the men, even though two of the men (the sheriff and the county attorney) were professionals in law enforcement? Explain the different attitudes the two genders have and the different approaches they took to looking for, defining, and categorizing "evidence."

8. How can something be a "trifle" (nothing important) to one person and something significant to another? How does the following exchange of dialogue between two of the men in the story point up the gender issue—how the world of women is different from the world of men—in the story?

> Sheriff Peters: Held for murder and worryin' about preserves.
> Mr. Hale: Well, women are used to worrying over trifles.

9. Find examples of sexism in the play's characters. Which character comes across as the most sexist? After Mrs. Hale says, "I don't think a place'd be any cheerfuller for John Wright's being in it," the county attorney says, "I'd like to talk more of that a little later." Explain why you think he never does.

10. At one point, Mrs. Peters tells about a boy who, when she was a young girl, took a hatchet to her kitten. "If they hadn't held me back," she goes on, "I would have—" and then catching herself, "—hurt him." How did Mrs. Peters originally mean to finish her statement? What bearing does this have on the story?

11. After Mrs. Hale fixes Mrs. Wright's nervous, uneven sewing, she suggests that Mrs. Peters bring the quilt to Mrs. Wright in jail, to which Mrs. Peters agrees: "There couldn't possibly be any objection to it, could there?" What do you think?

How do Mrs. Hale and Mrs. Peters circumvent the law? Where do they mislead the men, and where do they downplay, change, destroy, hide, or remove evidence? At what point in the play are you certain that they will do what is necessary to keep the men from discovering any evidence that will help them determine a motive? How do you feel about all this? Is this justice or obstruction of justice? Explain your thinking.

12. A year after she wrote "Trifles" as a one-act play, the author, Susan Glaspell, rewrote it in the form of a short story, and changed the title to "A Jury of Her Peers." Explain why you prefer one title over the other.

DETECTWRITE: Plot

1. Considering the evidence, do you think it probable that Mrs. Wright will be found "not guilty" by a jury of her peers when her case comes to trial? Is this justice? Explain. As a prospective writer of mystery and detective stories, how do you feel about stories with this kind of outcome? Would you write such a story? Why or why not?

2. Another kind of justice is "poetic justice." Poetic justice (which can be separate from or part of legal justice) involves the rewarding of virtue and the punishment of vice in a manner that is particularly appropriate or ironic. Several stories in this collection demonstrate "poetic justice" at work. Do you find "poetic justice" in "Trifles"? Explain. Would you write a story in which there is poetic justice outside of and contrary to legal justice? Why or why not?

3. Point out examples of irony in "Trifles." How do you feel about the place of irony in mysteries? Explain your position.

DetectWrite: Characterization

1. How are Mrs. Hale and Mrs. Peters different? How are they similar? Compare and contrast their appearance, their social and economic backgrounds, their life's experiences, and their relationships with their husbands and with Mrs. Wright.

   Based on the stage directions, dialogue, and action of the play, whom would you cast in the roles of Mrs. Hale and Mrs. Peters? Would you choose name actors? If you were to audition unknown actors, what qualities would you be looking for? Defend your choices.

2. What kinds of casting decisions would go into your choices for the three men in the play?

3. Let's suppose that farmer Hale's description in the play of Mrs. Wright when he came upon her in the kitchen was shown in a movie as a flashback. We would need an actress to study the character and play her. Give written instructions to the actress who will play Mrs. Wright on everything she needs to know about her character. Base your directions on all of the evidence in the play and on everything else you know about Mrs. Wright's background and life from having read the entire play.

DetectWrite: Setting

1. How do the details of the scenic design for the Wright kitchen mirror Mrs. Wright's life with her husband?

2. How do the details of the scenic design for the Wright kitchen reflect the suddenness of Mrs. Wright's decision to kill her husband?

3. Why doesn't the audience ever go with the men upstairs or outside? How does the author's use of the "unit set" (in this case, the kitchen of the farmhouse) reflect the focus of interest of the play? Would you change this in a film version of the play? Explain.

4. In a film version of the play, would you create a scene in which Mr. Hale questions Mrs. Wright in the kitchen and then finds her husband dead in bed upstairs—or would you convey these details as exposition in the scene in which Mr. Hale responds to the county attorney's request to "tell just what happened when you came here yesterday morning"? Defend your decision.

DetectWrite: Plot and Dialogue

1. In the short story version of "Trifles," the author adds the following line of dialogue for the county attorney after he has asked Mrs. Peters to "keep an eye out for anything that might be of use to us": "No telling you women might come upon a clue to the motive—and that's the thing we need."

Do you think this additional piece of dialogue adds to or detracts from the story? Give the reasoning behind your opinion.

2. In the play, right after Mrs. Hale hides the box with the dead canary in it in her coat pocket, the county attorney comments to the effect that their investigation at the house was pretty much a failure, that about all they found out was something as insignificant, as trifling, as the fact that Mrs. Wright was going to knot her sewing, not quilt it. Then the play ends.

    In the short story version, "A Jury of Her Peers," the author omits that conversation, ending the story with action instead: "There was the sound of a knob turning in the inner door. Martha Hale snatched the box from the sheriff's wife, and got it in the pocket of her big coat just as the sheriff and the county attorney came back into the kitchen."

    Which ending do you prefer and why?

DETECTWRITE: Characterization and Stage Directions

"The law has got to punish crime," Mrs. Peters, the sheriff's wife, says to Mrs. Hale, disagreeing with Mrs. Hale's implication that John Wright deserved to be killed. The county attorney says a little bit later that "a sheriff's wife is married to the law."

However, throughout the play the sheriff's wife has moved—in motion and emotion—considerably closer to Mrs. Hale, both in terms of geographical position and emotional position. Trace this change in Mrs. Peters in the stage directions of the play, noting where the actress playing Mrs. Peters is physically located in relation to the actress playing Mrs. Hale. As the play progresses, how does the "blocking" of Mrs. Peters' stage position correspond with her emotional alignment with Mrs. Hale's position on justice and the law.

In a mystery or detective play that you write, use stage directions not only as cues to the actor's positions, actions, and body language but also as a way of making a symbolic or thematic statement.

The Interrogation

Eric Weiner

THE HEADMISTRESS OPENED HER OFFICE DOOR WIDE. SHE stared out at the slump-shouldered girl who sat stranded on the wide leather sofa of the outer office, waiting for her. The headmistress smiled without warmth. "Come in," she said.

It wasn't an invitation, it was an order. The girl got up. She gathered the books she had piled beside her on the sofa and, cradling them against her chest as if for protection, filed past the headmistress into the room.

The headmistress's office at the Hadley School for Girls looked as if it had been designed specifically to wring confessions from students. Walnut wainscoting and a paneled wooden ceiling made the room dark and foreboding. Large oil portraits of former headmistresses, all of whom seemed to stare down accusingly, hung on the walls. At the far end of the room loomed the headmistress's wide mahogany desk, dominating the entire space like a judge's platform. Across from the desk stood a high-backed wooden chair, floating alone in a sea of red Oriental carpet. This was the seat for students who must face the headmistress. This was the seat of the accused.

"Sit down," the headmistress said curtly.

The girl sat. She was fifteen and in her third year at Hadley but she was a mousy sort of girl who made little impression. Miss Kendrick, the headmistress, only vaguely recognized her.

"I presume you know why you're here."

The girl shook her head no.

"Oh, come now," the headmistress scoffed. She leaned against her desk, arms folded. "You didn't hear about the trouble with Mr. Carr?"

The girl squirmed. "I haven't heard a thing," she said. Behind her glasses, she kept blinking.

Miss Kendrick stared at the girl.

"I haven't," the girl insisted. But even as she said it, her heart was pounding out the words *I have, I have, I have.* Every girl at Hadley already knew about the picture in Mr. Carr's classroom.

It showed Mr. Carr and the headmistress locked together in a wild position, which was probably physically impossible. Both figures were stark naked, and certain parts of their bodies had been drawn crudely out of proportion. And just in case the picture might seem to lack the old school spirit, the artist had added the Hadley school insignia as a tattoo on Mr. Carr's—.

The girl lowered her gaze to the red carpet. Not only did she know about the picture, she thought the picture was very funny. But she wasn't about to say so.

Miss Kendrick sat down. Her chair was larger than the girl's, and a little higher. "Well then," she said, "I guess you're the last to know." She smiled briefly. "It seems that someone has painted an obscenity in Mr. Carr's classroom. Mr. Carr is understandably upset. And deeply hurt. As am I."

"I'm sorry to hear that," the girl said, shifting in her seat.

"Are you?"

"Yes, ma'am." The girl started biting her nails, then quickly put her hand back under her books in her lap.

"Well, let me tell you why I'm so concerned," the headmistress said. "You know about the term *in loco parentis*?"

The girl did. In fact, it seemed to her it was all they ever talked about at Hadley. *In loco parentis,* "in the place of a parent." What it meant was there was always someone at Hadley telling you what to do.

"While you are within these walls," the headmistress intoned in her deep voice, "we are responsible for you girls in every way. From the moment you wake up to the moment you go to bed, it's our job to see that you are educated physically, spiritually, mentally, and morally. To do that, it is imperative that we command your utmost respect. Understood?"

"Yes, ma'am."

The headmistress placed her hands on the glossy wood of her desktop and pushed herself slowly to her full majestic height. She began pacing the room, circling around the girl. The girl could feel sweat beading on her upper lip. But she kept her hands under the books on her lap.

"Now. We know the picture was done during third period, because that's the only time Mr. Carr's classroom is idle. We've talked to almost every girl who has third period free. You're second to last."

The girl blinked nervously, gave a little smile. "I'm used to that," she said.

Miss Kendrick didn't smile back. "Are you?" she asked. She was by the window now. She turned her back on the girl. Outside, it was a dingy November afternoon and the girl could see one of her dormmates making her way through the quad, looking cold, forlorn, and depressed. Probably on an errand for some senior, the girl thought.

Miss Kendrick's next question sounded almost casual, "Did you do it?"

It took the girl a second to respond. "No!" Her voice was raspy with tension.

The headmistress sighed. "I didn't think so. It seems that no-body did." She chuckled dryly as she sat down again. "I guess that picture just painted itself."

The headmistress fixed the girl with her pale gray eyes. "Where were you third period?"

"I . . . I . . . I don't want to say."

"You don't want to say? What are you talking about?"

"I . . . I just can't say, I'm sorry."

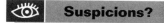

Suspicions?

Whom do you suspect of having painted the picture in Mr. Carr's classroom? Why?

"You can't." Smiling, the headmistress glanced around the room as if she were sharing a joke with the paintings on the walls "Good. So then you admit you painted the picture?"

"No!"

"Then where were you?"

The girl didn't answer.

The headmistress stared at the books on the girl's lap. "Put your books down," she ordered.

The girl's hands were shaking as she transferred the books to the carpet. She shoved her hands into the side pockets of her school uniform's plaid skirt.

The headmistress studied her for several moments, until the girl shivered. "All right," the headmistress said. "Let me see your hands."

"My what?"

"You heard me. Your hands. Let me see them."

At first the girl didn't move. Then she drew her hands out of her pockets. For a moment, she kept them in her lap palms down. Then slowly, reluctantly, the girl raised her hands.

"Closer!"

The girl stretched her hands out toward the desk. The headmistress leaned forward.

The girl's palms were spattered with black paint.

Miss Kendrik looked up slowly, her eyes boring into those of the girl. The girl looked down at her hands.

Then she started crying, large tears rolling down her cheeks. "OK, I admit it," she said softly, "I painted it. I painted it! OK? I painted the picture."

"You did."

"Y—yes."

"You're sure?"

"Yes! Yes!"

"You snuck in there and painted it?"

"Right."

"And that's why your hands are covered with black paint, is that correct?"

"Yes! Yes! That's what I'm saying! I painted that awful picture!" The girl's eyes were blurry with tears.

"Now why would someone do such a thing?" Miss Kendrick asked.

The girl snuffled loudly as she wiped her nose with the back of her hand. "I don't know. I guess I thought it would be funny."

"Funny? You call that filth funny?"

"Well, no, I don't, not anymore. I'm sorry. I really am." The girl waited, but the headmistress didn't say anything, so the girl said it again. "What else can I say? I'm really, really sorry."

"You are."

"Yes, ma'am."

The headmistress shook her head slowly, gravely. "OK, let's have it," she said. "What's going on?"

"What do you mean?"

"Why are you lying to me?"

"I don't know what—"

"Your hands are the wrong color."

"What? I don't under—"

Suspicions?

Why do you think the headmistress has concluded that something is going on and that the girl's confession is a lie? Explain.

"That little obscenity in Mr. Carr's classroom . . . it was painted in red."

The girl was about to speak, but she closed her mouth, swallowing the words.

"*All* red," the headmistress said.

The girl could feel her face flushing deeply. The headmistress's face reddened as well. They stared at one other. Then, abruptly, the girl started crying again. They were noisy sobs this time "I'm . . . sorry," she struggled to say. "Oh, God. I'm sorry. I didn't mean . . . to lie."

"We'll deal with that later," the headmistress said. Her tone was almost gentle now. "Right now we just want to know who did it."

"But I . . . I can't!"

"Oh now, of course you can," said Miss Kendrick. The gentleness disappeared as abruptly as it had come. "I want the name. Now."

A last tear ran down into the corner of the girl's mouth. "If I tell, she won't get—suspended. Will she?"

"That's not your concern."

The girl looked down at her hands, studying her black stained fingers. "Laura did it," she said at last.

"Laura who?" the headmistress demanded, though there was only one Laura the girl could mean.

"Laura Templeton," the girl said. She covered her mouth, apparently horrified by what she had done. "Oh, God," she said, "I shouldn't have told, I—"

"Of course you should have," Miss Kendrick snapped. Her eyes were flashing. She was obviously stunned. "Well, come on," she said. "Let's have the rest of it."

"No, I can't, I—"

The headmistress snapped her fingers hard—twice—as if she were commanding a small animal. "Stop your whining," she ordered. The girl was silent. "Why did Laura Templeton paint that picture?"

"Well, she just did it for a gag, you know. She never thought Mr. Carr would get so mad. She really didn't—"

The girl gave the headmistress a pleading look, but Miss Kendrick's face offered her no hope.

"And?" Miss Kendrick asked.

"Well, when Mr. Carr got so furious, Laura got really scared. And she told me—" The girl hesitated.

"She told you what?"

"She told me that if I didn't take the blame for it, she'd fix it so"—a fresh sob escaped her—"so no girl ever talked to me again."

"I see."

Laura Templeton was a student Miss Kendrick knew and liked. She was pretty, popular, athletic. This year, as a senior she'd been appointed proctor of Bingham Dorm. Proctors were in charge of checking that the other students observed all dorm rules. From everything that Miss Kendrick had heard, Laura was handling the job beautifully.

"I know, I know it doesn't seem like her," the girl said. "But . . . " She trailed off.

"But what? Listen, young lady, we're going to sit here until I've heard everything, so you can save yourself a lot of time and trouble by telling me exactly what is going on!"

The girl sighed. "It's like we're her slaves," she said quietly.

"Slaves? What kind of nonsense is this? She's only a proctor."

The girl nodded. "If she wants to, she can make your life a living . . . well . . . hell," the girl said.

"Go on," the headmistress ordered. "I want to hear it all."

The girl did as she was told. She told all, all the things the faculty didn't know about Laura. How Laura demanded total respect. And if you crossed her, she would get you. Laura and her friends would shortsheet your bed. Knock your books out of your arms when they passed you on the paths. Spill coffee on your homework. Reset your alarm clock so you'd be late for class. If Laura was really angry with someone, she'd get the whole dorm chanting that girl's name before assembly.

Hearing this last item, the headmistress reddened again. She had heard plenty of chanting this year at assembly, and she had never managed to stop it.

"A lot of it's just little stuff, you know?" the girl continued. "But it kind of adds up. And, and if you want to get back in her good graces? Well, it's like, you have to be Laura's maid. And you have to do all these favors for her. It doesn't matter what she asks you, you have to do it and—"

The girl stopped short as if she had just realized where her words had taken her.

"And that's what happened to you," the headmistress said.

The girl nodded, blinking back fresh tears.

"So now you had to do her *this* favor, confessing to a crime you didn't commit?"

She nodded again.

Miss Kendrick thought for several moments. "All right," she said at last. "You can go."

She walked the girl to the door. Before she opened the door, Miss Kendrick told her she should keep their discussion private for the time being. The girl promised that she would. Then the headmistress opened the door and said, "Laura, you may come in now."

Laura Templeton was sitting and waiting on the same sofa where the girl herself had waited. The girl stopped short when she saw her.

Laura stood, smiling brightly at Miss Kendrick.

As much as the girl hated Laura, the sight of her caused her a sharp stab of remorse.

Then the girl left. Her heart was pounding like crazy.

At one-thirty that night, long after all the other young residents in Bingham Dorm had gone to sleep, the girl was still wide awake. She slipped out of her room and went softly down the hall to the bathroom.

The bathroom was deserted. Still, the girl was taking no chances. She took off her robe and stepped into one of the two shower stalls, which had the privacy of a curtain. She turned the faucets on full blast.

That afternoon, the dorm head had searched Laura's room and found a red-stained paintbrush. Rumor had it that she was going to be expelled.

The girl carefully scrubbed her hands. The black paint ran down her legs and swirled down the little metal drain.

Then she went to work on the red stains underneath.

 Suspicions?

1. Why do you think the girl's hands are "spattered with black paint"?

2. Who painted the picture in Mr. Carr's classroom—Laura Templeton or "the girl"—and why do you think so?

3. If your final suspect is different from who it was before, what caused you to change your mind? If your suspect has stayed the same, explain why.

 How Clever?

1. What is an interrogation? Which professionals do you usually associate with the conducting of an interrogation? As the headmistress conducts her interrogation, how does she, in effect, function as an amateur detective?

2. Is the headmistress successful at "playing detective"? How does the end of the story use an indirect means to reveal that "the girl" and not Laura Templeton was guilty of painting the picture in Mr. Carr's classroom? Why didn't the girl wash the paint off her hands before she was called for the interrogation?

3. Miss Kendrick tells the girl, "We've talked to almost every girl who has third period free. You're second to last," and the girl replies, "I'm used to that." What does it mean to the girl psychologically to feel that she is always second to last? How is this feeling confirmed by the fact that the girl is described as "a mousy sort of girl who made little impression" and the fact that "Miss Kendrick, the headmistress, only vaguely recognized her"?

4. Based on what you know about Miss Kendrick's feelings about Laura Templeton, explain why it is understandable that Laura would be the last student with a free third period to be interrogated.

5. Why is it important to both the girl and to the plot of the story that the girl keep her hands covered or hidden during the early stages of the interrogation?

6. What alibi, if any, does the girl have for her whereabouts during the third period?

7. How does the girl manage to distract the headmistress so that Miss Kendrick does not return to the question of the girl's whereabouts during the third period? How successful can a detective (amateur or professional) be if he or she is easily distracted? Explain.

8. What was the girl's motive? Why did she choose Laura Templeton to "frame" for the crime? Do you think the girl committed the crime for reasons having to do with her feelings about the school and then decided to frame Laura, or do you think the girl committed the crime for the purpose of framing Laura? Explain why you chose the motive that you did.

9. "The girl stopped short as if she had just realized where her words had taken her." How does the girl make it seem as if Miss Kendrick has to pull all the incriminating information out of her when actually the girl's objective in the interrogation is to wrongly place the responsibility for the crime on Laura? Find in the story other specific instances of a character's action or dialogue where it appears that Miss Kendrick is in control of the interrogation when actually the girl is.

DETECTWRITE: Characterization

1. From the point of view of an author of mystery stories, explain why you believe that not giving "the girl" an actual name makes the story more effective or less effective.

2. Find details in the author's characterization of the girl and of Miss Kendrick that later turn out to be misleading. In your opinion, would this qualify as a red herring (misleading clue)? Explain.

3. The headmistress in this particular story turns out to be an unsuccessful amateur detective. Do you think that that would be true for educators in general? Explain. For a detective story you would write, explain why you would or would not choose a teacher as the amateur detective.

DETECTWRITE: Plot

1. Were the author's repeated references to the girl's covered or hidden hands during the early part of the interrogation too many, too few, or about right for a reader trying to figure out what is going on? Explain.

2. Create a brief piece of dialogue in which the change of just one or two words (like Miss Kendrick's use of "black paint" instead of "paint" and "someone" instead of "you") would communicate a different enough meaning to affect the development of the plot. Explain.

3. What do you like or dislike about the author's indirect way of revealing the girl as the perpetrator of the crime? Explain.

4. How do you feel about the resolution of a mystery story in which the guilty party gets away with the crime? Why do you feel this way? Do you feel the same way in the case of this particular story? Were your feelings the same or different for similar stories in this collection? Explain. Why would you or wouldn't you write such a story?

DETECTWRITE: Setting

How did the author's use of particular details of the physical setting of the story create the false impression that no student could be a match for the headmistress? Could the story's setting be considered a red herring? Explain. What other possible settings for a story might suggest, correctly or not, that one character has more power than another?

Part two

Professional Private Eyes at Work

DDS 10752 Libra

John Lutz and Josh Pachter

DWIGHT STONE SAT HUNCHED OVER THE TELEPHONE IN THE yellow glow from the antique lamp atop his desk. His voice was pitched low but excited. The huge oak rolltop was the dominant feature of Stone's cluttered living room, which also served as his office. Most of the furniture scattered around was ancient, because he couldn't afford anything newer; the desk and lamp, legacies from a long-dead aunt, were the only valuable pieces in the apartment.

A mischievous smile flickered briefly across his lips as he cradled the receiver, but his clear brown eyes were still troubled. He crossed to the tiny cubicle his landlord called a kitchenette, made coffee on a hot plate, and carried a steaming mug back to his desk. He pulled a blank expense account form from one of the drawers and laboriously began to fill it in, now and then darting out a hand for coffee or to work the cantankerous old adding machine at his side. He was a large man, with too much upholstery straining the material of his clothes; he and his overstuffed furniture were perfectly compatible.

In a silence between ratchety growls of the adding machine, Stone suddenly sat up straight. A slight noise from behind had alerted him. He turned, and saw the tarnished brass knob of the front door slowly rotating, heard a floorboard creak outside in the hall. Fear lanced through his bowels like a shaft of ice as he realized that he *had* been followed home, after all.

Fright momentarily numbed him. Like most small-town private investigators, he never carried a gun, didn't even own one. He regretted that now, because he had no illusions about who it was that stood outside his door. Or about what it was the man had come for.

True, the door was locked, but the lock was a joke and would offer little resistance. It would slow down the man outside for a moment, but it wouldn't stop him.

There wasn't much time. Within the next few minutes, Stone knew, he would be out of time forever.

Swallowing his terror, he scribbled hastily at the bottom of the paper he was working on. There was an ominous click from the doorway, and he dropped his pen and reached for one of the desk's many cubbyholes.

Seconds later, the apartment door swung open behind him.

Nudger watched the two detectives nosing around the ransacked apartment. The place was a mess. Stone hadn't been much of a housekeeper to begin with, and whoever had killed him had taken the time to toss the four small rooms with frantic thoroughness.

The policemen were both in their fifties; they moved with the studied nonchalance of the typical small-town cop. They were a team: one was named Byrnes (the plodder, Nudger soon decided), the other was Allen (the brains of the operation). Nudger resisted making the obvious crack about George and Gracie. He didn't figure this pair for a comedy act.

"Go through it again," said Byrnes, standing in the light from the front window. The lamp on the big old rolltop where Stone had died was still on. Nudger had found it on when he'd arrived, an hour earlier, and had left it that way. He hadn't touched the body, either; it lay slumped across the surface of the desk, as he had discovered it. The expression on the half of Stone's face he could see was twisted, terrorized. There was no blood on the desk or the floor, because the small-caliber bullet that had left a neat little hole in the back of Stone's head on entry hadn't come out the other side. Nudger was glad about that; he hated the sight of blood. Murder scared him plenty all by itself, without the accompanying gore.

"Stone had been hired to recover a set of drawings which had been stolen from the office of a fashion designer here in town," he said tiredly, starting in on the story for the third time. "He phoned me in the city last night and told me about the case. He'd only been brought in a couple of days ago, but he'd already managed to get his hands on the drawings. He was worried that the thief would try to get them back again, though, so he'd hidden them someplace where he was sure they'd be safe. He wouldn't tell me where they were, but he seemed pretty clear that the thief would never be able to find them. He was going to work up an expense account, he said, then catch some sleep. He wanted me to meet him here this morning and go with him to pick up the drawings and deliver them to his client. Just in case the thief tried to get him back, he said."

Byrnes and Allen listened impassively.

"When I showed up here," Nudger went on, "he didn't answer my knock. I slipped the lock with a credit card and came in to wait for him."

Byrnes stirred. "That's breaking and entering," he remarked.

Actually it was trespassing, but Nudger decided not to quibble. Somehow the time seemed wrong for a discussion of legal niceties. "Bull," he said. "Dwight Stone and I have been friends for years. I let myself in whenever I came calling and found him out. He didn't mind; he did the same thing at my place." He motioned toward the body at the desk. "Anyway, I found him like that and phoned the police immediately."

Allen's pale blue eyes were unreadable. If he held any particular opinion about Nudger's story, he wasn't letting it show. Byrnes, on the other hand, had a more provincial personality; he was making no effort to conceal his disdain for the hotshot city-slicker P.I.

"You didn't touch anything?" Allen asked.

"Of course not."

"Just like on TV," said Byrnes. Nudger couldn't tell if he was kidding.

"Tell us more about this case Stone was working on," Allen suggested.

"There's not much to tell. Geoffrey Devane's got a small but very successful fashion house here in your town. He does all the designing himself, and employs about two-dozen people to manufacture and market the clothing. When he opened up his safe on Monday morning, the drawings for his spring line were missing. Four of the people who work for him knew the combination of the safe, and Devane figured one of the four must have swiped the designs, planning on selling them to one of the firm's competitors."

"Industrial espionage," Allen murmured.

"Exactly. Devane reported the theft, but the police didn't seem very encouraging, so he decided to bring in a private investigator. He got Stone's number out of the Yellow Pages, and it took Dwight three days to pin down the thief's identify and recover the drawings."

"Only the thief wanted them back"—Allen picked up the narrative— "so he followed Stone home and killed him and turned the place upside down looking for them."

"That's the way I figure it," Nudger agreed.

Allen trudged to the window, gazed outside, then turned to face Nudger. He was framed by sunlight, and Nudger had to squint to look at him. That was the sort of technique cops used on suspects, not fellow professionals. Nudger's stomach twitched out a warning. He thumbed back the foil on a roll of antacid tablets and popped two of the chalky disks into his mouth.

"Nervous?" Allen asked.

"My stomach is. Almost always."

"Ulcer?"

"Don't know. Afraid to find out."

"Dumb."

"I guess."

"You say you used a credit card to slip the lock this morning?"

Nudger nodded. "The killer must have locked the door behind him when he left last night."

"Why last night? Why not this morning, sometime before you arrived?"

"The lamp on the desk," said Nudger. "It must have been dark outside when Stone was shot, that's why he had it switched on."

 Suspicions?

"That was the sort of technique cops used on suspects, not fellow professionals." Nudger's nervous stomach warns him that the police may not be buying his story, that he may be a suspect. Nudger contends that he discovered the body that morning and that Stone had to have been murdered the night before. What clue in the story so far might help conclude that Stone had been murdered not in the morning but some time at night?

"You look good for this, you know." Byrnes scowled. "In spite of your pretty story." He seemed to relish the opportunity to speak in Hollywood cliches.

"You mean I'm a suspect?" Nudger asked, as if the thought had just now occurred to him. It was uncomfortable, standing there in a room with two homicide detectives as they plied their trade. It was uncomfortable standing there in a room with a dead body in it. The combination of cops and corpse was lousy. "Don't forget," he said to Allen, who seemed much the more open-minded of the two, "I'm the one who called this in in the first place."

"Subterfuge," Allen suggested. "You and Stone were pals. You figured we'd get around to you sooner or later, so you called in the murder to convince us you had nothing to do with it."

Now they were ganging up on him. It didn't seem fair. "I'm not that devious," Nudger said. "And what about the murder weapon? I'm not carrying a gun, and you haven't found one in the apartment. And the door was locked when I got here."

"That's *your* story," said Byrnes doggedly. He shot a glance at the corpse. "What's *his* story?"

"What about my motive?" Nudger tried.

"We might just find one."

Or invent one, Nudger thought. He popped another antacid tablet into his mouth. Small-town murder, small-town cops, small-town judge and jury. Put it all together and it might spell big-time trouble.

"Mind if I look at the desk for a minute?" he asked.

"Be our guest," Allen told him.

Nudger crossed the room, riffled through the papers on the rolltop's surface, explored its cubbyholes carefully.

"The expense account," he said at last, straightening and looking over at Allen. "Stone told me he was going to work it up for Devane after he got through talking with me, but there's no sign of the form on his desk."

"*You* say he told you," Byrnes reminded Nudger." What *I* say is that you and Stone were together last night. You had an argument, or you've got some other motive we haven't tumbled to yet. You shot him, then realized we'd tie you to him eventually. So you went away and ditched the gun, then came back this morning so you could 'find' the body and call us in and feed us your carefully rehearsed version of the facts."

Nudger thought back over the last fifteen hours and realized he'd been completely alone between the time he'd hung up the phone after talking with Stone and his discovery of the body this morning. Alone on the phone with Stone; the words ran through his mind and kept him from thinking clearly. The law couldn't prove he was here when Stone was murdered, that was certain—but Nudger couldn't prove he wasn't here, either. His stomach dived and did a few tight loops.

"The fingerprint man and photographer ought to be here soon," Byrnes announced. "When they show up, we'll be leaving."

"I know," Nudger said. "You're going to take me downtown for another little chat."

"This *is* downtown," Allen told him. "You can call your lawyer from headquarters."

"I'll wait until I'm charged before I do that," Nudger muttered. He wasn't at all sure Byrnes and Allen had enough evidence to hold him on a murder rap.

Allen shrugged. Byrnes smiled. Nudger figured they probably thought they had enough.

 Suspicions?

Sometimes in detective stories the absence of something that should be present is a more significant clue than the presence of something that shouldn't be there. Which important item seems to be missing from the scene of the crime? (To have another look: review both Stone's actions in the beginning of the story and Nudger's account to the detectives about the arrangements he had made with Stone.)

Staring at the big rolltop desk and the position of the body, he had an idea. Or maybe it was just a final straw to clutch at before drowning in a sea of lawyers, judges, and jurors. And then jailers.

"Maybe he hid it," he said.

"Hid what?" That was Allen, of course. Byrnes had better things to do than pay attention to anything Nudger might offer.

"The expense account form. Stone was sitting at his desk when he was shot. What if he heard someone at the door behind him? He might have had just enough time to scrawl a message on that form and hide it from his killer."

"That's right," said Byrnes, deadpan, "he was working on his expenses when he bought it."

"Which would explain how come there's no expense account form in plain view on the desk now," Nudger continued. "He wrote a message on it and hid it before the killer entered the apartment."

That line of reasoning seemed to sway Allen slightly. He gave Nudger an encouraging smile. Byrnes looked like he was wishing they could wind this whole thing up, so he could file his report and head for home. Police work, this minor matter of the rest of Nudger's life, was apparently annoying him.

Nudger walked back to the desk, and neither officer moved to stop him.

"We looked and you looked," Byrnes said.

"Can I look again?"

"Why not?" Allen shrugged. "With a minimum of touching, please."

Nudger stood back from the desk and scanned it carefully. Nothing he could see even remotely resembled an expense account form.

"We already checked under the body," said Byrnes, hoping to hurry things along. "We did everything but take the damn desk apart."

"You didn't look where you couldn't see, though, did you?"

 Suspicions?

Where do you think Nudger can possibly look that the police didn't because they couldn't see? (The police say they "already checked under the body" and "did everything but take the damn desk apart.")

"What do you mean?" Allen's forehead wrinkled with puzzlement.

Ignoring him, Nudger stepped to the desk and eased the rolltop down as far as possible, almost to the point where it would have touched Stone's body.

A printed form was attached to the accordion S-roll of the retractable top with a bit of cellophane tape. Stone must have had just enough time to use the tape, then push the rolltop up and out of sight before his murderer came into the room.

Nudger tore the form away from the wooden rolltop triumphantly. Byrnes and Allen had already moved to flank him, and the three of them read the combination of letters and numbers scribbled across the bottom of the sheet:

DDS 10752 LIBRA

"Libra," said Byrnes, with a disgusted look at his partner. "Don't tell me this turns out to be another one of your damn zodiac cases."

"'Zodiac cases'?" Nudger repeated, turning the words into a question.

Allen frowned. "A couple years back," he explained, "I solved a case where a dying man's last word was *Gemini,* and Byrnes here thinks that makes me some kind of astrology expert."

"Libra," Byrnes grumbled. "And DDS. And 10752. What the hell's it all supposed to mean?"

Nudger fumbled with his roll of antacid tablets, then changed his mind and slipped the roll back into his pocket. "The DDS part I understand," he said. "Stone once told me he was born during Eisenhower's first presidential campaign. His parents were staunch Republicans, so they named him Dwight David. Which made his initials DDS."

"And," Allen mused, "he was born during Ike's campaign." He bent over the body and slid a thin billfold from the dead man's hip pocket. Unfolding it, he leafed through its half-dozen plastic windows until he located Stone's driver's license. "Uh-huh. He was born on October seventh, 1952: that's 10/7/52."

"Which makes him a Libra, all right," Byrnes contributed. "Same as my wife." Suddenly he faced Nudger and snapped, "What's *your* sign?"

"No smoking," Nudger told him.

"Get serious, tough guy."

"I'm not tough and I am serious. I don't have any idea what my sign is. My birthday's September thirteenth, does that help any?"

"Virgo," said Byrnes, as if a lot of things had just been explained.

"So the letters are his initials, the numbers are his birthdate, and Libra is his astrological sign," Allen nodded. "But—I mean, so *what?*"

 Suspicions?

This is a crucial clue: it is the message Stone "scribbled hastily at the bottom of the paper he was working on." Try to decipher it. What possible meanings does each of what appears to be three distinct elements have for you? What possible meanings might they have in combination? What might they have meant to Dwight Stone?

"Maybe the killer was a Libra, too," Byrnes suggested feebly.

"Or a dentist," said Nudger, glad to see that the focus of the investigation had shifted away from him for a change. "DDS might stand for Doctor of Dental Surgery, you know, instead of Dwight David Stone."

Before Byrnes could formulate an appropriately snide comeback, the fingerprint man and photographer arrived. They turned out to be the same man, a wiry scarecrow with bristling gray hair and a genuine Speed Graphic camera, like the press used to rely on in the thirties and forties. Then a second man turned up, the county's medical examiner and town's mortician. There was a lot of versatility in this backwater. Stone hadn't had any family, and the M.E. was sizing up the furniture to see how big a funeral the estate could be expected to cover.

Suspicions?

If Stone was born during Eisenhower's first presidential campaign that would mean that he was born in the year 1952. How does that fact help you with any other part of the message Stone scribbled?

While the experts went about their tasks, Nudger, Byrnes, and Allen turned back to Dwight Stone's last desperate message.

"We oughta check his horoscope for today," Byrnes proposed.

Nudger thought that was as logical an idea as he'd heard so far.

"Never mind that," Allen said, snapping his fingers. There was a hunter's gleam in his eye. "Let's go."

"Go?" Byrnes asked gruffly. "Go where?"

"You'll see," said Allen. "And you're not going to like it when I tell you Nudger here gave me the idea."

"Me?" Nudger looked around blankly, making sure there was nobody else with that name in the apartment. "What'd I say?"

"You said maybe the killer was a dentist." Allen smiled mysteriously, and they couldn't get another word out of him.

They left Stone's apartment and crossed the street to a dusty unmarked car parked illegally next to a fire hydrant. Halfway to their destination, Nudger finally realized where they were headed, and why. He was impressed. Maybe there was something to be said for small-town detective work, after all.

If Allen turned out to be right, that is.

The building was suitably quiet. There were people there—old ladies in padded armchairs devouring Barbara Cartland romances, college types copying term papers from assorted encyclopedias, a prim woman with her hair in a bun pulling outdated periodicals out of plastic covers and replacing them with more recent issues—but all of them went about their business in silence.

 Suspicions?

Based on the specific details of this paragraph, what building has Detective Allen driven his partner and Nudger to? Why do you think Allen has gone there, of all places?

It took only a few moments for Allen to find the shelf he was looking for, and he ran his index finger along the spines of the books lined up there until he reached one whose white gummed label read 107.52 and, beneath that, Mol. He eased the book from the shelf and pronounced its title aloud: *"Teaching Philosophy,* by Vincent Molloy. Should make fascinating reading, if that's the sort of reading that fascinates you. Me, I like the 87th Precinct."

There were several sheets of paper sandwiched between the book's removable dust jacket and permanent hard cover. Allen slid them free and unfolded them. Each page displayed a sketch of a woman dressed in delicate pastel clothing, and each drawing had been signed by Geoffrey Devane at the lower-right corner.

On the top sheet, in Dwight Stone's handwriting, the name of Devane's comptroller had been penciled in.

"I'm still not sure I understand it all," Byrnes said, as Nudger and the two detectives sat over coffee in a closet-sized office at headquarters. Luther Higham, Devane's comptroller, had confessed to the theft of the drawings and the murder of Dwight Stone, and was in a holding cell awaiting arraignment on charges of industrial espionage and murder.

Nudger was glad to explain. "Higham opened up the safe and stole his boss's drawings, planning to sell them to a competitor. But unfortunately—for the thief, that is—Stone was able to recover the sketches. He was afraid to keep them in his apartment, though, figuring—correctly, as it turned out—that the thief might know who he was and come after them. So he stashed them at the local library, figuring he and I would pick them up the next morning and deliver them to Devane."

Byrnes finished his coffee and set down his Styrofoam cup, still looking perplexed. "That much I get," he said. "And to make sure he wouldn't forget which book he'd hidden the drawings in, he used the volume whose call number matched his birthdate. But why did he put his initials on that note he left you? And why the hell did he bother writing down his sign?"

"They weren't his initials," said Allen. "And it wasn't his sign, either. It was Nudger who tipped me off to that, when he pointed out that DDS didn't *have* to stand for Dwight David Stone. Well, it didn't stand for a dentist, either:

it stood for Dewey decimal system, the cataloging system used for classifying nonfiction books by subject. Stone was telling Nudger that he'd hidden the drawings in the book shelved under Number 107.52 according to the Dewey decimal system."

 Suspicions?

Can you answer Detective Byrnes' questions and solve the puzzle? Consider the possibility that Byrnes' questions contain red herrings (false clues) that have distracted you.

"But why Libra?" Byrnes demanded.

Nudger grinned. "Stone didn't have time to finish his message and hide it away before Devane's comptroller broke into his apartment. It was more important to hide it than to finish it, so he stopped writing, two letters before what he'd intended to be the end of the message, and counted on Nudger to realize what he meant."

"Library," Byrnes sighed. "Dewey decimal system number 107.52, in the public library."

"Only I managed to miss it," said Nudger. "I guess I'm not as bright as Stone thought. Good thing for me your partner worked it out."

Byrnes washed a hand across his face. "Yeah, sure is. Listen, Nudger, looks like I owe you an apology. I jump to conclusions, sometimes. It's a lousy habit, I know, but I do it anyway. Like with that astrology business—"

Nudger stood up from his straight-backed chair, feeling his stomach beginning to react to the acidic coffee he'd only half finished. He smiled and waved a hand negligently and said, "Forget the apology. Let's just say you owe me a decent cup of coffee. That stuff you guys drink is awful."

"Actually, we usually drink tea." Byrnes grinned. "So the Zodiac Detective here can read the leaves."

 How Clever?

1. Detective Byrnes' first comment to Detective Allen after reading the combination of letters and numerals—DDS 10752 LIBRA—was: "Libra. Don't tell me this turns out to be another one of your damn zodiac cases." How did this comment influence the reasoning of all the detectives in the story who were trying to break the code of Stone's message? How did Byrnes' comment affect your trying to beat him, Allen, and Nudger to the solution of the puzzle?

2. Sometimes when we look head-on at something we narrow our focus too much and get fixated on just one possible meaning. If we don't look from a different distance, angle, slant, or perspective (this kind of thinking is called "lateral thinking"), we may miss out completely on the more accurate view

from the sidelines. "Lateral thinking" encourages a kind of reasoning process that unlocks us from our traditional or automatic way of looking at things so that we don't jump to conclusions and block out other possibilities.

Did you stop thinking about what DDS stood for after Nudger matched the letters to Stone's initials? If so, do you see how you got trapped by non-lateral, fixated thinking? Where else in the story did you get trapped into non-lateral thinking?

3. What does Nudger later offer as a second possible meaning of DDS? What connection does Allen make between Nudger's less-than-serious explanation of the meaning of DDS and what LIBRA might refer to? How is Allen making use of lateral thinking?

4. Byrne asks Allen why Stone wrote LIBRA after the letters and numbers of the Dewey Decimal System. What explanation for LIBRA is Nudger, at last, able to supply?

DETECTWRITE: Characterization

This short story features a "hotshot city-slicker P.I." (a private investigator by the name of Nudger) whose friend, another private investigator by the name of Dwight Stone, has been murdered. Officially conducting the investigation, however, is a team of two policemen (homicide detectives) employed by the small town in which the crime has taken place.

When it comes time for you to create your own detective character, whether he or she is a police officer, private investigator ("P. I." or "private eye"), or detective, you will need to decide not only what kind of portrait to paint but also how visible that portrait is. In other words, some writers of detective fiction have very detailed detectives and others are barely sketched in.

In this story, you might have expected Nudger to solve the crime since he is the one who realizes that the rolltop desk's top needs to be examined. But it is actually Detective Allen who makes the connections in the body of evidence necessary for understanding the meaning of DDS 10752 LIBRA.

In preparation for creating your own detective, list in separate columns the character traits and personality features that are stated or implied in the story "DDS 10752 LIBRA" that help you to distinguish among the three "detectives" in its cast of characters.

Death and Diamonds

Susan Dunlap

"**T**HE THING I LIKE MOST ABOUT BEING A PRIVATE investigator is the thrill of the game. I trained in gymnastics as a kid. I love cases with lots of action. But, alas, you can't always have what you love." Kiernan O'Shaughnessy glanced down at her thickly bandaged foot and the crutches propped beside it.

"Kicked a little too much ass, huh?" The man in the seat beside her at the Southwest Airlines gate grinned. There was an impish quality to him. Average height, sleekly muscled, with the too-dark tan of one who doesn't worry about the future. He was over forty but the lines around his bright green eyes and mouth suggested quick scowls, sudden bursts of laughter, rather than the folds of age setting in. Amid the San Diegans in shorts and T-shirts proclaiming the Zoo, Tijuana, and the Chargers, he seemed almost formal in his chinos and sports jacket and the forest green polo shirt. He crossed, then recrossed his long legs and glanced impatiently at the purser standing guard at the end of the ramp.

The Gate 10 waiting area was jammed with tanned families ready to fly from sunny San Diego to sunnier Phoenix. The rumble of conversations was broken by children's shrill whines and exasperated parents barking their names in warning.

"We are now boarding all passengers for Southwest Airlines flight twelve forty-four to Oakland, through gate nine."

A mob of the Oakland-bound crowded closer to their gate, clutching their blue plastic boarding passes.

Beside Kiernan the man sighed. But there was a twinkle in his eyes. "Lucky them. I hate waiting around like this. It's not something I'm good at. One of the reasons I like flying Southwest is their open seating. If you move fast you can get whatever seat you want."

"Which seat is your favorite?"

"One-B or one-C. So I can get off fast. *If* they ever let us *on.*"

The Phoenix-bound flight was half an hour late. With each announcement of a Southwest departure to some other destination, the level of grumbling in the Phoenix-bound area had grown till the air seemed thick with frustration, and at the same time old and overused, as if it had held just enough oxygen for the scheduled waiting period, and now, half an hour later, served only to dry out noses and to make throats raspy and tempers short.

The loudspeaker announced the Albuquerque flight was ready for boarding. A woman in a rhinestone-encrusted denim jacket raced past them toward the Albuquerque gate. Rhinestones. Hardly diamonds, but close enough to bring the picture of Melissa Jessup to Kiernan's mind. When she'd last seen her, Melissa Jessup had been dead six months, beaten and stabbed, her corpse left outside to decompose. Gone were her mother's diamonds, the diamonds her mother had left her as security. Melissa hadn't been able to bring herself to sell them, even to finance her escape from a life turned fearful and the man who preferred them to her. It all proved, as Kiernan reminded herself each time the memory of Melissa invaded her thoughts, that diamonds are *not* a girl's best friend, that Mother (or at least a mother who says "don't sell them") does *not* know best, and that a woman should never get involved with a man she works with. Melissa Jessup had done all of those things. Her lover had followed her, killed her, taken her mother's diamonds, and left not one piece of evidence. Melissa's brother had hired Kiernan, hoping that with her background in forensic pathology she would find some clue in the autopsy report, or that once she could view Melissa's body she would spot something the local medical examiner had missed. She hadn't. The key that would nail Melissa's killer was not in her corpse, but with the diamonds. Finding those diamonds and the killer with them had turned into the most frustrating case of Kiernan's career.

She pushed the picture of Melissa Jessup out of her mind. This was no time for anger or any of the emotions that the thought of Melissa's death brought up. The issue now was getting this suitcase into the right hands in Phoenix. Turning back to the man beside her, she said "The job I'm on right now is baby-sitting this suitcase from San Diego to Phoenix. This trip is not going to be 'a kick'."

"Couldn't you have waited till you were off the crutches?" he said, looking down at her bandaged right foot.

"Crime doesn't wait." She smiled, focusing her full attention on the conversation now. "Besides, courier work is perfect for a hobbled lady, don't you think, Mr.—uh?"

He glanced down at the plain black suitcase, then back at her. "Detecting all the time, huh?" There was a definite twinkle in her eyes as he laughed. "Well, this one's easy. Getting my name is not going to prove whether you're any good as a detective. I'm Jeff Siebert. And you are?"

"Kiernan O'Shaughnessy. But I can't let that challenge pass. Anyone can get a name. A professional investigator can do better than that. For a start, I surmise you're single."

He laughed, the delighted laugh of the little boy who's just beaten his parent in rummy. "No wedding ring, no white line on my finger to show I've taken the ring off. Right?"

"Admittedly, that was one factor. But you're wearing a red belt. Since it's nowhere near Christmas, I assume the combination of red belt and green turtleneck is not intentional. You're color-blind."

"Well, yeah," he said buttoning his jacket over the offending belt. "But they don't ask you to tell red from green before they'll give you a marriage license. So?"

"If you were married, your wife might not check you over before you left each morning, but chances are she would organize your accessories so you could get dressed by yourself, and not have strange women like me commenting on your belt."

"This is the final call for boarding Southwest Airlines flight twelve forty-four to Oakland at gate nine."

Kiernan glanced enviously at the last three Oakland-bound passengers as they passed through gate 9. If the Phoenix flight were not so late, she would be in the air now and that much closer to getting the suitcase in the right hands. Turning back to Siebert, she said, "By the same token, I'd guess you have been married or involved with a woman about my size. A blonde."

He sat back down in his seat, and for the first time was still.

"Got your attention, huh?" Kiernan laughed. "I really shouldn't show off like that. It unnerves some people. Others, like you, it just quiets down. Actually, this was pretty easy. You've got a tiny spot of lavender eyeshadow on the edge of your lapel. I had a boyfriend your height and he ended up sending a number of jackets to the cleaners. But no one but me would think to look at the edge of your lapel, and you could have that jacket for years and not notice that."

"But why did you say a blonde?"

"Blondes tend to wear violet eyeshadow."

He smiled, clearly relieved.

"Flight seventeen sixty-seven departing gate ten with service to Phoenix will begin boarding in just a few minutes. We thank you for your patience."

He groaned. "We'll see how few those minutes are." Across from them a woman with an elephantine carry-on bag pulled it closer to her. Siebert turned to Kiernan, and giving her that intimate grin she was beginning to think of as *his look,* Siebert said, "You seem to be having a good time being a detective."

The picture of Melissa Jessup popped up in her mind. Melissa Jessup had let herself be attracted to a thief. She'd ignored her suspicions about him until it was too late to sell her mother's jewels and she could only grab what was at hand and run.

Pulling her suitcase closer, Kiernan said, "Investigating can be a lot of fun if you like strange hours and the thrill of having everything hang on one maneuver. I'll tell you the truth—it appeals to the adolescent in me, particularly if I can pretend to be something or someone else. It's fun to see if I can pull that off."

"How do I know you're not someone else?"

"I could show you ID, but, of course, that wouldn't prove anything," she laughed. "You'll just have to trust me, as I am you. After all, *you* did choose to sit down next to me."

"Well, that's because you were the best-looking woman here sitting by herself."

"Or at least the one nearest the hallway where you came in. And this is the only spot around where you have room to pace. You look to be a serious pacer." She laughed again. "But I like your explanation better."

Shrieking, a small girl in yellow raced in front of the seats. Whooping gleefully, a slightly larger male version sprinted by. He lunged for his sister, caught his foot on Kiernan's crutch and sent it toppling back as he lurched forward, and crashed into a man at the end of the check-in line. His sister skidded to a stop. "Serves you right, Jason. Mom, look what Jason did!"

Siebert bent over and righted Kiernan's crutch. "Travel can be dangerous, huh?"

"Damn crutches! It's like they've got urges all their own," she said. "Like one of them sees an attractive crutch across the room and all of a sudden it's gone. They virtually seduce underage boys."

He laughed, his green eyes twinkling impishly. "They'll come home to you. There's not a crutch in the room that holds a *crutch* to you."

She hesitated a moment before saying, "My crutches and I thank you." This was, she thought, the kind of chatter that had been wonderfully seductive when she was nineteen. And Jeff Siebert was the restless, impulsive type of man who had personified freedom then. But nearly twenty years of mistakes—her own and more deadly ones like Melissa Jessup's—had shown her the inevitable end of such flirtations.

Siebert stood up and rested a foot against the edge of the table. "So what else is fun about investigating?"

She shifted the suitcase between her feet. "Well, trying to figure out people, like I was doing with you. A lot is common sense, like assuming that you are probably not a patient driver. Perhaps you've passed in a no-passing zone, or even have gotten a speeding ticket."

He nodded, abruptly.

"On the other hand," she went on, "sometimes I know facts beforehand, and then I can fake a Sherlock Holmes and produce anything-but-elementary deductions. The danger with that is getting cocky and blurting out conclusions before you've been given evidence for them."

"Has that happened to you?"

She laughed and looked meaningfully down at her foot. "But I wouldn't want my client to come to that conclusion. We had a long discussion about whether a woman on crutches could handle his delivery."

"Client?" he said, shouting over the announcement of the Yuma flight at the next gate. In a normal voice, he added, "In your courier work, you mean? What's in that bag of your client's that so very valuable?"

She moved her feet till they were touching the sides of the suitcase. He leaned in closer. He was definitely the type of man destined to be trouble, she thought, but that little-boy grin, that conspirational tone, were seductive, particularly in a place like this where any diversion was a boon. She wasn't surprised he had been attracted to her; clearly, he was a man who liked small women. She glanced around, pleased that no one else had been drawn to this spot. The nearest travelers were a young couple seated six feet away and too involved in each other to waste time listening to strangers' conversation. "I didn't pack the bag. I'm just delivering it."

He bent down with his ear near the side of the suitcase. "Well, at least it's not ticking." Sitting up, he said, "But seriously, isn't that a little dangerous?

Women carrying bags for strangers, that's how terrorists have gotten bombs on planes."

"No!" she snapped. "I'm not carrying it for a lover with an M-1. I'm a bonded courier."

The casual observer might not have noticed Siebert's shoulders tensing, slightly, briefly, in anger at her rebuff. Silently, he looked down at her suitcase. "How much does courier work pay?"

"Not a whole lot, particularly compared to the value of what I have to carry. But then there's not much work involved. The chances of theft are minuscule. And I do get to travel. Last fall I drove a package up north. That was a good deal since I had to go up there anyway to check motel registrations in a case I'm working on. It took me a week to do the motels, and then I came up empty." An entire week to discover that Melissa's killer had not stopped at a motel or hotel between San Diego and Eureka. "The whole thing would have been a bust if it hadn't been for the courier work."

He glanced down at the suitcase. She suspected he would have been appalled to know how visible was his covetous look. Finally he said, "What was in that package, the one you delivered?"

She glanced over at the young couple. No danger from them. Still Kiernan lowered her voice. "Diamonds. Untraceable. That's really the only reason to go to the expense of hiring a courier."

"Untraceable, huh?" he said, grinning. "Didn't you even consider taking off over the border with them?"

"Maybe," she said slowly, "if I had known they were worth enough to set me up for the rest of my actuarial allotment, I might have."

"We will begin preboarding Southwest Airlines flight seventeen sixty-seven with service to Phoenix momentarily. Please keep your seats until preboarding has been completed."

She pushed herself up and positioned the crutches under her arms. It was a moment before he jerked his gaze away from the suitcase and stood, his foot tapping impatiently on the carpet. All around them families were hoisting luggage and positioning toddlers for the charge to the gate. He sighed loudly. "I hope you're good with your elbows."

She laughed and settled back on the arm of the seat.

His gaze went back to the suitcase. He said, "I thought couriers were handcuffed to their packages."

"You've been watching too much TV." She lowered her voice. "Handcuffs play havoc with the metal detector. The last thing you want in this business is buzzers going off and guards racing in from all directions. I go for the low-key approach. Always keep the suitcase in sight. Always be within lunging range."

He took a playful swipe at it. "What would happen if, say, that bag were to get stolen.?"

"Stolen!" She pulled the suitcase closer to her. "Well, for starters, I wouldn't get a repeat job. If the goods were insured, that might be the end of it. But if it were something untraceable"—she glanced at the suitcase—"it could be a lot worse." With a grin that matched his own, she said, "You're not a thief, are you?"

He shrugged. "Do I look like a thief?"

"You look like the most attractive man here." She paused long enough to catch his eye. "Of course, looks can be deceiving." She didn't say it, but she could picture him pocketing a necklace carelessly left in a jewelry box during a big party, or a Seiko watch from under a poolside towel. She didn't imagine him planning a heist, but just taking what came his way.

Returning her smile, he said, "When you transport something that can't be traced, don't they even provide you a backup?"

"No! I'm a professional. I don't need backup."

"But with your foot like that?"

"I'm good with the crutches. And besides, the crutches provide camouflage. Who'd think a woman on crutches carrying a battered suitcase had anything worth half a mi—Watch out! The little girl and her brother are loose again." She pulled her crutches closer as the duo raced through the aisle in front of them.

"We are ready to begin boarding Southwest Airlines flight number seventeen sixty-seven to Phoenix. Any passengers traveling with small children or those needing a little extra time may begin boarding now."

The passengers applauded. It was amazing, she thought, how much sarcasm could be carried by a nonverbal sound.

She leaned down for the suitcase. "Preboarding. That's me."

"Are you going to be able to handle the crutches and the suitcase?" he asked.

"You're really fascinated with this bag, aren't you?"

"Guilty." He grinned. "Should I dare to offer to carry it? I'd stay within lunging range."

She hesitated.

In the aisle a woman in cerise shorts, carrying twin bags, herded twin toddlers toward the gate. Ahead of her an elderly man leaned precariously on a cane. The family with the boy and girl were still assembling luggage.

He said, "You'd be doing me a big favor letting me preboard with you. I like to cadge a seat in the first row on the aisle."

"The seat for the guy who can't wait?"

"Right. But I got here so late that I'm in the last boarding group. I'm never going to snag one-B or one-C. So help me out. I promise," he said, grinning, "I won't steal."

"Well . . . I wouldn't want my employer to see this. I assured him I wouldn't need any help. But . . ." She shrugged.

"No time to waver now. There's already a mob of preboarders ahead of us." He picked up the bag. "Some heavy diamonds."

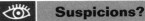 **Suspicions?**

Before P.I. Kiernan O'Shaughnessy, Jeff Siebert, and their fellow passengers board their plane to Phoenix, have any of the characters' words or actions created any suspicions in your mind? Explain.

"Good camouflage, don't you think? Of course, not everything's diamonds."

"Just something untraceable?"

She gave him a half wink. "It may not be untraceable. It may not even be valuable."

"And you may be just a regular mail carrier," he said, starting toward the gate.

She swung after him. The crutches were no problem, and the thickly taped right ankle looked worse than it was. Still, it made things much smoother to have Siebert carrying the suitcase. If the opportunity arose, he might be tempted to steal it, but not in a crowded gate at the airport with guards and airline personnel around. He moved slowly, staying right in front of her, running interference. As they neared the gate, a blond man carrying a jumpy toddler hurried in front of them. The gate phone buzzed. The airline rep picked it up and nodded at it. To the blond man and the elderly couple who had settled in behind him, Kiernan, and Siebert, he said, "Sorry, folks. The cleaning crew's a little slow. It'll just be a minute."

Siebert's face scrunched in anger. "What's 'cleaning crew' a euphemism for? A tire fell off and they're looking for it? They've spotted a crack in the engine block and they're trying to figure out if they can avoid telling us?"

Kiernan laughed. "I'll bet people don't travel with you twice."

He laughed. "I just hate being at someone else's mercy. But since we're going to be standing here awhile, why don't you do what you love more than diamonds, Investigator: tell me what you've deduced about me."

"Like reading your palm?" The crutches poked into her armpits; she shifted them back, putting more weight on her bandaged foot. Slowly she surveyed his lanky body, his thin agile hands, con man's hands, hands that were never quite still, always past *ready*, coming out of *set*. "Okay. You're traveling from San Diego to Phoenix on the Friday evening flight, so chances are you were here on business. But you don't have on cowboy boots, or a Stetson. You're tan, but it's not that dry tan you get in the desert. In fact, you could pass for a San Diegan. I would have guessed that you travel for a living, but you're too impatient for that, and if you'd taken this flight once or twice before you wouldn't be surprised that it's late. You'd have a report to read, or a newspaper. No, you do something where you don't take orders, and you don't put up with much." She grinned. "How's that?"

"That's pretty elementary, Sherlock," he said with only a slight edge to his voice. He tapped his fingers against his leg. But all in all he looked only a little warier than any other person in the waiting area would as his secrets were unveiled.

"Southwest Airlines flight number seventeen sixty-seven with service to Phoenix is now ready for preboarding."

"Okay, folks," the gate attendant called. "Sorry for the delay."

The man with the jittery toddler thrust his boarding pass at the gate attendant and strode down the ramp. The child screamed. The elderly couple moved haltingly, hoisting and readjusting their open sacks with each step. A family squeezed in in front of them, causing the old man to stop dead and move his bag to the other shoulder. Siebert shifted from foot to foot.

Stretching up to whisper in his ear, Kiernan said, "It would look bad if you shoved the old people out of your way."

"How bad?" he muttered, grinning, then handed his boarding pass to the attendant.

As she surrendered hers, she said to Siebert, "Go ahead, hurry. I'll meet you in one-C and D."

"Thanks." He patted her shoulder.

She watched him stride down the empty ramp. His tan jacket had caught on one hip as he balanced her suitcase and his own. But he neither slowed his pace nor made an attempt to free the jacket; clutching tight to her suitcase, he hurried around the elderly couple, moving with the strong stride of a hiker. By the time she got down the ramp the elderly couple and a family with two toddlers and an infant that sucked loudly on a pacifier crowded behind Siebert.

Kiernan watched irritably as the stewardess eyed first Siebert, then her big suitcase. The head stewardess has the final word on carry-on luggage, she knew. With all the hassle that was involved with this business anyway, she didn't want to add a confrontation with the stewardess. She dropped the crutches and banged backward into the wall, flailing for purchase as she slipped down to the floor. The stewardess caught her before she hit bottom. "Are you okay?"

"Embarrassed," Kiernan said, truthfully. She hated to look clumsy, even if it was an act, even if it allowed Siebert and her suitcase to get on the plane unquestioned. "I'm having an awful time getting used to these things."

"You sure you're okay? Let me help you up," the stewardess said. "I'll have to keep your crutches in the hanging luggage compartment up front while we're in flight. But you go ahead now; I'll come and get them from you."

"That's okay. I'll leave them there and just sit in one of the front seats," she said, taking the crutches and swinging herself on board the plane. From the luggage compartment it took only one long step on her left foot to get to row 1. She swung around Siebert, who was hoisting his own suitcase into the overhead bin beside hers, and dropped into seat 1-D, by the window. The elderly couple was settling into seats 1-A and 1-B. In another minute Southwest would call the first thirty passengers, and the herd would stampede down the ramp, stuffing approved carry-ons in overhead compartments and grabbing the thirty most prized seats.

"That was a smooth move with the stewardess," Siebert said, as he settled into his coveted aisle seat.

"That suitcase is just about the limit of what they'll let you carry on. I've had a few hassles. I could see this one coming. And I suspected that you"—she patted his arm—"were not the patient person to deal with that type of problem. You moved around her pretty smartly yourself. I'd say that merits a drink from my client."

He smiled and rested a hand on hers. "Maybe," he said, leaning closer, "we could have it in Phoenix."

For the first time she had a viscerally queasy feeling about him. Freeing her hand from his, she gave a mock salute. "Maybe so." She looked past him at the elderly couple.

Siebert's gaze followed hers. He grinned as he said, "Do you think they're thieves? After your loot? Little old sprinters?"

"Probably not. But it pays to be alert." She forced a laugh. "I'm afraid constant suspicion is a side effect of my job."

The first wave of passengers hurried past. Already the air in the plane had the sere feel and slightly rancid smell of having been dragged through the filters too many times. By tacit consent they watched the passengers hurry on board, pause, survey their options, and rush on. Kiernan thought fondly of that drink in Phoenix. She would be sitting at a small table, looking out a tinted window; the trip would be over, the case delivered into the proper hands; and she would feel the tension that knotted her back releasing with each swallow of scotch. Or so she hoped. The whole frustrating case depended on this delivery. There was no fallback position. If she screwed up, Melissa Jessup's murderer disappeared.

That tension was what normally made the game fun. But this case was no longer a game. This time she had allowed herself to go beyond her regular rules, to call her former colleagues from the days when she had been a forensic pathologist, looking for some new test that would prove culpability. She had hoped the lab in San Diego could find something. They hadn't. The fact was that the diamonds were the only "something" that would trap the killer, Melissa's lover, who valued them much more than her, a man who might not have bothered going after her had it not been for them. Affairs might be brief, but diamonds, after all, are forever. They would lead her to the murderer's safe house, and the evidence that would tie him to Melissa. *If* she was careful.

She shoved the tongue of the seat belt into the latch and braced her feet as the plane taxied toward the runway. Siebert was tapping his finger on the armrest. The engines whirred, the plane shifted forward momentarily, then flung them back against their seats as it raced down the short runway.

The FASTEN SEAT BELT sign went off. The old man across the aisle pushed himself up and edged toward the front bathroom. Siebert's belt was already unbuckled. Muttering, "Be right back," he jumped up and stood hunched under the overhead bin while the old man cleared the aisle. Then Siebert headed full-out toward the back of the plane. Kiernan slid over and watched him as he strode down the aisle, steps firmer, steadier than she'd have expected of a man racing to the bathroom in a swaying airplane. She could easily imagine him hiking in the redwood forest with someone like her, a small, slight woman. The blonde woman with the violet eyeshadow. She in jeans and one of those soft Patagonia jackets Kiernan had spotted in the L.L. Bean catalog, violet with blue trim. He in jeans, turtleneck, a forest green down jacket on his rangy body. Forest green would pick up the color of his eyes and accent his dark, curly hair. In her picture, his hair was tinted with the first flecks of autumn snow and the ground still soft like the spongy airplane carpeting beneath his feet.

When he got back he made no mention of his hurried trip. He'd barely settled down when the stewardess leaned over him and said, "Would you care for something to drink?"

Kiernan put a hand on his arm. "This one's on my client."

"For that client who insisted you carry his package while you're still on crutches? I'm sorry it can't be Lafite-Rothschild. Gin and tonic will have to do." He grinned at the stewardess. Kiernan could picture him in a bar, flashing that grin at a tall redhead, or maybe another small blonde. She could imagine him with the sweat of a San Diego summer still on his brow, his skin brown from too many days at an ocean beach that is too great a temptation for those who grab their pleasures.

"Scotch and water," Kiernan ordered. To him, she said, "I notice that while I'm the investigator, it's you who are asking all the questions. So what about you, what do you do for a living?"

"I quit my job in San Diego and I'm moving back to Phoenix. So I'm not taking the first Friday night flight to get back home, I'm taking it to get to my new home. I had good times in San Diego: the beach, the sailing, Balboa Park. When I came there a couple years ago I thought I'd stay forever. But the draw of the desert is too great. I miss the red rock of Sedona, the pines of the Mogollon Rim, and the high desert outside Tucson." He laughed. "Too much soft California life."

It was easy to picture him outside of Show Low on the Mogollon Rim with the pine trees all around him, some chopped for firewood, the ax lying on a stump, a shovel in his hand. Or in a cabin near Sedona lifting a hatch in the floorboards.

The stewardess brought the drinks and the little bags of peanuts, giving Jeff Siebert the kind of smile Kiernan knew would have driven her crazy had she been Siebert's girlfriend. How often had that type of thing happened? Had his charm brought that reaction so automatically that for him it had seemed merely the way women behave? Had complaints from a girlfriend seemed at first unreasonable, then melodramatic, then infuriating? He was an impatient man, quick to anger. Had liquor made it quicker, as the rhyme said? And the prospect of unsplit profit salved his conscience?

He poured the little bottle of gin over the ice and added tonic. "Cheers."

She touched glasses, then drank. "Are you going to be in Phoenix long?"

"Probably not. I've come into a little money and I figure I'll just travel around, sort of like you do. Find someplace I like."

"So we'll just have time for our drink in town then?"

He rested his hand back on hers. "Well, now I may have reason to come back in a while. Or to San Diego. I just need to cut loose for a while."

She forced herself to remain still, not to cringe at his touch. *Cut loose—* what an apt term for him to use. She pictured his sun-browned hand wrapped around the hilt of a chef's knife, working it up and down, up and down, cutting across pink flesh till it no longer looked like flesh, till the flesh mixed with the blood and the organ tissue, till the knife cut down to the bone and the metal point stuck in the breastbone. She pictured Melissa Jessup's blond hair pink from the blood.

Suspicions?

Who do you think murdered Melissa Jessup? Explain your choice.

She didn't have to picture her body lying out in the woods outside Eureka in northern California. She had seen photos of it. She didn't have to imagine what the cracked ribs and broken clavicle and the sternum marked from the knife point looked like now. Jeff Siebert had seen that too, and had denied what Melissa's brother and the Eureka sheriff all knew—knew in their hearts but could not prove—that Melissa had not gone to Eureka camping by herself as he'd insisted, but had only stopped overnight at the campground she and Jeff had been to the previous summer because she had no money and hadn't been able to bring herself to sell the diamonds her mother had left her. Instead of a rest on the way to freedom, she'd found Siebert there.

Now Siebert was flying to Phoenix to vanish. He'd pick up Melissa's diamonds wherever he'd stashed them, and he'd be gone.

"What about your client?" he asked. "Will he be meeting you at the airport?"

"No. No one will meet me. I'll just deliver my goods to the van, collect my money, and be free. What about you?"

"No. No one's waiting for me either. At least I'll be able to give you a hand with that bag. There's no ramp to the terminal in Phoenix. You have to climb down to the tarmac there. Getting down those metal steps with a suitcase and two crutches would be a real balancing act."

All she had to do was get it into the right hands. She shook her head. "Thanks. But I'll have to lug it through the airport just in case. My client didn't handcuff the suitcase to me, but he does expect I'll keep hold of it."

He grinned. "Like you said, you'll be in lunging range all the time."

"No," she said firmly. "I appreciate your offer, Jeff; the bag weighs a ton. But I'm afraid it's got to be in my hand."

Those green eyes of his that had twinkled with laughter narrowed, and his lips pressed together. "Okay," he said slowly. Then his face relaxed almost back to that seductively impish smile that once might have charmed her, as it had Melissa Jessup. "I want you to know that I'll still find you attractive even if the bag yanks your shoulder out of its socket." He gave her hand a pat, then shifted in his seat so his upper arm rested next to hers.

The stewardess collected the glasses. The plane jolted and began its descent. Kiernan braced her feet. Through his jacket, she felt the heat of his arm, the arm that had dug that chef's knife into Melissa Jessup's body. She breathed slowly and did not move.

To Kiernan he said, "There's a great bar right here in Sky Harbor Airport, the Sky Lounge. Shall we have our drink there?"

She nodded, her mouth suddenly too dry for speech.

 Suspicions?

Predict what you will think will happen between this point and the end of the story. Tell why you have made those predictions.

The plane bumped down, and in a moment the aisles were jammed with passengers ignoring the stewardess's entreaty to stay in their seats. Siebert stood up and pulled his bag out of the overhead compartment and then lifted hers onto his empty seat. "I'll get your crutches," he said, as the elderly man across the aisle pushed his way out in front of him. Siebert shook his head. Picking up both suitcases, he maneuvered around the man and around the corner to the luggage compartment.

Siebert had taken her suitcase. *You don't need to take both suitcases to pick up the crutches.* Kiernan stared after him, her shoulders tensing, her hands clutching the armrests. Her throat was so constricted she could barely breathe. For an instant she shared the terror that must have paralyzed Melissa Jessup just before he stabbed her.

"Jeff!" she called after him, a trace of panic evident in her voice. He didn't answer her. Instead, she heard a great thump, then him muttering and the stewardess's voice placating.

The airplane door opened. The elderly man moved out into the aisle in front of Kiernan, motioning his wife to go ahead of him then they moved slowly toward the door.

Kiernan yanked the bandage off her foot, stepped into the aisle. "Excuse me," she said to the couple. Pushing by them as Siebert had so wanted to do, she rounded the corner to the exit.

The stewardess was lifting up a garment bag. Four more bags lay on the floor. So that was the thump she'd heard. A crutch was beside them.

She half heard the stewardess's entreaties to wait, her mutterings about the clumsy man. She looked out the door down onto the tarmac.

Jeffrey Siebert and the suitcase were gone. In those few seconds he had raced down the metal steps and was disappearing into the terminal. By the time she could make it to the Sky Lounge he would be halfway to Show Low, or Sedona.

Now she felt a different type of panic. *This* wasn't in the plan. She couldn't lose Siebert. She jumped over the bags, grabbed one crutch, hurried outside to the top of the stairs, and thrust the crutch across the hand rails behind her to make a seat. As the crutch

 Suspicions?

Explain, as fully as you can, what you think "the plan" involves.

slid down the railings, she kept her knees bent high into her chest to keep from landing and bucking forward onto her head. Instead the momentum propelled her on her feet, as it had in gymnastics. In those routines, she'd had to fight the momentum; now she went with it and ran, full-out.

She ran through the corridor toward the main building, pushing past businessmen, between parents carrying children. Siebert would be running ahead. But no one would stop him, not in an airport. People run through airports all the time. Beside the metal detectors she saw a man in a tan jacket. Not him. By the luggage pickup another look-alike. She didn't spot him till he was racing out the door to the parking lot.

Siebert ran across the roadway. A van screeched to a halt. Before Kiernan could cross through the traffic, a hotel bus eased in front of her. She skirted behind it. She could sense a man following her now. But there was no time to deal with that. Siebert was halfway down the lane of cars. Bent low, she ran down the next lane, the hot dusty desert air drying her throat.

By the time she came abreast of Siebert, he was in a light blue Chevy pickup backing out of the parking slot. He hit the gas, and, wheels squealing, drove off.

She reached toward the truck with both arms. Siebert didn't stop. She stood watching as Jeffrey Siebert drove off into the sunset.

There was no one behind her as she sauntered into the terminal to the Sky Lounge. She ordered the two drinks Siebert had suggested, and when they came, she tapped "her" glass on "his" and took a drink for Melissa Jessup. Then she swallowed the rest of the drink in two gulps.

By this time Jeff Siebert would be on the freeway. He'd be fighting to stay close to the speed limit, balancing his thief's wariness of the highway patrol against his gnawing urge to force the lock on the suitcase. Jeffrey Siebert was an impatient man, a man who had nevertheless made himself wait nearly a year before leaving California. His stash of self-control would be virtually empty. But he would wait awhile before daring to stop. Then he'd jam a knife between the top and bottom of the suitcase, pry and twist it till the case fell open. He would find diamonds. More diamonds. Diamonds to take along while he picked up Melissa Jessup's from the spot where he'd hidden them.

She wished Melissa Jessup could see him when he compared the two collections and

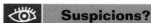 **Suspicions?**

How would you explain the ease with which O'Shaughnessy goes about the actions in the Sky Lounge. What does she have to be so confident about? Why?

realized the new ones he'd stolen were fakes. She wished she herself could see his face when he realized that a woman on crutches had made it out of the plane in time to follow him to point out the blue pickup truck.

Kiernan picked up "Jeff's" glass and drank more slowly. How sweet it would be if Melissa could see that grin of his fade as the surveillance team surrounded him, drawn by the beepers concealed in those fake diamonds. He'd be clutching the evidence that would send him to jail. Just for life, not forever. As Melissa could have told him, only death and diamonds are forever.

 How Clever?

1. At the very start of the story P. I. Kiernan O'Shaughnessy tells the murderer and jewel thief Jeff Siebert: "The thing I like most about being a private investigator is the thrill of the game" and "I love cases with lots of action." In this story how and where does Kiernan O'Shaughnessy demonstrate her preference for "the thrill of the game" and "lots of action?"

2. In this story, why weren't diamonds "a girl's best friend," despite the song lyric that insists that they are? How weren't they Jeff Seibert's "best friend" either, even though he made away with a suitcase filled with them?

3. How does Kiernan O'Shaughnessy's second statement to Siebert in the story—"I trained in gymnastics as a kid"—foreshadow the action in the last pages of the story?

4. Where is the earliest moment in the story that you began to suspect that P. I. Kiernan O'Shaughnessy's sitting next to Jeff Siebert in the airport lounge and striking up a conversation with him was not accidental? What specifically gave you the idea at that point?

5. P. I. O'Shaughnessy tells Siebert that "investigating can be a lot of fun," and she gives as an example, "trying to figure out people, like I was doing with you." Discuss several conclusions that O'Shaughnessy made about Siebert's life and habits that you found impressive, given the acts of detection (observations) they were based on.

6. In her airport lounge conversation with Siebert, P. I. Kiernan O'Shaughnessy admits: "Sometimes I know facts beforehand, and then I can fake a Sherlock Holmes and produce anything-but-elementary deductions." In this particular case, which facts about Siebert does O'Shaughnessy know beforehand? Why, according to O'Shaughnessy, is there danger in "faking a Sherlock Holmes"?

7. What three things did O'Shaughnessy fake as part of her plan to catch Siebert with the evidence that would help convict him of Melissa Jessup's murder? Explain how they figured in the development of the plot.

8. Consider both of the following thoughts O'Shaughnessy has that the author shares with the reader:

"The issue now was getting this suitcase into the right hands in Phoenix" and, later, "She would be sitting at a small table, looking out a tinted window; the trip would be over, the case delivered into the proper hands; and she would feel the tension that knotted her back releasing with each swallow of scotch. Or so she hoped. The whole frustrating case depended on this delivery. There was no fallback position. If she screwed up, Melissa Jessup's murderer disappeared."

How do these two thoughts foreshadow Siebert's stealing O'Shaughnessy's suitcase from the overhead compartment when the plane lands?

9. O'Shaughnessy says to Siebert in the airport lounge that her "crutches provide camouflage. Who'd think a woman on crutches carrying a battered suitcase had anything worth half a mi—Watch out! The little girl and her brother are loose again." Do you think O'Shaughnessy would have completed her statement—"half a million dollars"—if the two children had not then raced through the aisle in front of her and Siebert? Explain your reasoning.

10. How did O'Shaughnessy avoid a confrontation with the head stewardess over the size of her carry-on luggage? Why was this essential to her plan?

11. Explain why you think the following is either a genuine clue or a red herring: "Siebert had taken her suitcase. *You don't need to take both suitcases to pick up the crutches.* Kiernan stared after him, her shoulders tensing, her hands clutching the armrests. Her throat was so constricted she could hardly breathe. For an instant she shared the terror that must have paralyzed Melissa Jessup just before he stabbed her. 'Jeff!' she called after him, a trace of panic evident in her voice."

12. "She couldn't lose Siebert." Why wasn't losing sight of Siebert as the plane landed part of O'Shaughnessy's plan? What was the plan?

13. Who was the man O'Shaughnessy sensed was following her as she raced after Siebert in the airport parking lot?

14. What was O'Shaughnessy actually doing when, as Siebert hit the gas of the pickup and drove off, she "reached toward the truck with both arms"?

15. What does O'Shaughnessy mean by "only death and diamonds are forever"?

DETECTWRITE: Characterization and Plot

1. How did disguising Private Investigator Kiernan O'Shaughnessy as an injured, slow-moving courier contribute to the development of the plot of "Death and Diamonds"? Consider how you might use disguise and visual trickery in a mystery story you would write.

2. Private Investigator Kiernan O'Shaughnessy's training, background, and specialty are in forensic pathology. Nevertheless, in this particular case, O'Shaughnessy could find nothing in either Melissa Jessup's autopsy report or in an examination of her body that had been missed by the local med-

ical examiner. Consequently, "the key that would nail Melissa's killer was not in her corpse, but with the diamonds" and "finding those diamonds and the killer with them had turned into the most frustrating case of Kiernan's career." Find examples in the story of frustration on the part of its major character. What ways did O'Shaughnessy use to control her frustration that would be helpful for any detective, including the one you might feature in a mystery story you would write?

3. Consider the kind of specialty the private investigator or detective might have in a mystery story you would write. How might that specialty make a difference in the development of the story's plot and in the detective's solving of the case?

4. O'Shaughnessy comments that "Investigating can be a lot of fun if you like strange hours and the thrill of having everything hang on one maneuver. I'll tell you the truth—it appeals to the adolescent in me, particularly if I can pretend to be something or someone else. It's fun to see if I can pull that off." Later in the story she adds: "I'm afraid constant suspicion is a side effect of my job," and the author goes on to comment that for O'Shaughnessy it was the tension of the job that "normally made the game fun."

Consider all of the various points O'Shaughnessy makes about the kind of person who would take to private investigating and the kind of life she or he would lead. What character traits seem essential? Where does O'Shaughnessy herself reveal them in the course of "Death and Diamonds"?

5. Can you think of any other profession that requires most of these same traits? Explain.

6. Which of these traits would you consider incorporating into the personality and nature of the private investigator to be featured in the mystery story you would write? Which of these traits would you find the easiest and the hardest to make use of and put into action? Explain why. Do you know someone you can model your private investigator or detective on? What kind of work does that person do, and what kinds of things is he or she into?

7. If private investigating appeals to "the adolescent" in some of us, why do you think an actual adolescent would or would not be a good fictional private investigator for a mystery story you would write?

DETECTWRITE: Plot

1. Consider the "props" (short for properties) that are essential to the development of the plot of "Death and Diamonds." What props might be useful to the development of the story line of a mystery you would write?

2. On ten separate slips of paper write the names of ten different objects. Fold the slips in half so that your words cannot be read and mix the slips up.

Then randomly choose at least two and no more than four slips and develop the outline of a mystery story you would write that makes use of those objects.

DETECTWRITE: Setting

1. The setting of "Death and Diamonds" is a fairly constricted one: an airport's waiting lounge and the inside of the airplane for the most part, with a brief scene near and inside the airport's parking lot and another brief scene inside the lounge. Explain why you think a constricted setting is easier or harder to use in a mystery story. Why would you want or not want to make use of a similarly constricted setting in a mystery story you would write? Explain.

2. On ten separate slips of paper write the name of ten different places or locations. Fold the slips in half so that your words cannot be read and mix the slips up. Then randomly choose anywhere from two to four slips and develop an outline of a mystery story you would write that makes use of the locations listed on one of those slips.

Candala

George C. Chesbro

INDIRI TAMIDIAN WAFTED INTO MY DOWNTOWN OFFICE LIKE a gossamer breath of incense from some Hindu temple in her native India. Her young, lithe body rippled beneath the rustling silk folds of her sari; her coal black eyes, sheened by that enormous zest for life which was Indiri's very quintessence, smoldered in their sockets. Blue-black hair tumbled to her shoulders, perfectly complementing the translucent, light chocolate colored flesh of her face. Indiri was stunningly beautiful. And troubled; the light from her eyes could not disguise the fact that she had been crying.

Self-pity, unexpected and unbidden, welled up within me like a poisonous cloud, a hated stench from a dark, secret place deep inside my soul. Some thoughts have teeth; just as it is dangerous for an artist to search too hard for the murky headwaters of his power, it is folly for a dwarf to entertain romantic thoughts of beautiful women. I fall into the second category.

I pushed the cloud back to its wet place and clamped the lid on. I stood and smiled as Indiri glanced around her.

"So this is where the famous criminologist spends his time when he's not teaching," Indiri said with a forced gaiety that fell just short of its mark.

I grunted. "You could have seen the criminology professor anytime on campus, even if you are majoring in agriculture," I said easily. "You didn't have to come all the way down here."

"I didn't come to see the professor," Indiri said, leaning forward on my desk. "I came to see the detective. I would like to hire you."

"Now what would a lovely, intelligent young woman like you want with a seedy private detective?" Immediately my smile faded. The girl's flesh had paled, isolating the painted ceremonial dot in the center of her forehead, lending it the appearance of an accusing third eye. It had been a stupid thing to say. Worse, it had sounded patronizing, and Indiri Tamidian was not a woman to be patronized. "How can I help you, Indiri?"

"I want you to find out what's bothering Pram."

"What makes you think anything is bothering him?"

"He hasn't called or come to see me for a week. Yesterday I went over to his room and he refused to see me."

I turned away before my first reaction could wander across my face. Pram Sakhuntala was one of my graduate students, and a friend of sorts. A good athlete, Pram often worked out with me in the gym as I struggled to retain and polish the skills that were a legacy of the nightmare years I had spent headlining with the circus as Mongo the Magnificent. Like Indiri, Pram was part of a U.N.-funded exchange program designed to train promising young Indians for eventual return to their own land, where their newly acquired skills could be put to optimum use. Pram was taking a degree in sociology, which explained his presence in one of my criminology sections. He was also Indiri's fiance and lover. Or had been. Losing interest in a woman like Indiri might be an indication that Pram was losing his mind, but that was his business. It certainly did not seem the proper concern of a private detective, and that's what I told Indiri.

"No, Dr. Frederickson, you don't understand," Indiri said, shaking her head. "There would be no problem if it were simply a matter of Pram not loving me anymore. That I could understand and accept. But he *does* love me, as I love him. I know that because I see it in his eyes; I feel it. Perhaps that sounds silly, but it is true."

It did not sound silly; Indiri came from a people who had produced the *Kama Sutra,* a land where life is always a question of basics. "Still, you don't have any idea what could have caused him to stop seeing you?"

"I'm not sure," Indiri said hesitantly.

"But you do have a suspicion."

"Yes. Do you know Dr. Dev Reja?"

"Dev Reja. He's chairman of Far Eastern Studies." I knew him, and didn't like him. He strode about the campus with all the imperiousness of a reincarnated Gautama Buddha with none of the Buddha's compensating humility.

"Yes," Indiri said softly. "He is also the advisor to the Indo-American Student Union, and coordinator of our exchange program. Last week Pram told me that Dr. Dev Reja had asked to speak with him. I don't know if there's any connection, but it was after that meeting that Pram changed toward me."

It suddenly occurred to me that I had not seen Pram for more than a week. He had missed my last class. This, in itself, was not significant. At least it hadn't seemed so at the time.

"What could Dev Reja have said to Pram that would cause him to change his attitude toward you?"

"That is what I would like you to find out for me, Dr. Frederickson."

I absently scratched my head. Indiri reached for her purse and I asked her what she was doing.

"I don't know how much you charge for your services," the girl said, looking straight into my eyes. "I don't have too much—"

"I only charge for cases," I said abruptly. "So far, this doesn't look like anything I could help you with." Tears welled in Indiri's eyes. "Not yet, it doesn't," I added quickly. "First I'll have to talk to Dr. Dev Reja before I can decide whether or not there's going to be any money in this for me. If I think there's anything I can do, we'll talk about fees later."

I was beginning to feel like the editor of an advice to the lovelorn column, but the look Indiri gave me shook me right down to my rather modest dwarf toes and made it all worthwhile.

Famous. That was the word Indiri had used—half in jest, half seriously—to describe me. It was true that I'd generated some heat and some headlines with my last two cases, both of which I'd literally stumbled across. But *famous?* Perhaps. I never gave it much thought. I'd had enough of fame; Mongo the Magnificent had been famous, and that kind of freak fame had almost destroyed me. What Indiri—or anyone else, for that matter, with the possible exceptions of my parents and Garth, my six-foot police detective brother—could not be expected to understand were the special needs and perspective of a four-foot-seven-inch dwarf with an I.Q. of 156 who had been forced to finance his way to a Ph.D. by working in a circus, *entertaining* people who saw nothing more than a freak who just happened to be a highly gifted tumbler and acrobat. Long ago I had developed the habit of not looking back, even to yesterday. There were just too many seemingly impossible obstacles I had already crossed, not to mention the ones coming up; the look of disbelief in the eyes of an unsuspecting client seeing me for the first time, choking back laughter at the idea of a *dwarf* trying to make it as a private detective.

I squeezed the genie of my past back into its psychic bottle as I neared the building housing the Center for Far Eastern Studies. Mahajar Dev Reja was in his office. I knocked and went in.

Dev Reja continued working at his desk a full minute before finally glancing up and acknowledging my presence. In the meantime I had glanced around his office; elephant tusks and other Indian trinkets cluttered the walls. I found the display rather gauche compared to the Indian presence Indiri carried *within* her. Finally Dev Reja stood up and nodded to me.

"I'm Frederickson," I said, extending my hand. "I don't think we've ever been formally introduced. I teach criminology."

Dev Reja considered my hand in such a way that he gave the impression he believed dwarfism might be catching. But I left it there and finally he took it.

"Frederickson," Dev Reja said. "You're the circus performer I've heard so much about."

"Ex-performer," I said quickly. "Actually, I'd like to speak to you about a mutual acquaintance. Pram Sakhuntala."

That raised Dev Reja's eyebrows a notch and I thought I detected a slight flush high on his cheekbones.

"My time is limited, Mr.—Dr.—Frederickson. How does your business with Pram Sakhuntala concern me?"

I decided there was just no way to sneak up on it. "Pram has been having some difficulty in my class," I lied. "There's an indication his troubles may stem from a talk he had with you." It wasn't diplomatic, but Dev Reja didn't exactly bring out the rosy side of my personality. "I thought I would see if there was any way I could help."

"He *told* you of our conversation?" This time his reaction was much more obvious and recognizable; it was called anger. I said nothing. *"Candala!"* Dev Reja hissed. It sounded like a curse.

"How's that?"

"Pram asked you to come and see me?"

"Is Pram in some kind of trouble?"

Dev Reja's sudden calm was costing him. "It must have occurred to you before you came here that any discussion Pram and I may have had would be none of your business. You were right."

I didn't have to be told that the interview was at an end. I turned and walked to the door past a blown-up photograph of a tiger in an Indian jungle. It was night and the eyes of the startled beast glittered like fractured diamonds in the light of the enterprising photographer's flash. In the background the underbrush was impenetrably dark and tangled. I wondered what had happened to the man who took the shot.

Pram showed up at the gym that evening for our scheduled workout. His usually expressive mouth was set in a grim line and he looked shaky. I made small talk as we rolled out the mats and began our warm-up exercises. Soon Pram's finely sculpted body began to glisten, and he seemed to relax as his tension melted and merged with the sweat flowing from his pores.

"Pram, what's a 'candala'?"

His reaction was immediate and shocking. Pram blanched bone white, then jumped up and away as though I had grazed his stomach with a white-hot poker.

"Where did you hear that?" His words came at me like bullets from the smoking barrel of a machine gun.

"Oh, Dr. Dev Reja dropped it in conversation the other day and I didn't have time to ask him what it meant."

"He was talking about me, wasn't he?!"

Pram's face and voice were a torrent of emotions, a river of tortured human feeling I was not yet prepared to cross. I'd stuck my foot in the water and found it icy cold and dark. I backed out.

"As far as I know, it had nothing to do with you," I said lamely. Pram wasn't fooled.

"You don't usually lie, Professor. Why are you lying now?"

"What's a 'candala,' Pram? Why don't you tell me what's bothering you?"

"What right do you have to ask me these questions?"

"None."

"Where did you get the idea of going to see Dr. Dev Reja?"

Like it or not, it seemed I'd just been pushed right into the middle of the water. This time I struck out for the other side. "Indiri's been hurt and confused by the way you've been acting," I said evenly. "Not hurt for herself, but for you. She thinks you may be in some kind of trouble, and she asked me to try to help if I can. She loves you very much, Pram. You must know that. If you are in trouble, I can't help you unless you tell me what it's all about."

Pram blinked rapidly. His skin had taken on a greenish pallor and for a moment I thought he would be sick. The fire in his eyes was now banked back to a dull glow as he seemed to stare through and beyond me. Suddenly he turned and, still in his gym clothes, walked out of the gym and into the night. I let him go. I had already said too much for a man who was working blind.

I showered and dressed, then made my way over to the women's residence where Indiri was staying. I called her room and she immediately came down to meet me in the lobby. I wasted no time.

"Indiri, what's a 'candala'?"

The question obviously caught her by surprise. "It's a term used to refer to a person of very low caste," she said quietly, after a long hesitation. "A candala is what you in the West could call an 'untouchable.' But it is even worse—I'm sorry to have to tell you these things, Dr. Frederickson. I love my country, but I am so ashamed of the evil that is our caste system. Mahatma Gandhi taught us that it was evil, and every one of our leaders have followed his example. Still, it persists. I am afraid it is just too deeply ingrained in the souls of our people."

"Don't apologize, Indiri. India has no monopoly on prejudice."

"It's not the same, Dr. Frederickson. You cannot fully understand the meaning and implications of *caste* unless you are Indian."

I wondered. I had a few black friends who might give her an argument, but I didn't say anything.

"Actually," Indiri continued, "the most common name for an untouchable is 'sutra.' A candala is—or was—even lower."

"Was?"

"You rarely hear the word anymore, except as a curse. Once, a candala was considered absolutely apart from other men. Such a man could be killed on the spot if he so much as allowed his shadow to touch that of a man in a higher caste. However, over the centuries it was realized that this practice ran counter to the basic Indian philosophy that every man, no matter how 'low,' had *some* place in the social system. In Indian minds—and in day-to-day life—the concept of candala fell under the weight of its own illogic."

"Go on."

"Candalas were forced to wear wooden clappers around their necks to warn other people of their presence. They were allowed to work only as executioners and burial attendants. They were used to cremate corpses, then forced to wear the dead man's clothing."

I shuddered involuntarily. "Who decides who's who in this system?"

"It is usually a question of birth. A person normally belongs to the caste his parents belonged to, except in the case of illegitimate children who are automatically considered sutras."

"What about Pram?" I said, watching Indiri carefully. "Could he be a sutra, or even a candala?"

I had expected some kind of reaction, but not laughter. It just didn't go with our conversation. "I'm sorry, Dr. Frederickson," Indiri said, reading my face. "That just struck me as being funny. Pram's family is Ksatriyana, the same as mine."

"Where does a Ksatriyana fit into the social scheme of things?"

"A Ksatriyana is very high," she said. I decided it was to her credit that she didn't blush. "Ksatriyana is almost interchangeable with Brahman, which is usually considered the highest caste. Buddha himself was a Ksatriyana. A member of such a family could never be considered a sutra, much less a candala."

"What about Dr. Dev Reja? What's his pedigree?"

"He is a Brahman."

I nodded. I had no time to answer Indiri's unspoken questions; I still had too many of my own. I thanked her and left. The subject of our conversation had left a dusty residue on the lining of my mind and I gulped thirstily at the cool night air.

I needed an excuse to speak to Pram so I picked up his clothes from the common locker we shared in the gym and cut across the campus to his residence.

It was a small building, a cottage really, converted into apartments for those who preferred a certain kind of rickety individuality to the steel-and-glass anonymity of the high-rise student dorms. There was a light on in Pram's second-floor room. I went inside and up the creaking stairs. The rap of my knuckles on the door coincided with another sound that could have been a chair

 Suspicions?

Based on the two sounds Dr. Frederickson hears, what do you think was going on in Pram Sakhuntala's room? Explain.

tipping over onto the floor. I raised my hand to knock again, and froze. There was a new sound, barely perceptible but real nonetheless; it was the strangling rasp of a man choking to death.

I grabbed the knob and twisted. The door was locked. I had about three feet of space on the landing and I used every inch of it as I stepped back and leaped forward, skipping off the floor, kicking out with my heel at the door just above the lock. It gave. The door flew open and I hit the floor, slapping the wood with my hands to absorb the shock and immediately springing to my feet. The scene in the room branded its image on my mind even as I leaped to right the fallen chair.

Two factors were responsible for the fact that Pram was still alive: He had changed his mind at the last moment, and he was a lousy hangman to begin with. The knot in the plastic clothesline had not been tied properly and there had not been enough slack to break his neck; he had sagged rather than fallen through the air. His fingers clawed at the thin line, then slipped off. His legs thrashed in the air a good two feet above the floor; his eyes bulged and his tongue, thick and black, protruded from his dry lips like an obscene worm. His face was blue. He had already lost control of his sphincter and the air was filled with a sour, fetid smell.

I quickly righted the chair and placed it beneath the flailing feet, one of which caught me in the side of the head, stunning me. I fought off the dizziness and grabbed his ankles, forcing his feet onto the chair. That wasn't going to be enough. A half-dead, panic-stricken man with a rope around his neck choking the life out of him doesn't just calmly stand up on a chair. I jumped up beside him, bracing and lifting him by his belt while, with the other hand, I stretched up and went to work on the knot in the clothesline. Finally it came loose and Pram suddenly went limp. I ducked and let Pram's body fall over my shoulder. I got down off the chair and carried him to the bed. I put my ear to his chest; he was still breathing, but just barely. I grabbed the phone and called for an ambulance. After that I called my brother.

Pram's larynx wasn't damaged and, with a little difficulty, he could manage to talk; but he wasn't doing any of it to Garth.

"What can I tell you, Mongo?" Garth said. He pointed to the closed door of Pram's hospital room where we had just spent a fruitless half hour trying to get Pram to open up about what had prompted him to try to take his own life. "He says nobody's done anything to him. Actually, by attempting suicide, he's the one who's broken the law."

I muttered a carefully selected obscenity.

"I didn't say I was going to press charges against him," Garth grunted. "I'm just trying to tell you that I'm not going to press charges against anyone else either. I can't. Whatever bad blood there is between your friend and this Dev Reja, it obviously isn't a police matter. Not until and unless some complaint is made."

I was convinced that Pram's act was linked to Dev Reja, and I'd hoped that a talk with Pram would provide the basis for charges of harassment—or worse—against the other man. Pram had refused to even discuss the matter, just as he had refused to let Indiri even see him. I thanked my brother for his time and walked him to the elevator. Then I went back to Pram's room.

I paused at the side of the bed, staring down at the young man in it who would not meet my gaze. The fiery rope burns on his neck were concealed beneath bandages, but the medication assailed my nostrils. I lifted my hands in a helpless gesture and sat down in a chair beside the bed, just beyond Pram's field of vision.

"It does have something to do with Dev Reja, doesn't it, Pram?" I said after a long pause.

"What I did was a terrible act of cowardice," Pram croaked into the silence. "I must learn to accept. I *will* learn to accept and live my life as it is meant to be lived."

"Accept what?" I said very carefully, leaning forward.

Tears welled up in Pram's eyes, brimmed at the lids, then rolled down his cheeks. He made no move to wipe them away. "My birth," he said in a tortured whisper. "I must learn to accept the fact of my birth."

"What are you talking about? You are a Ksatriyana. Indiri told me."

Pram shook his head. "I am a . . . sutra." I tried to think of a way to frame my next question, but it wasn't necessary. Now Pram's words flowed out of him like pus from a ruptured boil. "You see, I am adopted," Pram continued. "That I knew. What I did not know is that I am illegitimate, and that my real mother was a sutra. Therefore, on *two* counts, I am a sutra. Dr. Dev Reja discovered this because he has access to the birth records of all the Indian exchange students. He had no reason to tell me until he found out that Indiri and I intended to marry. It was only then that he felt the need to warn me."

"*Warn you?*" The words stuck in my throat.

"A sutra cannot marry a Ksatriyana. It would not be right." I started to speak but Pram cut me off, closing his eyes and shaking his head as though he was in great pain. "I cannot explain," he said, squeezing the words out through lips that had suddenly become dry and cracked. "You must simply accept what I tell you and know that it is true. I know why Dr. Dev Reja called me a candala; he thought I had gone to you to discuss something which has nothing to do with someone who is not Indian. It does not matter that it was said in anger, or that he was mistaken in thinking it was me who had come to you; he was right about me being a candala. I have proved it by my actions. I have behaved like a coward. It is in my blood."

"If you want to call yourself a fool, I might agree with you," I said evenly. "Do you think Indiri gives a damn what caste you come from?" There was a rage building inside me and I had to struggle to keep it from tainting my words.

Pram suddenly looked up at me. Now, for the first time, life had returned to his eyes, but it was a perverted life, burning with all the intensity of a fuse on a time bomb. "Having Indiri know of my low station would only increase my humiliation. I have told you what you wanted to know, Dr. Frederickson. Now you must promise to leave me alone and to interfere no further."

"You haven't told me anything that makes any sense," I said, standing up and leaning on the side of the bed. "A few days ago you were a fairly good-looking young man, a better than average student deeply loved by the most beautiful girl on campus. Now you've refused to even see that girl and, a few hours ago, you tried to take your own life. You're falling apart, and all because some silly bastard called you a name! Explain *that* to me!"

I paused and took a deep breath. I realized that my bedside manner might leave something to be desired, but at the moment I felt Pram needed something stronger than sympathy; something like a kick in the ass. "*I'm* not going to tell Indiri," I said heatedly. "*You* are. And you're going to apologize to her for acting like such a . . . jerk. Then maybe the three of us can go out for a drink and discuss the curious vagaries of the human mind." I smiled to soften the blow of my words, but Pram continued to stare blankly, shaking his head.

"I am a candala," he said, his words strung together like a chant. "What I did was an act of pride. Candalas are not allowed pride. I must learn to accept what my life has—"

I couldn't stand the monotonous tones, the corroding, poisonous mist that was creeping into his brain and shining out through his eyes; I struck at that sick light with my hand. Pram took the blow across his face without flinching, as if it was someone else I had hit. The nurse who had come into the room had no doubts as to whom I had hit and she didn't like it one bit. I shook off her hand and screamed into Pram's face.

"A name means nothing!" I shouted, my voice trembling with rage. "What the hell's the *matter* with you?! You can't allow yourself to be defined by someone else! You must define *yourself*! Only *you* can determine what you are. Now stop talking crazy and pull yourself together!"

But I was the one being pulled out of the room by two very husky young interns. I continued to scream at the dull-faced youth in the bed even as they pulled me out through the door. I could not explain my own behavior, except in terms of blind rage and hatred in the presence of some great evil that I was unable to even see, much less fight.

Outside in the corridor I braced my heels against the tiles of the floor. "Get your goddam hands off me," I said quietly. The two men released me and I hurried out of the hospital, anxious to get home and into a hot bath. Still, I suspected even then that the smell I carried with me out of that room was in my mind, and would not be so easily expunged.

"He's changed, Dr. Frederickson," Indiri sobbed. I pushed back from my desk and the Indian girl rushed into my arms. I held her until the violent shuddering of her shoulders began to subside.

"He's told you what the problem is?" Pram had been released from the hospital that morning, and it had been my suggestion that Indiri go to meet him.

Indiri nodded. "He's becoming what Dr. Dev Reja says he is."

I didn't need Indiri to tell me that. I knew the psychiatrist assigned to Pram and a little gentle prodding had elicited the opinion that Pram had, indeed, accepted Dev Reja's definition of himself and was adjusting his personality, character, and behavior accordingly. It had all been couched in psychiatric mumbo jumbo, but I had read Jean Paul Sartre's existential masterpiece, *Saint Genet,* and that was all the explanation I needed.

"How do you feel about what he told you?" I said gently. Indiri's eyes were suddenly dry and flashing angrily. "Sorry," I added quickly. "I just had to be sure where we stood."

"What can we do, Dr. Frederickson?"

If she was surprised when I didn't answer she didn't show it. Perhaps she hadn't really expected a reply, or perhaps she already knew the answer. And I knew that I was afraid, afraid as I had not been since, as

Suspicions?

What do you think Dr. Frederickson intends to do? Explain.

a child, I had first learned I was different from other children and had lain awake at night listening to strange sounds inside my mind.

I burst into the room and slammed the door behind me. My timing was perfect; Dev Reja was about halfway through his lecture.

"Ladies and gentlemen," I intoned, "class is dismissed. Professor Dev Reja and I have business to discuss."

Dev Reja and the students stared at me, uncomprehending. Dev Reja recovered first, drawing himself up to his full height and stalking across the room. I stepped around him and positioned myself behind his lectern. "Dismiss them now," I said, drumming my fingers on the wood, "or I deliver my own impromptu lecture on bigotry, Indian style."

That stopped him. Dev Reja glared at me, then waved his hand in the direction of the students. The students rose and filed quickly out of the room, embarrassed, eager to escape the suppressed anger that crackled in the air like heat lightning before a summer storm.

"What do you think you're doing, Frederickson?" Dev Reja's voice shook with outrage. "This behavior is an utter breach of professional ethics, not to mention common courtesy. I will have this brought up—"

"Shut up," I said easily. It caught him by surprise and stopped the flow of words. He stared at me, his mouth open. My own voice was calm, completely belying the anger and frustration behind the words. "If there's anyone who should be brought before the Ethics Committee, it's you. You're absolutely unfit to teach."

Dev Reja walked past me to the window, but not before I caught a flash of what looked like pain in his eyes. I found that incongruous in Dev Reja, and it slowed me. But not for long.

"Let me tell you exactly what you're going to do," I said to the broad back. "I don't pretend to understand all that's involved in this caste business, but I certainly can recognize rank prejudice when I see it. For some reason that's completely beyond me, Pram has accepted what you told him about himself, and it's destroying him. Do you know that he tried to kill himself?"

"Of course I know, you fool," Dev Reja said, wheeling on me. I was startled to see that the other man's eyes were glistening with tears. I was prepared for anything but that. I continued with what I had come to say, but the rage was largely dissipated; now I was close to pleading.

"You're the one who put this 'untouchable' crap into his head, Dev Reja, and you're the one who's going to have to take it out. I don't care how you do it; just do it. Tell him you were mistaken; tell him he's really the reincarnation of Buddha, or Gandhi. Anything. Just make it so that Pram can get back to the business of living. If you don't, you can be certain that I'm going to make your stay at this university—and in this country—very uncomfortable. I'll start with our Ethics Committee, then work my way up to your embassy. I don't think they'd like it if they knew you were airing India's dirty laundry on an American campus."

"There's nothing that can be done now," Dev Reja said in a tortured voice that grated on my senses precisely because it did not fit the script I had written for this confrontation. Dev Reja was not reacting the way I had expected him to.

"What kind of man are you, Dev Reja?"

"I am an Indian."

"Uh-huh. Like Hitler was a German."

The remark had no seeming effect on the other man and I found that disappointing.

"Dr. Frederickson, may I speak to you for a few minutes without any interruption?"

"Be my guest."

"I detest the caste system, as any right-thinking man detests a system that traps and

 Suspicions?

Based on the flash of pain and the tears that had appeared in Dr. Dev Reja's eyes and his tortured voice that did "not fit the script" that Dr. Frederickson had written in his mind for this confrontation, what do you think that Dr. Dev Reja intends to say to Dr. Frederickson? Why?

dehumanizes men. However, I can assure you that Pram's mentality and way of looking at things is much more representative of Indian thinking than is mine. The caste system is a stain upon our national character, just as your enslavement and discrimination against blacks is a stain upon yours. But it *does* exist, and must be dealt with. The ways of India are deeply ingrained in the human being that is Pram Sakhuntala. I can assure you this is true. I know Pram much better than you do, and his reaction to the information I gave him proves that I am correct."

"Then why did you give him that information? Why did you give him something you knew he probably couldn't handle?"

"Because it was inevitable," Dev Reja said quietly. "You see, Dr. Frederickson, you or I could have overcome this thing. Pram cannot, simply because he is not strong enough. Because he is weak, and because he would have found out anyway, for reasons which I think will become clear to you, he would have destroyed himself, and Indiri as well. This way, there is a great deal of pain for Pram, but the catastrophe that would otherwise be is prevented."

"I don't understand."

"Pram was going to marry a Ksatriyana. Don't you suppose Indiri's family would have checked the circumstances of Pram's birth before they allowed such a marriage to take place? I tell you they would, and then things would have been much worse for everyone involved."

"But he could have married her and lived here."

"Ah, Dr. Frederickson, he could *still* do that, couldn't he? But I think you will agree that that does not seem likely. You see, what you fail to understand is that Pram is an *Indian,* and his roots are in India. Pram's adoptive parents are extremely liberal and farseeing people. Not at all like most people in India, in the United States or, for that matter, in the world. Pram himself failed to learn the great truth that was implicit in his adoption. I know that if Pram was to attempt to return to India and marry Indiri—as he would most certainly have done if I had not told him what I did—he would have been ridiculed and derided by Indiri's family; perhaps even stoned for even presuming to do such a thing. In other words, Dr. Frederickson, Pram has the same options he had before: to marry Indiri or not; to live here or in India. I'm sure Indiri is as indifferent to Pram's origins as his own family is. He is not able to do this because, as you say, the knowledge that he could come from sutra origins is destroying him. You see, in effect, Pram is prejudiced against himself. I had hoped that telling him the truth as I did would give him time to adjust, to prepare himself."

I suddenly felt sick at the image of a young man doing battle with shadows; Pram had had a glittering treasure within his grasp and had ended with an empty pot at the end of a fake rainbow. And all because of a label he had swallowed and internalized but which, for him, was no more digestible than a stone.

"I didn't know you'd said those things to him," I said lamely. "But now he's obsessed with this candala thing."

"I'm afraid you'll have to take the responsibility for that, Dr. Frederickson."

"You said it."

"In anger, without thinking. You felt the need to repeat it."

I could feel a cloak of guilt settling over my shoulders. I made no attempt to shrug it off for the simple reason that Dev Reja was right.

"It doesn't really matter, Dr. Frederickson. Even without you the problem would still remain. However, now I am curious. What would you have done in my place?"

I wished I had an answer. I didn't. I was in over my head and knew it.

"All right," I said resignedly, "what do we do now?"

"What we have been doing," Dev Reja said. "Help Pram the best we can, each in our own way."

"He has a psychiatrist looking after him now. The university insisted."

"That's good as far as it goes," Dev Reja said, looking down at his hands. "Still, you and I and Indiri must continue to talk to him, to try to make him see what you wanted him to see: that a man is not a label. If he is to marry Indiri and return to India, he must strengthen himself; he must prepare an inner defense against the people who will consider his love a crime."

"Yes," I said, "I think I see." It was all I said, and I could only hope Dev Reja could sense all of the other things I might have said. I turned and walked out of the classroom, closing the door quietly behind me.

Pram's soul was rotting before my eyes. He came to class, but it was merely a habitual response and did not reflect a desire to actually learn anything. Once I asked him how he could expect to be a successful sociologist if he failed his courses; he had stared at me blankly, as though my words had no meaning.

He no longer bathed, and his body smelled. The wound on his throat had become infected and suppurating; Pram had wrapped it in a dirty rag which he did not bother to change. His very presence had become anathema to the rest of his class, and it was only with the greatest difficulty that I managed to get through each lecture that Pram attended. Soon I wished he would no longer come, and this realization only added to my own growing sense of horror. He came to see me each day, but only because I asked him to. Each day I talked, and Pram sat and gave the semblance of attention. But that was all he gave, and it was not difficult to see that my words had no effect; I could not even be sure he heard them. After a while he would ask permission to leave and I would walk him to the door, fighting back the urge to scream at him, to beat him with my fists.

The infected wound landed him back in the hospital. Three days later I was awakened in the middle of the night by the insistent ring of the telephone. I picked it up and Indiri's voice cut through me like a knife.

"Dr. Frederickson! It's Pram! I think something terrible is going to happen!"

Her words were shrill, strung together like knots on a wire about to snap. "Easy, Indiri. Slow down and tell me exactly what's happened."

"Something woke me up a few minutes ago," she said, her heavy breathing punctuating each word. "I got up and went to the window. Pram was standing on the lawn, staring up at my window."

"Did he say anything, make any signal that he wanted to talk to you?"

"No. He ran when he saw me." Her voice broke off in a shudder, then resumed in the frightened croak of an old woman. "He was wearing two wooden blocks on a string around his neck."

"Wooden blocks?"

"Clappers," Indiri sobbed. "Like a candala might wear. Do you remember what I told you?"

I remembered. "In what direction was he running?"

"I'm not sure, but I think Dr. Dev Reja's house is in that direction."

I slammed down the phone and yanked on enough clothes to keep from being arrested. Then, still without knowing exactly why, I found myself running through the night.

My own apartment was a block and a half off campus, about a half mile from Dev Reja's on-campus residence. I hurdled a low brick wall on the east side of the campus and pumped my arms as I raced across the rolling green lawns.

Suspicions?

1. Indiri Tamidian thinks that "something terrible is going to happen." Do you agree? Explain.

2. As Dr. Frederickson runs after Pram and toward Dr. Dev Reja's house, it is possible that he has figured out what is going to happen. He tells us, "I ran in a panic, pursued by thoughts of clappers and corpses." Make as specific and exact a prediction as you can about what you think Dr. Frederickson thinks is going to happen—and explain why you made that particular prediction.

I ran in a panic, pursued by thoughts of clappers and corpses. My lungs burned and my legs felt like slabs of dough; then a new surge of adrenalin flowed and I ran. And ran.

The door to Dev Reja's house was ajar, the light on in the living room. I took the porch steps three at a time, tripped over the door jamb and sprawled headlong on the living room floor. I rolled to my feet; and froze.

Pram might have been waiting for me, or simply lost in thought, groping for some last thread of sanity down in the black, ether depths where his mind had gone. My mouth opened, but no sound came out. Pram's eyes were like two dull marbles, too large for his face and totally unseeing.

Dev Reja's naked corpse lay on the floor. The handle of a kitchen knife protruded from between the shoulder blades. The clothes Dev Reja should have been wearing were loosely draped over Pram. The room reeked with the smell of gasoline.

Candala. Pram had made the final identification, embracing it completely.

I saw Pram's hand move and heard something that sounded like the scratching of a match; my yell was lost in the sudden explosion of fire. Pram and the corpse beside him blossomed into an obscene flower of flame: its petals seared my flesh as I stepped forward.

I backed up slowly, shielding my face with my hands. Deep inside the deadly pocket of fire Pram's charred body rocked back and forth, then fell across Dev Reja's corpse. I gagged on the smell of cooking flesh.

Somewhere, thousands of miles and years from what was happening in the room, I heard the scream of fire engines, their wailing moans blending with my own.

 How Clever?

1. Explain the caste system of India on the basis of the various parts of the story that provide information about it. What is the position of the "candala"? Where in Indiri Tamidian's explanation to Dr. Frederickson of "candala" does she indirectly provide two clues to Pram Sakhuntala's true origins?

2. Indiri tells Dr. Frederickson: "'You cannot fully understand the meaning and implications of *caste* unless you are Indian.'" Do you agree with Indiri? Explain.

3. Dr. Frederickson thinks, in response to Indiri's statement (in question 2): "I wondered. I had a few black friends who might give her an argument, but I didn't say anything." Do you agree with Dr. Frederickson? Explain.

4. Review questions 2 and 3 above. Based on his actions and comments in the story, whom do you think Dr. Dev Reja would agree with more—Indiri or Dr. Frederickson? Explain.

5. What personal reasons might Dr. Frederickson have in the context of Pram Sakhuntala's suicide attempt for feeling such "blind rage and hatred in the presence of some great evil that I was unable to even see, much less fight"? Explain.

6. Explain what Dr. Frederickson means when he tells Pram: "You can't allow yourself to be defined by someone else! You must define *yourself!* Only *you* can determine what you are. Now stop talking crazy...!"

7. Why had Dr. Dev Reja asked Pram to come speak with him? What motive did he have for telling Pram about his sutra origins and the circumstances of his birth? Do you agree with what Dr. Dev Reja did and with his reasons for doing it? Explain.

8. Is Dr. Dev Reja correct when he says that "Pram has the same options he had before: to marry Indiri or not; to live here or in India"? Explain.

9. How was Dr. Dev Reja right (Dr. Frederickson agrees) when he held Dr. Frederickson responsible for "this candala thing"?

10. When Dr. Frederickson leaves Dr. Dev Reja's classroom he says to him, "Yes, I think I see," and then lets the reader know that "It was all I said, and I could only hope Dr. Dev Reja could sense all of the other things I might have said." What would those other things have been? Explain how this might make Dr. Dev Reja's character a kind of red herring in the story.

11. Explain why Dr. Frederickson's "sense of horror" increased when he realized that he wished that Pram would no longer attend his class.

12. Why did Pram put wooden clapper boxes around his neck when he went to Dr. Dev Reja's house? What intention was he signaling to Dr. Dev Reja?

13. Where in Indiri's explanation to Dr. Frederickson of the kind of work candalas are permitted to do did she provide four clues to the ending of the story? How are those clues remembered by Dr. Frederickson when he tells the reader, "I ran in a panic, pursued by thoughts of clappers and corpses"?

14. Do you feel that the story had to end the way it did? Explain the reasons behind your feelings.

15. What does Dr. Frederickson mean when he concludes his narration of the story with these words: "Somewhere, thousands of miles and years from what was happening in the room, I heard the scream of fire engines, their wailing moans blending with my own"?

DETECTWRITE: Characterization

1. Review the details of the portrait of university criminology professor Dr. Robert Frederickson—private detective, four-foot-seven-inch

dwarf, ex-circus performer and famous headliner "Mongo the Magnificent" (tumbler and acrobat)—that leads off the story "Candala." Explain why you think the author began this particular story with such a clear and exact picture of the story's detective.

2. Compare and contrast Dr. Frederickson with other private detectives you have met in this collection. In what specific ways is he different? How is he similar?

3. If you were to create a private detective for a mystery story you might write, would you make him as distinctive as Dr. Frederickson is? Explain.

4. Why is "self-pity" rejected by Dr. Frederickson as part of his nature—and how is this fact critical to Dr. Frederickson's involvement in the plot of this story?

5. Contrast the author's portrait of Indiri Tamidian's "zest for life" in the opening paragraph of the story with the author's portrait of Pram Sakhuntala's "death wish" in the final two pages of the story. How does this contrast indirectly convey the essence of the point the story makes?

6. Explain how Dr. Dev Reja is an example of a character who is either wholly or partly misunderstood by the detective in the story and how this misconception serves as a red herring (false clue) for the reader.

DETECTWRITE: Plot

1. The plot of "Candala" depends upon the reader's already knowing or learning an aspect of another culture's way of life. How did the author structure sufficient background information into the story so that readers could learn what they needed to know without the story's sounding like a history or anthropology lesson?

2. What specialized background information might you want to structure into a mystery story you would write so that your plot would have a distinctive exotic aspect?

3. How would you communicate this information so that it read as an integral part of the story and not as awkward insertions of background material?

DETECTWRITE: Setting

1. Rethink the university setting of "Candala" so that the same story is now set in your high school. What changes would you have to make and why? Do you consider these changes to be major or minor? Explain.

2. Think about how you might use your high school and the people in it as the setting for a detective story you might write. What ideas come immediately to mind?

Out the Window

Lawrence Block

T HERE WAS NOTHING SPECIAL ABOUT HER LAST DAY. SHE seemed a little jittery, preoccupied with something or with nothing at all. But this was nothing new for Paula.

She was never much of a waitress in the three months she spent at Armstrong's. She'd forget some orders and mix up others, and when you wanted the check or another round of drinks you could go crazy trying to attract her attention. There were days when she walked through her shift like a ghost through walls, and it was as though she had perfected some arcane technique of astral projection, sending her mind out for a walk while her long lean body went on serving food and drinks and wiping down empty tables.

She did make an effort, though. She damn well tried. She could always manage a smile. Sometimes it was the brave smile of the walking wounded and other times it was a tight-jawed, brittle grin with a couple tabs of amphetamine behind it, but you take what you can to get through the days and any smile is better than none at all. She knew most of Armstrong's regulars by name and her greeting always made you feel as though you'd come home. When that's all the home you have, you tend to appreciate that sort of thing.

And if the career wasn't perfect for her, well, it certainly hadn't been what she'd had in mind when she came to New York in the first place. You no more set out to be a waitress in a Ninth Avenue gin mill than you intentionally become an ex-cop coasting through the months on bourbon and coffee. We have that sort of greatness thrust upon us. When you're as young as Paula Wittlauer you hang in there, knowing things are going to get better. When you're my age you just hope they don't get too much worse.

She worked the early shift, noon to eight, Tuesday through Saturday. Trina came on at six so there were two girls on the floor during the dinner rush. At eight Paula would go wherever she went and Trina would keep on bringing cups of coffee and glasses of bourbon for another six hours or so.

Paula's last day was a Thursday in late September. The heat of the summer was starting to break up. There was a cooling rain that morning and the sun never did show its face. I wandered in around four in the afternoon with a copy of the *Post* and read through it while I had my first drink of the day. At eight o'clock I was talking with a couple of nurses from Roosevelt Hospital who wanted to grouse about a resident surgeon with a messiah complex. I was making sympathetic noises when Paula swept past our table and told me to have a good evening.

I said, "You too, kid." Did I look up? Did we smile at each other? Hell, I don't remember.

"See you tomorrow, Matt."

"Right," I said. "God willing."

But he evidently wasn't. Around three Justin closed up and I went around the block to my hotel. It didn't take long for the coffee and bourbon to cancel each other out. I got into bed and slept.

My hotel is on Fifty-seventh Street between Eighth and Ninth. It's on the uptown side of the block and my window is on the street side looking south. I can see the World Trade Center at the tip of Manhattan from my window.

I can also see Paula's building. It's on the other side of Fifty-seventh Street a hundred yards or so to the east, a towering high-rise that, had it been directly across from me, would have blocked my view of the trade center.

She lived on the seventeenth floor. Sometime after four she went out a high window. She swung out past the sidewalk and landed in the street a few feet from the curb, touching down between a couple of parked cars.

In high school physics they teach you that falling bodies accelerate at a speed of thirty-two feet per second. So she would have fallen thirty-two feet in the first second, another sixty-four feet the next second, then ninety-six feet in the third. Since she fell something like two hundred feet, I don't suppose she could have spent more than four seconds in the actual act of falling.

It must have seemed a lot longer than that.

I got up around ten, ten-thirty. When I stopped at the desk for my mail Vinnie told me they'd had a jumper across the street during the night. "A dame," he said, which is a word you don't hear much anymore. "She went out without a stitch on. You could catch your death that way."

I looked at him.

"Landed in the street, just missed somebody's Caddy. How'd you like to find something like that for a hood ornament? I wonder if your insurance would cover that. What do you call it, act of God?" He came out from behind the desk and walked with me to the door. "Over there," he said, pointing. "The florist's van there is covering the spot where she flopped. Nothing to see anyway. They scooped her up with a spatula and a sponge and then they hosed it all down. By the time I came on duty there wasn't a trace left."

"Who was she?"

"Who knows?"

I had things to do that morning, and as I did them I thought from time to time of the jumper. They're not that rare and they usually do the deed in the hours before dawn. They say it's always darkest then.

Sometime in the early afternoon I was passing Armstrong's and stopped in for a short one. I stood at the bar and looked around to say hello to Paula but she wasn't there. A doughy redhead named Rita was taking her shift.

Dean was behind the bar. I asked him where Paula was. "She skipping school today?"

"You didn't hear?"

"Jimmy fired her?"

He shook his head, and before I could venture any further guesses he told me.

I drank my drink. I had an appointment to see somebody about something, but suddenly it ceased to seem important. I put a dime in the phone and canceled my appointment and came back and had another drink. My hand was trembling slightly when I picked up the glass. It was a little steadier when I set it down.

I crossed Ninth Avenue and sat in St. Paul's for a while. Ten, twenty minutes. Something like that. I lit a candle for Paula and a few other candles for a few other corpses, and I sat there and thought about life and death and high windows. Around the time I left the police force I discovered that churches were very good places for thinking about that sort of thing.

After a while I walked over to her building and stood on the pavement in front of it. The florist's truck had moved on and I examined the street where she'd landed. There was, as Vinnie had assured me, no trace of what had happened. I tilted my head back and looked up, wondering what window she might have fallen from, and then I looked down at the pavement and then up again, and a sudden rush of vertigo made my head spin. In the course of all this I managed to attract the attention of the building's doorman and he came out to the curb anxious to talk about the former tenant. He was a black man about my age and he looked as proud of his uniform as the guy in the Marine Corps recruiting poster. It was a good-looking uniform, shades of brown, epaulets, gleaming brass buttons.

"Terrible thing," he said. "A young girl like that with her whole life ahead of her."

"Did you know her well?"

He shook his head. "She would give me a smile, always say hello, always call me by name. Always in a hurry, rushing in, rushing out again. You wouldn't think she had a care in the world. But you never know."

"You never do."

"She lived on the seventeenth floor. I wouldn't live that high above the ground if you gave me the place rent-free."

"Heights bother you?"

I don't know if he heard the question. "I live up one flight of stairs. That's just fine for me. No elevator and no, no high window." His brow clouded and he looked on the verge of saying something else, but then someone started to enter his building's lobby and he moved to intercept him. I looked up again, trying to count windows to the seventeenth floor, but the vertigo returned and I gave it up.

"Are you Matthew Scudder?"

I looked up. The girl who'd asked the question was very young, with long straight brown hair and enormous light brown eyes. Her face was open and defenseless and her lower lip was quivering. I said I was Matthew Scudder and pointed at the chair opposite mine. She remained on her feet.

"I'm Ruth Wittlauer," she said.

The name didn't register until she said, "Paula's sister." Then I nodded and studied her face for signs of a family resemblance. If they were there I couldn't find them. It was ten in the evening and Paula Wittlauer had been dead for eighteen hours and her sister was standing expectantly before me, her face a curious blend of determination and uncertainty.

I said, "I'm sorry. Won't you sit down? And will you have something to drink?"

"I don't drink."

"Coffee?"

"I've been drinking coffee all day. I'm shaky from all the damn coffee. Do I *have* to order something?"

She was on the edge, all right. I said, "No, of course not. You don't have to order anything." And I caught Trina's eye and warned her off and she nodded shortly and let us alone. I sipped my own coffee and watched Ruth Wittlauer over the brim of the cup.

"You knew my sister, Mr. Scudder."

"In a superficial way, as a customer knows a waitress."

"The police say she killed herself."

"And you don't think so?"

"I know she didn't."

I watched her eyes while she spoke and I was willing to believe she meant what she said. She didn't believe that Paula went out of the window of her own accord, not for a moment. Of course, that didn't mean she was right.

"What do you think happened?"

"She was murdered." She made the statement quite matter-of-factly. "I know she was murdered. I think I know who did it."

"Who?"

"Cary McCloud."

"I don't know him."

"But it may have been somebody else," she went on. She lit a cigarette, smoked for a few moments in silence. "I'm pretty sure it was Cary," she said.

"Why?"

"They were living together." She frowned, as if in recognition of the fact that cohabitation was small evidence of murder. "He could do it," she said carefully. "That's why I think he did. I don't think just anyone could commit murder. In the heat of the moment, sure, I guess people fly off the handle, but to do it deliberately and throw someone out of a—"

I put my hand on top of hers. She had long small-boned hands and her skin was cold and dry to the touch. I thought she was going to cry or break or something but she didn't. It was just not going to be possible for her to say the word *window* and she would stall every time she came to it.

"What do the police say?"

"Suicide. They say she killed herself." She drew on the cigarette. "But they don't know her, they never knew her. If Paula wanted to kill herself she would have taken pills. She liked pills."

"I figured she took ups."

"Ups, tranquilizers, ludes, barbiturates. And she liked grass and she liked to drink." She lowered her eyes. My hand was still on top of hers and she looked at our two hands and I removed mine. "I don't do any of those things. I drink coffee, that's my one vice, and I don't even do that much because it makes me jittery. It's the coffee that's making me nervous tonight. Not . . . all of this."

"Okay."

"She was twenty-four. I'm twenty. Baby sister, square baby sister, except that was always how she *wanted* me to be. She did all these things and at the same time she told me not to do them, that it was a bad scene. I think she kept me straight. I really do. Not so much because of what she was saying as that I looked at the way she was living and what it was doing to her and I didn't want that for myself. I thought it was crazy, what she was doing to herself, but at the same time I guess I worshipped her, she was always my heroine. I loved her, God, I really did, I'm just starting to realize how much, and she's dead and he killed her, I *know* he killed her, I just know it."

After a while I asked her what she wanted me to do.

"You're a detective."

"Not in an official sense. I used to be a cop."

"Could you . . . find out what happened?"

"I don't know."

"I tried talking to the police. It was like talking to the wall. I can't just turn around and do nothing. Do you understand me?"

"I think so. Suppose I look into it and it still looks like suicide?"

"She didn't kill herself."

"Well, suppose I wind up thinking that she did?"

She thought it over. "I still wouldn't have to believe it."

"No," I agreed. "We get to choose what we believe."

"I have some money." She put her purse on the table. "I'm the straight sister, I have an office job, I save money. I have five hundred dollars with me."

"That's too much to carry in this neighborhood."

"Is it enough to hire you?"

I didn't want to take her money. She had five hundred dollars and a dead sister, and parting with one wouldn't bring the other back to life. I'd have worked for nothing but that wouldn't have been good because neither of us would have taken it seriously enough.

And I have rent to pay and two sons to support, and Armstrong's charges for the coffee and the bourbon. I took four fifty-dollar bills from her and told her I'd do my best to earn them.

After Paula Wittlauer hit the pavement, a black-and-white from the Eighteenth Precinct caught the squeal and took charge of the case. One of the cops in the car was a guy named Guzik. I hadn't known him when I was on the force but we'd met since then. I didn't like him and I don't think he cared for me either, but he was reasonably honest and had struck me as competent. I got him on the phone the next morning and offered to buy him a lunch.

We met at an Italian place on Fifty-sixth Street. He had veal and peppers and a couple glasses of red wine. I wasn't hungry but I made myself eat a small steak.

Between bites of veal he said, "The kid sister, huh? I talked to her, you know. She's so clean and so pretty it could break your heart if you let it. And of course she don't want to believe sis did the Dutch act. I asked is she Catholic because then there's the religious angle but that wasn't it. Anyway your average priest'll stretch a point. They're the best lawyers going, the hell, two thousand years of practice, they oughta be good. I took that attitude myself. I said, 'Look, there's all these pills. Let's say your sister had herself some pills and drank a little wine and smoked a little pot and then she went to the window for some fresh air. So she got a little dizzy and maybe she blacked out and most likely she never knew what was happening.' Because there's no question of insurance, Matt, so if she wants to think it's an accident I'm not gonna shout suicide in her ear. But that's what it says in the file."

"You close it out?"

"Sure. No question."

"She thinks murder."

He nodded. "Tell me something I don't know. She says this McCloud killed sis. McCloud's the boyfriend. Thing is he was at an after-hours club at Fifty-third and Twelfth about the time sis was going skydiving."

"You confirm that?"

He shrugged. "It ain't airtight. He was in and out of the place, he coulda doubled back and all, but there was the whole business with the door."

"What business?"

"She didn't tell you? Paula Wittlauer's apartment was locked and the chain bolt was on. The super unlocked the door for us, but we had to send him back to the basement for a bolt cutter so's we could get through the chain bolt. You can only fasten the chain bolt from inside and you can only open the door a few inches with it on, so either Wittlauer launched her own self out the window or she was shoved out by Plastic Man, and then he went and slithered out the door without unhooking the chain bolt."

"Or the killer never left the apartment."

"Huh?"

"Did you search the apartment after the super came back and cut the chain for you?"

"We looked around, of course. There was an open window, there was a pile of clothes next to it. You know she went out naked, don't you?"

"Uh-huh."

"There was no burly killer crouching in the shrubbery, if that's what you're getting at."

"You checked the place carefully?"

"We did our job."

"Uh-huh. Look under the bed?"

"It was a platform bed. No crawl space under it."

"Closets?"

He drank some wine, put the glass down hard, glared at me. "What the hell are you getting at? You got reason to believe there was somebody in the apartment when we went in there?"

"Just exploring the possibilities."

"Jesus. You honestly think somebody's gonna be stupid enough to stay in the apartment after shoving her out of it? She musta been on the street ten minutes before we hit the building. If somebody did kill her, which never happened, but if they did they coulda been halfway to Texas by the time we hit the door, and don't that make more sense than jumping in the closet and hiding behind the coats?"

"Unless the killer didn't want to pass the doorman."

"So he's still got the whole building to hide in. Just the one man on the front door is the only security the building's got, anyway, and what does he amount to? And suppose he hides in the apartment and we happen to spot him. Then where is he? With his neck in the noose, that's where he is."

"Except you didn't spot him."

"Because he wasn't there, and when I start seeing little men who aren't there is when I put in my papers and quit the department."

There was an unvoiced challenge in his words. I had quit the department, but not because I'd seen little men. One night some years ago I broke up a bar holdup and went into the street after the pair who'd killed the bartender. One of my shots went wide and a little girl died, and after that I didn't see little men or hear voices, not exactly, but I did leave my wife and kids and quit the force and start drinking on a more serious level. But maybe it all would have happened just that way even if I'd never killed Estrellita Rivera. People go through changes and life does the damnedest things to us all.

"It was just a thought," I said. "The sister thinks it's murder so I was looking for a way for her to be right."

"Forget it."

"I suppose. I wonder why she did it."

"Do they even need a reason? I went in the bathroom and she had a medicine cabinet like a drugstore. Ups, downs, sideways. Maybe she was so stoned she thought she could fly. That would explain her being naked. You don't fly with your clothes on. Everybody knows that."

I nodded. "They find drugs in her system?"

"Drugs in her . . . oh, Jesus, Matt. She came down seventeen flights and she came down fast."

"Under four seconds."

"Huh?"

"Nothing," I said. I didn't bother telling him about high school physics and falling bodies. "No autopsy?"

"Of course not. You've seen jumpers. You were in the department a lot of years, you know what a person looks like after a drop like that. You want to be technical, there coulda been a bullet in her and nobody was gonna go and look for it. Cause of death was falling from a great height. That's what it says and that's what it was, and don't ask me was she stoned or was she pregnant or any of those questions because who the hell knows and who the hell cares, right?"

"How'd you even know it was her?"

"We got a positive ID from the sister."

I shook my head. "I mean how did you know what apartment to go to? She was naked so she didn't have any identification on her. Did the doorman recognize her?"

"You kidding? He wouldn't go close enough to look. He was along-side the building throwing up a few pints of cheap wine. He couldn't have identified his own ass."

"Then how'd you know who she was?"

"The window." I looked at him. "Hers was the only window that was open more than a couple of inches, Matt. Plus her lights were on. That made it easy."

"I didn't think of that."

"Yeah, well, I was there, and we just looked up and there was an open window and a light behind it, and that was the first place we went to. You'da thought of it if you were there."

"I suppose."

He finished his wine, burped delicately against the back of his hand. "It's suicide," he said. "You can tell the sister as much."

"I will. Okay if I look at the apartment?"

"Wittlauer's apartment? We didn't seal it, if that's what you mean. You oughta be able to con the super out of a key."

"Ruth Wittlauer gave me a key."

"Then there you go. There's no department seal on the door. You want to look around?"

"So I can tell the sister I was there."

"Yeah. Maybe you'll come across a suicide note. That's what I was looking for, a note. You turn up something like that and it clears up doubts for the friends and relatives. If it was up to me I'd get a law passed. No suicide without a note."

"Be hard to enforce."

"Simple," he said. "If you don't leave a note you gotta come back and be alive again." He laughed. "That'd start 'em scribbling away. Count on it."

The doorman was the same man I'd talked to the day before. It never occurred to him to ask me my business. I rode up in the elevator and walked along the corridor to 17G. The key Ruth Wittlauer had given me opened the door. There was just the one lock. That's the way it usually is in high-rises. A doorman, however slipshod he may be, endows tenants with a sense of security. The residents of unserviced walk-ups affix three or four extra locks to their doors and still cower behind them.

> **Suspicions?**
>
> Review police officer Guzik's response to Matthew Scudder's question, "How'd you know who she was?" Do you have any answers beyond the ones Guzik supplies? Explain.

The apartment had an unfinished air about it, and I sensed that Paula had lived there for a few months without ever making the place her own. There were no rugs on the wood parquet floor. The walls were decorated with a few unframed posters held up by scraps of red Mystik tape. The apartment was an L-shaped studio with a platform bed occupying the foot of the L. There were newspapers and magazines scattered around the place but no books. I noticed copies of *Variety* and *Rolling Stone* and *People* and the *Village Voice*.

The television set was a tiny Sony perched on top of a chest of drawers. There was no stereo, but there were a few dozen records, mostly classical with a sprinkling of folk music, Pete Seeger and Joan Baez and Dave Van Ronk. There was a dust-free rectangle on top of the dresser next to the Sony.

I looked through the drawers and closets. A lot of Paula's clothes. I recognized some of the outfits, or thought I did.

Someone had closed the window. There were two windows that opened, one in the sleeping alcove, the other in the living room section, but a row of undisturbed potted plants in front of the bedroom window made it evident she'd gone out of the other one. I wondered why anyone had bothered to close it. In case of rain, I supposed. That was only sensible. But I suspect the gesture must have been less calculated than that, a reflexive act akin to tugging a sheet over the face of a corpse.

I went into the bathroom. A killer could have hidden in the stall shower. If there'd been a killer.

Why was I still thinking in terms of a killer?

I checked the medicine cabinet. There were little tubes and vials of cosmetics, though only a handful compared with the array on one of the bedside tables. Here were containers of aspirin and other headache remedies, a tube of antibiotic ointment, several prescriptions and nonprescription hay fever preparations, a cardboard packet of Band-Aids, a roll of adhesive tape, a box of gauze pads. Some Q-Tips, a hairbrush, a couple of combs. A toothbrush in the holder.

There were no footprints on the floor of the stall shower. Of course he could have been barefoot. Or he could have run water and washed away the traces of his presence before he left.

I went over and examined the windowsill. I hadn't asked Guzik if they'd dusted for prints and I was reasonably certain no one had bothered. I wouldn't have taken the trouble in their position. I couldn't learn anything looking at the sill. I opened the window a foot or so and stuck my head out, but when I looked down the vertigo was extremely unpleasant and I drew my head back inside at once. I left the window open, though. The room could stand a change of air.

There were four folding chairs in the room, two of them closed and leaning against a wall, one near the bed, the fourth alongside the window. They were royal blue and made of high-impact plastic. The one by the window had her clothes piled on it. I went through the stack. She'd placed them deliberately on the chair but hadn't bothered folding them.

You never know what suicide will do. One man will put on a tuxedo before blowing his brains out. Another one will take off everything. Naked I came into the world and naked will I go out of it, something like that.

A skirt. Beneath it a pair of panty hose. Then a blouse, and under it a bra with two small, lightly padded cups. I put the clothing back as I had found it, feeling like a violator of the dead.

The bed was unmade. I sat on the edge of it and looked across the room at a poster of Mick Jagger. I don't know how long I sat there. Ten minutes, maybe.

On the way out I looked at the chain bolt. I hadn't even noticed it when I came in. The chain had been neatly severed. Half of it was still in the slot on the door while the other half hung from its mounting on the jamb. I closed the door and fitted the two halves together, then released them and let them dangle. Then I touched their ends together again. I unhooked the end of the chain from the slot and went to the bathroom for the roll of adhesive tape. I brought the tape back with me, tore off a piece and used it to fasten the chain back together again. Then I let myself out of the apartment and tried to engage the chain bolt from outside, but the tape slipped whenever I put any pressure on it.

I went inside again and studied the chain bolt. I decided I was behaving erratically, that Paula Wittlauer had gone out the window of her own accord. I looked at the windowsill again. The light dusting of soot didn't tell me anything one way or the other. New York's air is filthy and the accumulation of soot could have been deposited in a couple of hours, even with the window shut. It didn't mean anything.

I looked at the heap of clothes on the chair, and I looked again at the chain bolt, and I rode the elevator to the basement and found either the superintendent or one of his assistants. I asked to borrow a screwdriver. He gave me a long screwdriver with an amber plastic grip. He didn't ask me who I was or what I wanted it for.

I returned to Paula Wittlauer's apartment and removed the chain bolt from its moorings on the door and jamb. I left the building and walked around the corner to a hardware store on Ninth Avenue. They had a good selection of chain bolts but I wanted one identical to the one I'd removed and I had to walk down Ninth Avenue as far as Fiftieth Street and check four stores before I found what I was looking for.

Back in Paula's apartment I mounted the new chain bolt, using the holes in which the original had been mounted. I tightened the screws with

Suspicions?

1. Note the items Scudder finds in Paula's apartment. Sometimes the absence of something one expects to find can be more significant than the presence of something (expected or unexpected). Based on your reading of this scene and your knowledge of Paula, what would you have expected would be in Paula's apartment that Scudder doesn't find there?

   What conclusions can you draw from this absence?

2. Visualize Matt's itemization of the clothing he says Paula had placed deliberately on the chair but hadn't bothered folding. What conclusions can you draw from your visualization?

the super's screwdriver and stood out in the corridor and played with the chain. My hands are large and not terribly skillful, but even so I was able to lock and unlock the chain bolt from outside the apartment.

Suspicions?

How do you feel about Matt's experiment with the old and new chain bolt? Why?

I don't know who put it up, Paula or a previous tenant or someone on the building staff, but that chain bolt had been as much protection as the sanitized wrapper on a motel toilet seat. As evidence that Paula'd been alone when she went out the window, well, it wasn't worth a thing.

I replaced the original chain bolt, put the new one in my pocket, returned to the elevator, and gave back the screwdriver. The man I returned it to seemed surprised to get it back.

It took me a couple of hours to find Cary McCloud. I'd learned that he tended bar evenings at a club in the West Village called the Spider's Web. I got down there around five. The guy behind the bar had knobby wrists and an underslung jaw and he wasn't Cary McCloud. "He don't come on till eight," he told me "and he's off tonight anyway." I asked where I could find McCloud. "Sometimes he's here afternoons but he ain't been in today. As far as where you could look for him, that I couldn't tell you."

A lot of people couldn't tell me but eventually I ran across someone who could. You can quit the police force but you can't stop looking and sounding like a cop, and while that's a hindrance in some situations it's a help in others. Ultimately I found a man in a bar down the block from the Spider's Web who'd learned it was best to cooperate with the police if it didn't cost you anything. He gave me an address on Barrow Street and told me which bell to ring.

I went to the building but I rang several other bells until somebody buzzed me through the downstairs door. I didn't want Cary to know he had company coming. I climbed two flights of stairs to the apartment he was supposed to be occupying. The bell downstairs hadn't had his name on it. It hadn't had any name at all.

Loud rock music was coming through his door. I stood in front of it for a minute, then hammered on it loud enough to make myself heard over the electric guitars. After a moment the music dropped in volume. I pounded on the door again and a male voice asked who I was.

I said, "Police. Open up." That's a misdemeanor but I didn't expect to get in trouble for it.

"What's it about?"

"Open up, McCloud."

"Oh, Jesus," he said. He sounded tired, aggravated. "How did you find me, anyway? Give me a minute, huh? I want to put some clothes on."

Sometimes that's what they say while they're putting a clip into an automatic. Then they pump a handful of shots through the door and into you if you're still standing behind it. But his voice didn't have that kind of edge to it and I couldn't summon up enough anxiety to get out of the way. Instead I put my ear against the door and heard whispering within. I couldn't make out what they were whispering about or get any sense of the person who was with him. The music was down in volume but there was still enough of it to cover their conversation.

The door opened. He was tall and thin, with hollow cheeks and prominent eyebrows and a worn, wasted look to him. He must have been in his early thirties and he didn't really look much older than that but sensed that in another ten years he'd look twenty years older. If he lived that long. He wore patched jeans and a T-shirt with the Spider's Web silk-screened on it. Beneath the legend there was a sketch of a web. A macho spider stood at one end of it, grinning, extending two of his eight arms to welcome a hesitant girlish fly.

He noticed me noticing the shirt and managed a grin. "Place where I work," he said.

"I know."

"So come into my parlor. It ain't much but it's home."

I followed him inside, drew the door shut after me. The room was about fifteen feet square and held nothing you could call furniture. There was a mattress on the floor in one corner and a couple of cardboard cartons alongside it. The music was coming from a stereo, turntable and tuner and two speakers all in a row along the far wall. There was a closed door over on the right. I figured it led to the bathroom, and that there was a woman on the other side of it.

"I guess this is about Paula," he said. I nodded. "I been over this with you guys," he said. "I was nowhere near there when it happened. The last I saw her was five, six hours before she killed herself. I was working at the Web and she came down and sat at the bar. I gave her a couple of drinks and she split."

"And you went on working."

"Until I closed up. I kicked everybody out a little after three and it was close to four by the time I had the place swept up and the garbage on the street and the window gates locked. Then I came over here and picked up Sunny and we went up to the place on Fifty-third."

"And you got there when?"

"Hell, I don't know. I wear a watch but I don't look at it every damn minute. I suppose it took five minutes to walk here and then Sunny and I hopped right in a cab and we were at Patsy's in ten minutes at the outside, that's the after-hours place, I told you people all cf this, I really wish you would talk to each other and leave me the hell alone."

"Why doesn't Sunny come out and tell me about it?" I nodded at the bathroom door. "Maybe she can remember the time a little more clearly."

"Sunny? She stepped out a little while ago."

"She's not in the bathroom?"

"Nope. Nobody's in the bathroom."

"Mind if I see for myself?"

"Not if you can show me a warrant."

We looked at each other. I told him I figured I could take his word for it. He said he could always be trusted to tell the truth. I said I sensed as much about him.

He said, "What's the hassle, huh? I know you guys got forms to fill out, but why not give me a break? She killed herself and I wasn't anywhere near her when it happened."

He could have been. The times were vague, and whoever Sunny turned out to be, the odds were good that she'd have no more time sense than a koala bear. There were any number of ways he could have found a few minutes to go up to Fifty-seventh Street and heave Paula out a window, but it didn't add up that way and he just didn't feel like a killer to me. I knew what Ruth meant and I agreed with her that he was capable of murder but I don't think he'd been capable of this particular murder.

I said, "When did you go back to the apartment?"

"Who said I did?"

"You picked up your clothes, Cary."

"That was yesterday afternoon. The hell, I needed my clothes and stuff."

"How long were you living there?"

He hedged. "I wasn't exactly living there."

"Where were you exactly living?"

"I wasn't exactly living anywhere. I kept most of my stuff at Paula's place and I stayed with her most of the time but it wasn't as serious as actual living together. We were both too loose for anything like that. Anyway, the thing with Paula, it was pretty much winding itself down. She was a little too crazy for me." He smiled with his mouth. "They have to be a little crazy," he said, "but when they're too crazy it gets to be too much of a hassle."

Oh, he could have killed her. He could kill anyone if he had to, if someone was making too much of a hassle. But if he were to kill cleverly, faking the suicide in such an artful fashion, fastening the chain bolt on his way out, he'd pick a time when he had a solid alibi. He was not the sort to be so precise and so slipshod all at the same time.

"So you went and picked up your stuff."

"Right."

"Including the stereo and records."

"The stereo was mine. The records, I left the folk music and the classical shit because that belonged to Paula. I just took my records."

"And the stereo."

"Right."

"You got a bill of sale for it, I suppose."

"Who keeps that crap?"

"What if I said Paula kept the bill of sale? What if I said it was in with her papers and canceled checks?"

"You're fishing."

"You sure of that?"

"Nope. But if you did say that, I suppose I'd say the stereo was a gift from her to me. You're not really gonna charge me with stealing a stereo, are you?"

"Why should I? Robbing the dead's a sacred tradition. You took the drugs, too, didn't you? Her medicine cabinet used to look like a drugstore but there was nothing stronger than Excedrin when I took a look. That's why Sunny's in the bathroom. If I hit the door all the pretty little pills go down the toilet."

"I guess you can think that if you want."

"And I can come back with a warrant if I want."

"That's the idea."

"I ought to rap on the door just to do you out of the drugs but it doesn't seem worth the trouble. That's Paula Wittlauer's stereo. I suppose it's worth a couple hundred dollars. And you're not her heir. Unplug that thing and wrap it up, McCloud. I'm taking it with me."

"The hell you are."

"The hell I'm not."

"You want to take anything but your own ass out of here, you come back with a warrant. Then we'll talk about it."

"I don't need a warrant."

"You can't—"

"I don't need a warrant because I'm not a cop. I'm a detective McCloud, I'm private, and I'm working for Ruth Wittlauer, and that's who's getting the stereo. I don't know if she wants it or not, but that's her problem. She doesn't want Paula's pills so you can pop them yourself or give them to your girlfriend. You can shove 'em up your ass for all I care. But I'm walking out of here with that stereo and I'll walk through you if I have to, and don't think I wouldn't enjoy it."

"You're not even a cop."

"Right."

"You got no authority at all." He spoke in tones of wonder. "You said you were a cop."

"You can always sue me."

"You can't take that stereo. You can't even be in this room."

"That's right." I was itching for him. I could feel my blood in my veins. "I'm bigger than you," I said, "and I'm a whole lot harder, and I'd get a certain amount of satisfaction in beating the crap out of you. I don't like you. It bothers me that you didn't kill her because somebody did and it would be a pleasure to hang it on you. But you didn't do it. Unplug the stereo and pack it up so I can carry it or I'm going to take you apart."

I meant it and he realized as much. He thought about taking a shot at me and he decided it wasn't worth it. Maybe it wasn't all that much of a stereo. While he was unhooking it I dumped a carton of his clothes on the floor and we packed the stereo in it. On my way out the door he said he could always go to the cops and tell them what I'd done.

"I don't think you want to do that," I said.

"You said somebody killed her."

"That's right."

"You just making noise?"

"No."

"You're serious?" I nodded. "She didn't kill herself? I thought it was open and shut, from what the cops said. It's interesting. In a way, I guess you could say it's a load off my mind."

"How do you figure that?"

He shrugged. "I thought, you know, maybe she was upset it wasn't working out between us. At the Web the vibes were on the heavy side, if you follow me. Our thing was falling apart and I was seeing Sunny and she was seeing other guys and I thought maybe that was what did it for her. I suppose I blamed myself, like."

"I can see it was eating away at you."

"I just said it was on my mind."

I didn't say anything.

"Man," he said, "*nothing* eats away at me. You let things get to you that way and it's death."

I shouldered the carton and headed on down the stairs.

👁 **Suspicions?**

1. Do you agree with Matt when he concludes that Cary McCloud "was capable of murder but I don't think he'd been capable of this particular murder"? Explain why Matt draws this conclusion and why you either agree or disagree with it.

2. Does ruling out Cary McCloud as a suspect necessarily mean that Paula Wittlauer committed suicide? Explain.

Ruth Wittlauer had supplied me with an Irving Place address and a Gramercy 5 telephone number. I called the number and didn't get an answer, so I walked over to Hudson and caught a northbound cab. There were no messages for me at the hotel desk. I put Paula's stereo in my room, tried Ruth's number again, then walked over to the Eighteenth Precinct. Guzik had gone off duty but the deskman told me to try a restaurant around the corner, and I found him there drinking draft Heinekens with another cop named Birnbaum. I sat at their table and ordered bourbon for myself and another round for the two of them.

I said, "I have a favor to ask. I'd like you to seal Paula Wittlauer's apartment."

"We closed that out," Guzik reminded me.

"I know, and the boyfriend closed out the dead girl's stereo." I told him how I'd reclaimed the unit from Cary McCloud. "I'm working for Ruth, Paula's sister. The least I can do is make sure she gets what's coming to her. She's not up to cleaning out the apartment now and it's rented through the first of October. McCloud's got a key and God knows how many other people have keys. If you slap a seal on the door it'd keep the grave robbers away."

"I guess we can do that. Tomorrow all right?"

"Tonight would be better."

"What's there to steal? You got the stereo out of there and I didn't see anything else around that was worth much."

"Things have a sentimental value."

He eyed me, frowned. "I'll make a phone call," he said. He went to the booth in the back and I jawed with Birnbaum until he came back and told me it was all taken care of.

I said, "Another thing I was wondering. You must have had a photographer on the scene. Somebody to take pictures of the body and all that."

"Sure. That's routine."

"Did he go up to the apartment while he was at it? Take a roll of interior shots?"

"Yeah. Why?"

"I thought maybe I could have a look at them."

"What for?"

"You never know. The reason I knew it was Paula's stereo in McCloud's apartment. I could see the pattern in the dust on top of the dresser where it had been. If you've got interior pictures maybe I'll see something else that's not there anymore and I can lean on McCloud a little and recover it for my client."

"And that's why you'd like to see the pictures."

"Right."

He gave me a look. "That door was bolted from the inside, Matt. With a chain bolt."

"I know."

"And there was no one in the apartment when we went in there."

"I know that, too."

"You're still barking up the murder tree, aren't you? Jesus, the case is closed and the reason it's closed is the ditsy broad killed herself. What are you making waves for?"

"I'm not. I just wanted to see the pictures."

"To see if somebody stole her diaphragm or something."

"Something like that." I drank what remained of my drink. "You need a new hat anyway, Guzik. The weather's turning and a fellow like you needs a hat for fall."

"If I had the price of a hat, maybe I'd go out and get one."

"You got it," I said.

He nodded and we told Birnbaum we wouldn't be long. I walked with Guzik around the corner to the Eighteenth. On the way I palmed him two tens and a five, twenty-five dollars, the price of a hat in police parlance. He made the bills disappear.

I waited at his desk while he pulled the Paula Wittlauer file. There were about a dozen black-and-white prints, eight-by-tens, high-contrast glossies. Perhaps half of them showed Paula's corpse from various angles. I had no interest in these but I made myself look at them as a sort of reinforcement, so I wouldn't forget what I was doing on the case.

The other pictures were interior shots of the L-shaped apartment. I noted the wide-open window, the dresser with the stereo sitting on it, the chair with her clothing piled haphazardly upon it. I separated the interior pictures from the ones showing the corpse and told Guzik I wanted to keep them for the time being. He didn't mind.

He cocked his head and looked at me. "You got something, Matt?"

"Nothing worth talking about."

"If you ever do, I'll want to hear about it."

"Sure."

"You like the life you're leading? Working private, scuffling around?"

"It seems to suit me."

He thought it over, nodded. Then he started for the stairs and I followed after him.

Later that evening I managed to reach Ruth Wittlauer. I bundled the stereo into a cab and took it to her place. She lived in a well-kept brownstone a block and a half from Gramercy Park. Her apartment was inexpensively furnished but the pieces looked to have been chosen with care. The place was clean and neat. Her clock radio was turned to an FM station that was playing chamber music. She had coffee made and I accepted a cup and sipped it while I told her about recovering the stereo from Cary McCloud.

"I wasn't sure whether you could use it," I said, "but I couldn't see any reason why he should keep it. You can always sell it."

"No, I'll keep it. I just have a twenty-dollar record player that I bought on Fourteenth Street. Paula's stereo cost a couple of hundred dollars." She managed a smile. "So you've already more than earned what I gave you. Did he kill her?"

"No."

"You're sure of that?"

I nodded. "He'd kill if he had a reason but I don't think he did. And if he did kill her he'd never have taken the stereo or the drugs, and he wouldn't have acted the way he did. There was never a moment when I had the feeling that he'd killed her. And you have to follow your instincts in this kind of situation. Once they point things out to you, then you can usually find the facts to go with them."

"And you're sure my sister killed herself?"

"No. I'm pretty sure someone gave her a hand."

Her eyes widened.

I said, "It's mostly intuition. But there are a few facts to support it." I told her about the chain bolt, how it had proved to the police that Paula'd killed herself, how my experiment had shown it could have been fastened from the corridor. Ruth got very excited at this but I explained that it didn't prove anything in and of itself, only that suicide remained a theoretical possibility.

Then I showed her the pictures I'd obtained from Guzik. I selected one shot which showed the chair with Paula's clothing without showing too much of the window. I didn't want to make Ruth look at the window.

👁 **Suspicions?**

1. If you could closely examine the photographs Matt got from Guzik of the interior of Paula's apartment, what would you be looking for at this point and why?

2. What do you think of Matt's explanation to Ruth Wittlauer of why he thinks Cary McCloud did not kill her sister? Explain your opinion.

3. What is it about the chair with Paula's clothing on it that Matt noticed when he was in Paula's apartment and made him want "to make sure things hadn't been rearranged"? What does Matt understand that rules out suicide?

"The chair," I said, pointing to it. "I noticed this when I was in your sister's apartment. I wanted to see a photograph taken at the time to make sure things hadn't been rearranged by the cops or McCloud or somebody else. But that clothing's exactly the way it was when I saw it."

"I don't understand."

"The supposition is that Paula got undressed, put her clothes on the chair, then went to the window and jumped." Her lip was trembling but she was holding herself together and I went right on talking. "Or she'd taken her clothes off earlier and maybe she took a shower or a nap and then came back and jumped. But look at the chair. She didn't fold her clothes neatly, she didn't put them away. And she didn't just drop them on the floor, either. I'm no authority on the way women get undressed but I don't think many people would do it that way."

Ruth nodded. Her face was thoughtful.

"That wouldn't mean very much by itself. If she were upset or stoned or confused she might have thrown things on the chair as she took them off. But that's not what happened. The order of the clothing is all wrong. The bra's underneath the blouse, the panty hose are underneath the skirt. She took her bra off after she took her blouse off, obviously, so it should have wound up on top of the blouse, not under it."

"Of course."

I held up a hand. "It's nothing like proof, Ruth. There are any number of other explanations. Maybe she knocked the stuff onto the floor and then picked it up and the order of the garments got switched around. Maybe one of the cops went through the clothing before the photographer came around with his camera. I don't really have anything terribly strong to go on."

"But you think she was murdered."

"Yes, I guess I do."

"That's what I thought all along. Of course I had a reason to think so."

"Maybe I've got one, too. I don't know."

"What are you going to do now?"

"I think I'll poke around a little. I don't know much about Paula's life. I'll have to learn more if I'm going to find out who killed her. But it's up to you to decide whether you want me to stay with it."

"Of course I do. Why wouldn't I?"

"Because it probably won't lead anywhere. Suppose she was upset after her conversation with McCloud and she picked up a stranger and took him home with her and he killed her. If that's the case we'll never know who he was."

"You're going to stay with it, aren't you?"

"I suppose I want to."

"It'll be complicated, though. It'll take you some time. I suppose you'll want more money." Her gaze was very direct. "I gave you two hundred dollars. I have three hundred more that I can afford to pay. I don't mind paying it, Mr. Scudder. I already got . . . I got my money's worth for the first two hundred, didn't I? The stereo. When the three hundred runs out, well, you can tell me if you think it's worth staying with the case. I couldn't afford more cash right away, but I could arrange to pay you later on or something like that."

I shook my head. "It won't come to more than that," I said. "No matter how much time I spend on it. And you keep the three hundred for the time being, all right? I'll take it from you later on. If I need it, and if I've earned it."

"That doesn't seem right."

"It seems right to me," I said. "And don't make the mistake of thinking I'm being charitable."

"But your time's valuable."

I shook my head. "Not to me it isn't."

I spent the next five days picking the scabs off Paula Wittlauer's life. It kept turning out to be a waste of time but the time's always gone before you realize you've wasted it. And I'd been telling the truth when I said my time wasn't valuable. I had nothing better to do, and my peeks into the corners of Paula's world kept me busy.

Her life involved more than a saloon on Ninth Avenue and an apartment on Fifty-seventh Street, more than serving drinks and sharing a bed with Cary McCloud. She did other things. She went one evening a week to group therapy on West Seventy-ninth Street. She took voice lessons every Tuesday morning on Amsterdam Avenue. She had an ex-boyfriend she saw once in a while. She hung out in a couple of bars in the neighborhood and a couple of others in the Village. She did this, she did that, she went here, she went there, and I kept busy dragging myself around town and talking to all sorts of people, and I managed to learn quite a bit about the person she'd been and the life she'd led without learning anything at all about the person who'd put her on the pavement.

At the same time, I tried to track her movements on the final night of her life. She'd evidently gone more or less directly to the Spider's Web after finishing her shift at Armstrong's. Maybe she'd stopped at her apartment for a shower and a change of clothes, but without further ado she'd headed downtown. Somewhere around ten she left the Web, and I traced her from there to a couple of other Village bars. She hadn't stayed at either of them long, taking a quick drink or two and moving on. She'd left alone as far as anyone seemed to remember. This didn't prove a thing because she could have stopped elsewhere before continuing uptown, or she could have picked someone up on the street, which I'd learned was something she'd done more than once in her young life. She could have found her killer loitering on a street corner or she could have phoned him and arranged to meet him at her apartment.

Her apartment. The doormen changed off at midnight, but it was impossible to determine whether she'd returned before or after the changing of the guard. She'd lived there, she was a regular tenant, and when she entered or left the building it was not a noteworthy occasion. It was something she did every night, so when she came home for the final time the man at the door had no reason to know it was the final time and thus no reason to take mental notes.

Had she come in alone or with a companion? No one could say, which did suggest that she'd come in alone. If she'd been with someone her entrance would have been a shade more memorable. But this also proved nothing, because I stood on the other side of Fifty-seventh Street one night and watched the doorway of her building, and the doorman didn't take the pride in his position that the afternoon doorman had shown. He was away from the door almost as often as he was on it. She could have walked in flanked by six Turkish sailors and there was a chance no one would have seen her.

The doorman who'd been on duty when she went out the window was a rheumy-eyed Irishman with liver-spotted hands. He hadn't actually seen her land. He'd been in the lobby, keeping himself out of the wind, and then he came rushing out when he heard the impact of the body on the street.

He couldn't get over the sound she made.

"All of a sudden there was this noise," he said. "Just out of the blue there was this noise and it must be it's my imagination but I swear I felt it in my feet. I swear she shook the earth. I had no idea what it was, and then I came rushing out, and Jesus God, there she was."

"Didn't you hear a scream?"

"Street was empty just then. This side, anyway. Nobody around to scream."

"Didn't *she* scream on the way down?"

"Did somebody say she screamed? I never heard it."

Do people scream as they fall? They generally do in films and on television. During my days on the force I saw several of them after they jumped, and by the time I got to them there were no screams echoing in the air. And a few times I'd been on hand while they talked someone in off a ledge, but in each instance the talking was successful and I didn't have to watch a falling body accelerate according to the immutable laws of physics.

Could you get much of a scream out in four seconds?

I stood in the street where she'd fallen and I looked up toward her window. I counted off four seconds in my mind. A voice shrieked in my brain. It was Thursday night, actually Friday morning, one o'clock. Time I got myself around the corner to Armstrong's because in another couple of hours Justin would be closing for the night and I'd want to be drunk enough to sleep.

And an hour or so after that she'd be one week dead.

I'd worked myself into a reasonably bleak mood by the time I got to Armstrong's. I skipped the coffee and crawled straight into the bourbon bottle, and before long it began to do what it was supposed to do. It blurred the corners of the mind so I couldn't see the bad dark things that lurked there.

When Trina finished for the night she joined me and I bought her a couple of drinks. I don't remember what we talked about. Some but by no means all of our conversation touched upon Paula Wittlauer. Trina hadn't known Paula terribly well. Their contact had been largely limited to the two hours a day when their shifts overlapped, but she knew a little about the sort of life Paula had been leading. There'd been a year or two when her own life had not been terribly different from Paula's. Now she had things more or less under control, and maybe there would have come a time when Paula would have taken charge of her life, but that was something we'd never know now.

I suppose it was close to three when I walked Trina home. Our conversation had turned thoughtful and reflective. On the street she said it was a lousy night for being alone. I thought of high windows and evil shapes in dark corners and took her hand in mine.

She lives on Fifty-sixth between Ninth and Tenth. While we waited for the light to change at Fifty-seventh Street I looked over at Paula's building. We were far enough away to look at the high floors. Only a couple of windows were lighted.

That was when I got it.

I've never understood how people think of things, how little perceptions trigger greater insights. Thoughts just seem to come to me. I had it now, and something clicked within me and a source of tension unwound itself.

I said something to that effect to Trina.

"You know who killed her?"

"Not exactly," I said. "But I know how to find out. And it can wait until tomorrow."

The light changed and we crossed the street.

She was still sleeping when I left. I got out of bed and dressed in silence, then let myself out of her apartment. I had some coffee and a toasted English muffin at the Red Flame. Then I went across the street to Paula's building. I started on the tenth floor and worked my way up, checking the three or four possible apartments on each floor. A lot of people weren't home. I worked my way clear to the top floor, the twenty-fourth, and by the time I was done I had three possibles listed in my notebook and a list of over a dozen apartments I'd have to check that evening.

At eight-thirty that night I rang the bell of Apartment 21G. It was directly in line with Paula's apartment and four flights above it. The man who answered the bell wore a pair of Lee corduroy slacks and a shirt with a blue vertical stripe on a white background. His socks were dark blue and he wasn't wearing shoes.

I said, "I want to talk with you about Paula Wittlauer."

His face fell apart and I forgot my three possibles forever because he was the man I wanted. He just stood there. I pushed the door open and stepped forward and he moved back automatically to make room for me. I drew the door shut after me and walked around him, crossing the room to the window. There wasn't a speck of dust or soot on the sill. It was immaculate, as well scrubbed as Lady Macbeth's hands.

I turned to him. His name was Lane Posmantur and I suppose he was around forty, thickening at the waist, his dark hair starting to go thin on top. His glasses were thick and it was hard to read his eyes through them but it didn't matter. I didn't need to see his eyes.

"She went out this window," I said. "Didn't she?"

"I don't know what you're talking about."

"Do you want to know what triggered it for me, Mr. Posmantur? I was thinking of all the things nobody noticed. No one saw her enter the building. Neither doorman remembered it because it wasn't something they'd be likely to remember. Nobody saw her go out the window. The cops had to look for an open window in order to know who the hell she was. They backtracked her from the window she fell out of.

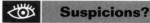

"And nobody saw the killer leave the building. Now that's the one thing that would have been noticed, and that's the point that occurred to me. It wasn't that significant by itself but it made me dig a little deeper. The doorman was alert once her body hit the street. He'd remember who went in or out of the building from that point on. So it occurred to me that maybe the killer was still inside the building, and then I got the idea that she was killed by someone who *lived* in the building, and from that point on it was just a question of finding you because all of a sudden it all made sense."

I told him about the clothes on the chair. "She didn't take them off and pile them up like that. Her killer put her clothes like that, and he dumped them on the chair so that it would look as though she undressed in her apartment and so that it would be assumed she'd gone out of her own window."

"But she went out of your window, didn't she?"

He looked at me. After a moment he said he thought he'd better sit down. He went to an armchair and sat in it. I stayed on my feet.

I said, "She came here. I guess she took off her clothes and you went to bed with her. Is that right?"

He hesitated then nodded.

"What made you decide to kill her?"

"I didn't."

I looked at him. He looked away, then met my gaze, then avoided my eyes again. "Tell me about it," I suggested. He looked away again and a minute went by and then he started to talk.

It was about what I'd figured. She was living with Cary McCloud but she and Lane Posmantur would get together now and then for a quickie. He was a lab technician at Roosevelt and he brought home drugs from time to time and perhaps that was part of his attraction for her. She'd turned up that night a little after two and they went to bed. She was really flying, he said, and he'd been taking pills himself, it was something he'd begun doing lately, maybe seeing her had something to do with it.

They went to bed and did the dirty deed, and then maybe they slept for an hour, something like that, and then she was awake and coming unglued, getting really hysterical, and he tried to settle her down and he gave her a couple of slaps to bring her around, except they didn't bring her around, and she was staggering and she tripped over the coffee table and fell funny, and by the time he sorted himself out and went to her she was lying with her head at a crazy angle and he knew her neck was broken and when he tried for a pulse there was no pulse to be found.

"All I could think of was she was dead in my apartment and full of drugs and I was in trouble."

"So you put her out the window."

"I was going to take her back to her own apartment. I started to dress her but it was impossible. And even with her clothes on I couldn't risk running into somebody in the hallway or on the elevator. It was crazy.

"I left her here and went to her apartment. I thought maybe Cary would help me. I rang the bell and nobody answered and I used her key and the chain bolt was on. Then I remembered she used to fasten it from outside. She'd showed me how she could do that. I tried with mine but it was installed properly and there's not enough play in the chain. I unhooked her bolt and went inside.

"Then I got the idea. I went back to my apartment and got her clothes and I rushed back and put them on her chair. I opened her window wide. On my way out the door I put her lights on and hooked the chain bolt again.

"I came back here to my own apartment. I took her pulse again and she was dead. She hadn't moved or anything, and I couldn't do anything for her, all I could do was stay out of it, and I, I turned off the lights here, and I opened my own window and dragged her body over to it, and, oh, God in heaven, God, I almost couldn't make myself do it but it was an accident that she was dead and I was so damned *afraid*—"

"And you dropped her out and closed the window." He nodded. "And if her neck was broken it was something that happened in the fall. And whatever drugs were in her system was just something she'd taken by herself, and they'd never do an autopsy anyway. And you were home free."

"I didn't hurt her," he said. "I was just protecting myself."

"Do you really believe that, Lane?"

"What do you mean?"

"You're not a doctor. Maybe she was dead when you threw her out the window. Maybe she wasn't."

"There was no pulse!"

"You couldn't find a pulse. That doesn't mean there wasn't any. Did you try artificial respiration? Do you know if there was any brain activity? No, of course not. All you know was that you looked for a pulse and you couldn't find one."

"Her neck was broken."

"Maybe. How many broken necks have you had occasion to diagnose? And people sometimes break their necks and live anyway. The point is that you couldn't have known she was dead and you were too worried about your own skin to do what you should have done. You should have phoned for an ambulance. You know that's what you should have done and you knew it at the time but you wanted to stay out of it. I've known junkies who left their buddies to die of overdoses because they didn't want to get involved. You went them one better. You put her out a window and let her fall twenty-one stories so that you wouldn't get involved, and for all you know she was alive when you let go of her."

"No," he said. "No. She was dead."

I'd told Ruth Wittlauer she could wind up believing whatever she wanted. People believe what they want to believe. It was just as true for Lane Posmantur.

"Maybe she was dead," I said. "Maybe that's your fault, too."

"What do you mean?"

"You said you slapped her to bring her around. What kind of a slap, Lane?"

"I just tapped her on the face."

"Just a brisk slap to straighten her out."

"That's right."

"Oh, hell, Lane. Who knows how hard you hit her? Who knows whether you may not have given her a shove? She wasn't the only one on pills. You said she was flying. Well, I think maybe you were doing a little flying yourself. And you'd been sleepy and you were groggy and she was buzzing around the room and being a general pain in the ass, and you gave her a slap and a shove and another slap and another shove and—"

"No!"

"And she fell down."

"It was an accident."

"It always is."

"I didn't hurt her. I liked her. She was a good kid, we got on fine, I didn't hurt her, I—"

"Put your shoes on, Lane."

"What for?"

"I'm taking you to the police station. It's a few blocks from here, not very far at all."

"Am I under arrest?"

"I'm not a policeman." I'd never gotten around to saying who I was and he'd never thought to ask. "My name's Scudder, I'm working for Paula's sister. I suppose you're under citizen's arrest. I want you to come to the precinct house with me. There's a cop named Guzik there and you can talk to him."

"I don't have to say anything," he said. He thought for a moment. "You're not a cop."

"No."

"What I said to you doesn't mean a thing." He took a breath, straightened up a little in his chair. "You can't prove a thing," he said. "Not a thing."

"Maybe I can and maybe I can't. You probably left prints in Paula's apartment. I had them seal the place a while ago and maybe they'll find traces of your presence. I don't know if Paula left any prints here or not. You probably scrubbed them up. But there may be neighbors who know you were sleeping with her, and someone may have noticed you scampering back and forth between the apartments that night, and it's even possible a neighbor heard the two of you struggling in here just before she went out the window. When the cops know what to look for, Lane, they usually find it sooner or later. It's knowing what you're after that's the hard part.

"But that's not even the point. Put your shoes on, Lane. That's right. Now we're going to go see Guzik, that's his name, and he's going to advise you of your rights. He'll tell you that you have a right to remain silent, and that's the truth, Lane, that's a right that you have. And if you remain silent and if you get a decent lawyer and do what he tells you, I think you can beat this charge, Lane. I really do."

"Why are you telling me this?"

"Why?" I was starting to feel tired, drained, but I kept on with it. "Because the worst thing you could do is remain silent, Lane. Believe me, that's the worst thing you could do. If you're smart you'll tell Guzik everything you remember. You'll make a complete voluntary statement and you'll read it over when they type it up and you'll sign your name on the bottom.

"Because you're not really a killer, Lane. It doesn't come easily to you. If Cary McCloud had killed her he'd never lose a night's sleep over it. But you're not a psychopath. You were drugged and half-crazy and terrified and you did something wrong and it's eating you up. Your face fell apart the minute I walked in here tonight. You could play it cute and beat this charge, Lane, but all you'd wind up doing is beating yourself.

"Because you live on a high floor, Lane, and the ground's only four seconds away. And if you squirm off the hook you'll never get it out of your head, you'll never be able to mark it Paid in Full, and one day or night you'll open the window and you'll go out of it, Lane. You'll remember the sound her body made when she hit the street—"

"*No!*"

I took his arm. "Come on," I said. "We'll go see Guzik."

 How Clever?

I. What acts of detection and reflection did Matt Scudder use to determine that someone who lived in the same apartment building had thrown Paula out of his apartment window and not hers? How did Matt's "just exploring the possibilities" over lunch with Police Officer Guzik provide the foundation for his later realizations about where Paula's killer lived?

2. After checking the apartments in Paula's building, Matt had "three possibles" listed in his notebook. What do you think all three had in common? Explain.

3. How did Matt know as soon as he met Lane Posmantur that "he was the man I wanted"? Why does Matt point out to the reader that the window sill of Lane's apartment was "as well scrubbed as Lady Macbeth's hands"?

4. What was significant about each of the three "things nobody noticed" that "triggered it" for Matt?

5. How did Paula Wittlauer die? What explanation does Lane give? What other possibilities does Matt offer? Which explanation do you find the most probable? How do you feel about not knowing for certain? Explain.

6. What does Matt mean when he tells Lane: "People believe what they want to believe"?

7. What different ways does Matt use to get Lane to think about his role and responsibility in the death of Paula Wittlauer? Why does he do this?

8. The story begins with the statement, "There was nothing special about her last day." How does Matt Scudder's involvement in proving that Paula Wittlauer did not take her own life add emotional meaning to the story's opening sentence?

9. Why does Matt believe it is in Lane's best interest for Lane to tell the police everything he remembers, even though with a decent lawyer Lane "could beat this charge"? How do you feel about his advice? Explain.

10. Matt talks about his intuition and states about his instincts that "once they point things out to you, then you can usually find the facts to go with them." He also tells Lane that when the cops know what to look for, they usually find it sooner or later, adding, "It's knowing what you're after that's the hard part."

    Is this more like "reflection followed by detection" rather than "detection and reflection"? Explain.

DETECTWRITE: Characterization

1. Compare and contrast Matt Scudder with the other private detectives or investigators you have met in this collection or elsewhere. In what ways is he representative or similar? How is he different? How would his differences help you to distinguish him from the others?

2. How did Matt wind up becoming "an ex-cop coasting through the months on bourbon and coffee"? What moral choice was involved? How do you feel about the choice Matt made? How does Matt's current professional situation reflect his values as a person?

3. Referring to how his life has changed, Matt says that that is the "sort of greatness thrust upon us." With what tone of voice would those words be

spoken? Matt then adds, "When you're my age you just hope they [things] don't get too much worse."

What does this tell us about Matt's nature? How do you feel about a person with this kind of attitude being the narrator and featured detective of the story? Explain.

4. Several authors of detective stories are partial to featuring ex-police officers as their private investigators. Explain why so many fictional private eyes share the same background.

5. If you were to feature a former police officer as the private eye in a detective story you planned to write, what specific reasons—physical, mental, political, moral, ethical, emotional, psychological, economic, social—would you provide for him or her to be no longer on the police force?

6. Explain why hardboiled detective stories are typically told in the first-person by the hardboiled detective. What would be lost if the voice were shifted to third-person narration? Explain.

7. Typically, in the hardboiled detective story, a woman knocks on the door, enters the P.I.'s office and his life, and triggers the plot of the story. Where else in the unfolding of the plot and in the portrayal of Matt Scudder does the author, Lawrence Block, show himself to be both a fan of and a master of the hardboiled detective story?

8. In a detective story you might write, would you choose to model your detective on the typical hardboiled detective? Explain.

9. In developing the cast of characters for a detective story you would write, you will want to make certain that your characters not only stay "in character" (act true to their individual nature) but also stay true to type (act true to nature without going over into stereotype). Where do you feel Lawrence Block has succeeded, or not succeeded, in this dual task? Explain.

10. Describe the people who live next door to you—both as individuals and as types. Tell how they might become either major or minor characters in a hardboiled detective story you would write.

DETECTWRITE: Dialogue

Select several of your favorite examples of dialogue from among the characters in "Out the Window" and explain how they help to establish the atmosphere needed in a hardboiled detective story.

DETECTWRITE: Setting

1. The Matt Scudder type of investigator—the hardboiled detective—is usually found working in urban areas. Review "Out the Window" for its references

to contemporary New York City and New York City life. How do these "local color" references both establish a hardboiled setting and atmosphere and assist in conveying characterization?

2. Think about the setting you might use for a hardboiled detective story you would write. What setting might that be? Why did you choose it? What atmosphere will you want that setting to convey? How will this particular setting affect the kind of character you choose your detective to be? How will this setting affect the plot of the story in important ways? Explain.

DETECTWRITE: Creating Plot Details

1. Find in the story "Out the Window" where the author, Lawrence Block, first indicates through narrator Matt Scudder's thoughts that Paula Wittlauer had shown physical evidence of being a drug user. Compare this first mention to the next two mentions by police officer Guzik of Paula's drug use.

   How are all three of these mentions more indirect than direct? Explain.

2. What would have been the effect on the story—and on the reader—if the author had used some form of the more detailed references first? Explain.

3. Re-read the paragraph on p. 126 in which Matt checks the medicine cabinet in Paula's bathroom and details its contents over the course of one medium-length sentence, one rather long sentence, and one quite short sentence. How do the content and rhythm of these sentences catch the reader up in what Matt sees?

4. How do the content and rhythm of the sentences in the paragraph on p. 126 attempt to hide from the reader what Matt and the reader should have expected to see that wasn't there, namely, "a medicine cabinet like a drugstore. Ups, downs, sideways"? What makes this paragraph a good example of the fact that in detective fiction, sometimes the absence of something one expects to find can be more significant than the presence of something expected or unexpected?

5. Re-read the references to the window of Paula's apartment in the order in which they appear in the opening sections of the story.

   How has the author made use of spare details in a particular sequence to enable his detective—and, perhaps, the reader, too—to "get it," to be in a position in which "little perceptions trigger greater insights"?

6. How does police officer Guzik's statement that "You can *only* fasten the chain bolt from inside and you can *only* open the door a few inches with it on" function as a red herring (false clue) in the story? (italics added)

7. How should statements with words like "only," "always," "never" be tested for accuracy? How many counter-examples need one find to disprove statements like these? How does the author advance the plot of the story by having Matt proceed with an experiment to test and disprove Guzik's "only" statement?

8. Note that when Matt reports to Ruth Wittlauer on his experiment that showed that the chain bolt "could have been fastened from the corridor," he is careful to explain that "it didn't prove anything in and of itself, *only* (italics added) that suicide remained a theoretical possibility." Explain.

9. How would close observation of detail have enabled the reader to realize, along with Matt Scudder, that there was something wrong about the sequence of the clothing on Paula's apartment chair?

10. Review the three "things nobody noticed" that "triggered" the solution of Paula's murder for Matt. How did the author both *logically* and *psychologically* present these three details so that they would "all make sense" not only to Matt but to the reader?

11. Select one ordinary, everyday action that could play a critical role in a detective story you might write. Write a brief paragraph of that story that includes enough of a mention of that action so that the reader is made aware of it and might remember it but *without* giving away the ultimate importance of the action as a clue in the plot of your story.

   Then, in a separate paragraph, explain how the everyday action you have planted would turn out to be a clue in your projected story.

Part three

Inside a Locked Room

The Locked Tomb Mystery

Elizabeth Peters

SENEBTISI'S FUNERAL WAS THE TALK OF SOUTHERN THEBES. Of course, it could not compare with the burials of Great Ones and Pharaohs, whose Houses of Eternity were furnished with gold and fine linen and precious gems, but ours was not a quarter where nobles lived; our people were craftsmen and small merchants, able to afford a chamber-tomb and a coffin and a few spells to ward off the perils of the Western Road—no more than that. We had never seen anything like the burial of the old woman who had been our neighbor for so many years.

The night after the funeral, the customers of Nehi's tavern could talk of nothing else. I remember that evening well. For one thing, I had just won my first appointment as a temple scribe. I was looking forward to boasting a little, and perhaps paying for a round of beer, if my friends displayed proper appreciation of my good fortune. Three of the others were already at the tavern when I arrived, my linen shawl wrapped tight around me. The weather was cold even for winter, with a cruel, dry wind driving sand into every crevice of the body.

"Close the door quickly," said Senu, the carpenter. "What weather! I wonder if the Western journey will be like this—cold enough to freeze a man's bones."

This prompted a ribald comment from Rennefer, the weaver, concerning the effects of freezing on certain of Senebtisi's vital organs. "Not that anyone would notice the difference," he added. "There was never any

150

warmth in the old hag. What sort of mother would take all her possessions to the next world and leave her only son penniless?"

"Is it true, then?" I asked, signaling Nehi to fetch the beer jar. "I have
heard stories—"

"All true," said the potter, Baenre. "It is a pity you could not attend the
burial, Wadjsen; it was magnificent!"

"You went?" I inquired. "That was good of you, since she ordered
none of her funerary equipment from you."

Baenre is a scanty little man with thin hair and sharp bones. It is said that
he is a domestic tyrant, and that his wife cowers when he comes roaring
home from the tavern, but when he is with us, his voice is almost a whisper.
"My rough kitchenware would not be good enough to hold the wine and
fine oil she took to the tomb. Wadjsen, you should have seen the boxes and
jars and baskets—dozens of them. They say she had a gold mask, like the
ones worn by great nobles, and that all her ornaments were of solid gold."

"It is true," said Rennefer. "I know a man who knows one of the servants of Bakenmut, the goldsmith who made the ornaments."

"How is her son taking it?" I asked. I knew Minmose slightly; a shy,
serious man, he followed his father's trade of stone carving. His mother
had lived with him all his life, greedily scooping up his profits, though
she had money of her own, inherited from her parents.

"Why, as you would expect," said Senu, shrugging. "Have you ever
heard him speak harshly to anyone, much less his mother? She was an old
she-goat who treated him like a boy who has not cut off the side lock; but
with him it was always 'Yes, honored mother,' and 'As you say, honored
mother.' She would not even allow him to take a wife."

"How will he live?"

"Oh, he has the shop and the business, such as it is. He is a hard
worker; he will survive."

In the following months I heard occasional news of Minmose. Gossip
said he must be doing well, for he had taken to spending his leisure time
at a local house of prostitution—a pleasure he never had dared enjoy
while his mother lived. Nefertiry, the loveliest and most expensive of the
girls, was the object of his desire, and Rennefer remarked that the maiden
must have a kind heart, for she could command higher prices than
Minmose was able to pay. However, as time passed, I forgot Minmose and
Senebtisi, and her rich burial. It was not until almost a year later that the
matter was recalled to my attention.

The rumors began in the marketplace, at the end of the time of inun-
dation, when the floodwater lay on the fields and the farmers were idle.
They enjoy this time, but the police of the city do not; for idleness leads to

crime, and one of the most popular crimes is tomb robbing. This goes on all the time in a small way, but when the Pharaoh is strong and stern, and the laws are strictly enforced, it is a very risky trade. A man stands to lose more than a hand or an ear if he is caught. He also risks damnation after he has entered his own tomb; but some men simply do not have proper respect for the gods.

The king, Nebmaatre (may he live forever!), was then in his prime, so there had been no tomb robbing for some time—or at least none had been detected. But, the rumors said, three men of west Thebes had been caught trying to sell ornaments such as are buried with the dead. The rumors turned out to be correct, for once. The men were questioned on the soles of their feet and confessed to the robbing of several tombs.

Naturally all those who had kin buried on the west bank—which included most of us—were alarmed by this news, and half the nervous matrons in our neighborhood went rushing across the river to make sure the family tombs were safe. I was not surprised to hear that that dutiful son Minmose had also felt obliged to make sure his mother had not been disturbed.

However, I was surprised at the news that greeted me when I paid my next visit to Nehi's tavern. The moment I entered, the others began to talk at once, each eager to be the first to tell the shocking facts.

"Robbed?" I repeated when I had sorted out the babble of voices. "Do you speak truly?"

"I do not know why you should doubt it," said Rennefer. "The richness of her burial was the talk of the city, was it not? Just what the tomb robbers like! They made a clean sweep of all the gold, and ripped the poor old hag's mummy to shreds."

At that point we were joined by another of the habitués, Merusir. He is a pompous, fat man who considers himself superior to the rest of us because he is Fifth Prophet of Amon. We put up with his patronizing ways because sometimes he knows court gossip. On that particular evening it was apparent that he was bursting with excitement. He listened with a supercilious sneer while we told him the sensational news. "I know, I know," he drawled. "I heard it much earlier—and with it, the other news which is known only to those in the confidence of the Palace."

He paused, ostensibly to empty his cup. Of course, we reacted as he had hoped we would, begging him to share the secret. Finally he condescended to inform us.

"Why, the amazing thing is not the robbery itself, but how it was done. The tomb entrance was untouched, the seals of the necropolis were unbroken. The tomb itself is entirely rock-cut, and there was not the slightest break in the walls or floor or ceiling. Yet when Minmose entered the burial chamber, he found the coffin open, the mummy mutilated, and the gold ornaments gone."

We stared at him, openmouthed.

"It is a most remarkable story," I said.

"Call me a liar if you like," said Merusir, who knows the language of polite insult as well as I do. "There was a witness—two, if you count Minmose himself. The sem-priest Wennefer was with him."

This silenced the critics. Wennefer was known to us all. There was not a man in southern Thebes with a higher reputation. Even Senebtisi had been fond of him, and she was not fond of many people. He had officiated at her funeral.

Pleased at the effect of his announcement, Merusir went on in his most pompous manner. "The king himself has taken an interest in the matter. He has called on Amenhotep Sa Hapu to investigate."

"Amenhotep?" I exclaimed. "But I know him well."

"You do?" Merusir's plump cheeks sagged like bladders punctured by a sharp knife.

Now, at that time Amenhotep's name was not in the mouth of everyone, though he had taken the first steps of that astonishing career that was to make him the intimate friend of Pharaoh. When I first met him, he had been a poor, insignificant priest at a local shrine. I had been sent to fetch him to the house where my master lay dead of a stab wound, presumably murdered. Amenhotep's fame had begun with that matter, for he had discovered the truth and saved an innocent man from execution. Since then he had handled several other cases, with equal success.

My exclamation had taken the wind out of Merusir's sails. He had hoped to impress us by telling us something we did not know. Instead it was I who enlightened the others about Amenhotep's triumphs. But when I finished, Rennefer shook his head.

"If this wise man is all you say, Wadjsen, it will be like inviting a lion to rid the house of mice. He will find there is a simple explanation. No doubt the thieves entered the burial chamber from above or from one side, tunneling through the rock. Minmose and Wennefer were too shocked to observe the hole in the wall, that is all."

We argued the matter for some time, growing more and more heated as the level of the beer in the jar dropped. It was a foolish argument, for none of us knew the facts; and to argue without knowledge is like trying to weave without thread.

This truth did not occur to me until the cool night breeze had cleared my head, when I was halfway home. I decided to pay Amenhotep a visit.

The next time I went to the tavern, I would be the one to tell the latest news, and Merusir would be nothing!

Most of the honest householders had retired, but there were lamps burning in the street of the prostitutes, and in a few taverns. There was a light, as well, in one window of the house where Amenhotep lodged. Like the owl he resembled, with his beaky nose and large, close-set eyes, he preferred to work at night.

The window was on the ground floor, so I knocked on the wooden shutter, which of course was closed to keep out night demons. After a few moments the shutter opened, and the familiar nose appeared. I spoke my name, and Amenhotep went to open the door.

"Wadjsen! It has been a long time," he exclaimed. "Should I ask what brings you here, or shall I display my talents as a seer and tell you?"

"I suppose it requires no great talent," I replied. "The matter of the Senebtisi's tomb is already the talk of the district."

"So I had assumed." He gestured me to sit down and hospitably indicated the wine jar that stood in the corner. I shook my head.

"I have already taken too much beer, at the tavern. I am sorry to disturb you so late—"

"I am always happy to see you, Wadjsen." His big dark eyes reflected the light of the lamp, so that they seemed to hold stars in their depths. "I have missed my assistant, who helped me to the truth in my first inquiry."

"I was of little help to you then," I said with a smile. "And in this case I am even more ignorant. The thing is a great mystery, known only to the gods."

"No, no!" He clapped his hands together, as was his habit when annoyed with the stupidity of his hearer. "There is no mystery. I know who robbed the tomb of Senebtisi. The only difficulty is to prove how it was done."

At Amenhotep's suggestion I spent the night at his house so that I could accompany him when he set out next morning to find the proof he needed. I required little urging, for I

👁 Suspicions?

1. "The tomb entrance was untouched, the seals of the necropolis were unbroken. The tomb itself is entirely rock-cut, and there was not the slightest break in the walls or floor or ceiling. Yet when Minmose entered the burial chamber, he found the coffin open, the mummy mutilated, and the gold ornaments gone."

Do you also believe at this point that there is no mystery because you think you know who robbed the tomb of Senebtisi? Whom do you think did it? Whom do you think Amenhotep suspects? What might the motive be?

was afire with curiosity. Though I pressed him, he would say no more, merely remarking piously, " 'A man may fall to ruin because of his tongue; if a passing remark is hasty and it is repeated, thou wilt make enemies'. "

I could hardly dispute the wisdom of this adage, but the gleam in Amenhotep's bulging black eyes made me suspect he took a malicious pleasure in my bewilderment.

After our morning bread and beer, we went to the temple of Khonsu, where the sem-priest Wennefer worked in the records office. He was copying accounts from pottery ostraca onto a papyrus that was stretched across his lap. All scribes develop bowed shoulders from bending over their writing; Wennefer was folded almost double, his face scant inches from the surface of the papyrus. When Amenhotop cleared his throat, the old man started, smearing the ink. He waved our apologies aside and cleaned the papyrus with a wad of lint.

"No harm was meant, no harm is done," he said in his breathy, chirping voice. "I have heard of you, Amenhotep Sa Hapu; it is an honor to meet you."

"I, too, have looked forward to meeting you, Wennefer. Alas that the occasion should be such a sad one."

Wennefer's smile faded. "Ah, the matter of Senebtisi's tomb. What a tragedy! At least the poor woman can now have a proper reburial. If Minmose had not insisted on opening the tomb, her ba would have gone hungry and thirsty through eternity."

"Then the tomb entrance really was sealed and undisturbed?" I asked skeptically.

"I examined it myself," Wennefer said. "Minmose had asked me to meet him after the day's work, and we arrived at the tomb

 Suspicions?

2. If the difficulty is to prove how it was done, consider the following statement about all locked room mysteries. Then offer whatever thoughts you may have at this point in the story about "how it was done."

The major question every locked room mystery poses is: How did the criminal get out of the room in which the crime was committed when all the means of escape are either locked or sealed?

As you will read in the short story "No One Likes to Be Played for a Sucker," by Michael Collins, the "locked" room of all locked room mysteries "is an exercise in illusion—a magician's trick. Otherwise it's impossible, and the impossible can't be done, period. Since it had been done, it must be a trick, a matter of distracting attention, and once you know what you're really looking for, the answer is never hard . . . just a matter of logic."

Logically, how did your suspect create the illusion of a locked tomb?

as the sun was setting; but the light was still good. I conducted the funeral service for Senebtisi, you know. I had seen the doorway blocked and mortared and with my own hands had helped to press the seals of the necropolis onto the wet plaster. All was as I had left it that day a year ago."

"Yet Minmose insisted on opening the tomb?" Amenhotep asked.

"Why, we agreed it should be done," the old man said mildly. "As you know, robbers sometimes tunnel in from above or from one side, leaving the entrance undisturbed. Minmose had brought tools. He did most of the work himself, for these old hands of mine are better with a pen than a chisel. When the doorway was clear, Minmose lit a lamp and we entered. We were crossing the hall beyond the entrance corridor when Minmose let out a shriek. 'My mother, my mother,' he cried—oh, it was pitiful to hear! Then I saw it too. The thing—the thing on the floor...."

"You speak of the mummy, I presume," said Amenhotep. "The thieves had dragged it from the coffin out into the hall?"

"Where they despoiled it," Wennefer whispered. "The august body was ripped open from throat to groin, through the shroud and the wrappings and the flesh."

"Curious," Amenhotep muttered, as if to himself. "Tell me, Wennefer, what is the plan of the tomb?"

Wennefer rubbed his brush on the ink cake and began to draw on the back surface of one of the ostraca.

"It is a fine tomb, Amenhotep, entirely rock-cut. Beyond the entrance is a flight of stairs and a short corridor, thus leading to a hall broader than it is long, with two pillars. Beyond that, another short corridor; then the burial chamber. The august mummy lay here." And he inked in a neat circle at the beginning of the second corridor.

"Ha," said Amenhotep, studying the plan. "Yes, yes, I see. Go on, Wennefer. What did you do next?"

"I did nothing," the old man said simply. "Minmose's hand shook so violently that he dropped the lamp. Darkness closed in. I felt the presence of the demons who had defiled the dead. My tongue clove to the roof of my mouth and—"

"Dreadful," Amenhotep said. "But you were not far from the tomb entrance; you could find your way out?"

"Yes, yes, it was only a dozen paces; and by Amon, my friend, the sunset light has never appeared so sweet! I went at once to fetch the necropolis guards. When we returned to the tomb, Minmose had rekindled his lamp—"

"I thought you said the lamp was broken."

"Dropped, but fortunately not broken. Minmose had opened one of the jars of oil—Senebtisi had many such in the tomb, all of the finest quality—and had refilled the lamp. He had replaced the mummy in its coffin and was kneeling by it praying. Never was there so pious a son!"

"So then, I suppose, the guards searched the tomb."

"We all searched," Wennefer said. "The tomb chamber was in a dreadful state; boxes and baskets had been broken open and the contents strewn about. Every object of precious metal had been stolen, including the amulets on the body."

"What about the oil, the linen, and the other valuables?" Amenhotep asked.

"The oil and the wine were in large jars, impossible to move easily. About the other things I cannot say; everything was in such confusion—and I do not know what was there to begin with. Even Minmose was not certain; his mother had filled and sealed most of the boxes herself. But I know what was taken from the mummy, for I saw the golden amulets and ornaments placed on it when it was wrapped by the embalmers. I do not like to speak evil of anyone, but you know, Amenhotep, that the embalmers . . ."

"Yes," Amenhotep agreed with a sour face. "I myself watched the wrapping of my father; there is no other way to make certain the ornaments will go on the mummy instead of into the coffers of the embalmers. Minmose did not perform this service for his mother?"

"Of course he did. He asked me to share in the watch, and I was glad to agree. He is the most pious—"

"So I have heard," said Amenhotep. "Tell me again, Wennefer, of the condition of the mummy. You examined it?"

"It was my duty. Oh, Amenhotep, it was a sad sight! The shroud was still tied firmly around the body; the thieves had cut straight through it and through the bandages beneath, baring the body. The arm bones were broken, so roughly had the thieves dragged the heavy gold bracelets from them."

"And the mask?" I asked. "It was said that she had a mask of solid gold."

"It, too, was missing."

"Horrible," Amenhotep said. "Wennefer, we have kept you from your work long enough. Only one more question. How do you think the thieves entered the tomb?"

The old man's eyes fell. "Through me," he whispered.

I gave Amenhotep a startled look. He shook his head warningly.

"It was not your fault," he said, touching Wennefer's bowed shoulder.

"It was. I did my best, but I must have omitted some vital part of the ritual. How else could demons enter the tomb?"

"Oh, I see." Amenhotep stroked his chin. "Demons."

"It could have been nothing else. The seals on the door were intact, the mortar untouched. There was no break of the smallest size in the stone of the walls or ceiling or floor."

"But—" I began.

"And there is this. When the doorway was clear and the light entered, the dust lay undisturbed on the floor. The only marks on it were the strokes of the broom with which Minmose, according to custom, had swept the floor as he left the tomb after the funeral service."

"Amon preserve us," I exclaimed, feeling a chill run through me.

Amenhotep's eyes moved from Wennefer to me, then back to Wennefer. "That is conclusive," he murmured.

"Yes," Wennefer said with a groan. "And I am to blame—I, a priest who failed at his task."

"No," said Amenhotep. "You did not fail. Be of good cheer, my friend. There is another explanation."

Wennefer shook his head despondently. "Minmose said the same, but he was only being kind. Poor man! He was so overcome, he could scarcely walk. The guards had to take him by the arms to lead him from the tomb. I carried his tools. It was the least—"

"The tools," Amenhotep interrupted. "They were in a bag or a sack?"

"Why, no. He had only a chisel and a mallet. I carried them in my hand as he had done."

Amenhotep thanked him again, and we took our leave. As we crossed the courtyard I waited for him to speak, but he remained silent; and after a while I could contain myself no longer.

"Do you still believe you know who robbed the tomb?"

"Yes, yes, it is obvious."

"And it was not demons?"

Amenhotep blinked at me like an owl blinded by sunlight.

"Demons are a last resort."

He had the smug look of a man who thinks he has said something clever; but his remark smacked of heresy to me, and I looked at him doubtfully.

"Come, come," he snapped. "Senebtisi was a selfish, greedy old woman, and if there is justice in the next world, as our faith decrees, her path through the Underworld will not be easy. But why would diabolical powers play tricks with her mummy when they could torment her spirit? Demons have no need of gold."

"Well, but—"

"Your wits used not to be so dull. What do you think happened?"

"If it was not demons—"

"It was not."

"Then someone must have broken in."

"Very clever," said Amenhotep, grinning.

"I mean that there must be an opening, in the walls or the floor, that Wennefer failed to see."

"Wennefer, perhaps. The necropolis guards, no. The chambers of the tomb were cut out of solid rock. It would be impossible to disguise a break in such a surface, even if tomb robbers took the trouble to fill it in—which they never have been known to do."

"Then the thieves entered through the doorway and closed it again. A dishonest craftsman could make a copy of the necropolis seal . . ."

"Good." Amenhotep clapped me on the shoulder. "Now you are beginning to think. It is an ingenious idea, but it is wrong. Tomb robbers work in haste, for fear of the necropolis guards. They would not linger to replace stones and mortar and seals."

"Then I do not know how it was done."

"Ah, Wadjsen, you are dense! There is only one person who could have robbed the tomb."

"I thought of that," I said stiffly, hurt by his raillery. "Minmose was the last to leave the tomb and the first to reenter it. He had good reason to desire the gold his mother should have left to him. But, Amenhotep, he could not have robbed the mummy on either occasion; there was not time. You know the funeral ritual as well as I. When the priests and mourners leave the tomb, they leave together. If Minmose had lingered in the burial chamber, even for a few minutes, his delay would have been noted and remarked upon."

"That is quite true," said Amenhotep.

"Also," I went on, "the gold was heavy as well as bulky. Minmose could not have carried it away without someone noticing."

"Again you speak truly."

Suspicions?

1. Have you changed your mind about whom Amenhotep suspects? What about your suspicions? Explain why or why not?

2. What additional clues to the identity of the grave robber and to the "how" of the crime has the story provided? What might Amenhotep have found "curious" about Wennefer's account of the despoiling of the mummy?

3. What might Amenhotep have seen, after he has studied Wennefer's drawing of the plan of the tomb, to cause him to say, "Ha. Yes, yes, I see"?

"Then unless Wennefer the priest is conspiring with Minmose—"

"That good, simple man? I am surprised at you, Wadjsen. Wennefer is as honest as the Lady of Truth herself."

"Demons—"

Amenhotep interrupted with the hoarse hooting sound that passed for a laugh with him. "Stop babbling of demons. There is one man besides myself who knows how Senebtisi's tomb was violated. Let us go and see him."

He quickened his pace, his sandals slapping in the dust. I followed, trying to think. His taunts were like weights that pulled my mind to its farthest limits. I began to get an inkling of truth, but I could not make sense of it. I said nothing, not even when we turned into the lane south of the temple that led to the house of Minmose.

Suspicions?

"We argued the matter for some time . . . It was a foolish argument, for none of us knew the facts; and to argue without knowledge is like trying to weave without thread." Do you think you have enough facts and enough knowledge to explain how Minmose created the illusion of a locked tomb? If you think you do, "weave with your thread" now before the seer Amenhotep provides his explanation of the crime.

There was no servant at the door. Minmose himself answered our summons. I greeted him and introduced Amenhotep.

Minmose lifted his hands in surprise. "You honor my house, Amenhotep. Enter and be seated."

Amenhotep shook his head. "I will not stay, Minmose. I came only to tell you who desecrated your mother's tomb."

"What?" Minmose gaped at him. "Already you know? But how? It is a great mystery, beyond—"

"You did it, Minmose."

Minmose turned a shade paler. But that was not out of the way; even the innocent might blanch at such an accusation.

"You are mad," he said. "Forgive me, you are my guest, but—"

"There is no other possible explanation," Amenhotep said. "You stole the gold when you entered the tomb two days ago."

"But, Amenhotep," I exclaimed. "Wennefer was with him, and Wennefer saw the mummy already robbed when—"

"Wennefer did not see the mummy," Amenhotep said. "The tomb was dark; the only light was that of a small lamp, which Minmose promptly dropped. Wennefer has poor sight. Did you not observe how he bent over his writing? He caught only a glimpse of a white shape, the size of a wrapped mummy, before the light went out. When next Wennefer saw the mummy, it was in the coffin, and his view of it then colored his confused memory of the first supposed sighting of it. Few people are good observers. They see what they expect to see."

"Then what did he see?" I demanded. Minmose might not have been there. Amenhotep avoided looking at him.

"A piece of linen in the rough shape of a human form, arranged on the floor by the last person who left the tomb. It would have taken him only a moment to do this before he snatched up the broom and swept himself out."

"So the tomb was sealed and closed," I exclaimed. "For almost a year he waited—"

"Until the next outbreak of tomb robbing. Minmose could assume this would happen sooner or later; it always does. He thought he was being clever by asking Wennefer to accompany him—a witness of irreproachable character who could testify that the tomb entrance was untouched. In fact, he was too careful to avoid being compromised; that would have made me doubt him, even if the logic of the facts had not pointed directly at him. Asking that same virtuous man to share his supervision of the mummy wrapping, lest he be suspected of connivance with the embalmers; feigning weakness so that the necropolis guards would have to support him, and thus be in a position to swear he could not have concealed the gold on his person. Only a guilty man would be so anxious to appear innocent. Yet there was reason for his precautions. Sometime in the near future, when that loving son Minmose discovers a store of gold hidden in the house, overlooked by his mother—the old do forget sometimes—then, since men have evil minds, it might be necessary for Minmose to prove beyond a shadow of a doubt that he could not have laid hands on his mother's burial equipment."

Minmose remained dumb, his eyes fixed on the ground. It was I who responded as he should have, questioning and objecting.

"But how did he remove the gold? The guards and Wennefer searched the tomb, so it was not hidden there, and there was not time for him to bury it outside."

"No, but there was ample time for him to do what had to be done in the burial chamber after Wennefer had tottered off to fetch the guards. He overturned boxes and baskets, opened the coffin, ripped through the mummy wrappings with his chisel, and took the gold. It would not take long, especially for one who knew exactly where each ornament had been placed."

Minmose's haggard face was as good as an admission of guilt. He did not look up or speak, even when Amenhotep put a hand on his shoulder.

"I pity you, Minmose," Amenhotep said gravely. "After years of devotion and self-denial, to see yourself deprived of your inheritance . . . And there was Nefertiry. You had been visiting her in secret, even before your mother died, had you not? Oh, Minmose, you should have remembered the words of the sage: 'Do not go in to a woman who is a stranger; it is a great crime, worthy of death.' She has brought you to your death, Minmose. You knew she would turn from you if your mother left you nothing."

Minmose's face was gray. "Will you denounce me, then? They will beat me to make me confess."

"Any man will confess when he is beaten," said Amenhotep, with a curl of his lip. "No, Minmose, I will not denounce you. The court of the vizier demands facts, not theories, and you have covered your tracks very neatly. But you will not escape justice. Nefertiry will consume your gold as the desert sands drink water, and then she will cast you off; and all the while Anubis, the Guide of the Dead, and Osiris, the Divine Judge, will be waiting for you. They will eat your heart, Minmose, and your spirit will hunger and thirst through all eternity. I think your punishment has already begun. Do you dream, Minmose? Did you see your mother's face last night, wrinkled and withered, her sunken eyes accusing you, as it looked when you tore the gold mask from it?"

A long shudder ran through Minmose's body. Even his hair seemed to shiver and rise. Amenhotep gestured to me. We went away, leaving Minmose staring after us with a face like death.

After we had gone a short distance, I said, "There is one more thing to tell, Amenhotep."

"There is much to tell." Amenhotep sighed deeply. "Of a good man turned evil; of two women who, in their different ways, drove him to crime; of the narrow line that separates the virtuous man from the sinner . . ."

"I do not speak of that. I do not wish to think of that. It makes me feel strange . . . The gold, Amenhotep—how did Minmose bear away the gold from his mother's burial?"

"He put it in the oil jar," said Amenhotep. "The one he opened to get fresh fuel for his lamp. Who would wonder if, in his agitation, he spilled a quantity of oil on the floor? He has certainly removed it by now. He has had ample opportunity, running back and forth with objects to be repaired or replaced."

"And the piece of linen he had put down to look like the mummy?"

"As you well know," Amenhotep replied, "the amount of linen used to wrap a mummy is prodigious. He could have crumpled that piece and thrown it in among the torn wrappings. But I think he did something else. It was a cool evening, in winter, and Minmose would have worn a linen mantle. He took the cloth out in the same way he had brought it in. Who would notice an extra fold of linen over a man's shoulders?

"I knew immediately that Minmose must be the guilty party, because he was the only one who had the opportunity, but I did not see how he had managed it until Wennefer showed me where the supposed mummy lay. There was no reason for a thief to drag it so far from the coffin and the burial chamber—but Minmose could not afford to have Wennefer catch even a glimpse of that room, which was then undisturbed. I realized then that what the old man had seen was not the mummy at all, but a substitute."

"Then Minmose will go unpunished."

"I said he would be punished. I spoke truly." Again Amenhotep sighed.

"You will not denounce him to Pharaoh?"

"I will tell my lord the truth. But he will not choose to act. There will be no need."

He said no more. But six weeks later Minmose's body was found floating in the river. He had taken to drinking heavily, and people said he drowned by accident. But I knew it was otherwise. Anubis and Osiris had eaten his heart, just as Amenhotep had said.

Author's note: Amenhotep Sa Hapu was a real person who lived during the fourteenth century B.C. Later generations worshiped him as a sage and scholar; he seems like a logical candidate for the role of ancient Egyptian detective.

 How Clever?

1. What specific illusionary tricks (tricks played on the eye) did Minmose pull on Wennefer in order to cause him to think that a grave robber has escaped from Senebtisi's tomb without leaving a trace behind? In what ways did Minmose succeed through "distracting attention"?

2. What three factors contributed to Minmose's successfully deceiving Wennefer into thinking he had seen Senebtisi's robed mummy when actually it was only a piece of white linen the shape and size of a mummy?

3. Why was it that Amenhotep Sa Hapu did not figure out how Minmose had managed to deceive Wennefer until after Wennefer drew for Amenhotep a plan of the tomb to show "where the supposed mummy lay"?

4. What is Amenhotep's thinking about how Minmose might have arranged for that piece of linen to be gotten into and out of the tomb?

5. Amenhotep is a "seer," and is, therefore, a wise individual. What specific observation had Amenhotep made that led him to conclude correctly that Wennefer had poor eyesight?

6. What does Amenhotep mean by his comment that "few people are good observers. They see what they expect to see"? How good a detective can those individuals who "see what they expect to see" be, instead of being seers? Explain.

7. Police detectives have always used "means, motive, and opportunity" as the three key ways of exploring possible suspects in a crime.

   Motive: what was Minmose's motive for robbing his mother's tomb? Why does Amenhotep believe that this is a case of "the narrow line that separates the virtuous man from the sinner," and of how "a good man turned evil"? Which two women does Amenhotep hold partly responsible for Minmose's actions? Why?

   Opportunity: why did Minmose wait almost a year after sealing and closing his mother's tomb before robbing it of its gold?

   Means: why did Minmose want Wennefer to accompany him to his mother's tomb? Why not someone else? How significant is it that Minmose is a professional stonecarver? Explain.

8. Amenhotep says that "the logic of the facts" pointed directly at Minmose. What logic? Which facts?

   a. What reason does Amenhotep give to Wadjsen to explain why diabolical powers—demons—cannot be the explanation for the despoiling of the mummy? Why would "demons" never be an explanation in a detective story?

   b. What reason does Amenhotep give to Wadjsen to explain why it is unlikely that "thieves entered through the doorway and closed it again"?

9. Amenhotep says that Minmose might need to "prove beyond a shadow of a doubt" that he had not taken gold from his mother's tomb. Explain how two specific precautionary actions that Minmose took on the day of his mother's burial could prevent suspicion from falling on him.

10. Amenhotep remarks that "only a guilty man would be so anxious to appear innocent." (He had expressed the same idea a little bit earlier when he said that Minmose "was too careful to avoid being compromised.") What do you think of this idea? Explain your position.

11. How did Minmose remove and hide the gold he stole from his mother's burial chamber without Wennefer's observing his actions? How did he transport the gold?

12. Amenhotep tells Minmose that he will not denounce him to the court of the vizier because Minmose has covered the tracks of his crime too neatly for the facts to convict him. However, Amenhotep believes that Minmose will "not escape justice." In this case, how does Amenhotep believe that justice will be served? Does he turn out to be correct? Explain.

13. How much of Amenhotep's solution of "the locked tomb mystery" was based on detection? How much was based on reflection? Explain.

14. How does Wadjsen's being a temple scribe make him a good choice as narrator of the story?

DetectWrite: Characterization

In an author's note at the end of the story, we are told that Amenhotep Sa Hapu was a real person who lived during the fourteenth century of the common era and that later generations worshipped him as a sage and scholar. The author, Elizabeth Peters, then adds that "he seems like a logical candidate for the role of an ancient Egyptian detective." (Within the story, Peters compares Amenhotep to an owl—telling us that he shared with owls a beaky nose, large, close-set eyes, and a preference for working at night—and refers to him as a seer, a see-er of truth.)

1. Explain in writing why you agree or disagree with Peters' reasoning behind her selection of Amenhotep as the detective in her story.

2. Choose an actual person living today from anywhere in the world and explain in writing why you think that person could be the model for a detective you would use in a contemporary mystery story you might write.

3. Choose an actual person from another time and place and explain in writing why that person could be the model for a fictional detective. Consider using this "historical detective" in a mystery story you would write.

DetectWrite: Characterization and Plot

1. Create a brief scenario for a criminal in a detective story you might write in which you clearly explain the means, motive, and opportunity behind your criminal's actions.

2. Explain how you as a writer would be careful not to have the criminal in your story "be so anxious to appear innocent."

DetectWrite: Setting

1. How does Peters make creative use of a tomb as the "room" for a locked room mystery?

2. What other non-traditional rooms might also lend themselves to the locked room format? Explain.

3. Honoring the conventions (requirements) of the plot of any locked room mystery, choose a "room" of your own, explain how it lends itself to becoming "a locked room," and then write the opening to a locked room mystery set in that room.

4. Complete the writing of your locked room mystery story after you read both "No One Likes to Be Played for a Sucker" and "The Man Who Read John Dickson Carr."

The Leopold Locked Room

Edward D. Hoch

CAPTAIN LEOPOLD HAD NEVER SPOKEN TO ANYONE ABOUT his divorce, and it was a distinct surprise to Lieutenant Fletcher when he suddenly said, "Did I ever tell you about my wife, Fletcher?"

They were just coming up from the police pistol range in the basement of headquarters after their monthly target practise, and it hardly seemed a likely time to be discussing past marital troubles. Fletcher glanced at him sideways and answered, "No, I guess you never did, Captain."

They had reached the top of the stairs and Leopold turned in to the little room where the coffee, sandwich, and soft-drink machines were kept. They called it the lunchroom, but only by the boldest stretch of the imagination could the little collection of tables and chairs qualify as such. Rather it was a place where off-duty cops could sit and chat, which was what Leopold and Fletcher were doing now.

Fletcher bought the coffee and put the steaming paper cups on the table between them. He had never seen Leopold quite this open and personal before, anxious to talk about a life that had existed far beyond the limits of Fletcher's friendship. "She's coming back," Leopold said simply, and it took Fletcher an instant to grasp the meaning of his words.

"Your wife is coming back?"

"My ex-wife."

"Here? What for?"

Leopold sighed and played with the little bag of sugar that Fletcher had given him with his coffee. "Her niece is getting married. Our niece."

"I never knew you had one."

"She's been away at college. Her name is Vicki Nelson, and she's marrying a young lawyer named Moore. And Monica is coming back east for the wedding."

"I never even knew her name," Fletcher observed, taking a sip of his coffee. "Haven't you seen her since the divorce?"

Leopold shook his head. "Not for fifteen years. It was a funny thing. She wanted to be a movie star, and I guess fifteen years ago lots of girls still thought about being movie stars. Monica was intelligent and very pretty—but probably no prettier than hundreds of other girls who used to turn up in Hollywood every year back in those days. I was just starting on the police force then, and the future looked pretty bright for me here. It would have been foolish of me to toss up everything just to chase her wild dream out to California. Well, pretty soon it got to be an obsession with her, really bad. She'd spend her afternoons in movie theaters and her evenings watching old films on television. Finally, when I still refused to go west with her, she just left me."

"Just walked out?"

Leopold nodded. "It was a blessing, really, that we didn't have children. I heard she got a few minor jobs out there——as an extra, and some technical stuff behind the scenes. Then apparently she had a nervous breakdown. About a year later I received the official word that she'd divorced me. I heard that she recovered and was back working, and I think she had another marriage that didn't work out."

"Why would she come back for the wedding?"

"Vicki is her niece and also her godchild. We were just married when Vicki was born, and I suppose Monica might consider her the child we never had. In any event, I know she still hates me, and blames me for everything that's gone wrong with her life. She told a friend once a few years ago she wished I were dead."

"Do you have to go to this wedding, too, Captain?"

"Of course. If I stayed away it would be only because of her. At least I have to drop by the reception for a few minutes." Leopold smiled ruefully. "I guess that's why I'm telling you all this, Fletcher. I want a favor from you."

"Anything, Captain. You know that."

"I know it seems like a childish thing to do, but I'd like you to come out there with me. I'll tell them I'm working, and that I can only stay for a few minutes. You can wait outside in the car if you want. At least they'll see you there and believe my excuse."

Fletcher could see the importance of it to Leopold, and the effort that had gone into the asking. "Sure," he said. "Be glad to. When is it?"

"This Saturday. The reception's in the afternoon, at Sunset Farms."

Leopold had been to Sunset Farms only once before, at the wedding of a patrolman who he'd especially liked. It was a low rambling place at the end of a paved driveway, overlooking a wooded valley and a gently flowing creek. If it had ever been a farm, that day was long past; but for wedding receptions and retirement parties it was the ideal place. The interior of the main building was, in reality, one huge square room, divided by accordion doors to make up to four smaller square rooms.

For the wedding of Vicki Nelson and Ted Moore three-quarters of the large room was in use, with only the last set of accordion doors pulled shut its entire width and locked. The wedding party occupied a head table along one wall, with smaller tables scattered around the room for the families and friends. When Leopold entered the place at five minutes of two on Saturday afternoon, the hired combo was just beginning to play music for dancing.

He watched for a moment while Vicki stood, radiant, and allowed her new husband to escort her to the center of the floor. Ted Moore was a bit older than Leopold had expected, but as the pair glided slowly across the floor, he could find no visible fault with the match. He helped himself to a glass of champagne punch and stood ready to intercept them as they left the dance floor.

"It's Captain Leopold, isn't it?" someone asked. A face from his past loomed up, a tired man with a gold tooth in the front of his smile. "I'm Immy Fontaine, Monica's stepbrother."

"Sure," Leopold said, as if he'd remembered the man all along. Monica had rarely mentioned Immy, and Leopold recalled meeting him once or twice at family gatherings. But the sight of him now, gold tooth and all, reminded Leopold that Monica was somewhere nearby, that he might confront her at any moment.

"We're so glad you could come," someone else said, and he turned to greet the bride and groom as they came off the dance floor. Up close, Vicki was a truly beautiful girl, clinging to her new husband's arm like a proper bride.

"I wouldn't have missed it for anything," he said.

"This is Ted," she said, making the introductions. Leopold shook his hand, silently approving the firm grip and friendly eyes.

"I understand you're a lawyer," Leopold said, making conversation.

"That's right, sir. Mostly civil cases, though. I don't tangle much with criminals."

They chatted for a few more seconds before the pressure of guests broke them apart. The luncheon was about to be served, and the more hungry ones were already lining up at the buffet tables. Vicki and Ted went over to start the line, and Leopold took another glass of champagne punch.

"I see the car waiting outside," Immy Fontaine said, moving in again. "You got to go on duty?"

Leopold nodded. "Just this glass and I have to leave."

"Monica's in from the west coast."

"So I heard."

A slim man with a mustache jostled against him in the crush of the crowd and hastily apologized. Fontaine seized the man by the arm and introduced him to Leopold. "This here's Dr. Felix Thursby. He came east with Monica. Doc, I want you to meet Captain Leopold, her ex-husband."

Leopold shook hands awkwardly, embarrassed for the man and for himself. "A fine wedding," he mumbled. "Your first trip east?"

Thursby shook his head. "I'm from New York. Long ago."

"I was on the police force there once," Leopold remarked.

They chatted for a few more minutes before Leopold managed to edge away through the crowd.

"Leaving so soon?" a harsh unforgettable voice asked.

"Hello, Monica. It's been a long time."

He stared down at the handsome, middle-aged woman who now blocked his path to the door. She had gained a little weight, especially in the bosom, and her hair was graying. Only the eyes startled him, and frightened him just a bit. They had the intense wild look he'd seen before on the faces of deranged criminals.

"I didn't think you'd come. I thought you'd be afraid of me," she said.

"That's foolish. Why should I be afraid of you?"

The music had started again, and the line from the buffet tables was beginning to snake lazily about the room. But for Leopold and Monica they might have been alone in the middle of a desert.

"Come in here," she said, "where we can talk." She motioned toward the end of the room that had been cut off by the accordion doors. Leopold followed her, helpless to do anything else. She unlocked the doors and pulled them apart, just wide enough for them to enter the unused quarter of the large room. Then she closed and locked the doors behind them, and stood facing him. They were two people, alone in a bare unfurnished room.

They were in an area about thirty feet square, with the windows at the far end and the locked accordion doors at Leopold's back. He could see the afternoon sun cutting through the trees outside, and the gentle hum of the air conditioner came through above the subdued murmur of the wedding guests.

"Remember the day we got married?" she asked.

"Yes. Of course."

She walked to the middle window, running her fingers along the frame perhaps looking for the latch to open it. But it stayed closed as she faced him again. "Our marriage was as drab and barren as this room. Lifeless, unused!"

"Heaven knows I always wanted children, Monica."

"You wanted nothing but your damned police work!" she shot back, eyes flashing as her anger built.

"Look, I have to go. I have a man waiting in the car."

"Go! That's what you did before, wasn't it? *Go, go!* Go out to your damned job and leave me to struggle for myself. Leave me to—"

"You walked out on me, Monica. Remember?" he reminded her softly. She was so defenseless, without even a purse to swing at him.

"Sure I did! Because I had a career waiting for me! I had all the world waiting for me! And you know what happened because you wouldn't come along? You know what happened to me out there? They took my money and my self-respect and what virtue I had left. They made me into a tramp, and when they were done they locked me up in a mental hospital for three years. Three years!"

"I'm sorry."

"Every day while I was there I thought about you. I thought about how it would be when I got out. Oh, I thought. And planned. And schemed. You're a big detective now. Sometimes your cases even get reported in the California papers." She was pacing back and forth, caged, dangerous. "Big detective. But I can still destroy you just as you destroyed me!"

He glanced over his shoulder at the locked accordion doors, seeking a way out. It was a thousand times worse than he'd imagined it would be. She was mad—mad and vengeful and terribly dangerous. "You should see a doctor, Monica."

Her eyes closed to mere slits. "I've seen doctors." Now she paused before the middle window, facing him. "I came all the way east for this day, because I thought you'd be here. It's so much better than your apartment, or your office, or a city street. There are one hundred and fifty witnesses on the other side of those doors."

"What in hell are you talking about?"

Her mouth twisted in a horrible grin. "You're going to know what I knew. Bars and cells and disgrace. You're going to know the despair I felt all those years."

"Monica—"

At that instant perhaps twenty feet separated them. She lifted one arm, as if to shield herself, then screamed in terror. "No! Oh, God, no!"

Leopold stood frozen, unable to move, as a sudden gunshot echoed through the room. He saw the bullet strike her in the chest, toppling her backward like the blow from a giant fist. Then somehow he had his own gun out of its belt holster and he swung around toward the doors.

They were still closed and locked. He was alone in the room with Monica.

He looked back to see her crumple on the floor, blood spreading in a widening circle around the torn black hole in her dress. His eyes went to the windows, but all three were still closed and unbroken. He shook his head, trying to focus his mind on what had happened.

There was noise from outside, and a pounding on the accordion doors. Someone opened the lock from the other side, and the gap between the doors widened as they were pulled open. "What happened?" someone asked. A woman guest screamed as she saw the body. Another toppled in a faint.

Leopold stepped back, aware of the gun still in his hand, and saw Lieutenant Fletcher fighting his way through the mob of guests. "Captain, what is it?"

"She . . . Someone shot her."

Fletcher reached out and took the gun from Leopold's hand—carefully, as one might take a broken toy from a child. He put it to his nose and sniffed, then opened the cylinder to inspect the bullets. "It's been fired recently, Captain. One shot." Then his eyes seemed to cloud over, almost to the point of tears. "Why the hell did you do it?" he asked. "Why?"

Leopold saw nothing of what happened then. He only had vague and splintered memories of someone examining her and saying she was still alive, of an ambulance and much confusion. Fletcher drove him down to headquarters, to the Commissioner's office, and he sat there and waited, running his moist palms up and down his trousers. He was not surprised when they told him she had died on the way to Southside Hospital. Monica had never been one to do things by halves.

The men—detectives who worked under him—came to and left the Commissioner's

Suspicions?

"The Leopold Locked Room" is quite unusual for a locked room mystery: not only is the victim in the locked room but so is the suspect. However, the reader feels pretty certain that Captain Leopold did not kill his former wife, despite Lieutenant Fletcher's assumption. Can you explain at this point who did kill Monica and how the evidence was made to incriminate Captain Leopold?

office, speaking in low tones with their heads together, occasionally offering him some embarrassed gesture of condolence. There was an aura of sadness over the place, and Leopold knew it was for him.

"You have nothing more to tell us, Captain?" the Commissioner asked. "I'm making it as easy for you as I can."

"I didn't kill her," Leopold insisted again. "It was someone else."

"Who? How?"

He could only shake his head. "I wish I knew. I think in some mad way she killed herself, to get revenge on me."

"She shot herself with *your* gun, while it was in *your* holster, and while *you* were standing twenty feet away?"

Leopold ran a hand over his forehead. "It couldn't have been my gun. Ballistics will prove that."

"But your gun had been fired recently, and there was an empty cartridge in the chamber."

"I can't explain that. I haven't fired it since the other day at target practise, and I reloaded it afterwards."

"Could she have hated you that much, Captain?" Fletcher asked. "To frame you for her murder?"

"She could have. I think she was a very sick woman. If I did that to her—if I was the one who made her sick—I suppose I deserve what's happening to me now."

"The hell you do," Fletcher growled. "If you say you're innocent, Captain, I'm sticking by you." He began pacing again, and finally turned to the Commissioner. "How about giving him a paraffin test, to see if he's fired a gun recently?"

The Commissioner shook his head. "We haven't used that in years. You know how unreliable it is, Fletcher. Many people have nitrates or nitrites on their hands. They can pick them up from dirt, or fertilizers, or fireworks, or urine, or even from simply handling peas or beans. Anyone who smokes tobacco can have deposits on his hands. There are some newer tests for the presence of barium or lead, but we don't have the necessary chemicals for those."

Leopold nodded. The Commissioner had risen through the ranks. He wasn't simply a political appointee, and the men had always respected him. Leopold respected him. "Wait for the ballistics report," he said. "That'll clear me."

So they waited. It was another 45 minutes before the phone rang and the Commissioner spoke to the ballistics man. He listened, and grunted, and asked one or two questions. Then he hung up and faced Leopold across the desk.

"The bullet was fired from your gun," he said simply. "There's no possibility of error. I'm afraid we'll have to charge you with homicide."

The routines he knew so well went on into Saturday evening, and when they were finished Leopold was escorted from the courtroom to find young Ted Moore waiting for him. "You should be on your honeymoon," Leopold told him.

"Vicki couldn't leave till I'd seen you and tried to help. I don't know much about criminal law, but perhaps I could arrange bail."

"That's already been taken care of," Leopold said. "The grand jury will get the case next week."

"I—I don't know what to say. Vicki and I are both terribly sorry."

 Suspicions?

The police commissioner tells Leopold that he will have to be charged with murder because "the bullet was fired from your gun" and adds "there's no possibility of error." Restate in your own words what the commissioner means by his words. How can that be possible? If you do not think it is possible, what explanation do you have for what occurred and for the police ballistics findings?

"So am I." He started to walk away, then turned back. "Enjoy your honeymoon."

"We'll be in town overnight, at the Towers, if there's anything I can do."

Leopold nodded and kept on walking. He could see the reflection of his guilt in young Moore's eyes. As he got to his car, one of the patrolmen he knew glanced his way and then quickly in the other direction. On a Saturday night no one talked to wife murderers. Even Fletcher had disappeared.

Leopold decided he couldn't face the drab walls of his office, not with people avoiding him. Besides, the Commissioner had been forced to suspend him from active duty pending grand jury action and the possible trial. The office didn't even belong to him anymore. He cursed silently and drove home to his little apartment, weaving through the dark streets with one eye out for a patrol car. He wondered if they'd be watching him, to prevent his jumping bail. He wondered what he'd have done in the Commissioner's shoes.

The eleven o'clock news on television had it as the lead item, illustrated with a black-and-white photo of him taken during a case last year. He shut off the television without listening to their comments and went back outside, walking down to the corner for an early edition of the Sunday paper. The front-page headline was as bad as he'd expected: *Detective Captain Held in Slaying of Ex-Wife.*

On the way back to his apartment, walking slowly, he tried to remember what she'd been like—not that afternoon, but before the divorce. He tried to remember her face on their wedding day, her soft laughter on their honeymoon. But all he could remember were those mad vengeful eyes. And the bullet ripping into her chest.

Perhaps he had killed her after all. Perhaps the gun had come into his hand so easily he never realized it was there.

"Hello, Captain."

"I—Fletcher! What are you doing here?"

"Waiting for you. Can I come in?"

"Well . . ."

"I've got a six-pack of beer. I thought you might want to talk about it."

Leopold unlocked his apartment door. "What's there to talk about?"

"If you say you didn't kill her, Captain, I'm willing to listen to you."

Fletcher followed him into the tiny kitchen and popped open two of the beer cans. Leopold accepted one of them and dropped into the nearest chair. He felt utterly exhausted, drained of even the strength to fight back.

"She framed me, Fletcher," he said quietly. "She framed me as neatly as anything I've ever seen. The thing's impossible, but she did it."

"Let's go over it step by step, Captain. Look, the way I see it there are only three possibilities: either you shot her, she shot herself, or someone else shot her. I think we can rule out the last one. The three windows were locked on the outside and unbroken, the room was bare of any hiding place, and the only entrance was through the accordion doors. These were closed and locked, and although they could have been opened from the other side you certainly would have seen or heard it happen. Besides, there were one

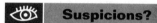

Suspicions?

Leopold is convinced that his former wife framed him for her murder, and yet he says, "The thing's impossible, but she did it." At this point in the story, can you help Leopold to understand how the "impossible" might be possible? Explain.

hundred and fifty wedding guests on the other side of those doors. No one could have unlocked and opened them and then fired the shot, all without being seen."

Leopold shook his head. "But it's just as impossible that she could have shot herself. I was watching her every minute. I never looked away once. There was nothing in her hands, not even a purse. And the gun that shot her was in my holster, on my belt. I never drew it till *after* the shot was fired."

Fletcher finished his beer and reached for another can. "I didn't look at her close, Captain, but the size of the hole in her dress and the powder burns point to a contact wound. The Medical Examiner agrees, too. She was shot from no more than an inch or two away. There were grains of powder in the wound itself, though the bleeding had washed most of them away."

"But she had nothing in her hand," Leopold repeated. "And there was nobody standing in front of her with a gun. Even I was twenty feet away."

"The thing's impossible, Captain."

Leopold grunted. "Impossible—unless I killed her."

Fletcher stared at his beer. "How much time do we have?"

"If the grand jury indicts me for first-degree murder, I'll be in a cell by next week."

Fletcher frowned at him. "What's with you, Captain? You almost act resigned to it! Hell, I've seen more fight in you on a routine holdup!"

"I guess that's it, Fletcher. The fight is gone out of me. She's drained every drop of it. She's had her revenge."

Fletcher sighed and stood up. "Then I guess there's really nothing I can do for you, Captain. Good night."

Leopold didn't see him to the door. He simply sat there, hunched over the table. For the first time in his life he felt like an old man.

Leopold slept late Sunday morning, and awakened with the odd sensation that it had all been a dream. He remembered feeling the same way when he'd broken his wrist chasing a burglar. In the morning, on just awakening, the memory of the heavy cast had always been a dream, until he moved his arm. Now, rolling over in his narrow bed, he saw the Sunday paper where he'd tossed it the night before. The headline was still the same. The dream was a reality.

He got up and showered and dressed, reaching for his holster out of habit before he remembered he no longer had a gun. Then he sat at the kitchen table staring at the empty beer cans, wondering what he would do with his day. With his life.

The doorbell rang and it was Fletcher. "I didn't think I'd be seeing you again," Leopold mumbled, letting him in.

Fletcher was excited, and the words tumbled out of him almost before he was through the door. "I think I've got something, Captain! It's not much, but it's a start. I was down at

Suspicions?

1. Lieutenant Fletcher says, "Look, the way I see it there are only three possibilities: either you shot her, she shot herself, or someone else shot her." Can you "look" again at the situation and come up any other possibilities besides these three?

2. What conclusions can you make from Leopold's repeated insistence that "there was nothing" in Monica's hands?

3. What conclusions can you make from the medical examiner's report that Monica was "shot from no more than an inch or two away"?

4. What conclusions can you make from the several conclusions you have just made?

headquarters first thing this morning and I got hold of the dress Monica was wearing when she was shot."

Leopold looked blank. "The dress?"

Fletcher was busy unwrapping the package he'd brought. "The Commissioner would have my neck if he knew I brought this to you, but look at this hole!"

Leopold studied the jagged, blood-caked rent in the fabric. "It's large," he observed, "but with a near-contact wound the powder burns would cause that."

"Captain, I've seen plenty of entrance wounds made by a .38 slug. I've even caused a few of them. But I never saw one that looked like this. Hell, it's not even round!"

"What are you trying to tell me, Fletcher?" Suddenly something stirred inside him. The juices were beginning to flow again.

"The hole in her dress is much larger and more jagged than the corresponding wound in her chest, Captain. That's what I'm telling you. The bullet that killed her couldn't have made this hole. No way! And that means maybe she wasn't killed when we thought she was."

Leopold grabbed the phone and dialed the familiar number of the Towers Hotel. "I hope they slept late this morning."

"Who?"

"The honeymooners." He spoke sharply into the phone, giving the switchboard operator the name he wanted, and then waited. It was a full minute before he heard Ted Moore's sleepy voice answering on the other end. "Ted, this is Leopold. Sorry to bother you."

The voice came alert at once. "That's all right, Captain. I told you to call if there was anything—"

"I think there is. You and Vicki between you must have a pretty good idea of who was invited to the wedding. Check with her and tell me how many doctors were on the invitation list."

Ted Moore was gone for a few moments and then he returned. "Vicki says you're the second person who asked her that."

"Oh? Who was the first?"

"Monica. The night before the wedding, when she arrived in town with Dr. Thursby. She casually asked if he'd get to meet any other doctors at the reception. But Vicki told her he was the only one. Of course we hadn't invited him, but as a courtesy to Monica we urged him to come."

"Then after the shooting, it was Thursby who examined her? No one else?"

"He was the only doctor. He told us to call an ambulance and rode to the hospital with her."

"Thank you, Ted. You've been a big help."

"I hope so, Captain."

Leopold hung up and faced Fletcher. "That's it. She worked it with this guy Thursby. Can you put out an alarm for him?"

"Sure can," Fletcher said. He took the telephone and dialed the unlisted squadroom number. "Dr. Felix Thursby? Is that his name?"

"That's it. The only doctor there, the only one who could help Monica with her crazy plan of revenge."

Fletcher completed issuing orders and hung up the phone. "They'll check his hotel and call me back."

"Get the Commissioner on the phone, too. Tell him what we've got."

Fletcher started to dial and then stopped, his finger in mid-air. "What *have* we got, Captain?"

> **Suspicions?**
>
> Lieutenant Fletcher says to Leopold, "What *have* we got, Captain?" What, specifically, do you believe they have on Monica and Dr. Thursby? Why was Monica interested in the number of doctors invited to Vicki and Ted's wedding? Who do you think killed Monica, how, and when?

The Commissioner sat behind his desk, openly unhappy at being called to headquarters on a Sunday afternoon, and listened bleakly to what Leopold and Fletcher had to tell him. Finally he spread his fingers on the desktop and said, "The mere fact that this Dr. Thursby seems to have left town is hardly proof of his guilt, Captain. What you're saying is that the woman wasn't killed until later—that Thursby killed her in the ambulance. But how could he have done that with a pistol that was already in Lieutenant Fletcher's possession, tagged as evidence? And how could he have fired the fatal shot without the ambulance attendants hearing it?"

"I don't know," Leopold admitted.

"Heaven knows, Captain, I'm willing to give you every reasonable chance to prove your innocence. But you have to bring me more than a dress with a hole in it."

"All right," Leopold said. "I'll bring you more."

"The grand jury gets the case this week, Captain."

"I know," Leopold said. He turned and left the office, with Fletcher tailing behind.

"What now?" Fletcher asked.

> **Suspicions?**
>
> Try to answer the Commissioner's two questions: How could Dr. Thursby have killed Monica "with a pistol that was already in Lieutenant Fletcher's possession, tagged as evidence?," and "how could he have fired the fatal shot without the ambulance attendants

"We go to talk to Immy Fontaine, my ex-wife's stepbrother."

Though he'd never been friendly with Fontaine, Leopold knew where to find him. The tired man with the gold tooth lived in a big old house overlooking the Sound, where on this summer Sunday they found him in the back yard, cooking hot dogs over a charcoal fire.

He squinted into the sun and said, "I thought you'd be in jail, after what happened."

"I didn't kill her," Leopold said quietly.

"Sure you didn't."

"For a stepbrother you seem to be taking her death right in stride," Leopold observed, motioning toward the fire.

"I stopped worrying about Monica fifteen years ago."

"What about this man she was with? Dr. Thursby?"

Immy Fontaine chuckled. "If he's a doctor, I'm a plumber! He has the fingers of a surgeon, I'll admit, but when I asked him about my son's radius that he broke skiing, Thursby thought it was a leg bone. What the hell, though, I was never one to judge Monica's love life. Remember, I didn't even object when she married you."

"Nice of you. Where's Thursby staying while he's in town?"

"He was at the Towers with Monica."

"He's not there any more."

"Then I don't know where he's at. Maybe he's not even staying for her funeral."

"What if I told you Thursby killed Monica?"

He shrugged. "I wouldn't believe you, but then I wouldn't particularly care. If you were smart you'd have killed her fifteen years ago when she walked out on you. That's what I'd have done."

Leopold drove slowly back downtown, with Fletcher grumbling beside him. "Where are we, Captain? It seems we're just going in circles."

> ### 👁 Suspicions?
>
> How does Immy Fontaine's comment about Dr. Thursby ("If he's a doctor, I'm a plumber! He has the fingers of a surgeon, I'll admit, but when I asked him about my son's radius that he broke skiing, Thursby thought it was a leg bone") give you a clue as to how Monica was shot with a pistol already in Lieutenant Fletcher's possession?

"Perhaps we are, Fletcher, but right now there are still too many questions to be answered. If we can't find Thursby I'll have to tackle it from another direction. The bullet, for instance."

"What about the bullet?"

"We're agreed it could not have been fired by my gun, either while it was in my holster or later, while Thursby was in the ambulance with

Monica. Therefore, it must have been fired earlier. The last time I fired it was at target practise. Is there any possibility—any chance at all—that Thursby or Monica could have gotten one of the slugs I fired into the target?"

Fletcher put a damper on it. "Captain, we were both firing at the same target. No one could sort out those bullets and say which came from your pistol and which from mine. Besides, how would either of them gain access to the basement target range at police headquarters?"

I could have an enemy in the department," Leopold said.

"Nuts! We've all got enemies, but the thing is still impossible. If you believe people in the department are plotting against you, you might as well believe that the entire ballistics evidence was faked."

"It was, somehow. Do you have the comparison photos?"

"They're back at the office. But with the narrow depth of field you can probably tell more from looking through the microscope yourself."

Fletcher drove him to the lab, where they persuaded the Sunday-duty officer to let them have a look at the bullets. While Fletcher and the officer stood by in the interests of propriety, Leopold squinted through the microscope at the twin chunks of lead.

"The death bullet is pretty battered," he observed, but he had to admit that the rifling marks were the same. He glanced at the identification tag attached to the test bullet: *Test slug fired from Smith & Wesson .38 Revolver, serial number 2420547.*

Leopold turned away with a sigh, then turned back.

2420547.

He fished into his wallet and found his pistol permit. *Smith & Wesson 2421622.*

"I remembered those two's on the end," he told Fletcher. "That's not my gun."

"It's the one I took from you, Captain. I'll swear to it!"

"And I believe you, Fletcher. But it's the one fact I needed. It tells me how Dr. Thursby managed to kill Monica in a locked room before my very eyes, with a gun that was in my holster at the time. And it just might tell us where to find the exclusive Dr. Thursby."

Suspicions?

Now that it has been established that the murder weapon was not Leopold's pistol, what do you think this tells Leopold about how Dr. Thursby managed to kill Monica and about where Leopold might find him?

By Monday morning Leopold had made six long-distance calls to California, working from his desk telephone while Fletcher used the squadroom phone. Then, a little before noon, Leopold, Fletcher, the Commissioner, and a man from the District Attorney's office took a car and drove up to Boston.

"You're sure you've got it figured?" the Commissioner asked Leopold for the third time. "You know we shouldn't allow you to cross the state line while awaiting grand jury action."

"Look, either you trust me or you don't," Leopold snapped. Behind the wheel Fletcher allowed himself a slight smile, but the man from the D.A.'s office was deadly serious.

"The whole thing is so damned complicated," the Commissioner grumbled.

"My ex-wife was a complicated woman. And remember, she had fifteen years to plan it."

"Run over it for us again," the D.A.'s man said.

Leopold sighed and started talking. "The murder gun wasn't mine. The gun I pulled after the shot was fired, the one Fletcher took from me, had been planted on me some time before."

"How?"

"I'll get to that. Monica was the key to it all, of course. She hated me so much that her twisted brain planned her own murder in order to get revenge on me. She planned it in such a way that it would have been impossible for anyone but me to have killed her."

"Only a crazy woman would do such a thing."

"I'm afraid she was crazy—crazy for vengeance. She set up the entire plan for the afternoon of the wedding reception, but I'm sure they had an alternate in case I hadn't gone to it. She wanted some place where there'd be lots of witnesses."

"Tell them how she worked the bullet hitting her," Fletcher urged.

"Well, that was the toughest part for me. I actually saw her shot before my eyes. I saw the bullet hit her and I saw the blood. Yet I was alone in a locked room with her. There was no hiding place, no opening from which a person or even a mechanical device could have fired the bullet at her. To you people it seemed I must be guilty, especially when the bullet came from the gun I was carrying.

"But I looked at it from a different angle—once Fletcher forced me to look at it at all! I knew I hadn't shot her, and since no one else physically could have, I knew no one did! If Monica was killed by a .38 slug, it must have been fired *after* she was taken from that locked room. Since she was dead on arrival at the hospital, the most likely time for her murder—to me, at least—became the time of the ambulance ride, when Dr. Thursby must have hunched over her with careful solicitousness."

"But you *saw* her shot!"

"That's one of the two reasons Fletcher and I were on the phones to Hollywood this morning. My ex-wife worked in pictures, at times in the technical end of movie-making. On the screen there are a number of ways to simulate a person being shot. An early method was a sort of compressed-air gun fired at the actor from just off-camera. These days, especially in the bloodiest of the Western and war films, they use a tiny explosive charge fitted under the actor's clothes. Of course the body is protected from burns, and the force of it is directed outward. A pouch of fake blood is released by the explosion, adding to the realism of it."

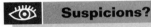

Suspicions?

If Monica was not shot while she was in the locked room with Captain Leopold, explain how he could have seen her shot.

"And this is what Monica did?"

Leopold nodded. "A call to her Hollywood studio confirmed the fact that she worked on a film using this device. I noticed when I met her that she'd gained weight around the bosom, but I never thought to attribute it to the padding and the explosive device. She triggered it when she raised her arm as she screamed at me."

"Any proof?"

"The hole in her dress was just too big to be an entrance hole from a .38, even fired at close range—too big and too ragged. I can thank Fletcher for spotting that. This morning the lab technicians ran a test on the bloodstains. Some of it was her blood, the rest was chicken blood."

"She was a good actress to fool all those people."

"She knew Dr. Thursby would be the first to examine her. All she had to do was fall over when the explosive charge ripped out the front of her dress."

"What if there had been another doctor at the wedding?"

Leopold shrugged. "Then they would have postponed it. They couldn't take that chance."

"And the gun?"

"I remembered Thursby bumping against me when I first met him. He took my gun and substituted an identical weapon—identical, that is, except for the serial number. He'd fired it just a short time earlier, to complete the illusion. When I drew it I simply played into their hands. There I was, the only person in the room with an apparently dying woman, and a gun that had just been fired."

"But what about the bullet that killed her?"

"Rifling marks on the slugs are made by the lands in the rifled barrel of a gun causing grooves in the lead of a bullet. A bullet fired through a smooth tube has no rifling marks."

"What in hell kind of gun has a smooth tube for a barrel?" the Commissioner asked.

"A home-made one, like a zip gun. Highly inaccurate, but quite effective when the gun is almost touching the skin of the victim. Thursby fired a shot from the pistol he was to plant on me, probably into a pillow or some other place where he could retrieve the undamaged slug. Then he reused the rifled slug on another cartridge and fired it with his home-made zip gun, right into Monica's heart. The original rifling marks were still visible and no new ones were added."

"The ambulance driver and attendant didn't hear the shot?"

"They would have stayed up front, since he was a doctor riding with a patient. It gave him a chance to get the padded explosive mechanism off her chest, too. Once that was away, I imagine he leaned over her, muffling the zip gun as best he could, and fired the single shot that killed her. Remember, an ambulance on its way to a hospital is a pretty noisy place—it has a siren going all the time."

They were entering downtown Boston now, and Leopold directed Fletcher to a hotel near the Common. "I still don't believe the part about switching the guns," the D.A.'s man objected. "You mean to tell me he undid the strap over your gun, got out the gun, and substituted another one—all without your knowing it?"

Leopold smiled. "I mean to tell you only one type of person could have managed it—an expert, professional pickpocket. The type you see occasionally doing an act in night clubs and on television. That's how I knew where to find him. We called all over Southern California till we came up with someone who knew Monica and knew she'd dated a man named Thompson who had a pickpocket act. We called Thompson's agent and discovered he's playing a split week at a Boston lounge, and is staying at this hotel."

"What if he couldn't have managed it without your catching on? Or what if you hadn't been wearing your gun?"

"Most detectives wear their guns off-duty. If I hadn't been, or if he couldn't get it, they'd simply have changed their plan. He must have signaled her when he'd safely made the switch."

"Here we are," Fletcher said. "Let's go up."

The Boston police had two men waiting to meet them, and they went up in the elevator to the room registered in the name of Max Thompson. Fletcher knocked on the door, and when it opened the familiar face of Felix Thursby appeared. He no longer wore the mustache, but he had the same slim surgeon-like fingers that Immy Fontaine had noticed. Not a doctor's fingers, but a pickpocket's.

"We're taking you in for questioning," Fletcher said, and the Boston detectives issued the standard warnings of his legal rights.

Thursby blinked his tired eyes at them, and grinned a bit when he recognized Leopold. "She said you were smart. She said you were a smart cop."

"Did you have to kill her?" Leopold asked.

"I didn't. I just held the gun there and she pulled the trigger herself. She did it all herself, except for switching the guns. She hated you that much."

"I know," Leopold said quietly, staring at something far away. "But I guess she must have hated herself just as much."

 ## How Clever?

1. Traditionally, the major question a locked room mystery poses is: How did the criminal get out of the room in which the crime was committed when all the means of escape are either locked or sealed from the inside? For this untraditional—and unconventional—locked room mystery, what is the answer to that question?

2. Explain the details of Monica's "crazy plan" to have herself murdered so that she could get revenge on her former husband. What "method" was there to Monica's "madness"?

3. Although it is a locked room mystery with a twist, "The Leopold Locked Room" is still "an exercise in illusion." How does this story demonstrate that what might "appear" to be impossible can be possible and that "seeing is not always necessarily believing"? Where was Monica's hand, like that of a magician's, "quicker than the eye"?

4. What false assumptions did Lieutenant Fletcher make after he found Captain Leopold in the locked room with the body of his former wife? What did he base those assumptions on?

5. What correct conclusions did Lieutenant Fletcher make from his close examination of Monica's dress?

6. How does the fact that Monica worked in Hollywood "as an extra, and some technical stuff behind the scenes" foreshadow the method by which Monica created the appearance of being shot by Leopold?

7. Just before being introduced to him, Leopold was aware that Dr. Thursby had "jostled against him in the crush of the crowd and hastily apologized." Later, Immy Fontaine comments that Dr. Thursby, while not a doctor, had "the fingers of a surgeon." How do these details provide clues as to how Captain Leopold's gun became the murder weapon?

8. Just before he hears what sounds to him like a gunshot, Leopold sees Monica lift "one arm, as if to shield herself" and hears her cry out, "No! Oh, God, no!" How does this moment provide a clue as to how Monica was able to distract attention and create the illusion that she was shot? How is Monica's illusionary "trick" typical of locked room mysteries?

9. Explain why you think Max Thompson, alias Dr. Thursby, will or will not be charged with murder.

10. Explain why you agree or disagree with the following statement: In "The Leopold Locked Room," Lieutenant Fletcher specializes in doing the detection and Captain Leopold specializes in doing the reflection.

11. How does this story demonstrate the idea that lateral thinking (looking at things from a different angle or perspective) can open the mind to realizations that might get shut out by straight or fixed thinking?

DETECTWRITE: Plot

1. Edward D. Hoch gives the traditional locked room mystery story a twist by placing the victim and the suspect together in a room. What differences does this twist make in the detailing of the plot of a locked room mystery?

2. What difficulties does this twist on the traditional locked room mystery pose for the writer? What opportunities does this twist create for the writer? In your opinion, how well did Hoch overcome the difficulties and capitalize on the opportunities? Explain.

3. For the detective story you would write, would you consider a locked room mystery that had the innocent suspect discovered in the room with the victim? Why or why not?

DETECTWRITE: Characterization and Plot

1. In order for there to be a story other than the simple one of the true criminal caught in the act, the suspect in Hoch's twist on the traditional locked room mystery had to be innocent. However, he did not have to be a police officer.

    How did the author's decision to make the innocent suspect a police officer affect the detailing of the events of the story? Explain why you think the story would have been less effective or more effective if the suspect caught in the locked room had not been a police officer.

2. The acts of detection and reflection involved in this story are generally split between the characters of Lieutenant Fletcher and the accused, Captain Leopold. Did this approach to plotting and characterization add to or detract from your interest in the story? Explain. Why would you consider or reject such a structure in a detective story you might write?

DETECTWRITE: Setting

1. In what ways does the choice of the accordioned-off locked room in this story fulfill the traditional requirements of a locked room mystery? In what ways is this particular locked room different or unique? In your opinion, did these ways add to or detract from the appeal of the story? Explain.

2. Honoring the conventions (requirements) of the plot of any locked room mystery, choose a "room" of your own, and explain how it lends itself to becoming "a locked room." Then write either the opening to the story set in that room or the scene in that locked room during which the murder takes place.

No One Likes to Be Played for a Sucker

Michael Collins

IT CAN BE A MISTAKE TO BE TOO SMART. DEVIOUSNESS TAKES real practice, judgment of human nature as fine as a hair, and something else—call it ice. The ice a person has inside.

Old Tercio Osso came to me with his suspicions on a Thursday morning. That alone showed his uneasiness. Old Tercio hadn't been out of his Carmine Street office in the morning for twenty years—not even for a relative's funeral.

"Business don't come and find you," Tercio pronounced regularly.

Osso & Vitanza, Jewelry, Religious Supplies, and Real Estate, and if you wanted to do business with Tercio, or pay your rent, you went to his office in the morning. In the afternoon Tercio presided in his corner at the Mazzini Political Club—a little cards, a little boccie out back.

Lean old Cology Vitanza, Tercio's partner of thirty years, reversed the procedure, and at night they both held down the office—thieves struck at night on Carmine Street, and there was safety in numbers.

It was Cology Vitanza that old Tercio came to me about.

"We got troubles, Mr. Fortune. I think Cology he makes plans."

The old man sat like a solemn frog on my one extra chair. He wore his usual ancient black suit, white shirt, and black tie with its shiny knot so small it looked as if it had been tied under pressure. The shabbiness of my one-room office did not bother Tercio. On Carmine Street, no matter how much cash a businessman has in various banks, he knows the value of a shabby front: it gives the poor confidence that a man is like them.

"What kind of plans?"

Tercio shrugged. "Business it's not good. We make some big mistakes. The stock market, buildings not worth so much as we pay, inventory that don't sell."

"I didn't know you made mistakes, Mr. Osso."

"So?" Tercio said. "Maybe I'm old. Vitanza he's old. We lose the touch, the neighborhood it's change. The new people they don't buy what we got. Maybe we been playin' too much boccie, sit around tellin' too many stories from the old days."

"All right," I said. "What plans do you figure Vitanza is making?"

Tercio folded his plump hands in his broad lap. "For six year Cology he got no wife. He got ten kids what got lotsa kids of their own. We both gettin' old. We got insurance, big. We talk about what we do next year and after and we don't think the same, so? Then I see Cology talking to people."

"What kind of insurance have you got?"

"On the inventory, on both of us, for the partners."

I sat back in the gray light from my one window that opens on the air shaft. "You're saying you think Vitanza is making plans to collect on the insurance?"

"I see him talk to Sid Nelson yesterday. Three days ago he drinks coffee alone with Don Primo."

Don Primo Veronese was a lawyer, a member of the Mazzini Club, and, by strong rumor, a fence for small hoods. Sid Nelson was a hood, not small but not big—sort of in between. A thief, a killer, and a careful operator.

"You and Vitanza talk to a lot of people."

"Sure, I talk to Don Primo myself," Tercio agreed. "I don't talk to no Sid Nelson. I don't say we should make a special inventory. I don't take big money from the bank, put in envelope, carry in my pocket. I don't go to mass five times in one week."

"What do you want me to do, Mr. Osso?"

A slow shrug. "In winter the wolf comes to the streets of the city. The old lion he got to learn new tricks or starve. Maybe I'm crazy, okay. Only you watch Cology. You be a detective."

"That's my work," I said. "All right, a hundred in advance."

"A horse works on hay," Tercio said, and counted out two nice crisp fifties. "You tell me nine o'clock every night."

After old Tercio had gone, I rubbed at the stump of my missing arm, then phoned Lieutenant Marx at the precinct. I told him Tercio's story.

"What do you want me to do?" Marx said.

"I don't know," I said. "Tell me that Tercio Osso is a smart old man."

"Tercio is a smart old man," Marx said. "All I can do is stand by, Dan.

At least until you get something that can be called reasonable suspicion."

"I know," I said.

"You can check out most of it," Marx pointed out.

That's what I did. I checked out old Osso's story.

It checked. Other people had seen Cology Vitanza talking to Don Primo Veronese, and, especially, to Sid Nelson. The firm of Osso & Vitanza was in trouble—cash tied up, notes overdue, interest not paid, a few bad deals the other Carmine Street financiers were grinning about, and the jewelry stock not moving at all.

Vitanza had been going to mass almost every day. He had withdrawn five thousand dollars in cash. (A teller I knew, and ten bucks, got me that information.) I had to take Tercio Osso's word about the special inventory of the unmoving stock, but I was sure it would turn out to be true.

I began tailing Cology Vitanza. It wasn't a hard tail. The tall old man was easy to follow and a man of routine. He never took me out of the ten-square-block area of Little Italy. I reported to Osso every night at nine o'clock by telephone.

On Friday I spotted Vitanza talking again to Sid Nelson. The hoodlum seemed interested in what Vitanza had to say.

I ate a lot of spaghetti and drank a lot of wine for two days. I saw one bad movie, and visited the homes of twenty old men. That is, Vitanza visited and I lurked outside in the cold, getting more bored every minute. I wore out my knees kneeling at the back of a dim church.

But I was there in the Capri Tavern at six o'clock Saturday night when Vitanza stopped to talk to a seedy-looking character in a rear booth. A white envelope passed from Vitanza to the seedy type. I waited until the new man downed his glass of wine and ambled out. Then I switched to tailing him.

I followed the seedy man through Little Italy and across to the East Side. He looked around a lot, and did all kinds of twists and turns, as if he figured he might be followed. That made it hard work, but I kept up with him. He finally headed for the Bowery.

A block south of Houston he suddenly ducked into a wino joint. I sprinted and went in, but he was out the back way and gone. I went around through the alleys and streets of the Bowery for another hour trying to pick up his trail, but I had no luck.

I went back to Carmine Street to find Cology Vitanza. He wasn't at the Mazzini Club, and neither was Osso. I tried their other haunts and didn't find them. The lights were on behind the curtained windows of the shop and office on Carmine Street, but I couldn't go in without tipping my hand, so I took up a stakeout.

Nothing happened for half an hour. Then some people tried to get into the store, but the front door was locked. That wasn't right for a Saturday night. It was almost nine o'clock by then. I made my call to Osso from a booth where I could watch the front door of the store. There was no answer, so I called Lieutenant Marx.

"I don't like how it sounds," Marx said. "Too bad you lost that Bowery character. I've done some checking on their insurance. They've got fifty thousand dollars on the inventory, twenty-five thousand dollars life on each payable to the other, and fifty thousand dollars surviving-partner insurance with option to buy out the heirs."

"A nice haul," I said. "What do we do?"

"Sid Nelson hasn't moved. I put a man on him for you."

"The commissioner wouldn't like that."

"The commissioner won't know," Marx said, and then was silent a few seconds. "We've got no cause to bust in yet."

"And if nothing's wrong we tip off Vitanza."

"But they shouldn't be locked up on Saturday night," Marx said. "The patrolman on the beat ought to be suspicious."

"I guess he ought to," I said.

"I'll be right over," Marx said.

Marx arrived with two of his squad inside three minutes. He'd picked up the beat patrolman on the way. I joined them at the door to the store. We couldn't see anything through the curtains.

"Pound the door and give a call," Marx instructed the beat patrolman.

The patrolman pounded and called out. Nothing happened. Marx chewed his lip and looked at me. Then, as if from far off, we heard a voice. It was from somewhere inside the store, and it was calling for help.

"I guess we go in," Marx said.

He kicked in the glass of the door and reached inside for the lock.

At first we saw nothing wrong in the jewelry store. Then Marx pointed to the showcases where the expensive jewelry was kept. They were unlocked and empty.

In the office in the back a rear window was open. A man lay on the floor in a pool of not-quite-dry blood. A .38-caliber automatic was on the floor about five feet from the body, toward the right wall of the office. There was a solid door in the right wall, and behind it someone was knocking and calling, "What's happen out there? Hey, who's out there?"

Marx and I looked at each other as one of his men bent over the body on the floor. It was not Tercio Osso, it was Cology Vitanza. Marx's second man swung the door of the safe open. It had been closed but not locked.

It was empty.

Marx went to the solid door. "Who's in there?"

"Osso! He knock me out, lock me in. What's happen?"

Marx studied the door. There was no key in the lock. I went and searched the dead man. I shook my head at Marx—no key. One of Marx's men pointed to the floor.

"There."

The key was on the floor not far from the gun. I picked it up. It was one of those common old house keys, rough and rusted, and there would be no prints. Marx took the key and opened the door.

Tercio Osso blinked at us. "Mr. Fortune, Lieutenant. Where's Cology, he—"

Osso stepped out into the office and saw his dead partner. He just stood and stared. Nothing happened to his face. I watched him. If anything had shown on his face I would have been surprised. Everyone knew he was a tough old man.

"So," he said, nodding, "he kill Cology. It figure. The crazy old man. Crazy."

"You want to tell us what happened?" Marx said.

"Sure, sure," the old man said. He walked to his desk and sat down heavily. I saw a trickle of blood over his left ear. He looked at Vitanza's body. "He come in maybe hour, two hours ago. What time is it?"

"Nine-twenty," Marx said.

"That long?" Osso said. "So two hours since. Seven-thirty, maybe. One guy. He comes in the front. I go out to see. He got a mask and a gun. He push me back to office, me and Cology. He makes us go lock the front door, clean out the cases and then the safe. He work fast. He shove me in storeroom, knock me out."

The old man touched his head, winced. "I wake up, I don't know what time. I listen. Nothing, no noise. I listen long time, I don't want him to come back for me. Nothing happen. I hear phone ring. So I start yelling. Then I hear you bust in."

Osso looked around. "He got it all, huh? Out the window. Only he don't keep the deal, no. Cology is crazy man. A guy like that don't keep no deals."

There was a long silence in the office. Sirens were growing in the cold night air outside as the police began to arrive at Marx's summons. Marx was chewing his lip and looking at me. I looked at Osso.

"You're telling us you figure Vitanza hired a guy to rob the store for the insurance, and then the guy killed him? Why?"

Osso shrugged. "Who know? Maybe the guy don't want to split with Cology. Maybe the guy figures the jewels is worth more than a cut of the insurance. They fight, Cology's dead. How do I know, I'm locked inside the storeroom."

The assistant medical examiner arrived, the fingerprint team, and two men from Safe and Loft. I went into the storeroom. It was small and windowless. There was no other door. The walls were white and clean, and the room was piled with lumber, cans, tools, and assorted junk. I found a small stain of blood on the floor near the door. The walls seemed solid.

When I went back out, Marx's men had finished marking the locations of the body, the gun, and the key. The ME stood up and motioned to his men to bring their basket.

"Shot twice in the back," the ME said. "Two hours ago, maybe more, maybe a little less. Rigor is just starting. He's a skinny old man. Died pretty quick, I'd say. The slugs are still in him—thirty-eight caliber looks about right."

"The gun's been fired twice," one of Marx's men said, "not long ago."

"Prints all over the place, all kinds," the fingerprint man said. "It won't be easy to lift them clean."

Marx growled. "Prints won't help. What about you Safe and Loft guys?"

A Safe and Loft man said, "Rear window opened from inside. Some marks on the sill could have been a man climbing out. The yard is all concrete, no traces, but we found this."

The Safe and Loft man held up a child's rubber Halloween mask. Marx looked at it sourly.

"They all use that trick now. The movies and TV tell them how to do everything," Marx said, and came over to me. He lit a cigarette. "Well, Dan?"

"Everything fits," I said. "Just about what I was supposed to figure that Vitanza was planning—except for his killing."

"Neat," Marx said.

"Too neat," I said. "Let's talk to Osso."

While his men and the experts went on working, Marx took Osso into the storeroom. I went with them. The old man watched us with cold, black eyes.

"This is just what you expected when you went to Fortune," Marx said to the old man.

"I got a hunch," Osso said.

"What does Cology figure on getting out of it, Tercio?" I said. "The insurance on the stock, no more. Maybe he figures on keeping most of the jewels, too, okay. But figure what you get out of it. You get the whole works—stock insurance, life insurance on Cology, partnership insurance, option to buy it all."

"So?" Osso said, watched me.

"So if Cology was going to set up a risky deal like this it ought to be you who's dead, not him. The thief should have killed you and knocked Cology out. Then there's a big pie to split with Cology."

"You think I set this up?"

I nodded. "It smells, Tercio. We're supposed to figure that Vitanza hired a punk to fake a holdup, but not kill you when there was more riding on you than on the stock? Then the hired hood kills Cology for some reason and leaves his gun here on the floor? Leaves his mask out in the yard to prove he was here? Leaves the key on the floor so we know you were locked in?"

Osso shrugged. "You figure I set it up, take me down and book me. I call my lawyer. You find the guy I hire. You do that. I tell the truth. I hire no one, you won't find no one. I'm inside the storeroom, so how I kill Cology?"

Marx said, "It's too neat, Osso. You practically told Fortune how it was going to happen."

"So book me. I get my lawyer. You find the man I hire." And the old man smiled. "Or maybe you figure I kill from inside locked room?"

Marx snapped, "Take the old man down, book him on suspicion. Go over the place with a vacuum cleaner. Send anything you find to Technical Services."

They took Osso. Marx followed and I left with him.

The police had gone, except for a patrolman posted at the broken door in front, when I jimmied the back window and went in. I dropped into the dark office and flicked on my flashlight. I focused the beam on the marks that showed where the gun, the key, and the body had been.

I heard the steps too late. The lights went on, and I turned from pure reflex. I never carry a gun, and if I'd had a gun I couldn't have pulled it with my flash still in my lone hand. I was glad I didn't have a gun. I might have shot by reflex, and it was Lieutenant Marx in the doorway. That's the trouble with a gun, you tend to depend on it if you have one.

Suspicions?

1. Do you agree with one-armed private investigator Dan Fortune and precinct lieutenant Marx that Tercio Osso's explanation of the death of his partner, Cology Vitanza, is "neat," in fact, "too neat"? Why or why not?

2. Marx has Osso taken downtown and booked for murder despite Osso's challenge: "You find the man I hire. Or maybe you figure I kill from inside locked room." What do you make of Osso's challenge? Explain your thoughts about it.

I said, "You, too, Lieutenant?"

"What's your idea?" Marx said.

"The old man's too confident," I said. "He damn near begged you to book him on suspicion of having hired a man to fake the robbery and kill Vitanza."

"Yeah," Marx said, "he did. You think he didn't hire anyone?"

I nodded. I didn't like it, but unless Cology Vitanza had set it up after all, which I didn't believe, there had to be another answer. Marx didn't like it either.

"You know what that gives us," Marx said.

"I know," I said, "but Tercio's too smart to hire a killer and have a monkey on his back the rest of his life. No, he'd do it himself."

"You got more than a hunch, Dan?"

"The gun," I said. "It's the flaw in the setup. It sticks out. A thief who kills takes his gun away with him. Osso would know that."

"So?"

"So the gun being in the office has to be the clue to the answer," I said. "It was here because Osso couldn't do anything else with it. The jewels are gone, the mask was out in the yard, the front door was locked on the inside out in the shop. If Osso had had a choice he'd have taken the gun away and the key too. He didn't. Why?"

Marx rubbed his jaw. "So if he did it, it reads like this: He took the ice and stashed it. He planted the mask and left the rear window open. He killed Vitanza, and then he got into that storeroom and somehow locked himself in with the key outside and a long way from the door."

"Yes and no," I said. "If he killed Vitanza *before* he got into that room, he could have disposed of the gun to make it look more like an outside killer. He didn't. So he must have killed Vitanza from *inside* the locked storeroom."

"And then got the gun and key out?"

"That's it," I said.

Marx nodded. "Let's find it."

We went to work. The locked room is an exercise in illusion—a magician's trick. Otherwise it's impossible, and the impossible can't be done, period. Since it *had* been done, it must be a trick, a matter of distracting attention, and once you know what you're really looking for, the answer is never hard.

Suspicions?

1. Review and react to Dan Fortune's remark that the gun is "the flaw in the setup" and that its being in the office "has to be the clue to the answer."

2. What do you think of Lieutenant Marx's summary of how Osso committed the crime "if he did it"? Explain.

3. What do you think of Dan Fortune's "yes and no" reaction and explanation? Explain.

When we had dismissed the distraction—the hired robber and killer theory—the rest was just a matter of logic. I sighted along the line from the body to the seemingly solid wall. The line pointed directly to a light fixture set in the wall. Sighting the other way, the line led to Vitanza's desk and telephone.

"Vitanza came in," I said. "Osso was already inside the locked room. Vitanza went to his desk. He probably always did that, and Osso could count on it. Or maybe he saw that the jewels were gone and went to his desk to telephone the police. Osso probably knew he would be sure to do that, too. They'd been partners thirty years."

"And Osso had to shoot him in the back," Marx said. "The desk faces the other way."

"Let's look at that light fixture," I said.

It was one of those small modern wall lamps with a wide circular metal base. It had been attached to the wall recently and was not painted over. The wall behind it sounded hollow, but we could not move the lamp.

"It doesn't come off, Dan," Marx said.

"Not from this side," I said.

We went into the storeroom. I measured off from the door to exactly where the light fixture was attached on the other side of the wall. We studied the wall. The whole wall had been recently painted. The cans of quick-drying paint were among the litter in the storeroom. On the floor there were a few crumbs of dried plaster.

"Quick-drying plaster," I said to Marx.

Marx found a hammer and chisel in the storeroom. There were flecks of plaster on the chisel. He opened a hole directly behind the light fixture. It opened easily. The back of the light fixture was clearly visible about two inches in, between vertical two-by-fours. The fixture had a metal eye on the back. It was held in place by a metal bar that passed through the eye and was angled to catch the two-by-fours.

"That's it," I said. "Simple and clever."

Marx had two hands. He reached in with his left, turned the metal bar, and held the fixture. He pushed the fixture out and to the left and aimed his pistol through the hole with his right hand. He had a clear shot at the desk five feet away—in direct line with where the body of Cology Vitanza had fallen.

I said, "He had this hole open on this side. He heard Vitanza come in and head for the desk. He pushed out the fixture. It didn't matter if Vitanza heard or not—Osso was ready, didn't care if he hit Vitanza front or back. He shot Vitanza, tossed the gun and key through the hole, pulled the fixture back and re-fastened it, plastered up the hole, and painted the wall. He knew no one would break in until after I called at nine o'clock. He hid here and waited."

I shook my head in admiration for the old man. "If we believe that Vitanza had set it up, fine, we'd be looking for a nonexistent thief and killer. If we think Osso hired a man, fine, too. We're still looking for a nonexistent thief and killer, and in a few weeks Osso cleans up this storeroom, and the new plaster sets so it can't be told from the old plaster. Maybe he fixes the light fixture so it's permanent in the wall. All the evidence is gone, and he's in the clear."

"Only now the lab boys should be able to prove some of the plaster is newer," Marx said, "the fixture moves out, and the evidence is in this room. We've got the old bastard."

Marx called in Captain Gazzo of Homicide. Gazzo took it to Chief of Detectives McGuire, who got a judge to order the office and storeroom sealed. The DA would want the jury to see the office and storeroom just as they were when Vitanza was killed.

I gave my statement, Marx made his report, and Gazzo faced the old man with it. Osso was a tough old bird.

"I want my lawyer," Osso said.

He got his lawyer, they booked the old man, and I went home to bed. I felt good. I don't get many locked rooms to play with, so I was pleased with myself.

Until morning.

"It's not the gun," Captain Gazzo said.

I was in Gazzo's office. So was Marx. Gazzo held the .38 automatic that had been on the office floor—the gun that had been the tip-off, the weak link, the key to it all.

"This gun didn't kill Vitanza," Gazzo said. "Ballistics just reported. Vitanza was killed with a thirty-eight, yes, but not this one."

I said nothing. Neither did Marx.

"A locked room," Gazzo said sarcastically. "Great work, boys. Clever, very clever."

I said it at the start: it can be a mistake to be too smart. A locked-room murder is an illusionist's trick, a matter of the misdirection of attention. And the one who had been too smart was me.

"All he threw out was the key," I said. "That was all he had to throw out all along. The rest was to distract us."

Suspicions?

1. What do you think of the solution to the locked room mystery that Dan Fortune and Lieutenant Marx have come up with? What evidence supports it? How?

2. What evidence, if any, has you still wondering? Explain.

3. What does the two-word paragraph "Until morning" lead you to expect? Why?

There had never been any reason why Osso had to kill from inside the storeroom, only that he lock himself in from the inside and get the key out. The whole locked room had been a trick to distract us. A gun on the floor by a dead man. The right caliber gun fired recently and the right number of times. Who would dream it was the wrong gun?

"The key now," Gazzo said. "First he's brought in on suspicion of having hired a man to fake a robbery and kill his partner. Next he's booked for having killed his partner from inside a locked room with a trick scheme. Now he killed his partner outside the room, switched guns, locked himself in, and tossed the key out. What next?"

"He killed Vitanza," Marx said. "I'm sure he did."

"I'm sure too," Gazzo agreed, "but what jury will believe us now with the speech his lawyer'll make about dumb cops and police persecution? You guys like fairy tales? How do you like the one about the boy who cried wolf? The DA is bawling on his desk thinking about facing a jury against Osso now."

"We'll find out what he did," Marx said. "We'll find the right gun and the jewels."

"Sure we will," Gazzo said. "Some day."

"And I bet it won't do us any good," I said.

It didn't. Three days after the killing the superintendent of a cheap rooming house on the Lower East Side reported that a tenant hadn't come out of his room for three days. The police broke in and found the man dead. It was the seedy character I had followed and lost.

He had been shot in the shoulder. The bullet was still in the wound. But that was not what had killed him. He had died from drinking whiskey with lye in it. The bottle was in the room. The police found some of the missing jewels in the room, but not all. They also found a .38-caliber automatic that had been fired twice.

"It's the gun that killed Vitanza," Ballistics reported.

"Only the bum's prints on the gun," Fingerprinting said.

"It's certain he died four or five hours *after* Vitanza died," the ME said. "The bad whiskey killed him. He might have been unconscious most of the time, but after three days we'll never prove it. He lost blood from that shoulder wound."

Ballistics then added the final touch. "The bullet in the bum's shoulder came from the gun you found on the floor of Osso and Vitanza's office. The gun was registered to Cology Vitanza himself."

With my statement and report on what I had observed Cology Vitanza do, on the actions Osso had reported and I had checked out, the evidence logically added up to only one story: the seedy character had been hired by Cology Vitanza to rob the jewelry store. For some reason there had been a fight while Osso was unconscious in the locked room. (Osso stated he had plastered the hole in the storeroom the day before. With the evidence against the bum his story was better than Marx's and mine.)

Vitanza had wounded the bum, and the bum had killed Vitanza. Then the wounded bum had run for his room with the loot but hid some of it on the way. In his room, weak from his wound, he had drunk the bad whiskey, passed out, and died. It was just the way a wounded bum would die.

I had a different story. The day after they dropped all charges against Tercio Osso I went to his office. He didn't try to evade me.

"I owe you a couple days and expenses," Osso said.

"You hired me in the first place just to make me and Marx suspicious," I said. "You figured I'd talk to the police and you knew we'd suspect a trick. You wanted us to accuse you right away of hiring someone to kill Vitanza."

Osso said nothing.

"You arranged all those suspicious acts of Vitanza's. It wouldn't have been hard. You were partners, old friends, and he'd do anything you asked him to do if you said it was business. You asked him to talk to Sid Nelson about something innocent, to take out five thousand dollars in cash for you, to meet the bum with a note, even to go to a lot of masses."

The old man was like a fat black frog in the chair.

"You played us like trout. It was too easy and not smart for you to have hired a killer. We were sure to look for more. That's when you handed us the locked room and the gun on the floor."

Osso smiled.

"That gun would have made any cop wonder, and you expected us to figure out the locked-room trick. You wanted us to charge you with it, and you wanted time. You needed at least a few hours to be sure the bum was dead, and the locked room would keep us nice and busy for at least a few hours."

The old man began to light a thin black cigar.

"You killed Vitanza while I was tailing the bum. You took the jewels, locked up, went out the back window. You went to the bum's room and

> ### ◉ Suspicions?
>
> Before Fortune gives his explanation of how the crime was committed and by whom, you try. Be sure to identify the criminal, state the motive, and detail in chronological order and in narrative form the steps taken in committing the crime.

filled him with the bad whiskey, then shot him with Vitanza's gun. A wound that would bleed but not kill.

"Then you planted the gun that had killed Vitanza in the bum's room with some of the jewels. You knew no one would look for the bum for days. You went back to the office and laid out Vitanza. You put the gun that had shot the bum on the office floor. You locked yourself in the storeroom from the inside and tossed out the key through the light fixture hole in the wall.

"Then you sat back and led me and Marx into being too smart for our own good. You got the time you needed. You kept us away from the bum until it was too late. You've got what you were after, and you're safe." I stopped and looked at the old man. "One thing I want to know, Osso. Why did you pick me?"

Old Tercio Osso blew smoke and looked solemn. He shrugged. He took the black stogie from his mouth and studied it. Then he laughed aloud.

"You got one arm," Osso said, grinned at me. "You're easy to spot. I got to know where you are all the time to make it work, see? I got to make it easy for that bum to spot you and lead you a chase before he loses you. And I got to make it easy for the man watching you all the time."

"You had a man watching me?"

"Sure, what else? Good man, a relative, never talk." Osso studied his cigar some more. "You got good friends on the cops, and you're a real smart man, see? I mean, I know you figure out that locked room."

And Osso laughed again. He was very pleased with his shenanigans. I said nothing, just stared at him. He studied me.

"I got to do it, see?" Osso said at last. "I'm in trouble. Vitanza he don't agree with me no more. He was gonna ruin me if I don't stop him. So I stop him. And I fix it so you smart guys outsmart yourselves."

I stood up. "That's okay, Osso. You see, you made the same mistake Marx and I made."

"So?" he said, his black eyes narrowing.

"That's right. You forgot other people can be as smart as you. You fixed it good so that no one can prove in court what you did. But you made it too good. Everyone knows you did it. You made it too complicated, Osso. You're the only one who could have worked it all. What I figured out, and just told you, I also told Vitanza's ten kids, and the members of the Mazzini Club. They're smart, too."

"I kill you too!" Osso croaked.

"You couldn't get away with it twice, not with everyone knowing what you did. You're too smart to try. Bad odds, and you always play the odds."

I left him chewing his lip, his shrewd mind working fast. Who knows, he's a smart man, and maybe he'll still get away with it. But I doubt it. As

I said, other men are smart, too, and Vitanza's kids and the Mazzini Club boys believed the story I had figured out.

I read the newspapers carefully now. I'm waiting for a small item about an old man named Tercio Osso being hit by a truck, or found in the river drowned by accident, or maybe the victim of an unfortunate food poisoning in a restaurant that just happens to be run by a member of the Mazzini Club.

Nothing fancy or complicated this time, just a simple, everyday accident. Of course, everyone will know what really happened, but no one will ever prove it. Whoever gets Tercio Osso won't even have to be particularly careful. A reasonably believable accident will do the trick.

After all, we're all human and have a sense of justice, and no one likes to be played for a sucker.

 ## How Clever?

1. Review pages 197 and 198. State Osso's motive. Then explain—in detail—how he outsmarted private investigator Dan Fortune and police lieutenant Marx.

2. If Osso did not outsmart you as you read the story and noted, tracked, and analyzed the clues, explain in detail how and why certain clues that were intended to distract and mislead you did not.

3. What aspect of Dan Fortune's physical condition was Osso able to put to use for his own purposes? Explain how he did that.

4. What aspect of Dan Fortune's character both as a person and as a private investigator did Osso understand so well that he was able to put it to use for his own purposes? Explain how he did that.

5. Re-read the opening paragraph of the story. Which parts of it apply to Dan Fortune? Which parts apply to Tercio Osso? Which parts apply to both of them? Explain your responses.

6. Re-read what Osso tells Fortune and Marx on page 192. How has Osso so carefully selected his words ("I hire no one, you won't find no one. I'm inside the storeroom, so how I kill Cology?") that he actually winds up telling Fortune and Marx what we later discover is absolutely true?

7. When Osso smiles and says, "Or maybe you figure I kill from inside the locked room?," how has he cleverly planted a distracting idea in Fortune's mind? Toward the end of the story, what specific reasons do we learn for Osso's doing this?

8. When Fortune concludes that "the gun being in the office has to be the clue to the answer," does this statement function as a red herring (misleading clue) in the story? Explain.

9. How do the following observations serve as both red herrings and authentic clues in the story?

   a. "On the floor there were a few crumbs of dried plaster."

   b. "There were flecks of plaster on the chisel."

   c. "He opened a hole directly behind the light fixture. It opened easily."

10. Re-read Fortune's summation of the case on page 194. Explain the "admiration" he says he feels for Osso. How smart does Fortune feel at this moment? Why?

11. Re-read Fortune's next summation of the case. Compare it with both his earlier summation and what he said before about the gun. Why is Fortune now certain that "there had never been any reason why Osso had to kill from inside the storeroom, only that he lock himself in from the inside and get the key out"? How and why did Fortune initially miss the logic of this in his reasoning?

12. Fortune points out that "the evidence logically added up to only one story." However, that story is not the truth of what happened. Explain how something can be "logical" but not "true."

13. There is "logical" and there is "psychological." Explain how Osso's understanding of the psychological enabled him to get Fortune to reason logically and miss the truth.

14. Explain how Fortune's understanding of the psychological enabled him to create a situation in which justice would triumph and Osso would be punished for his crime.

15. What reason does Fortune have for believing that Osso wound up being so smart as to outsmart himself?

16. Explain the meaning of the title "No One Likes to Be Played for a Sucker" and its relevance to the plot and characters of the story.

DETECTWRITE: Characterization

1. Dan Fortune has a physical condition—only one complete arm—that makes him stand out and a character trait—pride in feeling smart and not liking to be outsmarted and played for a sucker—that helps to define him. Think about the detective you might create for a series of mystery stories and then choose certain physical and psychological attributes that do the following:

   a. define him or her as a particular kind of person

   b. cause him or her to be noticeable, distinctive, remarkable

   c. contribute to or affect the special way he or she goes about solving crimes

2. Create a verbal portrait (picture in words) of your detective in which his or her uniqueness as a person and as a crime solver is apparent to the reader.

DETECTWRITE: Plot

1. Which aspects of the plot of "No One Like to Be Played for a Sucker" follow the conventions of a locked room mystery?
2. Which aspects of the plot follow the conventions of a private investigator crime story?
3. Which aspects follow the conventions of a police procedural?
4. How did the author combine all three of these kinds of detective stories into a story that the reader could follow, understand, appreciate, and enjoy?

DETECTWRITE: Setting

1. Compare the setting for this locked room mystery (which turns out to not be a locked room mystery after all!) with the settings for the other stories in this section. What generalizations can you make about the settings for locked room mysteries?
2. Compare and contrast the New York City setting of "No One Likes to Be Played for a Sucker" with the New York City settings of "Out the Window" or "The Sound of Murder," elsewhere in this collection. How did the "locked room" aspects of "No One Likes to Be Played for a Sucker" affect its use of its New York City setting? How did the fact that the story is not really a locked room mystery (or more than a locked room mystery) also affect how its New York City setting was used?

The Impossible Theft

John F. Suter

ROBERT CHISHOLM'S PALMS WERE FAINTLY DAMP. HE HAD less confidence in his ability to persuade than in the probability of his accomplishing the theft. Still, he hoped that theft would be unnecessary.

Donald Tapp looked up at him sardonically as he turned the second key to the double-locked room.

"Robert," he said in a voice that had been hoarse all his life, "you still haven't told me how you found out about my collection."

Chisholm's shrug was the smooth, practiced action of a man who knows and controls every muscle. He permitted his smile to be open and frank, instead of the faintly diabolical one which his lean face wore on certain occasions.

"I told you," he said. "A mutual friend. He just doesn't want to be identified."

Tapp reached around the metal doorframe and pressed a switch. Fluorescent lights hesitated, blinked, then came on.

He pursed his thick lips. "Mutual friend? I don't advertise what I own. There is always a clamor to have such items as these placed in a museum. Time enough for that when I'm dead." He studied Chisholm quizzically. "Would it have been Perry?"

Chisholm became poker-faced. "Sorry, Don."

Tapp still waited before ushering him into the room.

"Robert, I haven't seen you in—how many years? Even though we played together as boys and went to school together—clear through college. Now you arrive in town for a convention and after all these years you look me up. I'm delighted, Robert, delighted. I don't see old friends much any more. Chiefly my own fault. But, Robert, you arrive and make small talk and then, in the middle of it, you ask to see the collection."

Chisholm said, just a shade too casually, "If you'd rather not—"

Ask yourself, Don, he thought; *when you were a kid and somebody asked, "Whatcha got?" you'd always hide it, make a big secret of it.*

Tapp stepped away from the door, lifting a stubby right hand. "Come in and look. I'll be honest and say I'm particular. Not everybody can get into this room. But you're an old friend. At least, you were never grabby like the other kids."

If you only knew, Chisholm thought, entering the strongroom which Tapp devoted to his collection of rare historical documents.

It was a windowless room, about 12 feet by 20, lighted only by two rows of fluorescent tubes overhead. The only door was at the end of one long wall. To the left, on entering, the wall was decorated with a large rectangular mirror in a gilded frame. The borders of the glass itself were worked in elaborate scrolls and tracery. Ranged against the two long walls and the far end of the room were nine exhibition cases, four along each wall, one at the end. The cases were of beautifully grained wood, with glass tops.

Tapp beckoned Chisholm across the room.

"We'll begin here." He snapped a switch on the side of one cabinet, and the interior became evenly illuminated, showing a frayed yellowed paper on a background of black velvet.

As Chisholm bent his lean shoulders to look at the descriptive card, Tapp began to explain, "The last page of a letter by James Garfield. Identity of recipient unknown, but signature authenticated. Can you read it? It says, *As to your wish that I make a Fourth of July address in your community, this would give me the greatest of pleasure. I must defer my answer, however, because I feel that there is some prior commitment which I cannot identify at this moment. Should this prove to be only faulty memory, I shall be pleased to accept* . . . Of course, when you realize this was written just prior to that fatal July 2, it makes for interesting speculation, doesn't it?"

As Chisholm murmured an appropriate reply, Tapp switched off the light and moved to the right. "In this cabinet I have a receipt from William Tecumseh Sherman to Braxton Bragg for money that Bragg asked Sherman to invest for him in San Francisco in 1854, when Sherman was in the banking business. The accompanying letters have great historical significance."

Chisholm stared with a fascination he did not need to pretend as Tapp led him from case to case, showing him exceptionally valuable documents signed by George Washington, Abraham Lincoln, Andrew Johnson, Alexander Graham Bell, John C. Fremont, William H. Seward, and Carry Nation. This last name brought a chuckle from Tapp.

"Simple, isn't it? *No truce with Demon Rum! Carry Nation.*"

He snapped off the light in the eighth case and turned toward the last one, at the end of the room. He paused and glanced at Chisholm.

"Robert, what was it you told me you were doing these days?"

"Area man for Shaw and Pontz Lock Company." Chisholm reached toward his left lapel with supple, slender fingers and tapped the identity tag which was stuck to his coat by the adhesive on the back of the tag. "The convention is one of hardware dealers. I'm showing a new line of passage sets."

Tapp shrugged off a faint air of perplexity. "Well! Let's look at my prize exhibit." He illuminated the last cabinet.

In it lay a scrap of paper no bigger than the palm of the average-sized hand. It was even more yellowed than the other documents, the ink slightly more faded. It was charred along the top edge.

Tapp said nothing. Chisholm bent to look closely.

"Some kind of register or ledger?"

"That's right. From an inn."

"Three names. James—Allen? Samuel Green. That one's clear. But— *Button Gwinnett?*"

Tapp rubbed his stubborn chin with his solid-fleshed left hand. The tip of his broad nose wrinkled in amusement.

"You're amazed, Robert. Yes, the rarest of all signatures in United States history. Your amazement is justified. But it's genuine, I assure you—absolutely genuine."

"But how did you—? Where did you—?"

Tapp shook his head. "When I am dead, all information on these documents will be released to the museum which will inherit them. In the meantime, that information is my secret."

Chisholm glanced around the room. "I hope you have these well protected. And adequately insured."

"Both, you may be sure."

"What protection, Don? This interests me, since I'm in the lock business." He bent over the case containing the Button Gwinnett signature.

"I'm satisfied with it," said Tapp bluntly.

"Are you?" Chisholm drew a key ring from his pocket. It bristled with keys—and other odd-looking objects. His supple fingers gripped something which Tapp could not see, and he inserted it quickly into the lock on the edge of the glass top. Something clicked and he lifted the lid of the case. "You see?"

Instantly a clamor began somewhere in the big house.

"I see. And do you hear?" Tapp gave his old friend an exasperated look. "Come on. I'll have to shut off the alarm."

"Might I remain here, Don? I'd like to look some more. I promise I won't touch anything."

Tapp shook his head. "Nobody looks unless I'm here. But if you don't want to come with me, you may stand by the door, outside, until I come back."

After Tapp had locked both locks from the outside, Chisholm stood by the door thinking about the strongroom. All the cases were obviously wired to alarms. He had seen no wires. This meant that the wiring probably went through the legs of the cases, where it would be difficult to reach. Did each case activate a separate alarm, or trip a separate indicator, to show exactly which cabinet a burglar had attacked? Probably.

And the mirror on the left wall? What was a mirror doing in a room of this sort?

Tapp came bustling back, his chunky frame still radiating annoyance.

"Now, Robert," he said, unlocking the door for the second time, "I ask you, *please* don't try to sell me any locks—not this time."

"We have some things which would help you, if you'd let me demonstrate," Chisholm said, as he began to scan the room closely on re-entering.

Suspicions?

What explanation would you give for the presence of the mirror "in a room of this sort"?

"All right, all right—but show me a little later. In my den or in my office. Of course, I'm always interested in improving my safeguards. But not just now."

Chisholm moved slowly from case to case, keeping up a running conversation to distract Tapp's attention. But he could discover nothing other than the alarms and the puzzling mirror. There were, of course, the two locks in the door—which would be impossible to jimmy, or to pick. Then two tiny air passages, high in the end walls, protected by a fine, strong mesh caught his roving eye; but he dismissed them as irrelevant.

Finally he straightened and looked directly at Tapp.

"There's a lot of money represented here, Don."

Tapp nodded soberly. "I'd hate to tell you how much, Robert."

"And you'll put even more documents in this room, won't you?"

"If something good comes along."

"This, of course, means that you have the money to spend."

Tapp's expression grew pained. "You're being a bit ingenuous, Robert. Of course I have the money."

"Have you ever considered putting some of that money into something more worthwhile?"

Tapp grinned without humor. "I should have known there was more to this visit than a chat with an old friend. Now comes the touch. How much do you need?"

Chisholm shook his head. "The need isn't mine, Don. It's Green Meadows Hospital. A check for $50,000 from you would put their new equipment drive over the top."

Tapp grimaced. "Green Meadows! I've heard their pitch. A corny one, too. Green Meadows—even the name's corny. No, thanks, Robert. Why did you have to spoil our first meeting in years?"

Chisholm said seriously, "I don't consider geriatric problems corny, Don. Are you sure you just don't like to think of the kind of future any one of us might have to face? Look here: I've contributed $20,000 myself, and believe me, it'll hurt for a while. If I could give twenty, surely you can give fifty?"

Tapp grimaced again. "I don't like people telling me what I can or can't give to charity."

"It would be a deduction on your income tax return."

"Thanks. I know all the possible deductions upside down and backwards."

"Is there any way I can reach you on this, Don? Could I tell you some details of their program—"

Tapp shook his head firmly. "No way at all—not even for an old buddy. Especially not for an old buddy. I can't stand corn."

Chisholm's eyes narrowed, and his brows slanted up in a manner familiar to many people who had met him.

"All right, Don. You won't listen to a rational argument, so I'll make you an irrational proposition. Is your gambling blood still what it used to be?"

Tapp's smile was grim. "If it's a sure thing, I'll still bet."

"Would you bet a check for $50,000 that I can't steal something of value from this room?"

Shock and amazement crossed Tapp's heavy features. "Why, that's idiotic. I won't listen."

Chisholm held out a restraining hand. "No, wait. You have complete confidence in your safeguards. Let's see just how good they are. I don't know a thing about them except there are locks on the door and alarms connected with the cabinets. Yet I am willing to bet I can beat your system."

Tapp pondered. "There's nothing in the world which can't stand improvement. But $50,000—"

Chisholm pressed on. "Here's what I propose: shut me in this room for fifteen minutes—no more. In that short time I guarantee to steal one of these documents—*and get it out of here in spite of all your safeguards.* If I get that paper *out* of this room, you'll make the contribution to the hospital."

"And if you fail? What is your stake?"

"I'll guarantee to increase the efficiency of your safeguards one hundred per cent."

"That's hardly worth fifty thousand."

"I own a quarter interest in my company. I'll assign it to you."

Tapp eyed him shrewdly. "You seem pretty confident."

"I might be betting on a sure thing, Don. The way you like to do. Or I might be willing to take a bigger risk than you."

Tapp mused, "Fifteen minutes. And you have to get it *out* of the room by the end of that time. You know, I could just leave you locked in here."

"No, you must come and let me out. But I must agree to let you search me or put any reasonable restrictions on me until it's absolutely clear that you've lost."

"When do you want to do this?"

"Right now."

Tapp studied Chisholm speculatively. "Chisel—remember how we used to call you that?—when we were kids a lot of the others had contempt for me because I wouldn't take chances. I've done pretty well in life because of caution. But don't be misled: I *will* take a risk. I'll take this one."

Chisholm smiled broadly, but this time his smile had a Mephistophelian look. "Fine. Shall we begin?"

Suspicions?

After reviewing the language of Chisholm's proposal, do you have any clue as to how he intends to get a rare historical document out of the double-locked room?

Tapp held out his wrist silently and they compared watches.

"Fifteen minutes from the time you close the door," said Chisholm.

Tapp went out. As he pushed the door shut, he called through the narrowing crack, "Not that I think you have a snowball's chance, Chisel."

The door had scarcely closed before Chisholm was examining the mirror on the long wall with minute attention. He would have to proceed as though it were a two-way mirror, with only a thin layer of silver. He doubted that this was true, but he could not ignore the possibility. Finally he located what he was looking for: a circular loop in the border decoration on the glass. The glass within the loop looked subtly different.

His smile grew even more diabolical. He quickly stripped the convention badge from his left lapel and pasted it over the circle in the glass.

He then turned swiftly to the cases, taking out his keyring. Before he started to use it, he took a pair of thin rubber gloves from another pocket and put them on. Then, at a pace only a little slower than a walk, he went from case to case and opened the locks, which he had studied while looking at the documents the second time.

When he had lifted all the lids, he laughed at the thought of nine alarms ringing simultaneously in Tapp's ears, or nine position lights flashing at one time in Tapp's face. He then went from case to case and reached inside each. All his movements were swift. Most of them were intended as pure misdirection.

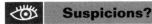

Suspicions?

What was Chisholm looking for—and what did he find—in the border decoration of the mirror?

Finally he had what he wanted. Now all he had to do was to make sure—doubly sure—that he was not being observed. To provide a cloak, he removed his jacket and slipped it over his shoulders backward, with the back of the jacket hanging in front of him and concealing his hands. His fingers made several rapid movements beneath the protection of the jacket. Then he suddenly reversed the process and put the coat back in its normal position.

He looked at his watch. Only eight minutes had passed.

For the remainder of the time Chisholm lounged against the doorframe singing slightly ribald songs in a clear, but not overloud, voice.

Precisely at the end of fifteen minutes, first one, then the other of the door locks was opened. The door itself, which was covered with a paneling of steel, swung back.

As Tapp stepped in, his glance already darting around the room, Chisholm clapped him lightly on the back.

"I hope you brought the check with you, Don."

Tapp half turned, and Chisholm felt a hard object bore into his ribs. He looked down. Tapp had shoved a pistol into his side.

"I have the check, Chisel, but you're going to earn it—if you get it at all. Step back."

Chisholm obeyed.

"Now, go over there to the opposite wall and sit on the floor by that first case. Extend your arms so that one is on either side of the leg of the case. Very good."

Chisholm, from his position on the floor, saw Tapp take a pair of handcuffs from his pocket. Warily, the shorter man approached him.

"Wrists out, Chisel. Good."

Tapp leaned over and snapped the cuffs on Chisholm's wrists. The tall diabolical-looking man had not ceased to smile.

"A lot of trouble, Don, just to find out what I did take. A lot of trouble to keep me from confusing you even more while you look. But I'll be glad to tell you without all this melodrama."

"Just be quiet, Chisel," Tapp said calmly. "If you aren't, I'll slug you with the butt of this gun."

"Violence wasn't in our agreement, Don."

"You were not completely honest with me, Chisel. After you put all your misdirections into action, the hunch I'd had about you came out into the open. I remembered your hobby when you were a boy. I made one phone call to a local convention delegate I happen to know, and he told me you still practice your hobby. You're still an amateur magician, aren't you, Chisel?"

Chisholm shrugged. "I do a little routine to catch the buyer's attention, then I work it into a sales talk for our products. It often helps."

"Spare me," Tapp muttered, peering into cases. His face darkened. "You lied to me, Chisel. You said you would take only one document. I count three of them: the Garfield letter we read, the Seward I mentioned, and the Button Gwinnett."

"I didn't lie," Chisholm replied calmly. "Figure it out for yourself."

"Misdirection again." Tapp turned and stared at him, but it was clear that his thoughts were elsewhere. In a moment he turned back to the cabinets and carefully lifted the velvet in the bottom of each. He found nothing.

He stood in thought for a few more minutes.

"The Garfield and the Alexander Graham Bell are the same size, and so are the Seward and the Lincoln. The Button Gwinnett doesn't match any, but it is *smaller* . . ."

Once more he went from case to case, this time lifting each of the remaining documents. When he had finished, he was smiling. He had found two of the missing papers carefully placed beneath others of the same size. He restored the Garfield and Seward documents to their proper cases.

"That leaves only the Button Gwinnett, Chisel. But this was what you had in mind all along. It's obvious. And if you're worth your salt as a magician, its hiding place won't be obvious. So let's eliminate the commonplace."

Tapp went over the cases carefully, first lifting out all the documents, then each piece of velvet. When he had replaced everything, he closed and locked the cases. Then he dropped to his knees and inspected the under sides of the cabinets.

He found nothing.

He walked to each end of the room in turn and reached up to the tiny air passages. The mesh in both was still firmly in place, and he could not budge it at either opening.

Then his eye caught the mirror.

"Oh, and another thing—" He walked to the mirror and stripped off the convention tag. "You're a sharp fellow, Robert."

Chisholm laughed. "Was my guess right? Closed-circuit TV? Did I cover the lens?"

"You put a patch on its eye, I must admit."

"No two-way mirror?"

"I considered it, but with several receivers on the TV, I can be at any one of several places in the house. A two-way mirror would only restrict me."

He walked over and stood in front of Chisholm. "Two possibilities still remain. One is that you might have slipped it into my own pocket at the door. So I'll check that out now."

He searched through all his pockets, but found nothing which had not been in them before.

He now stooped and unlocked the handcuffs, but made no move to take them from Chisholm's wrists.

"Drop the cuffs there, get up, and go to that corner," he said, motioning with the gun to the bare corner farthest away from the door.

Chisholm obeyed. When he had moved, Tapp inspected the area where the magician had been sitting.

"All right. Now take off your clothes—one garment at a time—and throw them over to me."

Chisholm complied, beginning with his coat jacket, until he stood completely stripped.

Tapp went over each item minutely, crushing cloth carefully, listening for the crackle of paper, inspecting shoes for false heels and soles and the belt for a secret compartment. From Chisholm's trousers he extracted a handkerchief and an ordinary keyring. In the pockets of the coat jacket he found a larger collection. The inside breast pocket yielded a wallet and two used envelopes with jottings on the back. The outside pockets contained the unusual keyring, the rubber gloves, a nearly full pack of cigarettes, a crumpled cigarette package, a ballpoint pen, and a rubber band.

Tapp examined all these things with intense concentration. In the wallet he found money, a driver's license, a miscellany of credit and identification cards, and a small receipt for the purchase of a shirt at a local department store. He searched for a hidden compartment in the wallet, but found none. He then shook the cigarettes from the pack, but neither the pack itself nor the individual cigarettes was the least out of the ordinary. Replacing them, he then smoothed out the crumpled pack. Several items inside it he dumped on the top of one of the cases: a twist of cellophane; two wadded bits of brownish, waxy-looking paper; a fragment of wrapper from a roll of peppermints; and part of a burned match. He snorted and swept this trash back into its container.

He drew in his breath with an angry hiss. "All right, Chisel, let's look *you* over. Turn around. Raise your arms. All right, now sit down on the floor and raise your feet."

"Nothing on the soles of my feet except dust from the floor. You should clean this place oftener," said Chisholm, leaning back on his arms.

Tapp's only answer was a growl.

"Have you checked the ceiling?" Chisholm asked.

Tapp looked up involuntarily. The ceiling was bare.

"See, you wouldn't have thought of that, would you?" Chisholm mocked.

Tapp leaned against one of the cabinets and aimed the pistol at Chisholm's midriff.

"Chisel, playtime is over. I want that Button Gwinnett back."

"Or else, eh? You forget a number of things. We haven't yet established whether the paper is in this room or out of it. We haven't exchanged your check for $50,000 for the stolen document. I haven't even put my clothes back on. And, incidentally, I give you my word: the missing paper isn't in my clothing."

Tapp tossed the clothing to Chisholm. "It doesn't matter. You're going to tell me where that piece of paper is."

Chisholm began to dress. "How do you propose to make me tell? Shoot me? On the grounds that I broke into your house to steal? A respected businessman like me— steal? If you killed me, then you'd never find your paper. If you only wounded me, I'd refuse to talk. So where are we, old friend?"

Tapp said grimly, "This bet of yours is just a stall. Once you get out of this room you'll take off with that signature to certain other collectors I could name. Why else won't you admit who told you about my collection? Only a handful of people know about it."

Chisholm was tempted to yield on this point and reveal to Tapp that it was the district manager of Tapp's own insurance company who had mentioned the collection to him in strict confidence. Had he not wished to show even the slightest sign of weakness, he would have told this.

"The whole thing was strictly honorable," Chisholm said. "This stunt was my own idea."

> ### 👁 Suspicions?
>
> Review Tapp's search of the cases, the room, the contents of his and Chisholm's clothing, and Chisholm himself. The Button Gwinnett document has to be either somewhere Tapp missed, thanks to Chisholm's movements of misdirection, or somewhere he searched. Where do you think the missing document is and what clues do you base your opinion on?

"And my idea," said Tapp heavily, "is to lock you in here without food and water until you return that paper. When you finally get out, I could always claim that I thought you had left the house and had locked you in without knowing."

Chisholm shook his head. "I had more respect for you, Don. If you did that, you'd either have to leave the other documents with me—and risk my destroying them—or take them out and have their absence disprove your story."

Inwardly, Chisholm was beginning to have qualms. If Tapp should abandon reason in favor of a collector's passion, as he seemed about to do, anything might happen. The best course was an immediate distraction.

"How do you know," he said challengingly, "that the paper isn't *already* outside the room?"

Tapp snorted. "Impossible!"

"Is it, now? There is a small trick I often do at dinner gatherings *which depends entirely on the victim's being too close to me to see what my hands are really doing.* I move a handkerchief or tissue from hand to hand near the victim's face, then throw it over his shoulder when my hand is too close for him to see exactly what I've done."

Tapp said warily, "But at no time were you outside this room."

"I didn't have to be."

Suddenly Tapp understood. "You mean when I came in!" He moved back and reached behind him to open the door. "Stay where you are." He stepped out and pushed the door shut again.

Chisholm waited tensely.

The door opened to a pencil-wide crack. "There's nothing out here, Chisel."

Chisholm answered evenly. "I didn't say there was. But if you'll use the brains I've always given you credit for, you'll realize that I don't *want* to steal your precious piece of paper. If I had, why make the bet? Let me out of here and give me the $50,000 check for the hospital, and I'll tell you where the Button Gwinnett signature is."

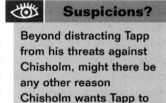

Suspicions?

Beyond distracting Tapp from his threats against Chisholm, might there be any other reason Chisholm wants Tapp to open the door and go out of the room? Explain.

A silence followed his words. Seconds dragged by. Minutes.

Finally Tapp spoke. "You swear that this will end here? That you won't even tell anyone about this incident? I used to think your word could be relied on, Chisel."

"I'll swear on anything you name."

"That won't be necessary." The door opened wide. "Now, where is it?"

Chisholm smiled and shook his head. "First, the $50,000 check."

Tapp eyed him shrewdly. "I don't know that the paper is out of the room. I don't owe you anything unless it *is* outside, and you're still *inside*. But you agreed to tell me where it is."

Chisholm kept smiling. "I'll swear again, if you like. The paper is outside the room, according to the conditions of our bet."

Tapp studied him. "Very well, come up to my den and I'll give you the check. You have my word that I'll keep my part of the bargain. Now— *where is that paper?*"

Chisholm stepped to Tapp's side and clapped him affectionately on the back. Then he held out his right hand.

"Here."

As Tapp all but snatched the document from him, Chisholm fished in his own jacket pocket. He took out the crumpled cigarette pack, opened it, and shook out the contents.

"Remember the convention badge I stuck over your TV camera lens? Such badges are only strips of cardboard coated on the back with a permanently tacky adhesive—the way surgical adhesive tape is coated." From the cigarette pack he took the two scraps of brownish, waxy paper. "That gave me the idea. It's easy to obtain tape with such an adhesive on *both* front and back. This brown paper protects the adhesive until it's peeled off, making the tape ready for use. In this case I kept a small bit of such tape in my pocket, removed the Button Gwinnett signature from the cabinet, exposed the adhesive on one side of the tape, and stuck the Button Gwinnett to that exposed side. Then I made the other side of the tape ready and palmed the whole thing."

Chisholm repeated an earlier gesture. A look of comprehension spread over Tapp's face.

"When you came into the room at the end of the fifteen minutes," Chisholm explained, "I simply put the Button Gwinnett paper in the one place you couldn't see—*on your back!*"

 How Clever?

1. The story opens with the third-person narrator telling us that Robert Chisholm "had less confidence in his ability to persuade than in the probability of his accomplishing the theft." How do the events of the story bear out Chisholm's assessment of his strengths and weaknesses as a persuader and as a thief?

2. "I guarantee to steal one of these documents—*and get it out of here in spite of all your safeguards.* If I get that paper *out* of this room, you'll make the contribution to the hospital." Where in the language of his proposal to Tapp did Chisholm take particular care in the selection of his words? Did the fact that Chisholm hid three documents violate either the letter or spirit of his proposal? Explain.

3. Why did Chisholm paste his convention badge over the circular loop that he had found in the border of the mirror?

4. How did Chisholm's experience as an amateur magician figure in his use of misdirection?

5. Why did Chisholm clap Tapp lightly on the back when Tapp re-entered the room at the end of the allotted fifteen minutes? In all probability, how did Tapp interpret the gesture?

6. When Tapp says that "two possibilities still remain," he sounds quite definitive. One of Tapp's possibilities was that Chisholm might have slipped the document into Tapp's own pocket at the door; the other was that Chisholm had hidden the document in his own clothing or on his own person. By stopping at these two possibilities, which possibility did Tapp not consider? Would Tapp have found the document if he had searched himself in exactly the same manner he searched Chisholm? Explain.

7. What did Tapp fail to pay sufficient attention to and reflect upon in his search of the contents of the crumpled cigarette pack?

8. Why was it necessary for Chisholm to get Tapp to leave the room? What was not accurate about Tapp's remark to Chisholm from the hall that "there's nothing out here"?

9. Explain why you think Tapp did or did not deserve to lose the bet.

DETECTWRITE: Setting and Plot

1. In what ways do the setting and plot of "The Impossible Theft" conform to the conventions of a locked room mystery? In what ways is the story unconventional? Explain.

2. Explain how something as simple as the childish prank of sticking a sign that says "Kick Me" on someone's back might have inspired the plot of "The Impossible Theft." Try thinking of some prank, trick, joke, or game from your childhood that might form the nucleus for a mystery story.

3. Compare and contrast the setting, plot, and placement of characters in "The Impossible Theft" with those elements in "The Leopold Locked Room."

DETECTWRITE: Characterization

Explain why you would or would not have a magician—amateur or professional—as a character in a locked room mystery you would write.

Part four

The Inspector Calls: Police Procedurals

The Sound of Murder

Donald E. Westlake

Detective Abraham Levine of Brooklyn's Forty-Third Precinct sat at his desk in the squadroom and longed for a cigarette. The fingers of his left hand kept closing and clenching, feeling awkward without the paper-rolled tube of tobacco. He held a pencil for a while but unconsciously brought it to his mouth. He didn't realize what he was doing till he tasted the gritty staleness of the eraser. Then he put the pencil away in a drawer, and tried unsuccessfully to concentrate on the national news in the news magazine.

The world conspired against a man who tried to give up smoking. All around him were other people puffing cigarettes casually and unconcernedly, not making any fuss about it at all, making by their very nonchalance his own grim reasons for giving them up seem silly and hypersensitive. If he isolated himself from other smokers with the aid of television or radio, the cigarette commercials with their erotic smoking and their catchy jingles would surely drive him mad. Also, he would find that the most frequent sentence in popular fiction was, "He lit another cigarette." Statesmen and entertainers seemed inevitably to be smoking whenever news photographers snapped them for posterity, and even the news items were against him: He had just reread for the third time an announcement to the world that Pope John XVIII was the first Prelate of the Roman Catholic Church to smoke cigarettes in public.

Levine closed the magazine in irritation, and from the cover smiled at him the Governor of a midwestern state, cigarette in F.D.R. cigarette-holder at a jaunty angle in his mouth. Levine closed his eyes, saddened by the knowledge that he had turned himself at this late date into a comic character. A grown man who tries to give up smoking is comic, a Robert Benchley or a W.C. Fields, bumbling along, plagued by trivia, his life an endless gauntlet of minor crises. *They could do a one-reeler on me*, Levine thought. *A great little comedy. Laurel without Hardy. Because Hardy died of a heart attack.*

Abraham Levine, at fifty-three years of age, was twenty-four years a cop and eight years into the heart attack range. When he went to bed at night, he kept himself awake by listening to the silence that replaced every eighth or ninth beat of his heart. When he had to climb stairs or lift anything heavy, he was acutely conscious of the labored heaviness of his breathing and of the way those missed heartbeats came closer and closer together, every seventh beat and then every sixth and then every fifth—

Some day, he knew, his heart would skip two beats in a row, and on that day Abraham Levine would stop, because there wouldn't be any third beat. None at all, not ever.

Four months ago, he'd gone to the doctor, and the doctor had checked him over very carefully, and he had submitted to it feeling like an aging auto brought to a mechanic by an owner who wanted to know whether it was worth while to fix the old boat up or should he just junk the thing and get another. (In the house next door to his, a baby cried every night lately. The new model, crying for the old and the obsolete to get off the road.)

So he'd gone to the doctor, and the doctor had told him not to worry. He had that little skip in his heartbeat, but that wasn't anything danger-ous, lots of people had that. And his blood pressure was a little high, but not much, not enough to concern himself about. So the doctor told him he was healthy, and collected his fee, and Levine left, unconvinced.

So when he went back again three days ago, still frightened by the skip and the shortness of breath and the occasional chest cramps when he was excited or afraid, the doctor had told him the same things all over again, and had added, "If you really want to do something for that heart of yours, you can give up smoking."

He hadn't had a cigarette since, and for the first time in his life he was beginning really to understand the wails of the arrested junkies, locked away in a cell with nothing to ease their craving. He was beginning to be ashamed of himself, for having become so completely dependent on something so useless and so harmful. Three days now. Comic or not, he was going to make it.

Opening his eyes, he glared at the cigarette-smoking Governor and shoved the magazine into a drawer. Then he looked around the squadroom, empty except for himself and his partner, Crawley, sitting over there smoking contentedly at his desk by the filing cabinet as he worked on a report. Rizzo and McFarlane, and the other two detectives on this shift, were out on a call but would probably be back soon. Levine longed for the phone to ring, for something to happen to distract him to keep mind and hands occupied and forgetful of cigarettes. He looked around the room, at a loss, and his left hand clenched and closed on the desk, lonely and incomplete.

When the rapping came at the door, it was so faint that Levine barely heard it, and Crawley didn't even look up. But any sound at all would have attracted Levine's straining attention. He looked over, saw a foreshortened shadow against the frosted glass of the door, and called, "Come in."

Crawley looked up. "What?"

"Someone at the door." Levine called out again, and this time the doorknob hesitantly turned, and a child walked in.

It was a little girl of about ten, in a frilly frock of pale pink, with a flared skirt, with gold-buckled black shoes and ribbed white socks. Her hair was pale blonde, combed and brushed and shampooed to gleaming cleanliness, brushed back from her forehead and held by a pink bow atop her head, then cascading straight down her back nearly to her waist. Her eyes were huge and bright blue, her face a creamy oval. She was a little girl in an ad for children's clothing in the *Sunday Times*. She was a story illustration in *Ladies' Home Journal*. She was Alice in Blunderland, gazing with wide-eyed curious innocence into the bullpen, the squadroom, the home and office of the detectives of the Forty-Third Precinct, the men whose job it was to catch the stupid and the nasty so that other men could punish them.

She saw, looking into this brutal room, two men and a lot of old furniture.

It was inevitable to Levine that the little girl spoke: "May I come in?" Her voice was as faint as her tapping on the door had been. She was poised to flee at the first loud noise.

Levine automatically lowered his own voice when he answered. "Of course. Come on in. Sit over here." He motioned at the straight-backed wooden chair beside his desk.

The girl crossed the threshold, carefully closed the door again behind, and came on silent feet across the room, glancing sidelong at Crawley, then establishing herself on the edge of the chair, her toes touching the floor, still ready for flight at any second. She studied Levine. "I want to talk to a detective," she said. "Are you a detective?"

Levine nodded. "Yes, I am."

"My name," she told him solemnly, "is Amy Thornbridge Walker. I live at 717 Prospect Park West, apartment 4-A. I want to report a murder, a quite recent murder."

"A murder?"

"My mother," she said, just as solemnly, "murdered my stepfather."

Levine glanced over at Crawley, who screwed his face up in an expression meant to say, "She's a nut. Hear her out, and then she'll go home. What else can you do?"

There was nothing else he could do. He looked at Amy Thornbridge Walker again. "Tell me about it," he said. "When did it happen?"

"Two weeks ago Thursday," she said. "November 27th. At two-thirty P.M."

Her earnest calm called for belief. But children with wild stories were not unknown to the precinct. Children came in with reports of dead bodies in alleys, flying saucers on rooftops, counterfeiters in basement apartments, kidnappers in black trucks—and once out of a thousand times what the child reported was real and not the product of a young imagination on a spree. More to save the little girl's feelings than for any other reason, therefore, Levine drew to him a pencil and a sheet of paper and took down what she told him. He said, "What's your mother's name?"

"Gloria Thornbridge Walker," she said. "And my stepfather was Albert Walker. He was an attorney."

To the side, Crawley was smiling faintly at the girl's conscious formality. Levine solemnly wrote down the names, and said, "Was your father's name Thornbridge, is that it?"

"Yes. Jason Thornbridge. He died when I was very small. I think my mother killed him, too, but I'm not absolutely sure."

"I see. But you *are* absolutely sure that your mother killed Albert Walker."

"My stepfather. Yes. My first father was supposed to have drowned by accident in Lake Champlain, which I consider very unlikely, as he was an excellent swimmer."

Levine reached into his shirt pocket, found no cigarettes there, and suddenly realized what he was doing. Irritation washed over him, but he carefully kept it from showing in his face or voice as he said, "How long have you thought that your mother killed your rea—your first father?"

"I'd never thought about it at all," she said, "until she murdered my stepfather. Naturally, I then started thinking about it."

Crawley coughed, and lit a fresh cigarette, keeping his hands up in front of his mouth. Levine said, "Did he die from drowning, too?"

"No. My stepfather wasn't athletic at all. In fact, he was nearly an invalid for the last six months of his life."

"Then how did your mother kill him?"

"She made a loud noise at him," she said calmly.

Levine's pencil stopped its motion. He looked at her searchingly, but found no trace of humor in her eyes or mouth. If she had come up here as a joke—on a bet, say from her schoolmates—then she was a fine little actress, for no sign of the joke was on her face at all.

Though how could he really tell? Levine, a childless man with a barren wife, had found it difficult over the years to communicate with the very young. A part of it, of course, was an envy he couldn't help, in the knowledge that these children could run and play with no frightening shortness of breath or tightness of chest, that they could sleep at night in their beds with no thought for the dull thudding of their hearts, that they would be alive and knowing for years and decades, for *decades,* after he himself had ceased to exist.

Before he could formulate an answer to what she'd said, the little girl jounced off the chair with the graceful gracelessness of the young and said, "I can't stay any longer. I stopped here on my way home from school. If my mother found out that I knew, and that I had told the police, she might try to murder me, too." She turned all at once and studied Crawley severely. "I am not a silly little girl," she told him. "And I am not telling a lie or making a joke. My mother murdered my stepfather, and I came in here and reported it. That's what I'm supposed to do. You aren't supposed to believe me right away, but you are supposed to investigate and find out whether or not I've told you the truth. And I have told you the truth." She turned suddenly back to Levine, an angry little girl—no, not angry, *definite*—a definite little girl filled with stern formality and a child's sense of rightness and duty. "My stepfather," she said, "was a very good man. My mother is a bad woman. You find out what she did, and punish her." She nodded briefly, as though to punctuate what she'd said, and marched to the door, reaching it as Rizzo and McFarlane came in. They looked down at her in surprise, and she stepped past them and out to the hall, closing the door after her.

Rizzo looked at Levine and jerked his thumb at the door. "What was that?"

It was Crawley who answered. "She came in to report a murder," he said. "Her Mommy killed her Daddy by making a great big noise at him."

Rizzo frowned. "Come again?"

"I'll check it out," said Levine. Not believing the girl's story, he still felt the impact of her demand on him that he do his duty. All it would take was a few phone calls. While Crawley recounted the episode at great length to Rizzo, and McFarlane took up his favorite squadroom position, seated at his desk with the chair canted back and his feet atop the desk, Levine picked up his phone and dialed the *New York Times*. He identified himself and said what he wanted, was connected to the right department, and after a few minutes the November 28th obituary notice on Albert Walker was read to him. Cause of death: a heart attack. Mortician: Junius Merriman. An even briefer call to Merriman gave him the name of Albert Walker's doctor, Henry Sheffield. Levine thanked Merriman, assured him there was no problem, and got out the Brooklyn yellow pages to find Sheffield's number. He dialed, spoke to a nurse, and finally got Sheffield.

"I can't understand," Sheffield told him, "why the police would be interested in the case. It was heart failure, pure and simple. What seems to be the problem?"

"There's no problem," Levine told him. "Just checking it out. Was this a sudden attack? Had he had any heart trouble before?"

"Yes, he'd suffered a coronary attack about seven months ago. The second attack was more severe, and he hadn't really recovered as yet from the first. There certainly wasn't anything else to it, if that's what you're getting at."

"I didn't mean to imply anything like that," said Levine. "By the way, were you Mrs. Walker's first husband's doctor, too?"

"No, I wasn't. His name was Thornbridge, wasn't it? I never met the man. Is there some sort of question about him?"

"No, not at all." Levine evaded a few more questions, then hung up, his duty done. He turned to Crawley and shook his head. "Nothing to—"

A sudden crash behind him froze the words in his throat. He half-rose from the chair, mouth wide open, face paling as the blood rushed from his head, his nerves and muscles stiff and tingling.

It was over in a second, and he sank back into the chair turning around to see what had happened. McFarlane was sheepishly picking himself up from the floor, his chair lying on its back beside him. He grinned shakily at Levine. "Leaned back too far that time," he said.

"Don't do that," said Levine, his voice shaky. He touched the back of his hand to his forehead, feeling cold perspiration slick against the skin. He was trembling all over. Once again, he reached to his shirt pocket for a cigarette, and this time felt an instant of panic when he found the pocket empty. He pressed the palm of his hand to the pocket, and beneath pocket and skin he felt the thrumming of his heart, and automatically counted the beats. Thum, thum, *skip*, thum, thum, thum, thum, thum, *skip*, thum, thum,—

On the sixth beat, the *sixth* beat. He sat there listening, head pressed to his chest, and gradually the agitation subsided and the skip came every seventh beat and then every eighth beat, and then he could dare to move again.

He licked his lips, needing a cigarette now more than at any other time in the last three days, more than he could ever remember needing a cigarette at any time in his whole life.

His resolve crumbled. Shamefacedly, he turned to his partner, "Jack, do you have a cigarette?"

Crawley looked away from McFarlane, who was checking himself for damage. "I thought you were giving them up, Abe," he said.

"Not around here. Please, Jack."

"Sure." Crawley tossed him his pack.

Levine caught the pack, shook out one cigarette, threw the rest back to Crawley. He took a book of matches from the desk drawer, put the cigarette in his mouth, feeling the comforting familiarity of it between his lips, and struck a match. He held the match up, then sat looking at the flame, struck by a sudden thought.

Albert Walker had died of a heart attack. "She made a loud noise at him." "The second attack was more severe, and he hadn't really recovered as yet from the first."

He shook the match out, took the cigarette from between his lips. It had been every sixth beat there for a while, after the loud noise of McFarlane's backward dive.

Had Gloria Thornbridge Walker *really* killed Albert Walker?

Would Abraham Levine *really* kill Abraham Levine?

The second question was easier to answer. Levine opened the desk drawer and dropped the cigarette and matches into it.

The first question he didn't try to answer at all. He would sleep on it. Right now, he wasn't thinking straight enough.

At dinner that night, he talked it over with his wife. "Peg," he said, "I've got a problem."

"A problem?" She looked up in surprise, a short solid stout woman three years her husband's junior, her iron-gray hair rigidly curled in a home permanent. "If you're coming to me," she said, "it must be awful."

He smiled, nodding. "It is." It was rare for him to talk about his job with his wife. The younger men, he knew, discussed their work with their wives as a matter of course, expecting and receiving suggestions and ideas and advice. But he was a product of an older upbringing, and still believed instinctively that women should be shielded from the more brutal aspects of life. It was only when the problem was one he couldn't discuss with Crawley that he turned to Peg for someone to talk to. "I'm getting old," he said suddenly, thinking of the differences between himself and the younger men.

She laughed. "That's your problem? Don't feel lonely, Abe, it happens to all kinds of people. Have some more gravy."

"Let me tell you," he said. "A little girl came in today, maybe ten years old, dressed nicely, polite, very intelligent. She wanted to report that her mother had killed her stepfather."

"A little girl?" She sounded shocked. She too believed that there were those who should be shielded from the more brutal aspects of life, but with her the shielded ones were children. "A little girl? A thing like that?"

"Wait," he said. "Let me tell you. I called the doctor and he said it was a heart attack. The stepfather—Mr. Walker—he'd had one attack already, and the second one on top of it killed him."

"But the little girl blames the mother?" Peg leaned forward. "Psychological, you think?"

"I don't know. I asked her how her mother had done the killing, and she said her mother made a loud noise at her father."

"A joke." She shook her head. "These children today, I don't know where they get their ideas. All this on the TV—"

"Maybe," he said. "I don't know. A man with a bad heart, bedridden, an invalid. A sudden shock, a loud noise, it might do it, bring on that second attack."

"What else did this little girl say?"

"That's all. Her stepfather was good, and her mother was bad, and she'd stopped off on her way home from school. She only had a minute, because she didn't want her mother to know what she was doing."

"You let her go? You didn't question her?"

Levine shrugged. "I didn't believe her," he said. "You know the imagination children have."

"But now?"

"Now, I don't know." He held up his hand, two fingers extended. "Now," he said, "there's two questions in my mind. First, is the little girl right or wrong? Did her mother actually make a loud noise that killed her stepfather or not? And if she did, the question number two: Did she do it on purpose, or was it an accident?" He waggled the two fingers and looked at his wife. "Do you see? Maybe the little girl is right, and her mother actually did cause the death, but not intentionally. If so, I don't want to make things worse for the mother by dragging it into the open. Maybe the little girl is wrong altogether, and if so it would be best to just let the whole thing slide. But maybe she's right, and it *was* murder, and then that child is in danger, because if I don't do anything, she'll try some other way, and the mother will find out."

Peg shook her head. "I don't like that, a little girl like that. Could she defend herself? A woman to kill her husband, a woman like that could kill her child just as easy, I don't like that at all, Abe."

"Neither do I." He reached for the coffee cup, drank. "The question is, what do I do?"

She shook her head again. "A child like that," she said. "A woman like that. And then again, maybe not." She looked at her husband. "For right now," she said, "you eat. We can think about it."

For the rest of dinner they discussed other things. After the meal, as usual, the craving for a cigarette suddenly intensified, and he was unable to concentrate on anything but his resolution. They watched television during the evening, and by bedtime he still hadn't made a decision. Getting ready for bed, Peg suddenly said, "The little girl. You've been thinking?"

"I'll sleep on it," he said. "Maybe in the morning. Peg, I am longing for a cigarette."

"Nails in your coffin," she said bluntly. He blinked, and went away silently to brush his teeth.

The lights turned out, they lay together in the double bed which now, with age, had a pronounced sag toward the middle, rolling them together. But it was a cold night out, a good night to lie close together and feel the warmth of life. Levine closed his eyes and drifted slowly toward sleep.

A sudden sound shook him awake. He blinked rapidly, staring up in the darkness at the ceiling, startled, disoriented, not knowing what it was. But then the sound came again, and he exhaled, releasing held breath. It was the baby from next door, crying.

Move over, world, and give us room, he thought, giving words to the baby's cries. *Make way for the new.*

And they're right, he thought. *We've got to take care of them, and guide them, and then make way for them. They're absolutely right.*

I've got to do something for that little girl, he thought.

In the morning, Levine talked to Crawley. He sat in the client's chair, beside Crawley's desk. "About that little girl," he said.

"You, too? I got to thinking about it myself, last night."

"We ought to check it out," Levine told him.

"I know. I figure I ought to look up the death of the first father. Jason Thornbridge, wasn't it?"

"Good," said Levine. "I was thinking of going to her school, talking to the teacher. If she's the kind of child who makes up wild stories all the time, then that's that, you know what I mean?"

"Sure. You know what school she's in?"

"Lathmore Elementary, over on Third."

Crawley frowned, trying to remember. "She tell you that? I didn't hear it if she did."

"No, she didn't. But it's the only one it could be." Levine grinned sheepishly. "I'm pulling a Sherlock Holmes," he said. "She told us she'd stopped in on her way home from school. So she was walking home, and there's only three schools in the right direction—so we'd be between them and Prospect Park—but they're close enough for her to walk." He checked them off on his fingers. "There's St. Aloysius, but she wasn't in a school uniform. There's PS 118, but with a Prospect Park West address and the clothing she was wearing and her good manners, she doesn't attend public school. So that leaves Lathmore."

"Okay, Sherlock," said Crawley. "You go talk to the nice people at Lathmore. I'll dig into the Thornbridge thing."

"One of us," Levine told him, "ought to check this out with the Lieutenant first. Tell him what we want to do."

"Fine. Go ahead."

Levine scraped the fingers of his left hand together, embarrassment reminding him of his need for a cigarette. But this was day number four, and he was going to make it. "Jack," he said, "I think maybe you ought to be the one to talk to him."

"Why me? Why not you?"

"I think he has more respect for you."

Crawley snorted. "What the hell are you talking about?"

"No, I mean it, Jack." Levine grinned self-consciously. "If I told him about it, he might think I was just dramatizing it, getting emotional or something, and he'd say thumbs down. But you're the level-headed type. If you tell him it's serious, he'll believe you."

"You're nuts," said Crawley.

"You *are* the level-headed type," Levine told him. "And I *am* too emotional."

"Flattery will get you everywhere. All right, go to school."

"Thanks, Jack."

Levine shrugged into his coat and plodded out of the squadroom, downstairs, and out to the sidewalk. Lathmore Elementary was three blocks away to the right, and he walked it. There was a smell of snow in the air, but the sky was still clear. Levine strolled along sniffing the snow-tang, his hands pushed deep into the pockets of his black overcoat. The desire for a smoke was less when he was outdoors, so he didn't hurry.

Lathmore Elementary, one of the myriad private schools which have sprung up to take the place of the enfeebled public school system long since emasculated by municipal politics, was housed in an old mansion on one of the neighborhood's better blocks. The building was mainly masonry, with curved buttresses and bay windows everywhere, looming three ivy-overgrown stories to a patchwork slate roof which dipped and angled and rose crazily around to no pattern at all. Gold letters on the wide glass pane over the double-doored entrance announced the building's new function, and just inside the doors an arrow on a wall was marked "OFFICE."

Levine didn't want to have to announce himself as a policeman, but the administrative receptionist was so officious and curious that he had no choice. It was the only way he could get to see Mrs. Pidgeon, the principal, without first explaining his mission in minute detail to the receptionist.

Suspicions?

1. What is your reaction to ten-year-old Amy Thornbridge Walker and the story she tells Brooklyn Detective Abraham Levine?

2. What reasons does Detective Levine have for pursuing this particular case?

3. Do you attach any significance to the story's constant references to Detective Levine's craving for a cigarette and his concern about his mortality? Explain.

Mrs. Pidgeon was baffled, polite, terrified and defensive, but not very much of any of them. It was as though these four emotions were being held in readiness, for one of them to spring into action as soon as she found out exactly what it was a police officer could possibly want in Lathmore Elementary. Levine tried to explain as gently and vaguely as possible.

"I'd like to talk to one of your teachers," he said. "About a little girl, a student of yours."

"What about her?"

"She made a report to us yesterday," Levine told her. "It's difficult for us to check it out, and it might help if we knew a little more about her, what her attitudes are, things like that."

Defensiveness began to edge to the fore in Mrs. Pidgeon's attitude. "What sort of report?"

"I'm sorry," said Levine. "If there's nothing to it, it would be better not to spread it."

"Something about this school?"

"Oh, no," said Levine, managing not to smile. "Not at all."

"Very well." Defensiveness receded, and a sort of cold politeness became more prominent. "You want to talk to her teacher, then."

"Yes."

"Her name?"

"Amy Walker. Amy Thornbridge Walker."

"Oh, yes!" Mrs. Pidgeon's face suddenly lit with pleasure, not at Levine but at his reminding her of that particular child. Then the pleasure gave way just as suddenly to renewed bafflement. "It's about Amy? She came to you yesterday?"

"That's right."

"Well." She looked helplessly around the room, aching to find out more but unable to find a question that would get around Levine's reticence. Finally, she gave up, and asked him to wait while she went for Miss Haskell, the fifth grade teacher. Levine stood as she left the room, then sank back into the maroon leather chair, feeling bulky and awkward in this hushed heavy-draped office.

He waited five minutes before Mrs. Pidgeon returned, this time with Miss Haskell in tow. Miss Haskell, unexpectedly, was a comfortable fortyish woman in a sensible suit and flat shoes, not the thin tall bird he'd expected. He acknowledged Mrs. Pidgeon's introduction, hastily rising again, and Mrs. Pidgeon pointedly said, "Try not to be too long, Mr. Levine. You may use my office."

"Thank you."

She left, and Levine and Miss Haskell stood facing each other in the middle of the room. He motioned at a chair. "Would you sit down, please?"

"Thank you. Mrs. Pidgeon said you wanted to ask me about Amy Walker."

"Yes, I want to know what kind of child she is, anything you can tell me about her."

Miss Haskell smiled. "I can tell you she's a brilliant and well-brought-up child," she said. "That she's the one I picked to be student in charge while I came down to talk to you. That she's always at least a month ahead of the rest of the class in reading the assignments, and that she's the most practical child I've ever met."

Levine reached to his cigarette pocket, cut the motion short, awkwardly returned his hand to his side. "Her father died two weeks ago, didn't he?"

"That's right."

"How did they get along, do you know? Amy and her father."

"She worshipped him. He was her stepfather actually, having married her mother only about a year ago, I believe. Amy doesn't remember her real father. Mr. Walker was the only father she knew, and having been without one for so long—" Miss Haskell spread her hands. "He was important to her," she finished.

"She took his death hard?"

"She was out of school for a week, inconsolable. She spent the time at her grandmother's, I understand. The grandmother caters to her, of course. I believe her mother had a doctor in twice."

"Yes, her mother." Levine didn't know what to do with his hands. He clasped them in front of him. "How do Amy and her mother get along?"

"Normally, so far as I know. There's never been any sign of discord between them that I've seen." She smiled again. "But my contact with Amy is limited to school hours, of course."

"You think there is discord?"

"No, not at all. I didn't mean to imply that. Just that I couldn't give you an expert answer to the question."

Levine nodded. "You're right. Is Amy a very imaginative child?"

"She's very self-sufficient in play, if that's what you mean."

"I was thinking about story-telling."

"Oh, a liar." She shook her head. "No, Amy isn't the tall tale type. A very practical little girl, really. Very dependable judgment. As I say, she's the one I left in charge of the class."

"She wouldn't be likely to come to us with a wild story she'd made up all by herself."

"Not at all. If Amy told you about something, it's almost certainly the truth."

Levine sighed. "Thank you," he said. "Thank you very much."

Miss Haskell rose to her feet. "Could you tell me what this wild story was? I might be able to help."

"I'd rather not," he said. "Not until we're sure, one way or the other."

"If I can be of any assistance—"

"Thank you," he said again. "You've already helped."

Back at the station, Levine entered the squadroom and hung up his coat. Crawley looked over from his desk and said, "You have all the luck, Abe. You missed the whirlwind."

"Whirlwind?"

"Amy's mama was here. Dr. Sheffield called her about you checking up on her husband's death, and just before she came over here she got a call from somebody at Lathmore Elementary, saying there was a cop there asking questions about her daughter. She didn't like us casting aspersions on her family."

"Aspersions?"

"That's what she said." Crawley grinned. "You're little Sir Echo this morning, aren't you?"

"I need a cigarette. What did the Lieutenant say?"

"She didn't talk to him. She talked to me."

"No, when you told him about the little girl's report."

"Oh. He said to take two days on it, and then let him know how it looked."

"Fine. How about Thornbridge?"

"Accidental death. Inquest said so. No question in anybody's mind. He went swimming too soon after lunch, got a stomach cramp, and drowned. What's the word on the little girl?"

"Her teacher says she's reliable. Practical and realistic. If she tells us something, it's so."

Crawley grimaced. "That isn't what I wanted to hear, Abe."

"It didn't overjoy me, either." Levine sat down at his desk. "What did the mother have to say?"

"I had to spill it, Abe. About what her daughter reported."

"That's all right," he said. "Now we've got no choice. We've got to follow through. What was her reaction?"

"She didn't believe it."

Levine shrugged. "She had to, after she thought about it."

"Sure," said Crawley. "Then she was baffled. She didn't know why Amy would say such a thing."

"Was she home when her husband died?"

"She says no," Crawley flipped open a memo pad. "Somebody had to be with him all the time, but he didn't want a professional nurse. So when Amy came home from school that afternoon, the mother went to the supermarket. Her husband was alive when she left and dead when she got back. Or so she says."

"She says Amy was the one who found him dead?"

"No. Amy was watching television. When the mother came home, she found him, and called the doctor."

"What about noises?"

"She didn't hear any, and doesn't have any idea what Amy means."

Levine sighed. "All right," he said. "We've got one timetable discrepancy. Amy says her mother was home and made a loud noise. The mother says she was out to the supermarket." His fingers strayed to his cigarette pocket, then went on to scratch his shoulder instead. "What do you think of the mother, Jack?"

"She's tough. She was mad, and she's used to having things her own way. I can't see her playing nursemaid. But she sure seemed baffled about why the kid would make such an accusation."

"I'll have to talk to Amy again," said Levine. "Once we've got both stories, we can see which one breaks down."

Crawley said, "I wonder if she'll try to shut the kid's mouth?"

"Let's not think about that yet. We've still got all day." He reached for the phone book and looked up the number of Lathmore Elementary.

Levine talked to the girl in Mrs. Pidgeon's office at eleven o'clock. At his request, they were left alone.

Amy was dressed as neatly as she had been yesterday, and seemed just as composed. Levine explained to her what had been done so far on the investigation, and that her mother had been told why the investigation was taking place. "I'm sorry, Amy," he said, "but we didn't have any choice. Your mother had to know."

Amy considered, solemn and formal. "I think it will be all right," she said. "She wouldn't dare try to hurt me now, with you investigating. It would be too obvious. My mother is very subtle, Mr. Levine."

Levine smiled, in spite of himself. "You have quite a vocabulary," he told her.

"I'm a very heavy reader," she explained. "Though it's difficult for me to get interesting books from the library. I'm too young, so I have to take books from the children's section." She smiled thinly. "I'll tell you a secret," she said. "I steal the ones I want to read, and then bring them back when I'm finished with them."

In a hurry, he thought, smiling, and remembered the baby next door. "I want to talk to you," he said, "about the day when your father died. Your mother said she went out to the store, and when she came back he was dead. What do you say?"

"Nonsense," she said, promptly. "*I* was the one who went out to the store. The minute I came home from school, she sent me out to the supermarket. But I came back too soon for her."

"Why?"

"Just as I was coming down the hall from the elevator, I heard a great clang sound from our apartment. Then it came again as I was opening the door. I went through the living room and saw my mother coming out of my stepfather's room. She was smiling. But then she saw me and suddenly looked terribly upset and told me something awful had happened, and she ran to the telephone to call Dr. Sheffield. She acted terribly agitated, and carried on just as though she really meant it. She fooled Dr. Sheffield completely."

"Why did you wait so long before coming to us?"

"I didn't know what to do." The solemn formality cracked all at once, and she was only a child after all, uncertain in an adult world. "I didn't think anyone would believe me, and I was afraid if Mother suspected what I knew, she might try to do something to me. But Monday in Civics Miss Haskell was talking about the duties of the different parts of government, firemen and policemen and everybody, and she said the duty of the police was to investigate crimes and see the guilty were punished. So yesterday I came and told you, because it didn't matter if you didn't believe me, you'd have to do your duty and investigate anyway."

Levine sighed. "All right," he said. "We're doing it. But we need more than just your word, you understand that, don't you? We need proof of some kind."

She nodded, serious and formal again.

"What store did you go to that day?" he asked her.

"A supermarket. The big one on Seventh Avenue."

"Do you know any of the clerks there? Would they recognize you?"

"I don't think so. It's a great big supermarket. I don't think they know any of their customers at all."

"Did you see anyone at all on your trip to the store or back, who would remember that it was you who went to the store and not your mother, and that it was that particular day?"

She considered, touching one finger to her lips as she concentrated, and finally shook her head. "I don't think so. I don't know any of the people in the neighborhood. Most of the people I know are my parents' friends or kids from school, and they live all over, not just around here."

The New York complication. In a smaller town, people know their neighbors, have some idea of the comings and goings around them. But in New York, next-door neighbors remain strangers for years. At least that was true in the apartment house sections, though less true in the quieter outlying sections like the neighborhood in which Levine lived.

Levine got to his feet. "We'll see what we can do," he said. "This clang you told me about. Do you have any idea what your mother used to make the noise?"

"No, I don't. I'm sorry. It sounded like a gong or something. I don't know what it could possibly have been."

"A tablespoon against the bottom of a pot? Something like that?"

"Oh, no. Much louder than that."

"And she didn't have anything in her hands when she came out of the bedroom?"

"No, nothing."

"Well, we'll see what we can do," he repeated. "You can go back to class now."

"Thank you," she said. "Thank you for helping me."

He smiled. "It's my duty," he said. "As you pointed out."

"You'd do it anyway, Mr. Levine," she said. "You're a very good man. Like my stepfather."

Levine touched the palm of his hand to his chest, over his heart. "Yes," he said. "In more ways than one, maybe. Well, you go back to class. Or, wait. There's one thing I can do for you."

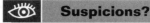

Suspicions?

1. How strong do you feel the case is against Mrs. Walker? Explain.

2. How concerned are you for Amy's life? Why?

She waited as he took a pencil and a small piece of memo paper from Mrs. Pidgeon's desk and wrote on it the precinct phone number and his home phone number, marking which each was. "If you think there's any danger of any kind," he told her, "any trouble at all, you call me. At the precinct until four o'clock and then at home after that."

"Thank you," she said. She folded the paper and tucked it away in the pocket of her skirt.

At a quarter to four, Levine and Crawley met again in the squadroom. When he'd come back in the morning from his talk with the little girl, Levine had found Crawley just back from having talked with Dr. Sheffield. It was Sheffield's opinion, Crawley had told him, that Amy was making the whole thing up, that her stepfather's death had been a severe shock and this was some sort of delayed reaction to it. Certainly he couldn't see any possibility that Mrs. Walker had actually murdered her husband, nor could he begin to guess at any motive for such an act.

Levine and Crawley had eaten lunch together in Wilton's, across the street from the station and then had separated, both to try to find someone who had either seen Amy or her mother on the shopping trip the afternoon Mr. Walker had died. This, aside from the accusation of murder itself, was the only contradiction between their stories. Find proof that one was lying, and they'd have the full answer. So Levine had started at the market and Crawley at the apartment building, and they'd spent the entire afternoon up and down the neighborhood, asking their questions and getting only blank stares for answers.

Crawley was there already when Levine came slowly into the squadroom, worn from an entire afternoon on his feet, climaxed by the climb to the precinct's second floor. He looked at Crawley and shook his head. Crawley said, "Nothing? Same here. Not a damn thing."

Levine laboriously removed his overcoat and set it on the coatrack. "No one remembers," he said. "No one saw, no one knows anyone. It's a city of strangers we live in, Jack."

"It's been two weeks," said Crawley. "Their building has a doorman, but he can't remember that far back. He sees the same tenants go in and out every day, and he wouldn't be able to tell you for sure who went in or out yesterday, much less two weeks ago, he says."

Levine looked at the wall-clock. "She's home from school by now," he said.

"I wonder what they're saying to each other. If we could listen in, we'd know a hell of a lot more than we do now."

Levine shook his head. "No. Whether she's guilty or innocent, they're both saying the exact same things. The death is two weeks old. If Mrs. Walker did commit murder, she's used to the idea by now that she's gotten away with it. She'll deny everything Amy says, and try to convince the girl she's wrong. The same things in the same words as she'd use if she were innocent."

"What if she kills the kid?" Crawley asked him.

"She won't. If Amy were to disappear, or have an accident, or be killed by an intruder, we'd know the truth at once. She can't take the chance. With her husband, all she had to do was fool a doctor who was inclined to believe her in the first place. Besides, the death was a strong possibility anyway. This time, she'd be killing a healthy ten-year-old, and she'd be trying to fool a couple of cops who wouldn't be inclined to believe her at all." Levine grinned. "The girl is probably safer now than she was before she ever came to us," he said. "Who knows what the mother might have been planning up till now?"

"All right, that's fine so far. But what do we do now?"

"Tomorrow, I want to take a look at the Walker apartment."

"Why not right now?"

"No. Let's give her a night to get rattled. Any evidence she hasn't removed in two weeks she isn't likely to think of now." Levine shrugged. "I don't expect to find anything," he said. "I want to look at the place because I can't think of anything else to do. All we have is the unsupported word of a ten-year-old child. The body can't tell us anything, because there wasn't any murder weapon. Walker died of natural causes. Proving they were induced won't be the easiest job in the world."

"If only *somebody*," said Crawley angrily, "had seen that kid at the grocery store! That's the only chink in the wall, Abe, the only damn place we can get a grip."

"We can try again tomorrow," said Levine, "but I doubt we'll get anywhere." He looked up as the door opened, and Trent and Kasper came in, two of the men on the four to midnight shift. "Tomorrow," he repeated.

"Maybe lightning will strike."

Levine shrugged back into his overcoat and left the office for the day. When he got home, he broke his normal habit and went straight into the house, not staying on the porch to read his paper. He went out to the kitchen and sat there, drinking coffee, while he filled Peg in on what little progress they'd made on the case during the day. She asked questions, and he answered them, offered suggestions and he mulled them over and rejected them, and throughout the evening, every once in a while, one or the other of them would find some other comment to make, but neither of them got anywhere. The girl seemed to be reasonably safe, at least for a while, but that was the best that could be said.

The baby next door was crying when they went to bed together at eleven o'clock. The baby kept him awake for a while, and his thoughts on the Walker death revolved and revolved, going nowhere. Once or twice during the evening, he had absent-mindedly reached for a cigarette, but had barely noticed the motion. His concentration and concern for Amy Walker and her mother was strong enough now to make him forget his earlier preoccupation with the problem of giving up smoking. Now, lying awake in the dark, the thought of cigarettes didn't even enter his head. He went over and over what the mother had said, what the daughter had told him, and gradually he drifted off into deep, sound sleep.

He awoke in a cold sweat, suddenly knowing the truth. It was as though he'd dreamed it, or someone had whispered it in his ear, and now he knew for sure.

She would kill tonight, and she would get away with it. He knew how she'd do it, and when, and there'd be no way to get her for it, no proof, nothing, no way at all.

He sat up, trembling, cold in the dark room, and reached out to the nightstand for his cigarettes. He pawed around on the nightstand, and suddenly remembered, and pounded the nightstand with his first in frustration and rage. She'd get away with it!

If he could get there in time—He could stop her, if he got there in time. He pushed the covers out of the way and climbed from the bed. Peg murmured in her sleep and burrowed deeper into the pillow. He gathered his clothes and crept from the bedroom.

He turned the light on in the living room. The clock over the television set read ten till one. There might still be time, she might be waiting until she was completely asleep. Unless she was going to do it with pills, something to help sleep, to make sleep a permanent, everlasting sure thing.

He grabbed the phone book and looked up the number of one of the private cab companies on Avenue L. He dialed, and told the dispatcher it was urgent, and the dispatcher said a car would be there in five minutes.

He dressed hurriedly, in the living room, then went out to the kitchen for pencil and paper, and left Peg a short note. "I had to go out for a while. Be back soon." In case she woke up. He left it on the nightstand.

A horn sounded briefly out front and he hurried to the front of the house, turning off lights. As he went trotting down the walk toward the cab, the baby next door cried out. He registered the sound, thought, *Baby next door,* and dismissed it from his mind. He had no time for extraneous thoughts, about babies or cigarettes or the rasp of his breathing from only this little exertion, running from the house. He gave the address, Prospect Park West, and sat back in the seat as the cab took off. It was a strange feeling, riding in a cab. He couldn't remember the last time he'd done it. It was a luxuriant feeling. To go so fast with such relaxing calm. If only it was fast enough.

It cost him four dollars, including the tip. If she was still alive, it was the bargain of the century. But as he hurried into the building and down the long narrow lobby to the elevators, the sound he'd heard as he'd left his home came back to him. He heard it again in his memory, and all at once he realized it hadn't been the baby next door at all. It had been the telephone.

He pressed the elevator button desperately, and the elevator slid slowly down to him from the eleventh floor. It had been the ring of the telephone.

So she'd made her move already. He was too late. When he'd left the house, he'd been too late.

The elevator doors opened, and he stepped in, pushed the button marked 4. He rode upward.

He could visualize that phone call. The little girl, hushed, terrified, whispering, beseeching. And Peg, half-awake, reading his note to her. And he was too late.

The door to apartment 4-A was ajar, the interior dark. He reached to his hip, but he'd been in too much of a hurry. The gun was at home, on the dresser.

He stepped across the threshold, cautiously, peering into the dark. Dim light spilled in from the hallway, showing him only this section of carpet near the door. The rest of the apartment was pitch black.

He felt the wall beside the door, found the light switch and clicked it on.

The light in the wall went out.

He tensed, the darkness now complete. A penny in the socket? And this was an old building, in which the tenants didn't pay directly for their own electricity, so the hall light was on the same line as the foyer of apartment A on every floor. They must have blown a fuse once, and she'd noticed that.

But why? What was she trying for?

The telephone call, as he was leaving the house. Somehow or other, she'd worked it out, and she knew that Levine was on his way here, that Levine knew the truth.

He backed away toward the doorway. He needed to get to the elevator, to get down and away from here. He'd call the precinct. They'd need flashlights, and numbers. This darkness was no place for him, alone.

A face rose toward him, luminous, staring, grotesque, limned in pale cold green, a staring devil face shining in green fire against the blackness. He cried out, instinctive panic filling his mouth with bile, and stumbled backwards away from the thing, bumping painfully into the doorpost. And the face disappeared.

He felt around him, his hands shaking, all sense of direction lost. He had to get out, he had to find the door. She was trying to kill him, she knew he knew and she was trying to kill him the same way she'd killed Walker. Trying to stop his heart.

A shriek jolted into his ears, loud, loud, incredibly loud, magnified far beyond the power of the human voice, a world-filling scream of hatred, grating him to the bone, and his flailing hands touched a wall, he leaned against it trembling. His mouth was open, straining for air, his chest was clogged, his heart beat fitfully, like the random motions of a wounded animal. The echoes of the shriek faded away, and then it sounded again, even louder, all around him, vibrating him like a fly on a pin.

He pushed away from the wall, blind and panic-stricken, wanting only to get away, to be away, out of this horror, and he stumbled into an armchair, lost his balance, fell heavily forward over the chair and rolled to the floor.

He lay there, gasping, unthinking, as brainlessly terrified as a rabbit in a trapper's snare. Pinwheels of light circled the corners of his stinging eyes, every straining breath was a searing fire in his throat. He lay on his back, encumbered and helpless in the heavy overcoat, arms and legs curled upward in feeble defense, and waited for the final blow.

But it didn't come. The silence lengthened, the blackness of the apartment remained unbroken, and gradually rationality came back to him and he could close his mouth, painfully swallow saliva, lower his arms and legs, and listen.

Nothing. No sound.

She'd heard him fall, that was it. And now she was waiting, to be sure he was dead. If she heard him move again, she'd hurl another thunderbolt, but for now she was simply waiting.

And the wait gave him his only chance. The face had been only phosphorescent paint on a balloon, pricked with a pin when he cried out. The shriek had come, most likely, from a tape recorder. Nothing that could kill him, nothing that could injure him, if only he kept in his mind what they were, and what she was trying to do.

My heart is weak, he thought, *but not that weak. Not as weak as Walker's, still recovering from his first attack. It could kill Walker, but it couldn't quite kill me.*

He lay there, recuperating, calming, coming back to himself. And then the flashlight flicked on, and the beam was aimed full upon him.

> **Suspicions?**
>
> When Detective Levine awoke in a cold sweat, why was he convinced that "she would kill tonight, and she would get away with it"?

He raised his head, looked into the light. He could see nothing behind it. "No, Amy," he said. "It didn't work."

The light flicked off.

"Don't waste your time," he said into the darkness. "If it didn't work at first, when I wasn't ready for it, it won't work at all.

"Your mother is dead," he said, speaking softly, knowing she was listening, that so long as she listened she wouldn't move. He raised himself slowly to a sitting position. "You killed her, too. Your father and mother both. And when you called my home, to tell me that she'd killed herself, and my wife told you I'd already left, you knew then that I knew. And you had to kill me, too. I'd told you that my heart was weak, like your father's. So you'd kill me, and it would simply be another heart failure, brought on by the sight of your mother's corpse."

The silence was deep and complete, like a forest pool. Levine shifted, gaining his knees, moving cautiously and without sound.

"Do you want to know how I knew?" he asked her. "Monday in Civics Miss Haskell told you about the duties of the police. But Miss Haskell told me that you were always at least a month ahead in your studies. Two weeks before your stepfather died, you read that assignment in your schoolbook, and then and there you decided how to kill them both."

He reached out his hand, cautiously, touched the chair he'd tripped over, shifted his weight that way, and came slowly to his feet, still talking. "The only thing I don't understand," he said, "is why. You steal books from the library that they won't let you read. Was this the same thing to you? Is it all it was?"

From across the room, she spoke, for the first time. "You'll never understand, Mr. Levine," she said. That young voice, so cold and adult and emotionless, speaking out contemptuously to him in the dark.

And all at once he could *see* the way it had been with Walker. Somnolent in the bed, listening to the frail fluttering of the weary heart, as Levine often lay at night, listening and wondering. And suddenly that shriek, out of the midafternoon stillness, coming from nowhere and everywhere, driving in at him—

Levine shivered. "No," he said. "It's you who don't understand. To steal a book, to snuff out a life, to you they're both the same. You don't understand at all."

She spoke again, the same cold contempt still in her voice. "It was bad enough when it was only *her*. Don't do this, don't do that. But then she had to marry him, and there were two of them watching me all the time, saying no no no, that's all they ever said. The only time I could ever have some peace was when I was at my grandmother's."

"Is *that* why?" He could hear again the baby crying, the gigantic ego of the very young, the imperious demand that *they* be attended to. And in the place of terror, he now felt only rage. That this useless half-begun thing should kill, and kill—

"Do you know what's going to happen to you?" he asked her. "They won't execute you, you're too young. They'll judge you insane, and they'll lock you away. And there'll be guards and matrons there, to say don't do this and don't do that, a million million times more than you can imagine. And they'll keep you locked away in a little room, forever and ever, and they'll let you do *nothing* you want to do, *nothing*."

He moved now, feeling his way around the chair, reaching out to touch the wall, working his way carefully toward the door. "There's nothing you can do to me now," he said. "Your bag of tricks won't work, and I won't drink the poison you fed your mother. And no one will believe the suicide confession you forged. I'm going to phone the precinct, and they'll come and get you, and you'll be locked away in that tiny room, forever and ever."

The flashlight hit the floor with a muffled thud, and then he heard her running, away from him, deeper into the apartment. He crossed the room with cautious haste, hands out before him, and felt around on the floor till his fingers blundered into the flashlight. He picked it up, clicked it on, and followed.

He found her in her mother's bedroom, standing on the window sill. The window was wide open, and the December wind keened into the room. The dead woman lay reposed on the bed, the suicide note conspicuous on the nightstand. He shone the light full on the girl, and she warned him, "Stay away. Stay away from me."

He walked toward her. "They'll lock you away," he said. "In a tiny, tiny room."

"*No, they won't!*" And she was gone from the window.

Levine breathed, knowing what he had done, that he had made it end this way. She hadn't ever understood death, and so it was possible for her to throw herself into it. The parents begin the child, and the child ends the parents. A white rage flamed in him at the thought.

He stepped to the window and looked down at the broken doll on the sidewalk far below. In another apartment, above his head, a baby wailed, creasing the night. Make way, make way.

He looked up. "We will," he whispered. "We will. But in our own time. Don't rush us."

 How Clever?

1. How did Brooklyn Detective Abraham Levine figure out that Amy Thorndike Walker was lying about her mother killing her stepfather? How did he realize, after he had left his apartment, that it must have been Amy who had called him at home? How did Amy conclude that if Detective Levine had already left his apartment, he must have figured out that Amy was both a liar and a killer?

2. What significance was there to the fact that according to Miss Haskell, Amy's fifth-grade teacher, Amy was always at least a month ahead of the rest of the class in her reading assignments?

3. The very first thing we are told about Detective Levine when we meet him at work is that he "longed for a cigarette." How is Detective Levine's constant desire for a cigarette linked to his worry that he will die from a heart attack? And how is that worry linked to Amy's killing of her stepfather and her plans for Detective Levine?

4. The reader's first awareness of Amy occurs in the words "the doorknob hesitantly turned, and a child walked in." How does this introduction predispose the reader in favor of Amy and the story she will tell? Does this predisposition and the description of Amy that immediately follows her entrance into the story constitute characterization as a red herring (misleading clue)? Explain.

5. There are quite a few references in the story to Detective Levine's envy of the next generation—young children or infants. Find the very first reference. How close to the beginning of the story does it occur and why? Why does Detective Levine envy the young?

6. Find the last reference in the story to Detective Levine's envy of the young. What is the effect on the reader with the story framed with these two references?

7. How does Amy come to symbolize or represent the entire next generation that Detective Levine fears (in fact, fears for his life)?

8. In the scene with his wife, Detective Levine indicates that he didn't believe Amy's story at first but then he's not so sure. He says that he has two questions: "First, is the little girl right or wrong? Did her mother actually make a loud noise that killed her stepfather or not? And if she did, then question number two: Did she do it on purpose, or was it an accident?" Using lateral thinking and your knowledge of the outcome of the story, what other questions should Detective Levine have thought to ask? Why did he only have these two?

9. Even though Detective Levine did not at first believe Amy's story, he decided to "check it out." Why was Amy so confident that Detective Levine would investigate her report? How did she count on it for what she was planning?

10. In what ways is Detective Levine "pulling a Sherlock Holmes" when he determines which school Amy attends? Where does he use detection and reflection?

11. How does Miss Haskell's characterization of the kind of child Amy is provide what will later turn out to be one solidly practical clue to Amy's guilt and several psychological clues?

12. What were Amy's motives in killing her stepfather and her mother? What is Detective Levine thinking and feeling when he reacts to Amy's main reason for killing her parents with the question "Is that why?" What was Amy's motive in attempting to kill Detective Levine? Do you think Amy killed her biological father? Explain.

13. Can an author's word choice be a red herring? Consider Donald Westlake's repeated use of the pronouns "she" and "her" in the five paragraphs that go from the middle of page 234.

14. What is ironic about the probable punishment Amy would have received for her crimes?

15. How do you feel about the fact that Detective Levine brought Amy to the point where she would commit suicide?

16. "The Sound of Murder" is the kind of detective story known as a police procedural. Explain why you think this is a good name for this kind of story.

DETECTWRITE: Setting

1. "Local color" refers to specific details authors incorporate into their stories to convey an accurate and recognizable sense of the setting's time and place. "The Sound of Murder" is set in contemporary New York City, more specifically in the Park Slope neighborhood of the borough of Brooklyn. Which particular examples of local color about New York City people, life, behavior, and institutions do you feel the author used most effectively to make the characters and plot of this contemporary urban crime story believable?

2. Compare and contrast the New York City location of this story with that in Lawrence Block's "Out the Window."

3. Think of some examples of local color for the setting of a detective or police procedural story that you might write.

DetectWrite: Plot Details

1. According to the author, Detective Levine believes that "the world conspired against a man who tried to give up smoking" and that he has turned himself into "a comic character" because he believed that "a grown man who tries to give up smoking is comic."

   Almost four decades have passed since the publication of "The Sound of Murder," and these attitudes have changed dramatically in the United States. Does the reversal of our feelings about people who try to break the smoking habit give "The Sound of Murder" a dated quality?

   Should an author concern himself or herself with examples of local color and current public attitudes that, while they give the story the life of its time, might also contribute to dating it over time? What is your opinion as a potential author of a detective story?

2. How does the author, Donald Westlake, create tension and suspense in the scene in which Detective Levine awakens and leaves for Amy's apartment?

3. How does Westlake create tension and suspense in the climactic scene in Amy's apartment?

4. What is effective about Westlake's saying that Detective Levine "stepped to the window and looked down at the broken doll on the sidewalk far below"?

5. It is a convention of every police procedural mystery story that the hero follow certain standard police operating procedures in his or her investigation and solution of a major crime. Review "The Sound of Murder" for the procedures Detective Levine and his partner Crawley follow. Which of these would you include in a police proedural mystery story that you might write? Why?

   Which additional procedures that you are aware of from your reading or viewing of other police procedural stories or from your knowledge of current police work would you have your police officer engage in? Why?

DetectWrite: Characterization

1. Compare and contrast Detective Levine with the other police officers you encounter in the stories in this section. In your opinion, which inspector contrasts most sharply with Detective Levine? Explain your decision.

2. Consider the possibility of writing a police procedural mystery with the hero of the story being a police officer. In what ways—physically and psychologically—would your hero be similar to Detective Levine? In what ways different?

3. How did you feel about a ten-year-old child as the criminal in "The Sound of Murder"? Under what circumstances would you have a child as the criminal in a detective story you might write?

4. How are Detective Levine's wife and his partner Crawley presented by the author as foils to Detective Levine?

5. How fully developed should secondary characters in a long short story or novella be? Consider Mrs. Walker in contrast to her daughter Amy and Mrs. Pidgeon (the principal of Amy's school) in contrast to Miss Haskell (Amy's fifth-grade teacher).

DETECTWRITE: Titling Your Story

Explain what appeals to you about the title of "The Sound of Murder." How might you use a similar approach in the titling of a detective story you would write?

Dial "M" for Murder

Frederick Knott

THE CHARACTERS

Margot Wendice
Max Halliday
Tony Wendice
Captain Lesgate
Inspector Hubbard
Thompson

ACT ONE

SCENE 1

The living room of the Wendices' flat in London.

It is about 6:20 P.M. on a Friday in September.

This is the ground floor apartment of a large house which has been converted into apartments. On the right are French windows which look out on to Charrington Gardens. There is a small terrace immediately outside. The heavy full-length curtains are at present drawn open. Inside the windows are shutters. These are folded back into the wall and are hardly noticeable. The fireplace is down left. On the wall above the mantelpiece is a mirror. Up left is a door leading to the bedroom; at the back two steps lead up into a small hall. Right of the hall is the kitchen. Back center of the hall is the entrance door to the flat (hall door). It has a Yale-type lock. When this door is open we can see through into a narrow passage outside which leads left to the street door. Back of the passage is a staircase leading up (from left to right) to the apartment above. The stairs pass the hall doorway at about the fifth step. Inside the hall door and to the left is a coat rack. At the back on the extreme right there are shelves with books in the top and bottles and drinking glasses on the bottom shelf. Underneath this bookshelf is a cupboard. In the wall on the extreme left there are corresponding shelves. Inside this are TONY'S *silver tennis trophies, a tennis racket is on the top shelf and on each side of the shelves, on the walls, are tennis photographs. In the extreme right upstage corner is a standard lamp. Right center is a flat table-desk on which there is a telephone and address book and a desk diary. The desk chair has its back to the windows. Below the desk is a wastepaper basket. Left center is a sofa. Right of this is a stool. Behind sofa is an oblong table on which there is a silver cigarette case and a vase of flowers. Down left is a chair and behind this chair is a small wall table with a wicker mending basket filled with stockings, scissors, etc. Below the sofa is a low, round coffee table.*

There is a chandelier over the center of the room and two wall brackets in the left wall above the fireplace. Both of these are controlled by light switches inside and on the right of the hall door. The standard lamp is switched on and off at the standard lamp itself.

At present no lights are on, it still being daylight outside, but the light begins to fade during the first scene between MAX *and* MARGOT.

The fire is burning brightly and the hall door is closed.

As the curtain rises, MARGOT *is handing* MAX *a drink. She suddenly hears something in the passage outside and opens and peeps through the hall door for a moment. Then she closes the hall door and turns to* MAX.

MARGOT: *[A little worried]* For a moment I thought it was Tony. I'm sorry I interrupted you. What were we talking about . . . ?

MAX: I was just telling you that I murdered exactly fifty-two people since I saw you last.

MARGOT: *[With a laugh, picking up her drink. Sits on couch]* Oh, yes—one a week. How *did* you do it?

MAX: Every way I could think of. I electrocuted some in their baths, locked others in the garage with the motor running or pushed them through windows and over cliffs. Other weeks I preferred to poison, shoot, strangle, stab, slug or suffocate.

MARGOT: Just according to how you felt?

MAX: When you write for that kind of television you don't have time to feel anything.

MARGOT: Where do you get all your ideas from?

MAX: Oh—newspaper stories—police files—bad dreams—other writers . . .

MARGOT: You once told me you'd never write anything that wasn't original.

MAX: Huh—you try being original fifty-two times a year!

MARGOT: Suppose you just dry up and can't think of anything?

MAX: If it comes to that I just use my three hats.

MARGOT: What do you mean?

MAX: I've got three old hats marked: Who kills who, How, and Why.

MARGOT: Which is what? I mean what's Why?

MAX: Why is the motive for killing. You've got to have a motive, you know. There are only five important ones. Fear—jealousy—money—revenge—and protecting someone you love. I just write them down on pieces of paper and pick one out of the Why hat.

MARGOT: Sounds rather like sorting the week's washing.

MAX: It's about as artistic as that. But better paid. It's no more frustrating than writing plays that aren't produced or novels that aren't published . . . And don't forget this: It all goes to prove that WITO makes teeth bright—white and *bite!* Makes amends and keeps your friends.

MARGOT: *[Laughs]* Let's have your glass, Max.

MAX: No . . . I'm all right, thanks.

MARGOT: I could hardly believe it when I heard your voice. At first I thought you were phoning from New York.

MAX: Yes, I thought you were shouting a little louder than necessary. As a matter of fact I was just around the corner. *[A pause, anxiously]* Was it all right . . . my phoning like that?

MARGOT: Yes, of course.

MAX: Was that—Tony who answered?

MARGOT: Yes, it was. *[An awkward pause]* I do hope he isn't going to be too late. Poor darling. He always gets caught when we're going to the theater. *[Pause]* So you're not here on a holiday—this time?

MAX: No, not this time. I came over to write some short TV films. After that I think I'll finally knock off for a year and write that novel. I've got to write it some day.

MARGOT: Another crime story?

MAX: I have to stick to crime—it's my stock in trade. But there's no reason why a murder story can't be as good as anything else. And I think I could write a good one if I took the time. I thought of a pretty fair gimmick on the plane coming over. There's a pair of twins—identical—one lives in Paris and the other in New York—all of a sudden they both decide to . . .

[MARGOT *has been growing anxious and loses interest in all this*]

MARGOT: *[Interrupting]* Max, before Tony comes I ought to explain something.

MAX: Yes?

MARGOT: I didn't tell him anything about us.

MAX: Oh.

MARGOT: When you rang up yesterday, I just said that you were a television writer I'd met when he was in America.

MAX: Well, that's true enough.

MARGOT: I said I'd met you again just before you went back to New York and you promised to look us up if you ever came back.

MAX: I see.

MARGOT: Max, I know you think it's silly, but when you get to know Tony, you'll understand why.

MAX: Margot, I'd like to get one thing straight. *[Rises, sits on arm of couch]* Things are O.K. now between you and Tony?

MARGOT: They couldn't be better. *[Rather intensely]* And I want to keep them that way.

MAX: *[Nods]* I'm very glad—at least I guess I will be when I get used to the idea.

MARGOT: *[Gratefully]* Thank you, Max.

MAX: *[Lightly]* I couldn't do this for anyone else, you know.

MARGOT: There's something else, Max.

MAX: Yes?

MARGOT: I wasn't going to tell you but . . .

MAX: Come on, let's have it . . .

MARGOT: Well, you remember those letters you wrote me?

MAX: Of course.

MARGOT: After I read them I burnt them. I thought it best. All except one. You probably know the one I mean.

MAX: I can guess. I never should have written it.

MARGOT: I know. But I loved it just the same. I used to carry it round wherever I went. Then one day Tony and I were going to spend the weekend with some friends in the country. While we were waiting on the platform I noticed my handbag was missing . . . and the letter was inside.

MAX: I see . . . Where was this?

MARGOT: Victoria Station. I thought I must have left it in the restaurant but when I went to look for it, it had gone.

MAX: You never found it?

MARGOT: I recovered the handbag about two weeks later from the lost and found. But the letter wasn't there. *[Pause]* Then a week after, I received a note. It told me what I had to do to get the letter back.

MAX: Go on.

MARGOT: I was to draw fifty pounds from my bank in five-pound notes, then change them for used one-pound notes. It said that if I went to the police or told anyone else—he would show the letter to my husband.

MAX: May I see it? [MARGOT *exits into bedroom.* MAX *gets up and paces uneasily around the room. He takes a cigarette from the silver box and lights it. Then* MARGOT *enters holding two white envelopes. She hands one of these to* MAX *who takes out the note and examines it*] Printed—all capitals. Anyone could have done this.

[MARGOT *hands him another envelope*]

MARGOT: Then—two days later—I got this one.

[MAX *takes out the second note*]

MAX: *[Glancing at the postmarks]* Both mailed in Brixton. *[Reading]* "Tie up money in a package and mail to John S. King, 23 Newport Street, Brixton, S.W.9. You will get your letter by return." Well, of all the . . .

MARGOT: That's a little shop. People use it as a forwarding address.

MAX: Did you mail the money?

MARGOT: Yes, but the letter was never returned. . . . So after waiting two weeks I went there. They said they'd never heard of a man by that name, and the parcel was still there. It had never been opened.

MAX: Well, I suppose that's something. [MAX *puts the notes back in the envelopes and puts them into his wallet*] May I keep these?

MARGOT: *[Hesitates]* Yes . . . If you like.

MAX: You didn't tell Tony?

MARGOT: No, I didn't tell anyone. *[Pause]* I can't understand why the man didn't collect the money.

MAX: He was probably in jail by that time. *[Pause]* You never heard from him again?

MARGOT: No.

MAX: Well, let me know if you do. I'll find him and fix him so he can't read, let alone write. *[Pause]* Is that why you asked me to stop writing?

MARGOT: Yes. I was in an awful panic. I imagined that every letter you wrote me would be opened and read by someone.

MARGOT: Why didn't you tell me?

MARGOT: You couldn't have done anything. You would probably have made me tell Tony and the police. As it was only fifty pounds I thought I'd pay up and have done with it.

MAX: Margot, are you ever going to tell Tony—about us?

MARGOT: [*Horrified*] No. I couldn't possibly tell him. Not now.

MAX: Why not? Don't you think we'd all get on better in the end if . . .

MARGOT: Please, Max, I know Tony—you don't.

MAX: You don't have to tell me. Just the thought of meeting him makes me, shall we say, uncomfortable.

MARGOT: Oh, you'll get on fine. He's changed a lot this last year. . . . Now, he's a model husband. [*Slowly and thoughtfully*] In fact, it was exactly a year ago that it happened.

MAX: What happened?

MARGOT: Tony suddenly grew up. He seemed to change overnight from a rather selfish little person into a perfectly reasonable grownup. You remember that night—I came to say good-bye?

MAX: How could I forget? Tony had gone off to play in a tennis tournament.

MARGOT: He did—but he came back. I'm not much good at writing about things like this, so I didn't try. But when I left you that night I came back here. I sat down on the sofa and had a good cry. Then I fell asleep. When I woke up he was standing in the hall with all his bags and tennis rackets. He just said that he had decided to give up tennis for good and settle down.

MAX: Just like that?

[MARGOT *gets up. Takes* MAX'S *glass and hers to drink bar and mixes drinks*]

MARGOT: Just like that. Of course I didn't believe him at first. I'd got so used to tagging around after him wherever he went, I could see no end to it. But he meant it all right. He went out the very next day and got himself a job. [*A church clock chimes*] What were we doing—exactly a year ago?

MAX: I was putting the mushrooms into the spaghetti. I nearly turned round and said, "I can't go through with this. Let's find Tony and have it out with him."

MARGOT: I felt that way, too. I wanted so much to say something—and all I could do was to stand there—quite uselessly—with a drip on the end of my nose. What did you do when I'd gone?

MAX: I walked along the Embankment and stared at the Chelsea gas works.

MARGOT: [*With a laugh*] Were you thinking about the gas works—or me?

MAX: Neither. I was writing a story. I always do when I'm miserable.

MARGOT: A sad story?

MAX: A triumphant story—my hero was an eminent writer coming from America with his pockets full of money ready to snatch his lady love from the arms of her jealous husband.

MARGOT: [Smiling] Only to find that husband and wife were very happy, thank you.

MAX: And that he was very glad to know it.

MARGOT: [Handing MAX his glass] Max, let's drink to—the way things turn out.

MAX: [Raising glass to MARGOT] Way things turn . . .

[But before they can drink, there is the sound of a key in the door. They both turn toward it, as if it had interrupted their toast. TONY enters. He is thirty-four and has an easy charm. His mind is always active and he usually seems very sure of himself]

MARGOT: Oh, there you are . . . We thought you were never coming . . . What have you been up to?

TONY: Sorry, darling. The boss blew in just as I was leaving.

[As TONY takes off his overcoat and hangs it up, MAX stands a little awkwardly, facing hall]

MARGOT: Tony, this is Max Halliday.

TONY: Hullo, Max.

MAX: [Shaking hands] Tony . . .

TONY: I'm terribly sorry to be so late. Has Margot been looking after you all right? How's your drink?

MARGOT: We've been drinking ourselves silly waiting for you.

TONY: [Mixing himself a drink] Well, how do you like it over here, Max?

MAX: Fine.

TONY: Is this your first visit to London?

MAX: Uh—no—I was here a year ago for a vacation.

TONY: Oh, yes, that's right. Margot told me. You write for the radio, don't you?

MAX: Television—for my sins.

TONY: Ah, yes. Television, poor fellow. Are you staying long?

MAX: I'm not sure. I've some writing to do. When that's finished I'd like to stay a while longer and do some traveling.

TONY: That's a good idea. But don't spend all your time in museums and cathedrals. Once you've seen one, you've seen the lot, if you ask me. Do you fish?

MAX: No, I'm afraid I don't.

TONY: Pity. If you did I'd suggest you went up to Scotland for the . . .

MARGOT: He doesn't fish, darling.

TONY: No, he doesn't. I guess that's that. Well, if you want showing around any time just let us know. [*To* MARGOT] Darling, we could take Max to the Tower of London.

MAX: I'm afraid I've already been there.

TONY: Oh, what a shame! I've always wanted to go to the Tower. But seriously, Max, if there's anything we can do any time . . .

MAX: Thank you, Tony. I'll remember that.

MARGOT: Darling, it's getting late. Did you reserve the table?

TONY: Yes. Seven o'clock.

MARGOT: [*Jumping up*] Well, come on then. [*Moving toward bedroom*] Get your coats on.

TONY: Oh, darling. Slight alteration in plans.

MARGOT: [*Turning*] Now don't say you can't go.

TONY: [*With a shrug*] I'm afraid so. Old man Burgess is flying to Brussels on Sunday and we all have to get our monthly reports in by tomorrow.

MARGOT: Oh, no! Can't you do it when you get back tonight?

TONY: 'Fraid not. It will take hours. I shall have to fake half of it.

MARGOT: Can you join us after the theater? We might go somewhere.

TONY: Give me a ring in the intermission. If I'm inspired I might make it . . .

MARGOT: Do try. I'll just get my things, Max.

[MARGOT *exits to bedroom*]

TONY: [*Handing tickets to* MAX] Here are the tickets, Max.

MAX: Thanks.

TONY: I'm afraid this is extremely rude of me.

MAX: Not at all. I'm sorry you can't come, though.

TONY: You must come to dinner one night.

MAX: Thanks, I'd like to.

TONY: I say—are you doing anything tomorrow night?

MAX: Saturday? I don't think so.

TONY: [*Delighted*] That's perfect. How would you like to come to a stag party—just down the road?

MAX: [*Puzzled*] A stag party?

TONY: Yes. Some American boys have been playing tennis all over the Continent and we're giving them a sort of farewell dinner.

MAX: But I'm no tennis player.

TONY: That doesn't matter. You know New York and all that.

[MARGOT *enters from bedroom. She wears overcoat and carries handbag*] Darling. Max is coming to the party tomorrow night.

MARGOT: Oh, good. [*To* MAX] You'd better drop in here first and have a drink.

TONY: That's the idea.

MARGOT: [*To* TONY] By the way, aren't you dressing?

TONY: Dinner jackets—yes. [*To* MAX] Is that all right?

MAX: Well, no. My trunk was supposed to arrive today, but I'm afraid it's not here yet.

TONY: [*Worried*] Oh. [*Pause*] You could rent one, of course.

MARGOT: Don't be silly. Darling, it isn't that important.

TONY: Just a minute. I've got an idea.

[TONY *exits quickly into bedroom leaving door open*]

MARGOT: Now we really are going to be late.

MAX: Shall I try and get a taxi?

MARGOT: No. We can usually pick one up. [*Glancing at bedroom*] Tony, we must go.

[TONY *returns with dinner jacket*]

TONY: Hold it a second. Just try this on, Max.

MARGOT: What on earth?

TONY: It's only my old single-breasted but it might do.

[*As* MAX *takes off coat reluctantly*]

MAX: Look—if dressing is as important as all this—let's forget it, shall we?

TONY: Nonsense.

[TONY *helps* MAX *on with dinner jacket*]

MARGOT: That dreadful old thing—it reeks of moth balls.

MAX: Well, they say that writers will do anything for a square meal.

TONY: Oh, it does look a little meager, doesn't it?

[MAX *gestures, indicating that dinner jacket is too small.* MARGOT *helps* MAX *off with dinner jacket and* TONY *helps him on with coat*]

MARGOT: I refuse to let you send Max out looking like a scarecrow. Surely he can go as he is.

[*Throws dinner jacket to* TONY]

MAX: Anyway, my stuff will be here by tomorrow. Let's hope that it is.

MARGOT: Come on, Max, let's go before he tries on the pants.

[MARGOT *and* MAX *exit.* TONY *stands in open doorway and watches them go*]

TONY: Enjoy yourselves. Hey, Max!

MAX: [*Offstage*] Yes?

TONY: Try and sell the odd ticket and have a drink on the proceeds. Good-bye—have a good time.

[TONY *closes the door. Turns bracket lights off and crosses to curtains. He closes curtains, switches on standard lamp and turns to telephone. After staring at the phone for a few seconds he picks it up and dials. After a pause* LESGATE'S *voice can be heard in the phone receiver*]

> **Suspicions?**
>
> Have any of the characters' words or actions created any suspicions in your mind so far? Explain.

LESGATE: Hullo.

TONY: Hullo? Hampstead 2837?

LESGATE: Yes.

TONY: Could I speak to Captain Lesgate, please?

LESGATE: Speaking.

TONY: Oh, good evening. You don't know me; my name's Fisher. . . . I understand you have a car for sale.

LESGATE: An American car.

TONY: That's right; I saw it at your garage. How much are you asking?

LESGATE: Eleven hundred.

TONY: Eleven hundred! I see. It certainly looks just the job for me but I don't like the price much.

LESGATE: I didn't like it when I bought it.

TONY: [*With a laugh*] Now when can we meet?

LESGATE: How about tomorrow afternoon?

TONY: I don't think I can manage that. [*Pause*] No, I can't. And I'm going to Liverpool on Sunday. I was rather hoping . . . I say, I suppose you couldn't come round to my flat tonight?

LESGATE: Where is it?

TONY: Maida Vale—I'd call on you only—I've twisted my knee rather badly.

LESGATE: Oh, I'm sorry. What's your address?

TONY: 61a Charrington Gardens.

LESGATE: Harrington . . .

TONY: No—Charrington.

LESGATE: Charrington . . .

TONY: That's right. Turn left at the underground. It's about two minutes' walk.

LESGATE: I'll be there in about an hour.

TONY: About an hour? That's extremely good of you. *[Anxiously]* By the way, will you be bringing the car?

LESGATE: I'm afraid I can't tonight because it's . . .

TONY: *[Relieved]* That doesn't matter. I had a good look at it. Perhaps you would bring the registration book and any necessary papers.

LESGATE: Of course.

TONY: I don't see why we shouldn't settle the whole thing here and now—provided you drop the price sufficiently.

LESGATE: I'm afraid that's quite out of the question.

TONY: Huh! We'll see what a couple of drinks can do.

LESGATE: *[Amused]* Huh, huh, huh.

TONY: Huh, huh, huh. Well—good-bye.

LESGATE: Good-bye.

[Hangs up]

TONY: *[Hangs up]* Captain Lesgate!

CURTAIN

SCENE 2

The same. One hour later. The room is softly lit by the standard lamp and brackets. A pair of white cotton gloves lies on the stool.

As the curtain rises, TONY *enters from the bedroom carrying an old leather suitcase which he places carefully against the wall left of drink cupboard. Then he turns and surveys the room. He looks at the cotton gloves for a moment, then goes and picks them up and lays them neatly on the left arm of the sofa. He considers the effect and is satisfied. He then starts for the bedroom. The doorbell rings and interrupts him. He turns and deliberately assumes a painful limp. He opens the hall door.* LESGATE *stands outside wearing an overcoat.*

LESGATE: Mr. Fisher?

TONY: Yes. Captain Lesgate?

LESGATE: Yes.

TONY: Do come in. This is very good of you. Let me have your coat. *[He takes it and hangs it up]* Have any difficulty finding your way?

LESGATE: None at all.

[*They enter the room*]

TONY: Do sit down.

LESGATE: Thank you.

TONY: Now, how about a drink?

[TONY *limps to the drink cabinet.*LESGATE *watches him curiously for a few moments*]

LESGATE: I can't help thinking I've seen you before somewhere.

TONY: [*Looking up sharply*] Funny you should say that. The moment I opened the door I . . . [*He stops suddenly*] Wait a minute . . . Lesgate? You're not Lesgate—Swann! C. J. Swann—or was it C. A.?

LESGATE: C. A. . . . . you've a better memory than I have . . . Fisher? When did we meet?

TONY: Weren't you at Cambridge?

LESGATE: Yes.

TONY: Must be twenty years ago. You wouldn't remember me . . . I only came your last year.

LESGATE: Well! What a coincidence!

[*They shake hands*]

TONY: [*Going to drink cupboard*] This calls for a special drink. I was planning to palm you off with an indifferent port. Let's see what we have here. [*Holding up the brandy*] How about this?

LESGATE: Perfect. [*Sits on sofa*] By the way—how did you know my car was for sale?

[TONY *pours brandy into two glasses before answering*]

TONY: Your garage told me.

LESGATE: That's odd. I don't think I mentioned it to anyone there.

TONY: I was stopping for a fill-up. I told them I was looking for an American car and they gave me your phone number. I say, it is for sale, isn't it?

LESGATE: [*Laughing*] Well, of course.

TONY: Good. But I refuse to discuss the price until you've had at least three brandies.

[TONY *hands* LESGATE *his glass*]

LESGATE: [*Taking it*] I warn you. I drive a hard bargain, drunk or sober.

TONY: So do I.

[*They laugh*]

LESGATE: You know, I think I must have seen you since we left Cambridge.

TONY: Ever been to Wimbledon?

LESGATE: That's it—Wendice—Tony Wendice . . . *[Bewildered]* Then what's all this about Fisher?

TONY: *[With a teasing glance]* What's all this about Lesgate? [LESGATE *looks embarrassed*] Do you like a cigar?

LESGATE: *[Taking out pipe]* I'll stick to this pipe, if you don't mind. [TONY *hesitates for a split second as if this throws him a little, then, turning away]*

TONY: That's one habit you've changed.

LESGATE: Oh?

[TONY *goes to wall and takes down a framed photograph of a group of young men at dinner*]

TONY: I remember at college you always used to smoke rather expensive cigars. Wait a minute, I think I have a picture of you. *[Showing the photograph to* LESGATE] Yes, look. Here's an old photo of you at a reunion dinner . . . There you are on the right with the biggest cigar in the business.

LESGATE: *[Amused]* Huh! That was the first and last reunion I ever went to. What a murderous thug I look.

TONY: *[Even more amused]* Yes—you do rather. Of course, I always remember you because of the College Ball. *[Pause]* You were the treasurer, weren't you?

LESGATE: Honorary treasurer. I used to organize the beastly things.

TONY: Yes. Some of the ticket money was stolen, wasn't it?

[TONY *sits on sofa*]

LESGATE: That's right. Nearly a hundred pounds. I'd left it in a cash box in my study. In the morning, it had gone. Still makes me sweat to think of it.

TONY: It was the college porter, of course.

LESGATE: Yes, poor old Alfred. He never could back a winner. They found the cash box in his back garden....

TONY: ...But not the money.

[LESGATE *hands the picture back to* TONY]

LESGATE: Good lord, twenty years ago!

TONY: What are you doing nowadays?

[Pause]

LESGATE: I deal in property. *[Changing the subject]* I don't follow tennis very closely. Did you play at Wimbledon this year?

TONY: No. I've given up tennis or rather tennis gave me up. One has to earn a living sometime, and I'd had a pretty good run for my money. I went round the world three times.

LESGATE: I suppose you were treated like a film star?

TONY: Film stars get paid.

LESGATE: There is that.

TONY: Of course I managed to save a bit on expenses. In seven years I put away just over a thousand pounds. Not much compared with your film stars!

LESGATE: What are you doing now? Making up for lost time?

TONY: I sell sports equipment. Not very lucrative but it gives me plenty of spare time.

LESGATE: *[Looking round the room]* Well, I'm here to tell you you manage to run a very comfortable place.

TONY: *[Modestly]* My wife has some money of her own. Otherwise I should hardly feel like blowing a thousand pounds on your car.

LESGATE: Eleven hundred. Yes, people with capital don't realize how lucky they are. I'm already resigned to living on what I can earn.

[Pause]

TONY: *[Thoughtfully]* Of course, you can still marry for money.

[Pause]

LESGATE: Yes, I suppose some people make a business of that.

TONY: *[Quietly]* I know I did.

[Pause]

LESGATE: *[With a laugh]* You mean the girl you fell in love with happened to have some money of her own.

TONY: No. *[Pause]* I always intended to marry for money. I had to. Whilst I was in first-class tennis I met wealthy people all over the world—I was somebody—while my wind lasted! I decided to snap up the first chance I got. I nearly married a tubby Boston deb with five million dollars; it got as far as pictures in the papers and then she threw me over for an heir to a chain of grocery stores. Funny how they stick together. I finally settled for a good deal less—a lot more easily. My wife had been a fan of mine for some time.

[Pause]

LESGATE: Well—that's putting it pretty bluntly.

TONY: Have I shocked you?

LESGATE: No, I always admire a man who knows what he wants.

TONY: To know what you want *to pay for*—that's the thing. Everything has its price. People fail because they want to buy cheap. I've learnt to pay a big price for anything I really want . . . I usually get it.

LESGATE: Yes, I'm sure you do. *[Looking at his wrist watch]* I haven't a great deal of time . . .

TONY: I was telling you about my wife. She got her money from her late aunt, who got it from her late husband, who got it from his first wife. Of course, a large chunk gets lopped off every time somebody dies but quite a bit has managed to filter through.

LESGATE: *[Joking]* You say you married for money. Why do you think she married you?

TONY: *[Quite simply]* I was a tennis star. She would never have married a commercial salesman.

LESGATE: But you've given up tennis. She hasn't left you.

[Pause]

TONY: She nearly did.

[TONY *starts to get up rather painfully*]

LESGATE: *[Rising]* Let me, Wendice. You've got a groggy knee.

TONY: Oh, thanks, old boy. Let's have that bottle over here, shall we?

LESGATE: Good idea.

[LESGATE *collects brandy from desk; he pours brandy into* TONY'S *glass and then into his own.* TONY *watches him all the time*]

TONY: Would you like to hear about it?

LESGATE: Hear what?

TONY: About my wife—how she nearly left me.

LESGATE: It's your privilege—you're the host.

TONY: Oh, thanks. To be frank, I think you might help. Just man to man advice, you know.

LESGATE: I'm at your service.

[LESGATE *puts bottle down on round table and sits down*]

TONY: After we were married I played in the various championships and Margot tagged along. I think she found it all a bit much. Hospitality—outside this country—can be pretty exhausting. When we got back she

> **Suspicions?**
>
> 1. What do you think is behind Tony's charade, his faking both a twisted knee and an interest in Swann's automobile?
>
> 2. What reasons might Tony have for choosing Swann, in particular (and not someone else), to be at his "service"?

tried to persuade me to give up tennis and play husband instead. *[Rises]* In the end, we compromised. I went alone to America for the grass court season and returned after the National Championships. I soon realized that a lot had happened while I was away. For one thing—she wasn't in love with me any more. There were phone calls that would end abruptly if I happened to walk in. And there was an old school friend she used to visit from time to time. Then one day we had a row; I wanted to play in a covered court tournament and as usual she didn't want me to go. I was in the bedroom—the phone rang. It all sounded pretty urgent. After that she seemed rather keen that I should play in that tournament after all, so I packed my kit into the car and drove off. *[Pause]* I parked the car two streets away and walked back on my tracks. Ten minutes later she came out of this house and took a taxi. I took another. *[Pause]* Her old school friend lived in a studio in Chelsea. I could see them through the studio window as he cooked spaghetti over a gas ring. They didn't say much. They just looked very natural together. Funny how you can tell when people are in love. Then I started to walk. I began to wonder what would happen if she left me. I'd have to find some way of earning a living to begin with. Suddenly I realized how much I'd grown to depend on her. All these expensive tastes I'd acquired while I was at the top—and now big tennis had finished with me—and so, apparently, had my wife. I can't ever remember being so scared. I dropped into a pub and had a few drinks. As I sat in the corner I thought of all sorts of things . . . I thought of three different ways of killing him. I even thought of killing her. That seemed a far more sensible idea—and just as I was working out how I could do it—I suddenly saw something which completely changed my mind. *[Pause]* I didn't go to that tournament after all. When I got back she was sitting exactly where you are now. I told her I'd decided to give up tennis and look after her instead.

[Pause]

LESGATE: Well?

TONY: *[Sharp change of mood]* As things turned out—I needn't have got so worked up after all. Apparently that spaghetti evening had been a sort of fond farewell. The boy friend had been called back to New York.

LESGATE: An American?

TONY: Yes. There were long letters from there . . . They usually arrived on Thursdays. She burnt all of them except one. That one she used to transfer from handbag to handbag. It was always with her. That letter became an obsession with me. I *had* to find out what was in it—and finally—I did. That letter made very interesting reading.

LESGATE: You mean you stole it?

TONY: Yes. I even wrote her two anonymous notes offering to sell it back.

LESGATE: Why?

TONY: I was hoping *that* would make her come and tell me all about him—but it didn't—so I kept the letter.

[TONY *takes out wallet, and lets the letter fall out of it onto sofa.* LESGATE *picks it up and examines envelope*]

LESGATE: Why are you telling me all this?

TONY: Because you're the only person I can trust. [LESGATE *puts the letter back in wallet and* TONY *snaps wallet shut*] Anyway, that did it. It must have put the fear of God into them because the letters stopped—and we lived happily ever after. *[Changes tone]* Funny to think that just a year ago I was sitting in that Knightsbridge pub—actually planning to murder her—and I might have done it if I hadn't seen something that changed my mind.

LESGATE: *[Tapping pipe on ash tray on table back of sofa]* Well. *[Tap—tap—tap]* What did you see? *[Tap—tap]*

TONY: *[Quietly]* I saw you.

[Long pause]

LESGATE: *[Turning round slowly to* TONY] What was so odd about that?

TONY: The coincidence. You see only a week before I'd been to a reunion dinner and the fellows had been talking about you. How you'd been court-martialed during the war—a year in prison! That was news. Mind you, at college we'd always said old Swann would end up in jail—that cash box, I suppose.

LESGATE: What about it?

TONY: *[With a laugh]* My dear fellow, everybody knew you took that money. Poor old Alfred.

Suspicions?

1. Tony tells Swann about Margot and Max, duplicating many of the details that Margot had shared with Max (and indirectly with the audience) at the beginning of the play. What might be the purpose of this duplication?

2. Of the five motives for a killing Max mentioned to Margot at the beginning of the play, which does Tony reveal to be his?

LESGATE: *[Rising]* Well, thanks for the drink. Interesting hearing about your matrimonial affairs, I'm sure. *[Moving to hall]* I take it you won't be wanting that car after all?

TONY: Don't you want me to tell you why I brought you here?

LESGATE: Yes, I think you'd better.

[*During his following speech,* TONY *gets up from the sofa. He has dropped his limp. He takes out his handkerchief, wipes fingerprints off the reunion photograph and returns it to wall. Then he carefully wipes ash tray, part of table and the brandy bottle. He crosses behind desk—takes ash tray and dumps ashes into fireplace—again wipes with handkerchief. He crosses to* LESGATE *and gets his glass, wipes it and puts it on coffee table*]

TONY: It was when I saw you in the pub that it happened. Suddenly everything became quite clear. Only a few months before, Margot and I had made our wills—quite short affairs leaving everything we had to each other in case of accidents. Hers worked out at just over ninety thousand pounds. Investments, mostly—all too easy to get at. And that was dangerous as they'd be bound to suspect me. I'd need an alibi—a very good one—and then I saw you. I'd often wondered what happened to people when they came out of prison—people like you, I mean. Can they get jobs? Do old friends rally round? Suppose they'd never had any friends. I was so curious to know that I followed you. I followed you home that night and—would you mind passing your glass? Thank you, thank you so much—and I've been following you ever since.

LESGATE: Why?

TONY: I was hoping that, sooner or later, I might—catch you at something and be able to . . .

LESGATE: Blackmail me?

TONY: Influence you. After a few weeks I got to know your routine which made it a lot easier.

LESGATE: Rather dull work.

TONY: To begin with, yes. But you know how it is—you take up a hobby and the more you get to know of it the more fascinating it becomes. You became quite fascinating. In fact, there were times when I felt that you—almost belonged to me.

LESGATE: That must have been fascinating.

TONY: You always went dog-racing on Mondays and Thursdays. I even took it up myself—just to be near you. You'd changed your name to Adams.

LESGATE: Yes, I got bored with Swann. Any crime in that?

TONY: No, none at all. And you used to go to a little private club in Soho. It had an odd name . . . *[Remembering]* The Kettle of Fish, that's it. The police closed it down recently, I believe—someone was caught taking drugs or something.

LESGATE: *[Casually]* I never heard about that. *I* went there to eat. There's no crime in that either.

TONY: None whatever. In fact, there was nothing really illegal about you. I got quite discouraged, and then one day you disappeared from your lodgings, so I phoned your landlady. I said, "Mr. Adams owed me five pounds.". . . Apparently that was nothing. Mr. Adams owes her six weeks' rent and her best lodger fifty-five pounds! And Mr. Adams had always been such a nice gentleman. That's what seemed to upset her most.

LESGATE: Yes, that's what always upsets them most.

[LESGATE *strolls to round table and reaches for the brandy bottle*]

TONY: I say, old boy, if you want another drink, do you mind putting on these gloves? [LESGATE *glances at the gloves on the arm of the sofa but does not pick them up*] Thanks. Now, where were we? Oh, yes, I'd lost you and then I found you one day at the dog-racing and tailed you home to your new lodgings in Belsize Park. There Mr. Adams became Mr. Wilson. Mr. Wilson left Belsize Park last July owing fifteen weeks' rent and somewhat richer for his brief encounter with a . . . Miss Wallace. You used to go out with Miss Wallace on Wednesdays and Sundays. She certainly was in love with you, wasn't she? I suppose she thought you were growing that handsome mustache to please her. Poor Miss Wallace.

LESGATE: This is all most interesting. Do go on.

TONY: July—August—September . . . Apartment one two seven Carlisle Court . . . Occupant . . . A Mrs. Van Dorn. Her late husband left her two hotels and a large apartment house—furnished. What a base to operate from, Captain Lesgate! The only trouble is, she does rather enjoy being courted, and she is so very expensive. Perhaps that's why you've been trying to sell her car for over a month.

LESGATE: Mrs. Van Dorn asked me to sell it for her.

TONY: I know. I called her up just before you arrived here. She only wanted eight hundred.

[*Pause.* LESGATE *remains perfectly still*]

LESGATE: [*Casually*] Where's the nearest police station?

TONY: Opposite the church. Two minutes' walk.

LESGATE: Suppose I walk there now?

TONY: What would you tell them?

LESGATE: Everything.

TONY: Everything? All about Mr. Adams and Mr. Wilson?

LESGATE: I shall simply tell them you are trying to blackmail me into . . .

TONY: Into?

LESGATE: Murdering your wife.

[Pause]

TONY: I almost wish you would. When she heard that we'd have the best laugh of our lives.

LESGATE: Aren't you forgetting something?

TONY: Am I?

LESGATE: You've told me a few things tonight.

TONY: What of it?

> **👁 Suspicions?**
>
> Is this something Tony has forgotten to take into account? Predict Tony's response.

LESGATE: Suppose I tell them how you followed her to that studio in Chelsea—how you watched them cooking spaghetti and all that rubbish. Wouldn't that ring a bell?

TONY: It certainly would. They'd assume you followed her there yourself.

LESGATE: Me? Why should I?

TONY: Why should you steal her handbag? Why should you write her all those blackmail notes? Can you prove that you didn't? You certainly can't prove that I did. It will be a straight case of your word against mine.

LESGATE: *[Amused]* Huh, that ought to puzzle them. What could you say?

TONY: I shall say that you came here tonight—half-drunk—and tried to borrow money on the strength that we were at college together. When I refused you said something about a letter belonging to my wife. As far as I could make out you were offering to sell it to me. I gave you what money I had and you gave me the letter. It has your fingerprints on it. Remember? *[Takes wallet out of pocket and shows it to him]* Then you said if I went to the police you'd tell some crazy story about my wanting you to murder my wife. But before we go any further, old boy—do consider the inconvenience. You see, I'm quite well known . . . and there would be pictures of you as well. Sooner or later a deputation of lodgers and landladies would come forward to testify to your character. And someone is almost certain to have seen you with Miss Wallace. *[Pause]* You were always careful not to be seen around with her—I noticed. You usually met in out-of-the-way places where no one would recognize you—like that little tea shop in Pimlico.

LESGATE: That was her idea, not mine.

TONY: Yes, it was a bit crummy, wasn't it? Hardly a place to take Mrs. Van Dorn. By the way, does Mrs. Van Dorn know about—Mr. Adams—and Mr. Wilson . . . and Miss Wallace? You were planning to marry Mrs. Van Dorn, weren't you?

LESGATE: Smart, aren't you?

TONY: Not really, I've just had time to think things out—putting myself in your position. That's why I know you're going to agree.

LESGATE: What makes you *think* I'll agree?

TONY: For the same reason that a donkey with a stick behind him and a carrot in front goes forwards and not backwards.

[Long pause]

LESGATE: Tell me about the carrot.

[Long pause, TONY *looks straight at* LESGATE]

TONY: One thousand pounds in cash.

[Long pause, LESGATE *looks up at* TONY *and their eyes meet]*

LESGATE: For a murder?

TONY: For a few minutes' work. That's all it is. And no risk. I guarantee. That ought to appeal to you. You've been skating on very thin ice.

LESGATE: *[With a great effort to appear amused]* I don't know what you're talking about . . .

TONY: You should know. It was in all the papers. A middle-aged woman found dead due to an overdose of cocaine. Appeared as though she'd been taking the stuff for quite a time—but no one knows where she got it . . . But we know—don't we? Poor Miss Wallace! *[This bites* LESGATE *and there is a long silence. Changing his tone]* Yes, you should take a long holiday abroad. Surely a honeymoon with Mrs. Van Dorn would be preferable to ten years' detention at Dartmoor. My thousand pounds should see you safely married to her. You'll find it makes such a difference to have some money in the family.

LESGATE: *[Amused and sarcastic]* This thousand pounds—where is it?

TONY: *[Quite serious]* It's in a small attaché case in a checkroom.

[Pause]

LESGATE: Where?

TONY: Somewhere in London. Of course, we don't meet again. As soon as you've—delivered the goods, I shall mail you the checkroom ticket and the key to the case. *[*TONY *opens drawer in desk and, using his handkerchief, takes out a bundle of one-pound notes. He throws this across the room so that it lands on the sofa]* You can take this hundred pounds on account.

*[*LESGATE *looks down at the money but doesn't touch it]*

LESGATE: *[Still skeptical]* The police would only have to trace one of those notes back to you and they'd hang us from the same rope.

TONY: They won't. For a whole year I've been cashing an extra twenty pounds a week. Always in fivers. I then change them for these at my leisure.

LESGATE: *[Rises, crosses to desk]* Let's see your bank statement.

TONY: By all means. [TONY *opens desk drawer and takes out his bank statement. He holds it open for* LESGATE *to see.* LESGATE *puts out his hands to touch it*] Don't touch!

LESGATE: Turn back a page. [TONY *turns back the page*] Your balance has dropped by over a thousand pounds in the year. Suppose the police ask you about that?

TONY: *[With a smile]* I go dog-racing twice a week.

LESGATE: They'll check with your bookmaker . . .

TONY: Like you—I always bet on the Tote . . . *[Pause]* Satisfied?

[Long pause. LESGATE *is standing right of desk with back to windows.* TONY *faces him from other side of desk]*

LESGATE: When would this take place?

TONY: Tomorrow night.

LESGATE: Tomorrow! Not a chance. I've got to think this over.

TONY: It's got to be tomorrow. I've arranged things that way.

LESGATE: Where?

TONY: Approximately where you're standing now.

*[*LESGATE *reacts to this. After a considerable pause]*

LESGATE: *[Quietly]* How?

TONY: Tomorrow evening, Halliday—that's the American boy friend— and I will go out to a stag party just down the road. She will stay here. She'll go to bed early and listen to Saturday Night Theater on the radio. She always does when I'm out. At exactly twenty-three minutes to eleven you will enter the house by the street door. *[Moving to hall]* You'll find the key of this door under the stair carpet—here.

*[*TONY *opens the hall door and leaves it wide open. He looks around to see that no one is watching and then points to one of the stairs which is clearly visible through the open door. He then comes in and closes the hall door]*

LESGATE: The fifth step.

TONY: That's the one. Go straight to the window and hide behind the curtains. *[Pause]* At exactly twenty minutes to eleven, I shall go to the telephone in the hotel to call my boss. I shall dial the wrong number—this number. That's all I shall do. *[Pause]* When the phone rings you'll see the lights go on under the bedroom door. When she opens it the light will stream across the room, so don't move until she answers the phone. *[Pause]* There must be as little noise as possible. *[Pause]* When you've finished, pick up the phone and give me a soft whistle. Then hang up. Don't speak, whatever you do. I shan't say a word. When I hear your whistle I shall hang up and redial—the *correct* number this time—I shall then speak to my boss as if nothing has happened and return to the party.

LESGATE: [*Looking round*] What happens then? Go on!

[TONY *picks up leather suitcase*]

TONY: You'll find this suitcase here. It will contain some clothes of mine for the cleaners. Open it and tip the clothes out onto the floor. [TONY *picks up the suitcase. He carries it back of couch to fireplace and puts it on the floor. He points to trophies on mantelpiece*] Then fill it with the cigarette box and some of these cups. Close the lid but don't snap the locks. [*Pause*] Then leave it here—just as it is now.

LESGATE: As if I left in a hurry?

TONY: That's the idea. Now—the window. If it's locked, unlock it and leave it open. [*Pause*] Then go out exactly the same way as you came in.

LESGATE: [*Indicating hall door*] By that door?

TONY: Yes—and here's the most important thing—as you go out, return the key to the place where you found it.

LESGATE: Under the stair carpet?

TONY: Yes.

[LESGATE *looks round the room, puzzled*]

LESGATE: Exactly what is supposed to have happened?

TONY: They'll assume you entered by the window. You thought the apartment was empty so you took the suitcase and went to work. She heard something and switched on her light. You saw the light go on under the door and hid behind the curtains. When she came in here you attacked her before she could scream. When you realized you'd actually killed her, you panicked and bolted into the garden leaving your loot behind.

LESGATE: [*Rises*] Just a minute . . . I'm supposed to have entered by the windows. What if they had been locked?

TONY: It wouldn't matter. You see, she often takes a walk round the garden before she goes to bed and she usually forgets to lock up when she gets back. That's what I shall tell the police.

LESGATE: But she may say that . . .

[*Pause*]

TONY: She isn't going to say anything—is she?

[*Pause, while* LESGATE *sees the logic of this*]

LESGATE: Is there any reason why I shouldn't leave by the garden?

TONY: Yes. You'd have to climb an iron gate. If anyone saw you, you might be followed.

LESGATE: [Turning to hall door] All right. I leave the flat—put the key back under the stair carpet, and go out by the street door. Suppose the street door's locked—how should I get in in the first place?

TONY: The street door's never locked.

LESGATE: When will you get back?

TONY: About twelve. I shall bring Halliday back for a nightcap—so we shall find her together. And we shall have been together since we left her—and there's my alibi.

[LESGATE looks round the room trying to visualize things. He moves slowly to hall door, opens it a few inches and peeps toward stairs. After a few seconds he closes it and turns to TONY]

LESGATE: You've forgotten something.

TONY: What?

LESGATE: When you return with—what's his name?—Halliday, how will you get into the apartment?

TONY: I shall let myself in.

LESGATE: But your key will be under the stair carpet. He's bound to see you take it out. That will give the whole show away.

[During TONY'S speech, TONY goes to door, wipes fingerprints off door handles, etc. Then crosses to desk and wipes desk and desk chair]

TONY: No, it won't be my key under the carpet. It will be hers. I shall take it from her handbag and hide it out there, just before I leave the flat. She won't be going out so she won't miss it. When I return with Halliday I'll use my own key to let us in. Then, while he's searching the garden or something, I'll take her key from under the stair carpet and return it to her handbag before the police arrive.

LESGATE: How many keys are there to that door?

TONY: Just hers and mine.

[The telephone rings. TONY hesitates, uncertain whether he should answer it. Then he goes to far side of desk so that he stands facing LESGATE with his back to the window. He picks up telephone. As soon as TONY answers phone, LESGATE picks up cotton gloves from arm of sofa and puts them on. He then moves around the room as follows: He opens the bedroom door and peers inside. He switches on bedroom light and, leaving door wide open, crosses to light switch and switches it off then crosses and switches off standard lamp so that room is *now lit only by the light from the bedroom. He crosses behind* TONY *to curtains and peers behind them. He draws the curtains aside. He unlocks the window, opens it and peers into the garden. He then opens and closes the window twice as if testing for a creak. He locks window and draws curtains shut. He switches on standard lamp and other lights and crosses to bedroom, switches off light and closes the door. He then strolls to sofa and stares down at the bundle of notes. He is doing this as* TONY *hangs up and looks across at him*]

[*Telephone conversation—*TONY *and* MARGOT. *Her voice can be heard through receiver and she is gay and very happy*]

TONY: Maida Vale 0401.

MARGOT: Tony, it's me.

TONY: [*Delighted*] Hullo, darling! How's it going?

MARGOT: [*With great enthusiasm*] Wonderfully! It's really a dreadful play—and we're enjoying every minute.

TONY: Oh—I'm sorry—I mean I'm glad.

MARGOT: How are you?

TONY: Very sleepy. [*Yawns*] I've just made myself some coffee to try and keep awake. Oh, darling, just a minute, I think there's someone at the door. [*To* LESGATE, *muffling telephone*] Careful, you can be seen from the bedroom window. [*To* MARGOT] Sorry, darling, false alarm.

MARGOT: You will join us, won't you?

TONY: I'm afraid not—I hardly seem to have started.

MARGOT: [*Really disappointed*] Oh, Tony! It never does work out, does it?

TONY: Oh, we'll manage it one day.

MARGOT: I say, darling . . .

TONY: Yes?

MARGOT: It seems awfully mean but—would you mind if Max and I went somewhere afterwards? You see . . .

TONY: Of course I don't mind. What do you want to do—dance?

MARGOT: Ummm!

TONY: Take him to Gerry's.

MARGOT: How do we get in?

TONY: Just mention my name. I don't know about the band but the food's good.

MARGOT: What are you doing about food?

TONY: Oh, I opened a tin of that luncheon meat.

MARGOT: Oh, you poor darling.

TONY: By the way, Maureen rang up just after you left. Wants us to go to dinner on Wednesday. You've got something down in your diary but I can't read your writing. *[He peers at the desk diary]* Looks like Al—Bentall. Who's he? Another of your boy friends?

MARGOT: Albert Hall, you idiot!

TONY: Oh, the Albert Hall, of course. I'm so glad we can't go to Maureen's—she's such a filthy cook . . .

MARGOT: There's the bell—I must fly.

TONY: All right. 'Bye, sweet—enjoy yourself. *[Looks across at* LESGATE*]* Well?

*[*LESGATE *picks up the notes and whisks them like a pack of cards]*

LESGATE: *[Quietly—with a nod]* It's a deal.

[As LESGATE *puts the notes in his inside pocket:]*

CURTAIN

> 👁 **Suspicions?**
>
> "Smart, aren't you?" says Swann, and Tony replies: "Not really, I've just had time to think things out." It appears that Tony has taken every possible detail into account—the perfect crime. Or is it? What possibly could go wrong? Speculate before you go on to Act Two.

ACT TWO

SCENE 1

The same. Saturday evening. The room is lit by the overhead lights and brackets. It is dark outside, the curtains are not drawn. The fire is burning brightly. The leather suitcase stands, as before, by the drink cabinet. MARGOT *and* MAX *are sitting on the sofa. She is showing him an album of press clippings. There are other clippings and folded newspapers on the round table in front of them.* TONY *is at drink shelf mixing drinks.* TONY *and* MAX *wear dinner jackets.* MARGOT *is not wearing evening dress. As the curtain rises they are all laughing.*

TONY: . . . After that, he lost concentration and didn't win another game.

MARGOT: *[To* TONY*]* Where's the picture of the Maharajah?

TONY: *[Moving behind sofa, hands drink to* MAX*]* It's somewhere among those loose ones. *[*MARGOT *searches among clippings on round table.* TONY *goes and stands with back to fire. To* MARGOT*]* Darling. When are you going to finish pasting in those press clippings?

MARGOT: I shall find time—one of these days. *[Unfolding piece of newspaper]* Oh, here we are. *[Showing it to* MAX*]* There's the Maharajah. Isn't he dreamy?

TONY: He had four Rolls Royces and enough jewels to sink a battleship, but all he really wanted was to play at Wimbledon.

[MARGOT *collects clippings from round table*]

MARGOT: The poor darling. He was so short-sighted he could hardly see the end of his racket—let alone the ball.

MAX: [*Turning pages of album*] You ought to write a book about all this.

[MAX *hands album to* MARGOT. *She puts the clippings inside it and lays it on the round table*]

MARGOT: Why don't you two collaborate? A detective novel with a tennis background.

TONY: Murder on the center court . . . How about it, Max? Will you provide me with the perfect murder?

MAX: Nothing I'd like better.

TONY: How do you start to write a detective story?

MAX: Forget the detection and concentrate on crime. The crime's the thing. Imagine you're going to steal something, or murder somebody.

TONY: Is that what you do? Hmm! Interesting.

MAX: I always just put myself in the criminal's shoes and keep saying: "Well, what do I do next?"

MARGOT: [*To* MAX] Do you really believe in the perfect murder?

[*Pause*]

MAX: Absolutely—on paper. And I think I could plan one better than most people—but I doubt if I could carry it out.

TONY: Why not?

[TONY *rises and moves to fireplace*]

MAX: Because in stories things turn out as the author plans them to. ...In real life they don't—always. [*He catches* MARGOT'S *eye and they give each other a little smile*] I imagine my murders would be rather like my bridge . . . I'd make some damned stupid mistake and never realize it until I found that everyone was looking at me.

[TONY *laughs and glances round at the clock*]

TONY: I think we'd better drink up, Max.

[*He finishes drink and crosses back of couch to drink shelf*]

MAX: All right, sir.

[*He rises*]

MARGOT: [*To* MAX] Are you doing anything tomorrow?

MAX: No. I don't think so.

MARGOT: [*To* TONY] Why don't we all drive down to Windsor for lunch?

TONY: Good idea. [*To* MAX] Come along early. At least—not too early. We may be nursing a hangover.

[TONY *crosses to stool*]

MAX: About eleven?

TONY: [*To* MAX] That'll do fine. [*To* MARGOT *as he moves to hall*] By the way, darling, did I lend you my latchkey? I can't find it anywhere.

MARGOT: [*Getting up*] I may have them both in my handbag. I'll just look.

[MARGOT *exits to bedroom.* MAX *goes to hall to get his overcoat.* TONY *goes to French windows. He unlocks and opens a window and peers outside*]

TONY: Raining pretty hard. I think I could lend you an old raincoat, if that's any good.

MAX: [*Taking down overcoat*] This will do. It isn't far, is it?

TONY: No—just around the corner.

[TONY *glances round at* MAX *to see if he is looking but he is putting on his overcoat and has his back to* TONY. TONY *deliberately opens one window a few inches, draws the curtains across the windows.* MARGOT *enters from the bedroom carrying a handbag. She opens it and takes out a zip purse. Out of this she takes a latchkey*]

MARGOT: I've only got one here. Are you sure yours isn't in your overcoat?

TONY: Yes, I've looked there. Could you lend me yours?

MARGOT: [*Holding key in hand*] Well, that's a bit awkward.

TONY: [*Turning to* MARGOT] Why?

MARGOT: I may want to go out.

[*Pause*]

TONY: Tonight?

MARGOT: Yes. I thought I might go to a movie or something.

TONY: But—aren't you going to listen to the radio—Saturday Night Theater?

MARGOT: [*Sitting on right end of sofa*] No, it's a thriller. I don't like thrillers when I'm alone.

TONY: [*Casually*] I see.

[*He goes and picks up raincoat on hall chair*]

MARGOT: In any case I'll be back before you so I can let you in.

TONY: [*Putting on raincoat*] We won't be back till after midnight. You may be asleep by then.

[He crosses to desk, taking gloves from raincoat pocket to put them on]

MAX: *[To* MARGOT*]* You can always leave your key under the proverbial mat.

*[*TONY *drops his key out of one of his gloves onto desk]*

TONY: *[Picking it up]* All right, chaps. Had it here in my glove all the time.

[Puts key back in raincoat pocket]

MARGOT: That settles that.

[She returns her key to her zip purse. She puts purse back in handbag, closes it and leaves it on oblong table]

TONY: What movie are you going to?

MARGOT: The Classic, I expect.

TONY: Will you get in? Saturday night.

MARGOT: I can always try. Now, don't make me stay in. You know how I hate doing nothing.

TONY: Nothing? But there're hundreds of things you can do. Have you written to Peggy about last weekend? And what about these clippings? It's an ideal opportunity.

MARGOT: Well, I like that! You two go gallivanting while I have to stay in and do those boring clippings.

*[*TONY *suddenly goes sullen]*

TONY: Oh, very well then, we won't go.

[He moves left above couch removing raincoat]

MARGOT: *[Astonished]* What do you mean?

TONY: Well, it's quite obvious you don't want us to go out tonight—so we won't. We'll stay here with you. What shall we do—play cards?

[Puts raincoat on chair]

MARGOT: Now, Tony darling . . .

[She rises and goes to front of coffee table]

TONY: *[Going to phone]* I'd better phone the Grendon and tell them we're not coming.

*[*MARGOT *stops* TONY *going to the phone]*

MARGOT: Tony, please. Don't let's be childish about this. I'll do your old press clippings.

TONY: You don't have to if you don't want to.

MARGOT: But I *do* want to. *[She picks up press clippings album]* Have we any paste?

TONY: There's some in the desk, I think.

MARGOT: Good. *[Takes album to desk]* And some scissors. In the mending basket. *[TONY goes to mending basket. He opens it, looks underneath a pair of MARGOT'S stockings and takes out a long pair of scissors. MARGOT, taking out empty paste tube from desk drawer]* Oh, look . . . the paste tube is empty. *[Exasperated]* It would be. *[TONY stares at the empty paste tube which MARGOT is holding]* Never mind. Mrs. Lucas is bound to have some.

TONY: Who's she?

MARGOT: She lives just across the road. I'll drop around later. *[TONY can't hide his annoyance. MARGOT reaches for scissors]* Thank you, darling.

[TONY passes her scissors]

MAX: Why not make some? All you need is some flour and starch.

TONY: Good idea. Do you know how to do it, Max?

MAX: *[Moving to kitchen]* In two shakes.

[MAX exits to kitchen]

TONY: Good old Max! *[To MARGOT]* I'm sorry, darling. Was I very unreasonable?

MARGOT: *[Moving to TONY]* No, I don't mind. I tell you what . . . I'll paste these in tonight and you put up that extra shelf in the kitchen . . . As you promised.

TONY: First thing tomorrow. Promise.

[He kisses her]

MAX: *[Calling from kitchen]* Where's the starch?

MARGOT: I'll show you.

[MARGOT exits to kitchen. We can hear them talking through the open door. TONY looks at oblong table. He glances quickly toward kitchen and then moves to MARGOT'S handbag and opens it. He takes out purse, zips it open and takes out key and puts it on table. He then zips the purse shut, returns it to handbag and closes bag, leaving it in exactly the same position as before. He picks up key and goes and opens hall door, leaving it wide open. He then looks along passage and to the landing above, then he lifts the stair carpet and places the key underneath. As he does this MARGOT gives a little peal of laughter from the kitchen. TONY turns back, a little startled; as he strolls back into the room, MARGOT enters from the kitchen with a cup and spoon. MAX follows her. As she is entering:]

It looks like vichysoisse without the chives.

MAX: If it starts to get thick, add a little water—and keep stirring.

[MARGOT puts down cup on desk and starts to arrange the newspapers and clippings. TONY and MAX stand in hall]

TONY: Keep the fire in for us, darling.

[He gets coat from chair]

MARGOT: I will.

TONY: Oh, and it's just possible old man Burgess will phone tonight. If he does, tell him I'm at the Grendon. It may be rather important.

MARGOT: What's the number?

TONY: It's in the book.

MARGOT: All right. Well, look after each other.

MAX: We will. Good night, Margot.

MARGOT: 'Night, Max. [*To* TONY] You'll run Max home in the car afterwards, won't you, darling?

TONY: Of course. We'll drop in here first for a nightcap. Sure you won't be up?

MARGOT: I shall be fast asleep. And I *don't* want to be disturbed.

TONY: Then we'll be as quiet as mice. [TONY *kisses* MARGOT] Good night, darling.

MARGOT: Good night.

TONY: Come on, Max.

Suspicions?

1. What details had Tony overlooked? How does he work things out so that Margot will be in the apartment when Swann arrives?

2. Why did Tony first ask about borrowing Margot's latchkey before removing it from her handbag?

3. Besides the latchkey, which objects has the author made you most aware of so far in the story? How might these objects figure in the development of the plot?

[They exit. MARGOT switches on lamp, turns on radio. Then she turns off chandelier and brackets. She turns to her work. She looks resigned to it. She unfolds a piece of newspaper, picks up scissors, starts cutting. Music swells to:]

CURTAIN

SCENE 2

The same. Later that night. MARGOT has finished pasting in TONY'S press clippings and has left the album lying open on the desk. By the album lie some pieces of newspaper and the scissors. The wastepaper basket is overflowing with cut pieces of newspaper.

When the curtain rises the room is lit only by the light from the fire which is still burning well. After a few seconds the hall door opens, but only about two inches, as if someone was listening.

Another few seconds and LESGATE enters. He stands in the doorway perfectly still—listening. He wears a raincoat and kid gloves but no hat. He closes the door without a sound except for the final click as it locks. As he crosses silently he takes off his scarf and ties two knots in it.

NOTE: *This scarf must have tassel ends, to emphasize, later, that it is a scarf and must be silk and tan colored so that* MARGOT *could mistake it for a stocking.*

LESGATE *crosses to French windows. The phone rings. He quickly hides behind curtains.*

After some time the light goes on under the bedroom door and MARGOT *enters from the bedroom. She leaves the door wide open and the light is thrown across the room.* MARGOT *puts on a dressing gown as she crosses to the telephone.*

She goes to the far side of the desk and answers the phone with her back turned to the window.

MARGOT: Hullo... [*She listens for several seconds, then louder*] Hullo!

[MARGOT *does not notice* LESGATE *as he comes from behind the curtains. His gloved hands hold each end of the silk scarf in which two knots have been tied.* MARGOT *has had the phone in her left hand. She puts phone hand down and jiggles the receiver with her right. Just as she is jiggling the receiver* LESGATE *attacks her, throwing the scarf over her head and drawing it back sharply against her throat. With a strangled gurgle she drops the phone.* LESGATE *holds her back against his body but* MARGOT'S *hands catch hold of the scarf and try to tear it away. They struggle for a moment, then* LESGATE *winds the scarf, with his left hand, right around her neck and at the same time she turns round so that she faces him with the scarf crossed at the back of her neck. He pushes her against the end of the desk and forces her down until she is bent right back along the top of the desk with her head downstage. In his efforts to tighten the scarf he leans right over her so that his body almost touches hers.* MARGOT'S *right hand leaves the scarf and waves over the end of the desk, groping for the scissors. She grabs them and strikes with one of the points into* LESGATE'S *back.* LESGATE *slumps over her and then very slowly rolls over the left side of the desk landing on his back with a strangled grunt.* MARGOT *continues to lie back over the desk, completely exhausted. Then she manages to get to her feet, all the time fighting for breath. She tears the scarf away from her throat but it remains looped around her shoulders. She grabs the telephone. At first she has difficulty in speaking. A sharp "Hullo" from* TONY *can be heard from the receiver*]

TONY: Hullo!

MARGOT: [*In short gasps*] Get the police—quickly—police!

TONY: Margot.

MARGOT: Who's that?

TONY: Darling, it's me . . .

MARGOT: Oh, thank God—Tony, come back at once!

TONY: What's the matter?

MARGOT: [Panicking] I can't explain now. Come quickly—*please!*

TONY: [Angrily] Darling, pull yourself together . . . What is it?

MARGOT: [Recovering slightly] A man—attacked me . . . tried to strangle me . . .

TONY: Has he gone?

MARGOT: No—he's dead . . . he's dead . . . [A long pause] Tony—Tony! Are you still there?

TONY: [Frozen] Margot!

MARGOT: Yes?

TONY: Now, listen very carefully.

MARGOT: Yes, I'm listening.

TONY: Don't touch anything! I'll be with you in a minute.

MARGOT: No, I won't.

TONY: Don't touch anything and don't speak to *anybody*—until I get back.

MARGOT: All right. I won't touch anything.

TONY: You promise?

MARGOT: [In angry panic] Yes, I promise—only please be quick!

[She begins to sob with fright as she replaces the phone. She staggers to window and opens it, goes outside. After several seconds she returns, having left scarf outside. The windows remain open. As she reaches desk and sees the body, she starts to door, stops and collapses on hall chair, sobs, then exits into bedroom and locks door. Chimes are heard from church clock outside. Sound of street door opening. Running footsteps. Sound of key in lock, door opens. TONY switches on wall bracket lights only. He takes in situation, stares at body, then at handbag and back to body, then he takes key out of door, puts it in raincoat pocket. He closes door quietly. He turns on standard lamp. He crosses to LESGATE and starts to turn body one way, then rolls him over toward the window. He sees scissors that are sticking in his back. He glances at hands for blood and then glances at bedroom door. Searches for key in LESGATE'S pockets. He can't find it. Sound of bedroom door unlocking. TONY rises and MARGOT comes rushing into his arms]

MARGOT: Oh, Tony, Tony, Tony . . .

TONY: It's all right—it'll be all right. What happened?

[MARGOT suddenly throws her arms round him and clings like a frightened child. TONY lifts her head slightly so he can see her throat]

MARGOT: He got something around my throat—it felt like a stocking.

TONY: Are you sure? Let me see. *[He touches her throat gently and she turns her head away quickly]* I'd better call a doctor.

MARGOT: *[Shocked at the thought]* But he's dead.

TONY: I know. When he fell he must have driven those scissors right through himself.

MARGOT: *[Turning away]* Horrible! Can't you . . . ?

TONY: Yes—right away. *[TONY exits quickly into bedroom. MARGOT suddenly puts her hand to her head. She turns and looks round the room. She sees her handbag on the sofa table, opens it, and fishes around inside. TONY enters from the bedroom carrying a blanket. When he sees what MARGOT is doing he stops dead and stares at her in horror]* What are you doing?

MARGOT: *[Taking out a bottle of aspirin]* Will you get me some water, please?

[MARGOT drops the handbag onto the table. TONY fills a glass with water from the drink cabinet and hands it to MARGOT who swallows some aspirin and takes a drink. TONY throws the blanket over LESGATE]

TONY: *[Quietly]* That's better.

[He covers the body]

MARGOT: Shut the window, please.

TONY: No—we mustn't touch anything until the police arrive. *[Looking at open window]* He must have broken in. *[Looking around room]* I wonder what he was after? *[Looking at bookcase]* Those cups, I expect.

MARGOT: When will the police get here?

TONY: *[Started]* Have you called them already?

MARGOT: No. You told me not to speak to anyone. Hadn't you better call them now?

TONY: *[Pause]* Yes, in a minute.

MARGOT: *[Moving to bedroom]* I'll get dressed.

TONY: Why?

MARGOT: They'll want to see me.

TONY: They're not going to see you.

MARGOT: But they'll have to ask me questions.

TONY: They can wait until tomorrow. I'll tell them all they want to know.

[As TONY is speaking he keeps looking around the desk, searching for something. MARGOT moves to bedroom door and then turns]

MARGOT: Tony.

TONY: Yes?

MARGOT: Why did you phone me?

[TONY *stares back at her for at least three seconds before answering*]

TONY: What? Er—sorry—I'll tell you about that later. I just thought of something. You said he used a stocking . . .

MARGOT: I think it was a stocking—or a scarf. Isn't it there?

TONY: [*Looking around*] No. But I expect they'll find it. Now you get back to bed. I'll phone them right away.

[*He goes over to* LESGATE. *Searches for key, finds it in raincoat pocket. Sighs with relief. Goes back to oblong table and returns key carefully to zip purse and closes handbag. Sighs with relief again. Returns to body and covers it with blanket. Then goes to phone and dials.* MARGOT *appears in bedroom door*]

MARGOT: Where's Max, Tony?

TONY: I told him to go straight home . . . Hullo, Operator—give me the Maida Vale Police quickly . . .

MARGOT: Did you tell him?

TONY: No. I wasn't sure what had happened, so I just said I was feeling rotten . . . Darling . . . go back to bed and . . .

[MARGOT *closes her door*]

POLICE: [*Offstage, heard through receiver*] Maida Vale Police.

TONY: Police? There's been a ghastly accident.

POLICE: Yes, sir?

TONY: A man has been killed.

POLICE: Your name, sir?

TONY: Wendice.

POLICE: [*Spelling*] D I double S . . . ?

TONY: No. D I C E.

POLICE: Your address, sir?

TONY: 61a Charrington Gardens. It's the ground-floor apartment.

POLICE: When was this 'ere accident?

TONY: About ten minutes ago. He broke in and attacked my wife . . .

POLICE: A burglar?

TONY: [*Impatiently*] Yes. I'll explain everything when you get here. How long will that take?

POLICE: About two minutes.

TONY: Two minutes.

POLICE: Don't touch anything, will you, sir?

TONY: No. We won't touch anything. Good-bye.

[He hangs up and looks around the room. Finally he goes to open window and steps out. Stoops down and picks something up. Comes back into room. He is holding each end of LESGATE'S *scarf with the two knots. Strolls thoughtfully to mending basket, searches in it and finds a stocking. He holds up scarf and stocking, comparing them. Then he drops stocking on stool and hides scarf in his pocket. He then kneels down beside* LESGATE *and takes out his wallet]*

MARGOT: *[Off, sharply]* Tony!

TONY: *[Calling back]* All right, darling. Won't be a minute.

*[*TONY *takes letter (*MAX'S*) out of his wallet and is about to put it in* LESGATE'S *pocket as:]*

CURTAIN

 Suspicions?

1. The perfect crime goes wrong! What hadn't Tony taken account of?
2. How does Tony overcome this reversal?
3. How does he handle Margot's latchkey?
4. Why does he substitute Margot's stocking for Lesgate's scarf?
5. Why does he place Max's letter to Margot in Lesgate's pocket?
6. What is Tony's new plan? Has he thought of everything?

SCENE 3

The same. Sunday morning. About 11 A.M.

The curtains are drawn open and it is bright and sunny outside. The wastepaper basket has been emptied. LESGATE'S *body has been removed but the blanket, folded once, still lies over "the spot" to hide bloodstains.*

The fire is out and has not been touched since last night. The dirty breakfast things lie on the coffee table. MARGOT *is still very nervous. She stands center as curtain rises.*

MARGOT: More coffee?

TONY: *[Off]* No, thank you.

[He enters from bedroom tying tie, goes to front of fire-place]

MARGOT: We'd better call Max—*[Quietly]*—and tell him.

TONY: I have. He's on his way over.

MARGOT: *[Trying to cheer up]* Did he like the party last night?

TONY: He certainly did. Made a remarkably good speech, except that he would keep referring to us as Limies. *[He laughs]* Oh, yes, he's all there, is Max . . . Where did you dig him up?

[Pause]

MARGOT: I—met him at Peggy's once—and then I met him again just before he went back to New York.

TONY: [*Lightly*] Oh, yes—so you told me.

[*Pause*]

MARGOT: Tony, why did you . . . ?)

Together

TONY: By the way, I . . .)

TONY: Sorry.

MARGOT: No, go on.

TONY: I've closed the shutters in the bedroom, that's all.

MARGOT: [*Anxiously*] Why?

TONY: People have started to go out for their Sunday papers. We now have a collection of refined snoopers.

MARGOT: How awful! Is it in the papers already?

TONY: I don't think so—not yet. But news travels fast. [*Pause*] What were you going to say?

MARGOT: I—can't remember—it's gone for the moment.

[*The phone rings.* MARGOT *gives a nervous start.* TONY *answers it*]

TONY: Hullo.

REPORTER: [*Offstage, heard through receiver*] Mrs. Wendice, please.

TONY: This is Mr. Wendice.

REPORTER: Oh, good morning, sir. I'm with the C. & S. News Service. Might I see Mrs. Wendice for a few minutes?

TONY: I'm afraid my wife can't see anyone just now—not for a day or two.

REPORTER: Oh. Was she hurt in any way?

TONY: No. She's all right now.

REPORTER: I just want one or two photographs.

TONY: [*Suddenly annoyed*] Well, how would you feel? I'm sorry—good-bye.

[TONY *rings off*]

MARGOT: Who was that?

TONY: Just a reporter—wanted to take some photographs of you.

MARGOT: I suppose we shall get a lot of that.

TONY: Not for long. As soon as the inquest's over they'll forget all about it . . . So will you.

MARGOT: When will it be?

TONY: The inquest? Tomorrow or Tuesday—I should think.

MARGOT: [*Nervously*] What will happen?

TONY: Nothing to worry about. The coroner will probably give you a pat on the back for putting up such a good show.

MARGOT: For killing a man?

TONY: Now don't start getting ideas about that. It was him or you. As the police surgeon said, it was lucky those scissors were on the desk.

MARGOT: I hope I don't have to see that doctor again.

TONY: No, he hadn't much bedside manner, had he?

MARGOT: Why were the police so long last night?

TONY: Were they? I didn't notice. I'm afraid I dropped off to sleep very quickly.

MARGOT: I know you did. They stayed for hours. Cars seemed to be coming and going all night.

TONY: I only saw the sergeant. Nice chap. He seemed to have it all under control.

MARGOT: At one time I thought they must be turning all the furniture round.

TONY: [Looking around the room] Well, they haven't made much mess. They've even emptied the wastepaper basket. That was thoughtful of them.

MARGOT: Someone kept flashing a light under the bedroom door.

TONY: Taking photographs, probably.

MARGOT: About two o'clock I couldn't stand it any longer. I got up and came in here.

TONY: [Surprised] You came in here? What for?

MARGOT: To ask them when they expected to finish. But when I saw them I—couldn't say anything. Two men were on the floor with a tape measure. Another was outside. He kept opening and shutting the window. They all stopped what they were doing and looked at me. I felt such a fool. [Slowly] And on the desk—were a pair of shoes . . . His, I suppose. [Putting hand to head] It was horrible!

[TONY has remembered something]

TONY: Darling—before I forget—the sergeant wanted to know why you didn't phone the police immediately.

MARGOT: [Flustered] But how could I? You were on the phone.

TONY: I know, but . . .

MARGOT: [Agitated] You distinctly told me not to speak to anyone until you got here.

TONY: I know, darling. But I told him a slightly different story.

MARGOT: Why?

TONY: I said that you didn't call the police because you naturally assumed that I would phone them from the hotel.

[*Pause*]

MARGOT: Why did you say that?

TONY: Because—it was the perfectly logical explanation—and he accepted it. You see, if they got the idea that we had delayed reporting it— even for a few minutes—they might get nosy and start asking a lot of questions and . . .

MARGOT: So you want me to say the same thing?

TONY: I think so. [*Doorbell rings*] Just in case it comes up again. I expect that's Max. Let him in, will you, darling? I'll just get rid of these.

[TONY *exits into kitchen with tray of dishes.* MARGOT *goes to hall door and opens it.* DETECTIVE INSPECTOR HUBBARD *is standing in the passage outside*]

HUBBARD: [*Removing hat*] Good morning, madam.

MARGOT: Oh! Good morning.

HUBBARD: Mrs. Wendice?

MARGOT: Yes.

HUBBARD: I'm a police officer. [*Pause*] May I come in?

MARGOT: Of course. [*Nervously*] Excuse me, I'll tell my husband you're here.

HUBBARD: Thank you.

[MARGOT *exits to kitchen.* HUBBARD *looks around for a place to hang his hat. He sees pegs by the door and hangs it up. He then strolls into the room and looks the place over, getting his bearings. He glances deliberately from the blanket to the window, to the telephone, to the bedroom door. He then looks around until he sees the mending basket.* TONY *and* MARGOT *enter*]

TONY: Good morning.

HUBBARD: Good morning, sir. I'm Chief Inspector Hubbard. I'm in charge of the Criminal Investigation of this division.

TONY: I think I gave your sergeant all the necessary information.

HUBBARD: Yes, I've seen his report, of course, but there are a few things I'd like to get first hand. I gather my sergeant only saw you for a few moments, Mrs. Wendice? [*Turning suddenly to* MARGOT] Mrs. Wendice?

MARGOT: Yes . . . I . . .

TONY: My wife was suffering from considerable shock.

HUBBARD: [*Sympathetically*] Yes, that was a very nasty experience you had. [*Turning to bedroom door*] Mind if I take a look around?

TONY: Go ahead. The bedroom and bathroom are through here. . . .

[TONY *follows* HUBBARD *into the bedroom.* MARGOT *starts to follow them, then hangs back. She is now very nervous. She looks at the blanket on the floor and stares at it for a moment. Then she goes to the cigarette box on the coffee table, opens it, takes out a cigarette, fingers it and then puts it back again.* HUBBARD *and* TONY *enter from bedroom*]

HUBBARD: Well, he certainly didn't get in by the bathroom.

TONY: And the kitchen has bars on the window. [TONY *opens the kitchen door.* HUBBARD *glances in for a moment and then comes back into the room*] We assume he must have come in through these windows.

HUBBARD: Hmmm. I understand that you weren't here when this happened, sir?

TONY: No. I was at a dinner party at the Grendon Hotel.

HUBBARD: Just down the road?

TONY: Yes. By a curious coincidence I was actually phoning my wife when she was attacked.

HUBBARD: So I gather. Can you tell me exactly what time it was?

TONY: I—I'm not sure.

HUBBARD: Did you notice—Mrs. Wendice?

MARGOT: No, I didn't.

HUBBARD: You phoned the police at three minutes to eleven, sir.

TONY: Let me see—in that case it must have been—about a quarter to eleven. By the way—won't you sit down, Inspector?

[TONY *waves* HUBBARD *to the sofa.* TONY *brings the stool to sofa and sits*]

HUBBARD: Thank you.

MARGOT: Have you any idea who he was?

HUBBARD: Yes. At least we've discovered where he lived. There still seems to be some confusion as to his real name.

MARGOT: Oh?

HUBBARD: He appeared to have several. [*Suddenly, looking at* MARGOT] Had you ever seen him before?

MARGOT: [*Bewildered*] Why—no. Of course not. [HUBBARD *takes out his notebook and produces two snapshots of different sizes. He hands them to* MARGOT, *one by one, and watches her very closely as she glances at them and hands them back*] Oh, is this—him?

HUBBARD: Yes. You don't recognize him?

MARGOT: No. I—I never saw him.

HUBBARD: Didn't you even—catch a glimpse of his face?

MARGOT: No. You see, he attacked me from behind and it was dark. I hardly saw him at all.

HUBBARD: [*Pleasantly*] But before I showed you those photographs, you said you'd never seen him before. [*A pause; he watches her face*] How could you know that—if you never saw his face last night?

[*Pause*]

MARGOT: I don't quite understand . . .

TONY: Inspector, my wife simply meant that, as far as she knew, she had never seen him before.

Suspicions?

Why might Detective Inspector Hubbard suspect that Margot has seen Lesgate before?

HUBBARD: [*To* MARGOT] Was that what you meant?

MARGOT: [*Nervously, returns photos*] Yes—I'm sorry.

HUBBARD: How about you, sir? Ever seen him before?

[HUBBARD *hands* TONY *one of the photographs.* TONY *looks and hands it back*]

TONY: No. [HUBBARD *hands him the other.* TONY *looks at it*] No ... [*He hands it back*] At least . . . [*Taking another look*]

HUBBARD: Yes?

TONY: [*Amazed*] It's very like someone I was at college with—the mustache makes quite a difference.

HUBBARD: What was his name?

TONY: Now you're asking . . . It's over twenty years since I left.

HUBBARD: Was it Lesgate?

TONY: No.

HUBBARD: Wilson?

TONY: No.

HUBBARD: Swann?

TONY: No . . . Swann? Wait a minute—Swann . . . Yes, that's it. [*Crosses back of couch, gets photo off wall and brings it to* HUBBARD] Look, here's an old photo taken at a reunion dinner. We were at the same college. There he is—it's unbelievable!

HUBBARD: Did you know him well?

TONY: No. He was senior to me.

HUBBARD: Have you met him since then?

TONY: No—at least—come to think of it, I did see him—quite recently [*Pause*] but not to speak to.

HUBBARD: When was that?

TONY: About six months ago. It was at a railway station . . . Waterloo, I think. I remember noticing how little he'd changed.

HUBBARD: Had he a mustache then?

TONY: [*Pauses for thought, then hands photo back to* HUBBARD] No.

[HUBBARD *makes a note of this. Then he turns to* MARGOT]

HUBBARD: [*Getting up*] Mrs. Wendice, would you show me exactly what happened last night?

MARGOT: Tony, do I have to?

TONY: Afraid so, darling.

[TONY *helps her up. As she talks,* MARGOT *crosses to bedroom and then back of couch to center and then to phone*]

MARGOT: I was in bed when the phone rang. I got up and came in here.

HUBBARD: Did you switch this light on?

MARGOT: No.

HUBBARD: Just show me exactly where you were standing.

[MARGOT *stands as she did, with back half-turned to window*]

MARGOT: I stood here. I picked up the phone.

HUBBARD: Are you sure you had your back to the window like that?

MARGOT: Yes.

HUBBARD: But why?

MARGOT: [*Bewildered*] Why not?

[HUBBARD *stands at left of desk facing window*]

HUBBARD: Why go around the desk? I should have picked it up from this side.

[HUBBARD *picks up the phone with right hand and then replaces it*]

TONY: Surely my wife can remember . . .

HUBBARD: Just a moment, sir.

MARGOT: But I always answer the phone from here.

HUBBARD: Why?

MARGOT: So that if I want to write anything down—I can hold the phone in my left hand.

[*She places her left hand on the phone*]

HUBBARD: I see. All right—go on.

MARGOT: I picked up the phone. Then he must have come from behind the curtain and attacked me. He got something round my neck . . .

HUBBARD: Something? What do you mean by "something"?

MARGOT: I think it was a stocking.

HUBBARD: I see. What happened then?

MARGOT: He pushed me over the desk. I remember distinctly feeling for the scissors . . .

HUBBARD: Where were those scissors usually kept?

MARGOT: [Pointing] In that mending basket. I'd forgotten to put them away.

HUBBARD: Now what makes you think he came from behind those curtains?

MARGOT: Where else could he have been?

HUBBARD: The curtains were drawn, I suppose?

MARGOT: Yes, they were.

HUBBARD: Did you draw them yourself?

TONY: [A little weary of all this] I drew them, Inspector—before I went out.

HUBBARD: Did you lock the window at the same time?

TONY: Yes.

HUBBARD: Are you quite sure of that, sir?

TONY: Perfectly sure. I always lock up when I draw the curtains.

HUBBARD: Then how do you suppose he got into this room?

TONY: We assumed—that he broke in.

HUBBARD: There's no sign of a break-in. The lock's quite undamaged.

TONY: But he must have done. When I got back that window was wide open. At least . . . Margot, are you sure you didn't go out into the garden last night and forget to lock up afterwards?

MARGOT: I did go out for a moment. After—after he attacked me. I wanted to get some air. I pushed the window open and stood on the terrace outside.

HUBBARD: Did you call for help?

MARGOT: I'd just spoken to my husband on the telephone.

HUBBARD: You say you pushed the window open. Are you sure you didn't unlock it first?

MARGOT: Yes. Quite sure.

HUBBARD: Was it already open?

MARGOT: I—I—don't remember.

[Pause]

HUBBARD: Mrs. Wendice, why didn't you ring the police immediately when this happened?

[TONY catches MARGOT'S eye and she looks at him for a moment]

MARGOT: [*Trying to remember what* TONY *told her*] I was trying to get through—to the police when I discovered that my husband was on the line. [*Pause*] I naturally thought he would call the police—from the hotel—before he came here.

[*Pause.* TONY *looks relieved*]

HUBBARD: [*Quietly*] Didn't it occur to you to call—for a doctor?

MARGOT: No.

HUBBARD: Why ever not?

MARGOT: He was—dead.

HUBBARD: [*Quietly*] How did you know that?

MARGOT: I—it was obvious.

HUBBARD: Did you feel his pulse?

MARGOT: No—of course I didn't. Anyone would have realized he was dead . . . One look at those staring eyes . . .

HUBBARD: So you did see his face, after all?

MARGOT: [*Losing control*] I saw his eyes. I can't remember his face!

TONY: Inspector, my wife has obviously never seen this man before. And if he didn't get in by those windows—how did he get in?

[HUBBARD *strolls across to hall door*]

HUBBARD: [*Slowly*] As a matter of fact we're quite certain he came in by this door.

[HUBBARD *opens it a few inches and closes it with a click. Then he looks across at* TONY]

MARGOT: [*Quietly*] But it was locked.

TONY: Margot, did you open this door at all—and forget to close it after we'd gone?

MARGOT: No.

HUBBARD: How many keys are there to this door?

MARGOT: Only two. Mine was in my handbag and [*To* TONY] you had yours with you.

TONY: That's right.

HUBBARD: Has the caretaker got a key?

MARGOT: No.

HUBBARD: [*To* MARGOT] Do you employ a charwoman?

 Suspicions?

What physical evidence and facts about the setting might have convinced Detective Inspector Hubbard that Lesgate came through the front door rather than through the window that overlooks the garden?

MARGOT: Yes, but she hasn't got one either. I'm always in when she comes.

TONY: What makes you think he came in that way?

HUBBARD: [Quite simply] His shoes.

TONY: His shoes?

[HUBBARD crosses to window]

HUBBARD: The ground was soaking wet last night. If he'd come in by the garden he'd have left marks all over the carpet. [Pause] He didn't leave any because he wiped his shoes on the front door mat.

TONY: How can you tell?

HUBBARD: It's a fairly new mat and some of its fibers came off on his shoes . . .

TONY: But surely . . .

HUBBARD: And there was a small tar stain on the mat and some of the fibers show that as well. There's no question about it.

TONY: [Suddenly] Wait a minute, I think I've got it. [To Margot] You remember when your bag was stolen?

MARGOT: Yes.

TONY: Wasn't your key inside?

MARGOT: Yes, but it was still there when—I got it back.

HUBBARD: [Interested] Just a moment. I'd like to hear about this. What sort of bag?

TONY: A handbag, Inspector. My wife lost it at Victoria Station.

MARGOT: I got it back from the lost and found office about two weeks later.

HUBBARD: Was anything missing?

MARGOT: All the money had gone.

HUBBARD: Anything else?

[MARGOT seems uncertain what to say]

MARGOT: No.

HUBBARD: [Casually] No papers—or letters?

MARGOT: No.

HUBBARD: [With sudden emphasis] Are you quite sure about that?

MARGOT: [Determined] Yes.

HUBBARD: And your latchkey was in your handbag when you lost it?

MARGOT: Yes, but it was still there when it was returned.

TONY: Whoever stole that money could have had the key copied.

HUBBARD: Where was the bag found eventually?

MARGOT: At Victoria Station.

TONY: But not until several days later. By which time he could have had a duplicate made and returned the original to the bag.

HUBBARD: Before you go any further with this—how did he get in through the street door?

TONY: The street door's always unlocked.

HUBBARD: I see. He could have had your key copied. And he could have used it to open this door—but of course, he didn't.

TONY: Why not?

HUBBARD: Because if he had—the key would still have been on him when he died. But no key was found when we went through his pockets.

[Pause]

TONY: I see. Well—we seem to be back where we started.

HUBBARD: Not quite. *[Pause]* You said you saw this man at Waterloo Station?

TONY: Yes.

HUBBARD: Are you sure it wasn't—Victoria?

[TONY *thinks for a moment*]

TONY: It may have been. [*Turning to* MARGOT *excitedly*] When did you lose the bag? Wasn't it that weekend when we went to Peggy's? Yes, it was. It was Victoria. I remember now. He was sitting in the restaurant when I saw him.

HUBBARD: [*To* MARGOT] And was that where you left your handbag?

TONY: Yes, it was. [*To* MARGOT] You were with me, of course—didn't I say something about—there's someone I was at college with?

MARGOT: I don't remember.

[TONY *looks at* HUBBARD *who looks at* MARGOT]

HUBBARD: It looks as if he may have had something to do with that handbag, after all. The next thing is to get all this down on paper. I'd like you both to make an official statement before the inquest. *[Pause]* My office is only a few minutes from here. Perhaps you could come now?

[The doorbell rings]

TONY: Excuse me.

[TONY *opens hall door and* MAX *enters*]

MAX: Hello, Tony. [MAX *goes to* MARGOT *and then notices* HUBBARD] Margot . . .

TONY: Max, this is Inspector Hubbard. This is Mr. Halliday, Inspector. He was with me last night.

MAX: *[Bewildered]* How do you do?

HUBBARD: Mr. Halliday, as you were with Mr. Wendice last night, you may be able to help us here. Did you notice what time it was when he went to the phone?

[MAX *thinks for a moment*]

MAX: Yes—it was about twenty to eleven.

HUBBARD: *[Making note]* How did you come to notice that?

MAX: Well, when Mr. Wendice got up from the table I thought for a moment we were leaving the party, so I looked at my watch.

HUBBARD: Thank you, sir. You see, it was when Mrs. Wendice came in here to answer his call that she was attacked.

MAX: You mean *[To* TONY] you were phoning Margot . . . ?

TONY: Yes.

MAX: But I don't get this. I asked you if we were leaving and you said you were just going out to phone . . . your boss . . .

MARGOT: *[Sitting up]* Tony, I know what I was going to ask you. Why did you phone me last night?

[*All turn on* TONY]

HUBBARD: *[Crossing to* TONY] Now, just a moment. Before I lose the thread of this. At about twenty to eleven you left your party to phone your boss?

TONY: Yes. I used the pay phone in the lobby.

HUBBARD: Now, how long were you on the phone to your boss before you called your wife?

TONY: *[Smugly]* As a matter of fact I never did speak to him. I couldn't remember his number—so I rang my wife to ask her to look it up in the address book on the desk.

MARGOT: You mean you hauled me out of bed just to give you his phone number?

TONY: I had to. *[To* HUBBARD] My boss was flying to Brussels this morning and I wanted to remind him of something. It was rather important.

HUBBARD: Wasn't there a telephone directory in the hotel?

TONY: *[Calmly]* Yes, but he was at home—his home number isn't listed.

HUBBARD: So you never called him, after all?

TONY: No. Naturally when I heard what had happened here—I forgot all about it.

HUBBARD: I see. *[To* MAX] Mr. Halliday, Mr. and Mrs. Wendice are coming to my office now to make their statements. *[Taking out notebook]* Would you give me your address, sir? I may want to get in touch with you.

[TONY goes out by hall door]

MAX: Certainly.

MARGOT: I'll get my coat.

[She exits into bedroom]

MAX: I'm staying at the Carfax Hotel . . .

HUBBARD: *[Handing MAX notebook and pencil]* Just write it down there, will you? Telephone number as well. *[Watching MAX write]* Ever been over here before, sir?

[MAX doesn't see the catch in this]

MAX: *[Writing]* Yes, about a year ago.

HUBBARD: Umhm.

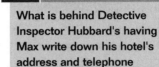

Suspicions?

What is behind Detective Inspector Hubbard's having Max write down his hotel's address and telephone number instead of Hubbard's taking it down himself? In short, what's the catch that Max misses?

[MAX hands notebook to HUBBARD who glances at address and returns it to his pocket. TONY enters by hall door]

TONY: Inspector, there's a devil of a crowd outside. Can't you send them away?

HUBBARD: They'll come back faster than they go, sir. I was going to suggest we left by the garden. Isn't there a gate at the far end?

TONY: Yes, but it may still be locked. I'll just see.

[TONY unlocks window and exits into garden. HUBBARD waits till he has gone and then turns to MAX]

HUBBARD: *[Confidentially]* How much does he know—about you and Mrs. Wendice?

MAX: *[Startled]* What are you talking about?

HUBBARD: You wrote a letter to Mrs. Wendice—from New York. *[MAX only stares at HUBBARD]* It was found in the dead man's inside pocket. I didn't mention it because I wasn't sure how much Mr. Wendice knew. Have you any idea how it got there?

MAX: No.

[MARGOT enters from bedroom. She is wearing an overcoat and carries her handbag]

MARGOT: Where's Tony?

MAX: He's just gone into the garden.

HUBBARD: Mrs. Wendice. When you lost your handbag, did you lose a letter as well?

[MARGOT looks quickly at MAX]

MARGOT: No.

MAX: Margot, it was found in this man's pocket.

HUBBARD: You did lose it—didn't you?

[Pause]

MARGOT: Yes, I did.

HUBBARD: I asked you that before, didn't I?

MARGOT: Yes—but you see—my husband didn't know about it.

HUBBARD: This man was blackmailing you, wasn't he?

[No reply]

MAX: It's no good, Margot. Tony will have to know about it now.

[MAX *takes out his wallet.* MARGOT *stares at him horrified*]

MARGOT: No!

MARGOT: It's the only thing to do. Inspector, after Mrs. Wendice lost my letter she received these two notes.

[MAX *hands the two blackmail notes to* HUBBARD *who reads them*]

HUBBARD: *[Glancing at postmarks]* Last February. *[To* MARGOT] How many times have you seen this man?

MARGOT: *[Angrily]* I've never seen him!

HUBBARD: *[To* MAX, *briskly]* Mr. Halliday, I'd like you to come along with us.

MAX: Yes, of course.

HUBBARD: Mrs. Wendice, when you come to make your statement there may be other police officers present. I shall warn you first that anything you say will be taken down and may be used in evidence. Now, never mind what you've told me so far. We'll forget all about that. From now on tell us exactly what you know about this man and exactly what happened last night. If you try and conceal anything at all it may put you in a very serious position.

MARGOT: I wish you'd explain what you mean by all this.

HUBBARD: I will. You admit that you killed this man. *[Enter* TONY] You say you did it in self-defense. Unfortunately, there were no witnesses, so we've only your word for that.

TONY: But I heard it all—over the telephone, Inspector.

HUBBARD: *[Turning to* TONY] What exactly did you hear, Mr. Wendice?

TONY: I heard—well, I heard a series of gasps.

HUBBARD: Did you hear anything to indicate that a struggle was going on?

TONY: Well, what I heard was perfectly consistent with what my wife told me.

HUBBARD: So all you really know of the matter is what your wife told you, isn't it? *[To* MARGOT] You suggest that this man came to burgle your flat, but there's no evidence of that. There is evidence, however, that he was blackmailing you.

TONY: Blackmail?

MAX: It's true, Tony.

HUBBARD: You suggest that he came in by the window—and we know he came in by that door.

MARGOT: [Frantically] But he can't have got in that way. That door was locked and there are only two keys. [Fumbling in her handbag] My husband had his with him and mine was in my handbag . . . [Takes out her latchkey and holds it up] Here!

[There is a pause]

HUBBARD: [Quietly] You could have let him in.

[Pause]

TONY: You're not suggesting that she let him in herself?

HUBBARD: At present, that appears to be the only way he could have entered.

MARGOT: Don't you even believe I was attacked? [Puts her hand to her throat] How do you think I got these bruises on my throat?

HUBBARD: You could have caused those bruises yourself. A silk stocking was found outside the window. It had two knots tied in it. Does that mean anything to you?

MARGOT: I suppose that must have been the stocking he used.

[Pause]

HUBBARD: We found the twin stocking wrapped in newspaper at the bottom of the wastepaper basket. Can you explain why your attacker should do that?

MARGOT: No.

HUBBARD: Those stockings were yours, weren't they?

MARGOT: [Horrified] No!

HUBBARD: We know they were. One of the heels had been darned with some silk that didn't quite match. We found a reel of that silk in your mending basket.

[MARGOT rushes to mending basket and searches inside]

MARGOT: [Thoroughly frightened] Tony, there was a pair of stockings in here!

[TONY goes to desk, picks up phone and dials frantically]

TONY: I've heard of police deliberately planting clues to make sure of a conviction. I just didn't realize they did it in this country.

MARGOT: [*Running across to* TONY] His men were in here for hours last night. They could easily have taken those stockings out and done anything with them.

TONY: Of course they did. And they wiped his shoes on the door mat as well.

[MARGOT *turns to* MAX]

ROGER: [*Offstage, heard through receiver*] Hullo.

TONY: [*Into phone*] Hullo, Roger. Thank God you're in. Tony Wendice, here. Now listen, Roger—we had a burglary last night. And Margot was attacked.

ROGER: Margot! Was she hurt?

TONY: No, she's all right, but the man was killed. The police are here now. And don't laugh—but they're suggesting that Margot killed him intentionally . . .

HUBBARD: [*Interrupting*] I wouldn't say that if I were you.

ROGER: Well! That's a good one!

TONY: It's funny, isn't it? Now, can you come round at once? To the Maida Vale Police Station . . .

ROGER: Be there right away.

TONY: Thanks, old boy. Good-bye. [TONY *rings off and crosses to* MARGOT] It's all right, darling, Roger's going to meet us at the police station.

HUBBARD: Mr. Wendice, I should advise you . . .

TONY: Our lawyer will give us all the advice we need, thank you.

[TONY *and* MARGOT *start to exit.* MAX *sees handbag on sofa*]

MAX: Here's your bag, Margot.

[TONY *opens French window*]

MARGOT: Oh, thank you, Max.

[*She takes bag, looks around the room, thoroughly bewildered. She turns and exits by French window.* MAX *follows her out.* HUBBARD *is about to exit, then turns to* TONY]

HUBBARD: You are coming, sir?

TONY: But of course, Inspector.

HUBBARD: [*Mumbling, half to himself*] Mm—I see—yes—I just wondered . . .

[HUBBARD *exits.* TONY *gives a brief glance around the room. He is now in complete control of the situation. He puts his hands in his pockets and follows* HUBBARD *out*]

CURTAIN

 Suspicions?

The stage directions indicate that the actor portraying Tony should convey that he feels that "he is now in complete control of the situation." What specific actions has Tony taken during Act Two to make him feel this way? Can you think of anything that Tony might have forgotten?

ACT THREE

The same. A few months later. Early afternoon.

The furniture has been rearranged. Curtains open but shutters have been fastened. No light except sharp rays through shutters. On the desk are a bottle of whiskey and a glass. The wastepaper basket is overflowing with odd junk and crumpled newspapers. Next to this there is a paper carrier containing groceries. A bed has been brought into the room with its head up-center. It has not been made properly for several days. Against the fireplace is the sofa. Odd clothing and robe are thrown over sofa. On the floor is TONY'S *leather suitcase with the lid open, half packed. The electric portable fire has been plugged in and stands between sofa and bed. When the curtain rises the room is in darkness. Footsteps are heard in the passage outside and a key turns in the hall door.* TONY *enters. He wears a raincoat, and carries a small blue fiber attaché case.* TONY *switches on the lights. He takes key out of door and puts it in raincoat pocket, then takes coat off. He puts coat on chair in hall. Closes door. He puts attaché case on bed, looks at watch, then crosses to table. He turns on radio. He returns to attaché case and unlocks it. He takes out a wad of pound notes, puts it in pocket and relocks case. Radio fades in. He looks up at the set and listens intently.*

ANNOUNCER: The main obstacles were the export of fruit and vegetables. Agreement has now been reached that the export quotas originally asked for be lowered by twelve and a half per cent. *[Pause]* The Home Secretary has written to the lawyers of Mrs. Margot Wendice to say that he has decided that there are not sufficient grounds to justify his recommending a reprieve. At the Old Bailey last November, Mrs. Wendice was found guilty of the murder of Charles Alexander Swann and was sentenced to death. *[Pause]* The official forecast is that there will be bright periods and showers in all districts today. Frost is expected again tonight, especially in the South. *[Phone rings]* The time is now eleven minutes past one and that is the end of the news . . .

[TONY *switches off radio and crosses to phone*]

TONY: *[Into phone]* Hullo!

PENDLETON: *[Offstage, heard through receiver]* Mr. Wendice?

TONY: Yes?

PENDLETON: Pendleton here.

TONY: Oh, good afternoon.

PENDLETON: Have you decided about the letters?

TONY: Yes—I'll be quite frank with you—the cost of the defense has been very high. I shall have to ask for five hundred pounds.

PENDLETON: Five hundred! But I'm only asking for her letters . . .

TONY: That's all very well—how would you like your wife's letters read by millions of people?

PENDLETON: I'm prepared to offer three fifty . . .

TONY: No, I'm sorry. I've quite made up my mind.

PENDLETON: Could you give me a little time to think this over?

TONY: By all means, think it over—only I'm going away the day after tomorrow. [*The door buzzer.* TONY *glances anxiously at the door. Quietly*] Excuse me. I shall have to ring you back.

[*He rings off. Goes to door and opens it.* MAX *stands in the passage outside. He wears neither coat nor hat. They stare at each other for a moment or two*]

MAX: Hello, Tony.

TONY: Hullo, Max.

MAX: May I come in?

TONY: Of course, you're quite a stranger.

MAX: [*Entering*] I'm sorry I haven't been around before. I wasn't I sure how you felt—after . . .

TONY: That's all right. It's rather chilly in here. I'll switch on . . . [TONY *stops short as he sees attaché case on bed*] I'll switch on the fire. Let's find somewhere for you to sit. [*Covers attaché case with clothes*] I've hardly seen anyone for weeks. I'm getting quite used to it. I've had to move in here because every-body stops in the street and peers in at the bedroom window. When the appeal failed they started climbing into the garden. You can't blame them, I suppose—it's cheaper than the zoo and far more topical.

MAX: I—had to come—in case there was anything . . .

[TONY *takes a typed letter from his pocket and hands it to* MAX]

TONY: [*Quietly*] I'm afraid it's settled, Max. Our lawyer received this from the Home Secretary this morning.

[MAX *reads letter and hands it back to* TONY]

MAX: You mustn't give up trying. It's not over yet.

TONY: I'm afraid it is. [*At bed*] We've done all we can. I went to the prison this morning to—say good-bye, but she wouldn't see me. I was rather glad—she never did like good-byes. [*Pause, simply*] I shan't see her again.

MAX: Tony. I take it you'd do anything—to save her life?

TONY: [*Surprised*] Of course.

MAX: Even if it meant going to prison for several years?

TONY: *[After a pause]* I'd do absolutely anything.

MAX: I think you can—I'm certain. *[Slowly]* If you tell the police *exactly* the right story.

TONY: The right story?

MAX: Listen, Tony. *[Sits on bed]* I've been working this out for weeks. Just in case it came to this. It may be her only chance.

TONY: Let's have it.

MAX: You'll have to tell the police that you hired Swann to murder her.

[Long pause. TONY *can only stare at* MAX*]*

TONY: *[Rises]* What are you talking about?

MAX: It's all right, Tony—I've been writing this stuff for years. I know what I'm doing. Margot was convicted because no one would believe her story. Prosecution made out that she was telling one lie after another— and the jury believed him. But what did his case amount to? Only three things. My letter—her stocking, and the idea that, because no key was found on Swann, she must have let him in herself. *[Pause]* Now Swann is dead. You can tell any story you like about him. You can say that you did know him. That you'd met him, and worked out the whole thing together. Not the blackmail. Swann was only suspected of blackmail for two reasons. Because my letter was found in his pocket and because you saw him the day Margot's bag was stolen.

TONY: Well?

MAX: You can now tell the police that you never saw him at Victoria. That the whole thing was an invention of yours to try and connect him with the letter.

TONY: But the letter was found in his pocket.

MAX: Because you put it there.

TONY: *[Pause]* You mean I should pretend that I stole her handbag?

MAX: Sure. You could have.

TONY: But why?

MAX: Because you wanted to find out who was writing to her. When you read my letter you were so mad you decided to teach her a lesson.

TONY: But I can't say that I wrote those blackmail notes.

MAX: Why not? No one can prove that you didn't.

*[*TONY *thinks it over]*

TONY: All right. I stole her bag and blackmailed her. What else?

MAX: You kept my letter and planted it on Swann after he'd been killed.

TONY: Wait a minute—when could I have done that?

MAX: After you got back from the party and before the police arrived. At the same time you took one of Margot's stockings from the mending basket and substituted it for whatever Swann had used.

[TONY *thinks it over*]

TONY: Max, I know you're trying to help but—can you imagine anyone believing this?

MAX: You've got to make them believe it.

TONY: But I wouldn't know what to say. You'd have to come with me.

MAX: No. I couldn't do that. They know the sort of stuff I write. If they suspected we'd talked this out they wouldn't even listen. They mustn't know I've been here.

TONY: Max! It's ridiculous. Why should I want anyone to murder Margot?

MAX: Oh, one of the stock motives. Had Margot made a will?

[Pause]

TONY: I—yes, I believe she had.

MAX: Are you the main beneficiary?

TONY: I suppose so.

MAX: Well, there you are.

TONY: But thousands of husbands and wives leave money to each other, without murdering each other. The police wouldn't believe a word of it! They'd take it for exactly what it is. A husband desperately trying to save his wife.

MAX: *[Rises]* Well, it's worth a try. They can't hang you for planning a murder that never came off. Face it. The most you'd get would be a few years in prison.

TONY: Thanks very much.

MAX: . . . And you'd have saved her life. That doesn't seem too big a price.

TONY: That's fine coming from you, Max. Her life might not be in danger at all if it hadn't been for you. It was because of your—association with her that she lost the sympathy of the jury. Don't get me wrong, Max. If there was the slightest chance of this coming off—of course I'd do it. But it's got to be convincing. How—how could I have persuaded Swann to do a thing like this?

MAX: You'd have to say you offered him money.

TONY: What money? I haven't got any.

[Pause]

MAX: You would have Margot's money.

TONY: It would be months before I could lay my hands on that. And people don't commit murder on credit. No, we'll have to think up something better than that . . .

MAX: [Fighting to concentrate] All right—we will. There is an answer and we've got to find it. [Pause] How much time have we got?

TONY: [As if he can hardly say it] It's tomorrow morning . . .

[Door buzzer. Offstage door slams. Footsteps]

MAX: Sssssssh!

[They stop and listen. They look at each other. TONY goes to open the door. MAX snaps his fingers to attract TONY'S attention. He motions tony to wait and crosses quietly and exits into kitchen. When tony opens the hall door INSPECTOR HUBBARD is standing in the passage outside. He carries a raincoat over his arm and a briefcase]

TONY: Oh—hullo, Inspector. [HUBBARD enters and TONY closes the door. Anxiously] Is it—about my wife?

HUBBARD: [Sympathetically] Er—no, sir. I'm afraid not.

TONY: [Surprised] What is it, then?

[HUBBARD hangs his briefcase on the same chair as TONY'S raincoat and then hangs up his hat and raincoat on coat rack]

HUBBARD: I'm making enquiries in connection with a robbery that took place about three weeks ago.

TONY: Can't this wait a few days?

HUBBARD: [Sincerely] Of course, sir, I'm very conscious of your position. If I may—I would like to say how deeply sorry I am that things . . .

TONY: [Curtly] Yes, Inspector—all right. How can I help you?

HUBBARD: The cashier of a factory in Ledbury Street was attacked in his office and two men made off with several hundred pounds—mostly in pound notes.

Suspicions?

1. Max tells Tony that he can save Margot from the death sentence by telling the police "*exactly* the right story." The "right story" that Max suggests to Tony perfectly matches in its details what Tony had actually done. Tony's response is: "Max, I know you're trying to help but—can you imagine anyone believing this?" Can you or is the story just too fantastic? Explain.

2. Do you think Max's story comes from his imagination as a crime writer ("I've been writing this stuff for years") or that he actually suspects Tony of doing everything the story details? Explain your reasoning.

TONY: What's all this got to do with me?

HUBBARD: In cases like this, all police divisions are asked to keep a look-out for anyone spending large sums of money.

[He pauses as if expecting TONY *to say something]*

TONY: I see.

HUBBARD: I was wondering if you had sold anything recently—for cash.

TONY: Why?

HUBBARD: My sergeant happened to be making enquiries at Wales' garage the other day. *[Pause]* It appears that you settled an account there recently for—*[Glancing at notebook]*—just over sixty pounds.

TONY: *[Casually]* Yes. I happened to have quite a lot on me at the time so I paid cash.

HUBBARD: I see. Had you just drawn this money from your bank?

[Pause]

TONY: *[On his guard]* Have you been to my bank, Inspector?

HUBBARD: *[With a smile]* As a matter of fact, I have. They wouldn't help me. Bank statements are always jealously guarded. *[Good-naturedly]* Where'd yer get it, sir?

TONY: Is that any of your business?

HUBBARD: If it was stolen money—yes, sir. It is my business. *[Taking out his pipe and holding it up]* Do you mind if I smoke?

TONY: Go ahead. *[With a laugh]* Do you really think I've been receiving stolen money?

HUBBARD: Until you tell me where you got it—I shan't know what to think—shall I? [HUBBARD *feels around in his pockets and then goes to hall and takes a tobacco pouch from one of the pockets of his raincoat]* You see, if you got that money from someone you didn't know—well, that might be the very person we're looking for. Hullo! *[He stoops down and appears to pick up something from the carpet just beneath his raincoat]* Is this yours, sir?

[He holds up a latchkey]

TONY: *[Moving nearer]* What is it?

HUBBARD: *[Casually]* Somebody's latchkey. It was lying on the floor—just here.

[TONY *crosses to hall and feels in the pockets of his raincoat. From one of them he takes out his latchkey and holds it up]*

TONY: No. I've got mine here.

[At the same time HUBBARD *opens hall door and tries to fit the other key into the lock]*

HUBBARD: No. It's not yours. [TONY *puts his key back into his raincoat pocket*] It may be mine, then. *[Feeling in pockets of his raincoat]* Yes, it is. It must have dropped out of my pocket. There's a small hole here. *[He walks a few paces back into the room, looking at key in his hand. Continuing as he goes]* That's the trouble with those keys—they're all alike. *[He puts key carefully into his side pocket]* I'm sorry, sir, you were saying . . . ?

[TONY *is at a loss*]

TONY: I—I don't think I was . . .

HUBBARD: *[At right of bed]* Oh, yes—about that money—I'd be grateful if you'd tell me where you got it. After all, a hundred pounds is quite a lot to carry around.

TONY: You said sixty a moment ago.

HUBBARD: Did I? Er—yes—my sergeant decided to dig a little deeper before he put in his report. *[Pulling at his pipe]* He said you'd also paid— a bill at your tailor's and another—for wines and spirits.

TONY: I'm sorry he went to all that trouble. If he'd come straight to me, I could have explained it at once. I simply won rather a large sum at dog-racing.

HUBBARD: Over a hundred pounds?

[TONY *glances anxiously toward the kitchen door*]

TONY: *[Quietly]* Yes, over a hundred pounds. It has been done before, you know. *[Sits]*

HUBBARD: I see. *[Smiling]* Why didn't you tell me this straight away, sir?

TONY: *[Coldly]* Because I'm a little ashamed to be caught going to dog-racing when my wife is under sentence of death.

HUBBARD: *[Sympathetically]* I know how it is, sir. Helps to take your mind off things. *[Moving to hall]* Well, that answers everything, doesn't it? I'm sorry to have had to bother you at this time.

TONY: *[Going to open hall door]* Not at all.

[HUBBARD *takes his hat off the peg and then turns to* TONY]

HUBBARD: *[Casually]* Oh, there is just one other thing, sir. Have you a small blue attaché case?

[TONY *is obviously shaken by this. He does not reply for several seconds*]

TONY: Don't say you've found it already?

[HUBBARD *strolls back into the room*]

HUBBARD: Why? Have you lost it?

TONY: Yes. I was going to report it this afternoon. I think I left it in a taxi. How did you know about that attaché case, Inspector?

[HUBBARD *watches* TONY *closely, takes out pad and pencil. The door of the kitchen opens a little, but neither* TONY *nor* HUBBARD *notices it*]

HUBBARD: The wine shop mentioned that you had it when you paid your bill. So my sergeant checked back on your garage and your tailor. They both remembered you having it with you when you paid them.

TONY: Yes. I use it instead of a briefcase.

HUBBARD: [*Going to hall door*] Well, these taxi-men are pretty good at turning things in. I hope you'll find it all right. [*Enter* MAX] Oh! Mr. Halliday.

[MAX *stands there staring curiously at* TONY]

MAX: [*Quietly*] Before you go, Inspector—I think Mr. Wendice has something to tell you.

HUBBARD: Oh, has he?

[HUBBARD *turns to* tony. tony *stares at* MAX. MAX *goes to sofa and looks under some of* TONY'S *clothes*]

MAX: Where did you put it, Tony?

TONY: [*At bed*] What's come over you?

MAX: [*Crossing to bed*] When I was in here just now there was a small attaché case. I can't remember just where I saw it but . . . [MAX *lifts* TONY'S *dressing gown and reveals the case. He carries it to desk and tries to open it but it is locked. Quietly*] Got the key, Tony?

TONY: Have you gone mad?

[MAX *takes metal ice pick from drinks tray*]

MAX: Very well. If there's no key we'll have to open it some other way.

HUBBARD: [*To* MAX] Just a moment, sir. [*To* TONY, *sharply*] Why did you say you left this in a taxi?

TONY: I thought I had. [MAX *is busily working on the lock*] Don't be a fool, Max. I've got the key somewhere. [*Searching in pockets*] I don't know what all the fuss is about . . . [MAX *suddenly fixes point of poker behind the lock and gives a twist*] Max, you . . .

MAX: It's all right, Tony, I'll buy you a new one.

[MAX *opens case and takes out an evening paper and six bundles of one-pound notes. He lays them on the desk.* MAX *stacks them on the desk, one by one.* HUBBARD *throws hat onto bed, crosses to desk and examines the money*]

HUBBARD: Must be over five hundred pounds here. [*Turning to* TONY] Where did you get it?

MAX: I can tell you *why* he got it. That money was to have been paid to a man named Swann—after he had murdered Mrs. Wendice in this room.

As you know, there was—an accident—so it wasn't necessary to pay Swann, after all. Obviously he couldn't produce all this without questions being asked—so he lived on it. He's been living on it ever since the twenty-eighth of September.

HUBBARD: [*To* TONY] Well, Mr. Wendice?

MAX: Just now you said you'd do anything to save Margot. What's made you change your mind?

TONY: [*To* HUBBARD] Before you came, Inspector, he was trying to persuade me to go to the police and tell the most fantastic story you ever heard. Apparently I bribed Swann to murder my wife so that—correct me if I go wrong, Max—so that I could inherit all her money. And that isn't all. You remember that letter of Mr. Halliday's? Well, it wasn't Swann who stole it. I did! And I wrote those two blackmail notes. And I kept Mr. Halliday's letter and planted it on the body . . .

MAX: [*To* HUBBARD] And that stocking which was found . . .

TONY: Oh, yes—the stocking. Perhaps I'd better tell this. It may sound more like a confession. I substituted . . . [*To* MAX] Is that the right word? I substituted one of my wife's stockings for—er—the other one—you follow me, don't you? Er—what else, Max?

[MAX *goes to hall door and opens it*]

MAX: [*To* HUBBARD] He told Swann he would hide his key somewhere out here. [*He looks up and feels along the ledge above and outside the door*] Probably on this ledge. Swann let himself in, then hid behind the curtains. Then Wendice phoned from the hotel and brought her . . .

[TONY *sits*]

HUBBARD: Just a minute. If Swann had used Mr. Wendice's key—it would still have been on him when he died. Besides, how did Mr. Wendice get in when he returned from the hotel?

[*Pause*]

MAX: [*Thinking it out as he goes*] She could have let him—and he could have taken his key out of Swann's pocket before the police arrived.

HUBBARD: But he let himself in with his own key. That was established at the trial—don't you remember?

[MAX *appears defeated by this*]

TONY: Come on, Max—your move.

[MAX *goes to hall door and looks up again at the ledge outside. As he speaks he demonstrates*]

MAX: [*Slowly, but not overemphasized*] Swann could have taken the key from here—unlocked the door—and then returned it to the ledge before he went in.

HUBBARD: [*Interrupting*] All right, Mr. Halliday. This is all very interesting, but it isn't getting me any nearer what I came to find out.

MAX: [*Frantic*] But this is a matter of life and death! What else matters?

HUBBARD: What matters to me is where Mr. Wendice got this money, that's all I want to know.

[MAX *closes the door and crosses quickly to desk*]

MAX: We'll soon find out how long he's had it.

[MAX *starts to go through top drawer*]

TONY: Now, what's the matter?

[MAX *takes out a checkbook and examines the stubs*]

MAX: [*Excitedly showing checkbook to* HUBBARD] There you are, Inspector. The last check he wrote was on the twenty-seventh of September. That was the day before this happened. I tell you he's been living off it ever since. [HUBBARD *looks through the checkbook stubs*] Here's his bank statement.

[MAX *opens drawer and takes out the black folder. He opens it on the desk and examines the entries*]

HUBBARD: [*Looking at bank statement*] He hasn't drawn any large sums from his bank. Nothing over—fifty-three pounds.

[HUBBARD *drops folder on desk.* MAX *picks it up and examines it*]

MAX: But just look at these, Inspector—nearly every week—thirty-five pounds—forty—thirty-five—forty-five . . . He could have saved it up.

TONY: Of course—I may have been planning all this for years!

MAX: [*Threatening*] Where did you get it?

TONY: Are you sure you want to know? [*To* MAX, *grimly*] I warn you, Max, you won't like it.

MAX: Come on.

TONY: Very well—you asked for it. [*Pause*] When she called me back from the party that

 Suspicions?

In telling his story about Tony and Swann to Chief Inspector Hubbard, Max goes further in his detailing than he did when he recommended the story to Tony. What new possibility is suggested about the whereabouts of the key that Swann used to enter the apartment? What contradiction, if any, is there between this theory and our seeing Tony, near the end of Act Two, Scene 2, place the key from Swann's raincoat pocket into Margot's purse?

night I found her kneeling beside Swann and going through his pockets. She kept saying he had something of hers—but she couldn't find it. She was almost hysterical. That's why I wouldn't let the police question her. In the state she was in she would have told every lie under the sun. The next morning she showed me that money—just like it is now—all in one-pound notes. She said, "If anything happens to me—don't let them find this." *[Pause]* After she was arrested I took the money in that case to Charing Cross Station and left it in the checkroom. Whenever I needed money I took it out and left it in some other checkroom. I knew that if you found it she wouldn't stand a chance. You see, she was just about to give it to him when she killed him instead.

MAX: Do you expect anyone to believe this?

TONY: I've really no idea. What about it, Inspector?

[Pause]

HUBBARD: Hmmmmmmmm? *[At desk]* Well, it certainly seems to fit in with the verdict at the trial.

MAX: *[Frantic]* You mean you're not even going to check up on this? She's being hanged tomorrow.

[TONY *goes to bed*]

HUBBARD: *[Wearily]* All this has been out of my hands for months. There's been a trial and an appeal . . .

MAX: Of course, it wouldn't do you much good, would it? You'd have to admit you arrested the wrong person.

TONY: I think you ought to go.

MAX: You bet I'll go. *[Goes to hall]* But you've made one mistake. *[Pause]* What will happen when Margot hears about all this?

[Pause]

TONY: She'll deny it, of course.

MAX: And perhaps she'll change her will. [*This gets under* TONY'S *skin.* MAX *opens hall door. He looks straight at* TONY. *Slowly*] You'll have done it all for nothing.

[MAX *exits. From now on* HUBBARD *speaks to* TONY *very gently, almost as if he was a child.* TONY *turns to* HUBBARD]

TONY: Suppose I had told that story of his. Would anyone have believed me?

HUBBARD: Not a chance, sir. Before nearly every execution someone comes forward like this. This must have been very distressing for you—coming as it did.

[TONY *sits*]

TONY: Do you think they'll let him see her? I—I don't want her upset just . . .

HUBBARD: Have a word with your lawyer. He might be able to prevent it. *[Nodding at money on desk]* And I should get all that money into the bank before someone pinches it.

TONY: Thank you—I think I will.

HUBBARD: *[Taking down hat from peg]* By the way, I was asked to tell you— there are a few things belonging to Mrs. Wendice at the police station.

TONY: What sort of things?

[During these next few speeches, HUBBARD takes down his own raincoat and changes it for TONY'S on the hall chair. TONY has his back turned and does not notice]

HUBBARD: Just some books—and a handbag, I believe. They'd like you to come and collect them sometime.

TONY: You mean—after tomorrow?

HUBBARD: Yes—or today, if you like. Just ask the desk sergeant—he knows all about it. *[HUBBARD picks up his briefcase and TONY'S raincoat and puts the latter over his arm. Crosses to TONY and puts out his hand]* Well, good-bye Mr. Wendice. I don't suppose we shall meet again.

TONY: *[Shaking hands]* Good-bye, Inspector— and thank you.

[HUBBARD exits. TONY waits till he hears the door slam. Then he crosses to desk and pours whiskey into a glass and drinks it. He picks up one of the bundles of notes and whisks it like a pack of cards. He picks up attaché case, examines lock, throws it on bed and looks around the room. He picks up the paper carrier bag, tips contents on desk, fills bag with bundles of notes, covers them with newspaper. He crosses to bed, leans across it and switches off electric fire. He then crosses to hall with paper bag and takes HUBBARD'S rain-coat and throws it over his arm. He switches off light and exits. Sound of footsteps and street door opening and slamming. The pink glow of electric fire dies slowly. There is a sound of key in lock. The hall door opens and HUBBARD enters. He switches on pencil torch and looks around the room. He looks at key and

Suspicions?

1. Max challenges the believability of Tony's explanation of how he got the money. In your opinion, how believable is Tony's story that it is the bribery money Margot was intending to give Swann before she decided, instead, to kill him? Explain your reasoning.

2. Do you think that Max truly suspects Tony along the lines of the story he wanted Tony to tell the police? Why or why not?

3. Why do you think Hubbard has intentionally taken Tony's raincoat and left him his own?

then pockets it carefully. He throws his briefcase and raincoat on the bed and crosses to the desk. He picks up the phone and dials a number]

POLICE: *[Offstage, heard through receiver]* Hullo.

HUBBARD: Maida Vale Police? Chief Inspector here. Give me Sergeant O'Brien quick.

[Pause]

O'BRIEN: O'Brien.

HUBBARD: Hubbard . . . Look, I've got back in again. Start the ball rolling.

O'BRIEN: Yes, sir.

[HUBBARD rings off. He looks around the desk until he finds TONY'S bank statement and starts to examine it again. There is a crash of broken glass from behind shutters. HUBBARD puts out torch and moves silently into the kitchen. Someone opens the French windows but the shutters bar his way. A knife is inserted through the crack where the shutters meet and the bar which holds them together is lifted off its pin. Shutters fly open, letting daylight into the room. MAX enters. He immediately goes to desk and starts searching for something. HUBBARD appears from kitchen]

> **👁 Suspicions?**
>
> After Hubbard uses Tony's key to re-enter the apartment, he calls police headquarters and instructs Sergeant O'Brien to "start the ball rolling." Try to predict what Chief Inspector Hubbard is up to.

HUBBARD: What are you up to? *[MAX looks up, startled]* What's the idea?

MAX: Where's his bank statement?

HUBBARD: Never mind about that. You've got to get out of here—quick.

MAX: *[Raising his voice]* Have you got it?

HUBBARD: Sssssssh! Not so loud.

MAX: But don't you see . . .

HUBBARD: *[Savagely, but in half-whisper]* Shut up! *[Almost frantic]* If you want to save Mrs. Wendice, keep quiet and let me handle this.

MAX: You?

[Sound of street door opening, footsteps. HUBBARD raises his hand to keep MAX quiet and then points to door]

HUBBARD: Ssssssssh! *[They both stand motionless watching the door. Sound of someone trying to insert key into lock. Then silence for a moment. Door buzzer rings twice. HUBBARD raises his hand to restrain any movement from MAX. Footsteps move away. Sound of street door shutting. HUBBARD breathes a sigh of relief. He opens bedroom door and peers toward the street]* Whew! You nearly ditched us then. I should have locked you up.

MAX: What in the hell is all this?

HUBBARD: *[Letting off steam]* They talk about flatfooted policemen! May the saints protect us from the gifted amateur! *[He crosses to the open window and looks out into the garden for several seconds. Quietly]* You'd better prepare yourself for a surprise, Mr. Halliday.

Suspicions?

Who do you think is the "someone" at the door who tries inserting a key into the apartment door's lock, rings the buzzer twice, and then goes away? Explain your reasoning.

[HUBBARD continues to stare outside and then suddenly backs into the room waving MAX away from the window. After several seconds MARGOT appears, followed by THOMPSON, a police constable in uniform. MARGOT is dressed in the same clothes she was wearing at the end of Act Two, and she carries the same handbag. She stops in the window as she sees the two men. Her appearance should indicate that she has been through a great deal during the last two or three months]

MARGOT: Hullo, Max. *[MAX goes to her]* Where's Tony?

MAX: He—he's gone out.

MARGOT: When will he be back?

HUBBARD: *[His manner is official and brisk]* We're not sure. All right, Thompson. *[THOMPSON exits. HUBBARD turns to MARGOT]* Was it you who rang just now?

MARGOT: Yes. *[Surprised]* Why didn't you let me in?

HUBBARD: You've got a key. Why didn't you use it?

MARGOT: I did. But it didn't fit the lock.

HUBBARD: And you know why—don't you?

MARGOT: No, I don't. *[Pause]* Has the lock been changed?

HUBBARD: May I have your bag? *[Goes to bed. MARGOT gives up her handbag. HUBBARD opens it, undoes the zip purse and takes out the key. He holds it up]* You knew this wasn't your key, didn't you?

MARGOT: No.

[HUBBARD picks up the attaché case from the bed. He shows it to her]

HUBBARD: Your husband has explained this, you know. You can tell us all about it now.

[MARGOT stares at it. HUBBARD watches her face]

MARGOT: *[Bewildered]* What is it? Why am I . . . ? I don't understand.

[HUBBARD looks at her steadily for a moment]

Suspicions?

What possible explanations are there for the fact that the key Margot used did not work? Which explanation among all these possibilities do you believe is the true one? Why?

HUBBARD: No. I don't believe you do. *[Kindly]* Come and sit down, Mrs. Wendice.

[MARGOT *crosses to sofa and sits down.* HUBBARD *puts key and purse back into handbag*]

MAX: What's going on here?

[HUBBARD *goes to desk and looks out of window*]

HUBBARD: *[Shouting into garden]* Thompson!

THOMPSON: *[From garden]* Sir.

[THOMPSON *enters*]

HUBBARD: Take this handbag to the police station.

THOMPSON: Yes, sir.

[THOMPSON *slips his arm through the straps of the handbag and exits*]

HUBBARD: Wait a minute, you clot. You can't go down the street like that. [HUBBARD *takes his briefcase from desk and exits into garden*] Put it in this.

MAX: Margot, what is this? Why are you here?

MARGOT: *[As if in a dream]* I don't know. *[Slowly]* About an hour ago the warden came to see me. He just said I was to be taken home. Two detectives drove me here. They parked just around the corner. Then that policeman came up and said I could go. But I couldn't get this door open. When I left the policeman was still outside and he brought me around by the garden. *[Getting up]* Where's Tony? He was supposed to visit me this morning but they said he couldn't come. Has anything happened to him?

MAX: No—nothing. [HUBBARD *enters from garden. He closes the window, locks it and closes shutters. Then he goes to hall and switches on light*] Inspector, do you think you could tell us what you're up to?

HUBBARD: Mrs. Wendice, what I've got to tell you may come as a shock.

MARGOT: Yes?

HUBBARD: We strongly suspect that your husband had planned to murder you.

[MARGOT *stares at* HUBBARD *for a moment and then turns to* MAX]

MAX: He's right, Margot. He arranged for Swann to come here that night and kill you.

[MARGOT *shows no sign of emotion*]

MARGOT: How long have you known this?

HUBBARD: *[Surprised]* Did you suspect it yourself?

MARGOT: *[Working it out in her mind]* No—never—and yet . . . *[She looks around the room for several seconds then turns suddenly to* MAX] What's the matter with me, Max? I don't seem able to feel anything. Shouldn't I break down or something?

MAX: It's delayed action, that's all. In a couple of days you're going to have one hellava breakdown. [*Puts an arm around her. To* HUBBARD] When did you find out?

HUBBARD: The first clue came quite by accident. We discovered that your husband had been spending large numbers of pound notes all over the place. It ran into over three hundred pounds and it appeared to have started about the time you were arrested. Now, I had to find out where he got this money and how. Then I remembered that, after you were arrested, we searched this flat and I saw a copy of his bank statement in that desk. So yesterday afternoon, I went to the prison and asked to see your handbag, and while I was doing this I managed to lift your latchkey. Highly irregular, of course, but my blood was up. Then, this morning when your husband was out, I came here to look at this bank statement. [*Pause*] I never saw it because I never got through the door . . . You see, the key I had taken from your handbag didn't fit the lock. [*Three loud knocks on the ceiling above. They all look up and* HUBBARD *rushes to the hall and switches off lights*] Don't make a sound. [*Sound of a street door opening and shutting. Footsteps move along passage to hall door and stop. Long pause and then footsteps move away. Street door opens and slams. After a few moments* HUBBARD *goes and opens the hall door. Calling up*] Williams.

WILLIAMS: [*From upstairs*] Sir!

HUBBARD: Who was it?

WILLIAMS: Wendice, sir.

HUBBARD: Which way did he go?

WILLIAMS: Hold on. [*Pause*] Toward the police station, sir.

HUBBARD: Good. [HUBBARD *closes hall door and switches on lights. Crosses to telephone*] That was a near one. [*Picks up phone and dials a number*] Maida Vale Police?

O'BRIEN: [*Offstage, on phone*] Yes, sir. O'Brien.

Suspicions?

1. Explain why the key Inspector Hubbard took from Margot's handbag "didn't fit the lock."

2. Whose footsteps were those outside the apartment door? Why did that person stop at the hall door, pause, and then leave?

HUBBARD: Hubbard here . . . Look, O'Brien, he's found out about his raincoat . . . He just came back and couldn't get in. I think he's on his way to the station now. Has Thompson arrived with the handbag?

O'BRIEN: Yes, sir.

HUBBARD: Good. Now, look—give Wendice those books and the handbag and make sure he sees the key . . . Better make him check the contents and sign for it. If he wants his own key and raincoat . . . er, tell him I've gone to Glasgow.

O'BRIEN: Yes, sir.

HUBBARD: Any questions?

O'BRIEN: No questions.

HUBBARD: Right . . . Call me back when he leaves the station . . . [*During the phone call*

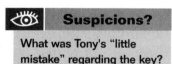

Suspicions?

Where do you think Margot's key is and why do you think so?

MAX *moves slowly to hall door and opens it. He looks up thoughtfully at the ledge above the door, then stares down at the spot where Swann died and then back to the ledge. He feels along it with his fingers and looks puzzled. To* MAX *as he rings off*] Well, Mr. Halliday, have you got it?

MAX: [*Puzzled*] I don't think so. [*Slowly*] Where is Mrs. Wendice's key?

[HUBBARD *goes through open door into passage. He takes her key from under the stair carpet and holds it up. Then he replaces it exactly in the same place*]

HUBBARD: It took me just half an hour to find it.

MAX: But if it was there—why didn't Wendice use it just now?

HUBBARD: He didn't use it because he doesn't realize it's there. He still thinks it's in his wife's handbag. You see, you were very nearly right. [*To* MARGOT] He told Swann that he would leave your key under the stair carpet, Mrs. Wendice, and told him to return it to the same place when he left. But as Swann was killed he naturally assumed that your key would still be in one of Swann's pockets. That was his little mistake. Because Swann had done exactly what you suggested, Mr. Halliday. [*Going through the motions*] He unlocked the door—and then returned the key *before* he came in . . .

MAX: And it's been out there ever since! And the key Wendice took out of Swann's pocket and returned to her handbag was . . .

Suspicions?

What was Tony's "little mistake" regarding the key?

HUBBARD: Swann's own latchkey! Mind you, even I didn't guess that at once. At first I thought your husband must have changed the lock. It had always surprised me that no key was found on Swann's body. After all, most men carry a latchkey about with them. Then I had a brainwave. I took the key that was in your handbag to Mrs. Van Dorn's and unlocked the door of her flat. Then I borrowed her telephone and called Scotland Yard.

MARGOT: Why did you bring me back here?

HUBBARD: Because you were the only other person who could possibly have left that key outside. I had to find out if you knew it was there.

MARGOT: Suppose I had known?

HUBBARD: [*With a smile*] You didn't!

MARGOT: [*Suddenly*] Max!

MAX: Yes, darling?

MARGOT: I think I'm going to have that breakdown right now!

[MARGOT *turns her head into* MAX'S *shoulder and begins to cry softly.* MAX *puts his arms around her. Phone rings*]

HUBBARD: O'Brien?

O'BRIEN: Yes, sir. He's just left the station.

HUBBARD: Right! [*Rings off. To* MARGOT *and* MAX *as he crosses to hall door*] Try and hang on a little longer. [*Opens door and calls up*] Williams!

WILLIAMS: [*Upstairs*] Sir!

HUBBARD: He's just left the station . . . Give me a thump if he comes this way.

WILLIAMS: [*From upstairs*] Right, sir.

[HUBBARD *closes door and makes sure it is locked properly*]

MARGOT: [*To* MAX] Handkerchief.

[MAX *produces his handkerchief and* Margot *wipes her eyes and gives her nose a good blow*]

MAX: [*To* HUBBARD] What happens now?

HUBBARD: Sooner or later he'll come back here. As I've pinched his key, he'll have to try the one in the handbag. When that doesn't fit he'll realize his mistake, put two and two together and look under the stair carpet.

MAX: But . . . if he doesn't do that—all this is pure guess work. We can't prove a thing.

HUBBARD: That's perfectly true. [*Slowly, with emphasis, pointing to hall door*] But once he opens that door—we shall know everything.

[*Pause*]

MAX: What will you do then?

HUBBARD: I'm to phone the Home Secretary personally. He's standing by for my call now.

MAX: And Mrs. Wendice?

HUBBARD: Will have nothing else to fear . . .

[*There are three thumps on the ceiling.* MAX *and* MARGOT *stand up.* HUBBARD *switches off the lights and stands by the telephone facing hall. Long silence*]

MAX: [*Gently*] All right, Margot?

MARGOT: [*In a whisper*] Yes—I'm all right.

[MAX *puts his arms around* MARGOT]

HUBBARD: [*Softly*] Quiet, now, you two. [*There is another long silence and then the sound of the street door opening and shutting. Footsteps to hall door.*

Pause. Sound of key in lock. It doesn't fit. Long pause. Footsteps moving back to front door. Slam. MAX *gives a start. He opens bedroom door and peeps through. In whisper:*] Careful!

MAX: He's going round by the garden. He'll see the broken glass.

HUBBARD: Ssssh!

[*Pause*]

MAX: [*In a low whisper*] He's coming back.

HUBBARD: He's remembered.

[*Long pause.* MAX *closes bedroom door silently and returns to* MARGOT. *Sound of street door opening and footsteps along passage to hall door. Silence for a few seconds . . . Then sound of key in door. The door opens and* TONY *enters. He is carrying* HUBBARD'S *raincoat,* MARGOT'S *handbag and some books. He stands silhouetted in the doorway and stares at the key in the door. Then he takes it out thoughtfully and stares back at the fifth step of the staircase, and then looks back at the key in his hand. Then he switches on the light and with his back to the audience closes the door shut, then turns and walks into the room. After several paces he sees* MARGOT *and* MAX, *stares at* MARGOT *for a long moment and then drops the books and the handbag to the ground. Then he turns and sees* HUBBARD *Suddenly he throws away his raincoat and rushes to the hall door in a panic. He opens the hall door but a* DETECTIVE *in plain clothes moves in from the left and blocks his way.* TONY *turns back into the room and stares at* MARGOT. MARGOT *turns her head away from* TONY *and toward* MAX. HUBBARD *looks* TONY *up and down for a moment then moves very slowly to the telephone and dials a number*]

CURTAIN

 How Clever?

1. Early in the second act of the play, Max tells Margot that he really believes in the perfect murder "on paper," but that in real life, things don't always turn out the way they are planned. Max, a writer of crime stories, is convinced that if he were ever to commit murder, he would "make some damned stupid mistake and never realize it." How do Max's comments sum up the "perfect" murder that Tony planned? When, where, and how did Tony "put two and two together" and realize his mistake?

2. Making assumptions—taking something for granted without thinking it through—can be costly, dangerous, and damaging. What simple assumption had Tony made about something as seemingly trivial as when Swann would return the key to its hiding place under the stair carpet?

3. Pretend you are Swann. Tell why you didn't act with Margot's latchkey the way Tony assumed you would? Why did you put the key back after you opened the apartment door instead of waiting until you had committed the murder and left the apartment?

4. There are dialogue references in both Acts Two and Three that when Swann's body was searched, "no key was found when we went through his pockets." How is this an important clue to the audience?

5. Since Tony apparently did not give any thought to the key he took out of Swann's raincoat pocket, what can the audience assume about the look and feel of Swann's key? How safe an assumption is this? Explain.

6. Was it a genuine clue or a red herring when, after he picked up his own key off the floor, Inspector Hubbard said to Tony, "That's the trouble with those keys—they're all alike." Explain your reasoning.

7. Besides the all-important mistake of assuming that the key in Swann's raincoat pocket was Margot's key and not Swann's own, did Tony make any other mistakes in his attempt to get away with murder? Would you consider how Tony handled his bank withdrawals and subsequent spending a mistake? Explain why or why not.

8. What assumption do you think Chief Inspector Hubbard first made about the fact that there was no key at all found on Swann's body? Why did the absence of a key continue to bother the detective?

9. Both Max and Inspector Hubbard suspect Tony. What has led Max to this suspicion? What has led the inspector to this suspicion? Is there any evidence to suggest that the two of them began to share their suspicions with each other? Is there any evidence to suggest that the two of them never shared their suspicions with each other?

10. At what point in Act Three does Inspector Hubbard reveal that he wasn't entirely convinced of Margot's innocence? Explain why you chose that moment in the play.

11. Hubbard states near the end of the play that once Tony "opens that door— we shall know everything." Explain why this is true. In your opinion, who solved this case—Max or Inspector Hubbard? Explain why you chose the person you did.

DetectWrite: Characterization and Plot

1. When we meet Max at the beginning of the play, he tells Margot that, as a writer of a weekly television crime program, whenever he cannot think of a story to write, he just uses his "three hats" marked: "Who kills who, How, and Why." How does this help him to overcome writer's block? As a prospective writer of a detective story, what do

you think of this method of writing crime stories? What do you think of it as a way of overcoming writer's block? How might it help you to write your own mystery story?

2. Max also tells Margot that there are only five "Whys"—five important motives for a killing: fear, jealousy, money, revenge, and protecting someone you love—and that he writes them down on pieces of paper and picks one out of the Why hat. Which of these "stock motives" (motives in ready supply) are behind Tony's plan to kill his wife, Margot? Can you think of any other "important" motives for a killing you might use in a detective story you would write? Of all these five or more motives, which would you make the major motive in your story and why?

3. Compare and contrast Chief Inspector Hubbard with Detective Levine in the novella "The Sound of Murder." Point out where and how the one is particularly British and the other is particularly American or New York-ish. How prominent a role does each play in the plotting of their respective stories? Explain.

DETECTWRITE: Plot

1. Margot told Tony that she might skip listening to the "Saturday Night Theater" program on the radio that particular night. "It's a thriller," she explained. "I don't like thrillers when I'm alone." How is this ironic? How does this plot twist almost spoil Tony's plan for the "perfect" crime? What makes the play "Dial 'M' for Murder" a thriller?

2. Find several places in the play where the playwright uses the device of placing an unidentified character on the other side of a locked or closed door. What effect does this have on the audience? Explain.

3. "Dial 'M' for Murder" is a good example of a detective story in which the reader or audience knows "whodunit" but not whether the criminal will ever be detected. Will the bad guy get away with it? Will the innocent be unjustly punished? Was the perfect crime committed and, therefore, did crime pay after all?

   What are your feelings about this type of mystery story? Would you consider writing such a story—one that reveals who the criminal is at or near the start of the story? Explain your feelings.

4. The detective in "Dial 'M' for Murder"—Chief Inspector Hubbard—doesn't enter the play until we're well into Act Two, and his acts of detection are done off-stage (out of the sight and knowledge of the audience), although they are revealed primarily through dialogue late in Act Three. What are your feelings about the way the detection is conveyed in "Dial 'M' for Murder," and why would you consider or not consider structuring a play of your own in this way?

5. Max believes that there is no reason that "a murder story can't be as good" as any other kind of story. Explain why you agree or disagree.

6. Max tells Margot that while flying on a plane to London he thought of "a pretty fair gimmick" for a mystery. "There's a pair of twins—identical," he begins, "one lives in Paris and the other in New York—all of a sudden they both decide to . . ." Try continuing Max's plot description of this story. Take it as far as you can, with as many plot and character details as you can think of, in ten minutes. What do you think of "your" story based on Max's "gimmick"? What do you like about it, and why? What possibilities does the story have for future development?

7. When Tony asks Max, "How do you start to write a detective story?" Max advises: "Forget the detection and concentrate on the crime. The crime's the thing. Imagine you're going to steal something, or murder somebody. I always just put myself in the criminal's shoes and keep saying, 'Well, what do I do next?'" As a potential writer of a detective story, what do you think of Max's advice? Explain.

8. Follow Max's advice on how to start writing your detective story: What does your criminal do? What does he or she do next? And after that? At what point in your story will you ignore Max's advice to "forget the detection" and start concentrating on the detection?

DETECTWRITE: Setting

1. Did you find "Dial 'M' for Murder" too British or dated (1950s)? If you did, where in particular and why? If you didn't, why do you think this particular setting has universal appeal?

2. If you were making a movie version right now of "Dial 'M' for Murder," what would you do to make the time and place of the setting contemporary American in their look and feel? How much like the setting of "The Sound of Murder" could you or would you make it? Explain.

3. "Dial 'M' for Murder" uses a unit set for all its scenes and three acts. Explain why this can be very economical for a stage play. Compare and contrast this play's use of a single set with that of the one-act play "Trifles" in the "Amateur and Off-Duty Detectives" section of this text. Does the fact that one of these plays is a one-act play and the other is full-length make a difference in your comparative analysis? Explain.

4. For some, the unit set can seem boring or claustrophobic, particularly when a full-length play is transferred from the stage to the movie screen. Do you feel this to be the case with "Dial 'M' for Murder"? Explain why you would or would not visually "open up" "Dial 'M' for Murder" if you were making your own film version of it. If you would open it up, where and how would you do it?

5. Alfred Hitchcock, the famed director of many movie thrillers, brought Frederick Knott's stage play "Dial 'M' for Murder" to the screen in 1954. According to the film critic David Denby in a 1998 article in *New York* magazine, "Hitchcock accepted and even reveled in the stage-derived claustrophobia of the action; his direction amounted to virtuoso manipulation of limited means." See Hitchcock's "Dial 'M' for Murder" on television or on video.

   Do you agree or disagree with Denby's belief that Hitchcock seems to have enjoyed not "opening up" the play but, instead, making the most of staying within the confines established by stage play conventions? Where and how does the movie look just like a filming of the stage play? Where doesn't the film do what you would expect movies to do better than plays? Where do you agree or disagree with Denby's comment that Hitchcock seems to have had fun being challenged by the limitations of the play's structure?

6. In 1998, thirty-four years after Alfred Hitchcock's movie version of "Dial 'M' for Murder," the director Andrew Davis brought out his "Dial 'M' for Murder" for the 1990s, which he called "A Perfect Murder." See "A Perfect Murder" or on video.

   Why do you think Davis has changed the title from "Dial 'M' for Murder" to "A Perfect Murder"? What else besides the title has Davis changed? (For example, who solves the crime in Davis's version?) Why do you think Davis has made not only these changes but these types of changes?

7. How has Davis "opened up" the stage play so that it looks and feels more like a movie than Hitchcock's version?

8. How has Davis's changing of the setting from 1950s London to 1990s New York affected characterization, dialogue, and plot? Which of Davis's changes coincide with your recommendations for your film version of "Dial 'M' for Murder"?

9. In what ways is "A Perfect Murder"—in its themes, plot details, or structure—still "Dial 'M' for Murder"?

10. Of all the versions of "Dial 'M' for Murder" you have experienced, which do you like best and why?

DETECTWRITE: Dialogue

1. What purposes were served by opening the play with the conversation between Margot and Max about the affair they had had? What purposes were served by the duplication of much of the same information in the later discussion between Tony and Lesgate?

2. How does Tony's following dialogue with Lesgate capture Tony's essential nature and character: "To know what you want *to pay for*—that's the thing. Everything has its price. People fail because they want to buy cheap. I've learnt to pay a big price for anything I really want . . . I usually get it"?

3. Find in the play at least one example of dialogue for each of the following characters that serves to convey that person's basic nature: Margot, Lesgate/Swann, Max, Inspector Hubbard. Explain why you chose that piece of dialogue.

4. Write what you believe to be a character-revealing piece of dialogue, and then test your dialogue's effectiveness by asking someone to read it aloud and tell you what he or she can conclude about the basic nature of the person who spoke those words.

5. Find examples of dialogue in the play that you find to be either rather British or old-fashioned, or both. Rewrite them for what might be your new American movie version of "Dial 'M' for Murder" to be set in either your own neighborhood or a neighborhood you are familiar with from your traveling, your reading, or your viewing of television and the movies. See and listen to "A Perfect Murder," the 1998 film version of "Dial 'M' for Murder" set in New York City, and compare and contrast its dialogue with the dialogue you have written for your "Dial 'M' for Murder" American update.

DETECTWRITE: Stage Directions

1. How did the author use particular stage directions during Tony's meeting with Swann/Lesgate to convey to the audience that while Tony's words were meant to win Swann over to doing the killing, his actions meant that Tony was confident that Swann would agree?

2. Find at least three other examples of stage directions in "Dial 'M' for Murder" that you found to be particularly meaningful or effective and explain why you chose them.

3. What is interesting about the fact that the final stage direction in the play shows Inspector Hubbard moving slowly to the telephone and starting to dial a number? Where else in the play has the telephone been used as a meaningful "prop" (short for stage property)? Who is Hubbard dialing?

DetectWrite: Creating a Title for Your Story

1. Explain why you think "Dial 'M' for Murder" is or is not a good title for this play. In what ways is it dated? Is "A Perfect Murder," the title of the 1998 film version, as good a title, not as good, or better?

2. The American author Sue Grafton uses repetition of sounds in the titles of her private eye novels, which she also writes in alphabetical order. *M is for Malice* is among her most recent works. Lawrence Treat, a prolific author of mystery novels and short stories and one of the founders of the Mystery Writers of America, wrote such novels as *H as in Hangman* and *V is for Victim*. A collection of his police procedural short stories was entitled *P as in Police*.

   For the detective story you would write, it is possible that you might first think of an effective title before you decided on any other aspect of the story. What is your opinion of the kind of title illustrated above in which there is, as in "Dial 'M' for Murder," the repetition of a particular sound? Explain why you feel the way you do.

A Dirge for Clowntown

James Powell

"**R**INGLING-RINGLING!" SHOUTED THE BEDSIDE TELEPHONE. When he fumbled the receiver out of its cradle, a familiar voice at the other end of the line said, "We've got a live one, Inspector. Three seventy-one Pagliacci Terrace, Apartment 2C."

Forcing a grunt as close to "I'm on my way" as he could muster, the man in the bed got his feet on the floor and staggered toward the bathroom, hitting a chair and the doorjamb on the way. Grabbing two tight fistfuls of sink porcelain, he stared down at the drain for a long moment. Then he raised his head and saw himself in the mirror. By Jumbo, he looked as bad as he felt! The dead-white skin, the great bloody slash of smile, the huge round maraschino nose, the perfect black triangles of his eyebrows, the dead white skullcap with the two side-tufts of bright-orange hair. There he was, Clowntown's finest, Inspector Bozo of the Homicide Squad. Talk about a three-ring hangover! Bozo ran the tips of his trembling fingers across his cheek. A trip to Makeup was long overdue. Well, it would have to wait. When Homicide said they had a live one, they meant they had a dead one.

Splashing water on his face, Bozo hurried back to the bedroom. The clock-radio on the bedside table said 11:15 in the morning. Shaking his head at himself, he got into his baggy pants, pulled the suspenders up over his shoulders, and sat down on the edge of the bed to put on his long yellow shoes. (Shoe length indicated rank on the Clowntown force. When two deputy chiefs met toe to toe, they had to raise their voices to communicate.)

Next came the high celluloid collar with the big bow tie of fluorescent orange and purple lightning bolts. Then he slipped into the paddy-green-plaid trenchcoat with all the belts and flaps, tabs and buttons, and the three-pound brass police badge pinned to a lapel. Slapping the pockets to make sure he had his revolver and his bicycle horn, he headed for the front door. He took the expensive pearl-grey fedora from the hatrack, set it carefully and properly on his head, and stepped out into the hall. Years ago, when he'd designed his outfit, he could have chosen one of those little umbrellas with the water spout in the ferrule or a squirting flower as the finishing touch. Instead he'd picked this perfect hat, feeling it set off the rest of his exaggerated costume. Yes, all in all he'd put together a damn good act. Why was it starting to fall apart?

As he passed through the lobby, Bozo exchanged horn-honk greetings with the building superintendent. Outside, a crew of Sanitation Department clowns armed with pushbrooms were sweeping spotlights out of the gutters. The Saturday-morning street was cold and blustery beneath an elephant-grey sky. Clowntown's wind was legendary, with newspapers scuttling around every corner and flags snapping like tent canvas overhead. The rawness came with early December.

Bozo decided to walk. Pagliacci Terrace wasn't that far and he needed to clear his head. He stumbled going up a curb and felt his nose budge. Damn, not that again. Almost twenty years on the force and the best nose he could afford was a wobbly mail-order number from Mr. Snoot. Last month, coming down the crowded city-hall steps with some buddies from Vice, the thing had dropped right off and gone bouncing high, wide, and handsome down the steps with Bozo cursing and chasing after it.

Oh, no one laughed. His embarrassed friends pretended not to notice. His Honor and the police chief and the rest of the brass looked the other way. They were all great admirers of his father, Big Bozo, who'd made the family name synonymous with clown. But Bozo knew they'd soon be clucking among themselves about how Big Bozo's boy was hitting the bottle, how he was going to seed, how he'd been in a tailspin since his divorce.

No, Bozo couldn't let that happen again. He made a mental note to have the nose looked after at the next sporting-goods store. The same people who custom-drilled the holes in bowling balls did nose refitting. And they always tried to sell him one of those flashy new Japanese noses all the trendy young clowns were wearing. But ever since the india-rubber-cartel people got their act together, the price of noses had gone through the roof.

Bozo reached the Pagliacci Terrace address and took the steps two at a time. The uniformed clown policeman guarding the apartment door saluted, using the hand holding his nightstick, rapping himself on the head and knocking his tall blue helmet askew. It was a stunt he did well and Bozo could see he was proud of it.

The dead clown lay on his back on the floor, toes pointed at the ceiling, the wreckage of a whole custard pie on his face. He was dressed in a convict's uniform of broad black and white horizontal stripes and brimless cap and had a black-plastic ball and chain shackled to one leg. Retrieving the victim's wallet, Bozo found the man's union card. He recognized the ferret face staring out at him from the photograph. Yes, he knew Clown Bunco very well. Like a few other clowns on the shady side of the law, Bunco, a small-time confidence man and hustler, had taken to wearing a convict outfit as if to openly challenge society and its values. Bozo glanced at the card again. Today was Bunco's birthday. Sending a friend a custard pie in the face on his birthday was an old Clowntown custom.

Over in the corner, the police medical examiner was cramming an immense cleaver, a butcher knife as big as a scimitar, and a vast hypodermic needle back into his black bag. "Well, Doctor?" asked Bozo coldly as he knelt down to clear away some of the custard and make sure it really was Bunco under the mess. He'd never cared for the medical examiner. The man had fled Clowntown soon after graduating from the Emmett Kelly School of Medicine to take a fling at burlesque, slouching across the stage and leering at females in low comic routines. When burlesque died, he'd crept back, happy to eke out a living as a police medical examiner. His lewd eyebrows, glasses, red nose, and moustache looked made from one piece and he walked like his tie was caught in the zipper of his fly. For Bozo the man would always have the smell of the rim-shot about him.

"Strychnine," said the doctor. "A massive dose in the birthday boy's custard pie." Reading Bozo's look of disbelief, he gave a take-it-or-leave-it shrug and loped for the door, adding over his shoulder, "The delivery man's waiting for you in there."

Bozo followed the direction of the medical examiner's cocked thumb into the bedroom, where a clown wearing a bright-yellow bellboy's uniform sat waiting with a very depressed look. His chest was decorated with large brass buttons and the words MIDWAY BAKING COMPANY were printed in chartreuse on his pillbox hat. "What the hell happened?" demanded Bozo.

"Search me," said the delivery man in a reedy, nervous voice. "This was almost my last stop of the day. I parked my van on the street. Up I came and honked at his keyhole. When he opened the door, I was standing there holding the pie behind my back. 'Clown Bunco?' I asked. 'Yeah, so what?' sez he. 'So Happy Birthday,' sez I and I let him have it right in the kisser. You know, the secret of my marksmanship is never taking my eyes off the target.

"But it's funny the reaction you get in that split second while the pie's in the air. Clown A's pleasantly surprised. Clown B's smug—he's already had so many pies in the face he hasn't gotten the custard out of his ears from the last one and I know there are three more pie-delivery men stacked up out on the staircase. But Bunco there gave me the kind of look you don't see very often, a kind of tearing up in the eyes like he was remembering how long a time it had been since anybody'd remembered his birthday. Then the pie hit." The delivery man looked at Bozo helplessly. "Then he fell over dead."

"The doctor says the pie was poisoned," said Bozo. "Which would mean he got custard in his mouth or up his nose. Well, I can't buy that." One of the first things a clown learned was the right way to take a custard pie in the face. Just before impact you closed your mouth tightly and breathed out through your nose.

"Believe me, it was the finger schtick that did him in," insisted the delivery man.

The great clown, Josef Schtick, the originator of many little routines clowns still use, came up with the business in question as a follow-up to being hit with a custard pie. He would stand there, a forlorn laughingstock, with the mess sliding down his face. Then he would take a scoop of the custard on his forefinger, look at it curiously, taste it, smile, smack his lips, and start eating. Bozo cursed his own obtuseness. The finger schtick. Of course.

Bozo sent the delivery man home, confident he couldn't have known the pie was poisoned. Clowns were totally incapable of causing direct physical harm to another person. That didn't mean a clown couldn't commit murder, only that he couldn't do it directly.

Bozo spent a good hour searching the apartment for something that might give him a clue to the murderer's identity. He found nothing until almost the last place he looked. In an envelope taped to the underside of the drawer in the telephone table, he discovered a manila envelope. Inside were a sheaf of sales receipts for furniture and other household furnishings made out to Bunco. He skimmed through them quickly. It was all expensive stuff and it wasn't anything here in the apartment. Strange.

But stranger still, why would a man hide sales receipts? Bozo made the envelope into a tube and stuffed it into his pocket. He left the apartment not sure what his next move should be. But back out on the sidewalk, he saw a Dinero's hamburger place across the street. All he'd found in Bunco's refrigerator was a wizened lemon and a moldy quart of buttermilk. Well, the guy had to eat somewhere. And that reminded Bozo he could use a shot of the feedbag himself.

The girl behind the lunch counter wore a blonde fright wig, a fashionable nose, an immense greasepaint smile, and, under her uniform, a big set of inflatable breasts. The portside one seemed to have a slow leak. When Bozo came in, she put down her copy of *Big Top Tid Bits* and ducked behind the coffee urn. He was sure he heard several strokes of a tire pump before she reappeared in full repair. "What'll it be?" she asked.

Bozo ordered his burger and sat watching the waitress prepare it. He knew her type well. The young girl fresh from Pratt Falls comes to Clowntown with stars in her eyes, so sure she'll land a job with the circus she can already smell the cotton candy. It ached to think about it. It made him remember his ex-wife, Calliope. She'd been new in town, too, the first time he met her and hell-bent to make her name in the circus. What a knockout she'd been, with her carrotred hair done up in braids and her great big freckles and the tasteful way she'd only blacked out a single tooth.

Those first years of their marriage had been times of big change for Clowntown. Until then, the city'd been a solidly blue-collar community. A lot of clowns worked for Ringmeister, the center-city brewery, or in the textile mills of Clowntown Tinsel and Spangle. But one of the biggies bought out Ringmeister and closed it down, and the Japanese computerized the hell out of the spangle industry. Center city declined, and the clowns began their flight out to the suburbs to Carneyville and Highwire.

Bozo and Calliope hadn't made the move. He was glad they hadn't. He had watched the suburban clowns trade in their floppy shoes for expensive sneakers and their baggy pants for designer jeans. And he saw their red-nosed faces at the commuter-train windows on the elevated tracks, looking sad—not clown sad, but stark, lonely, three-piece-suit sad. And he knew how their stories would end. Each year they'd buy a smaller-size nose until they got down to one no bigger than an angry boil. One morning they'd arrive at work with a band-aid on their nose and tell their secretary they'd had the boil lanced. When the band-aid came off, it would be goodbye, Clowntown.

But looking back on it, Bozo knew that he and his wife should have started a family. They put it off too long. Then all of a sudden Calliope wanted her own career. Bozo had argued strongly against it, but Calliope stood firm. "I can hear my slapstick clock ticking," she insisted. "It's now or never."

"Then it's never!" Bozo had shouted.

After the divorce, Calliope went to circus winter quarters in Florida. Bozo missed her. He tried not to think of her down there, just one more big red smile among a thousand big red smiles waiting for the big break. He got a card from her now and then. Sometimes he sent her money. But he knew he'd never see her again.

Bozo's food arrived. He ate it warily, unsure of his stomach, and set about organizing his thoughts on the case. So what did he have? The business of breathing out through the nose when you take a custard pie in the face was a clown trade-secret. So the murderer had to be a clown, a clown who knew Bunco well enough to know he still did the finger schtick.

And what about the hidden envelope? Bozo pulled it out and examined the contents again. A receipt from Crystal Palace Furniture for a bedroom and a living-room set. Another from ST Molding and Shelving

Suspicions?

What do you think Inspector Bozo "has" based on the observations he has made so far and the information he has gotten from interviewing the medical examiner and the pie-delivery man? Is there any reason to believe that the murderer is another clown? Explain.

for a fireplace mantel. A third from a company called PlexiGrandi for a piano. All were marked with the special instruction that the customer would pick them up at the warehouse. Why was stuff like this important enough for Bunco to hide? And was it connected with his murder?

Bozo pondered for a moment and then called the waitress over and showed her Bunco's union card. "Ever see this guy in here?"

She looked at the picture. "Him and his ball and chain? Sure—he was a regular," she said. "My first day here he gave me the honk and said if I played my cards right he'd introduce me to his bigwig pals in the circus. What a laugh. I sure told him where to get off."

"Somebody just told him where to get off permanently," said Bozo. "Bunco's been murdered." He waited for that to register before asking her, "Did he ever come in with anybody else?"

She snapped her gum thoughtfully before answering. "There was Waco. He was a rodeo clown—purple suspenders, hairy chaps, red-flannel long johns, a cowboy hat with the brim turned up in front—the whole ten yards. Distracting Brahman bulls from thrown riders was his life until rodeos went the way of the buffalo. He was a nice guy, Waco. Too nice to have anything to do with Bunco, I always thought. They used to sit over in that corner booth and talk. I haven't seen Waco for—how long's it been? Two months? Six weeks?"

She thought for a minute. "I let him take me out once. Oh, it was no big deal. He'd just come into some money and wanted to celebrate. He took me to one of those new wine bars where the mimes go. How harmless can it get, right, standing around for an hour or so pretending to drink?"

Bozo wasn't sure. In a recent try at cutting down on his own intake, he'd visited a wine bar some mimes had opened where Trapezio's, the great old Italian clown restaurant, used to be. It'd been a pleasant evening. A couple of those mime women would've been real knockouts if only they'd had big red noses. And the drinks had gone down smooth. But there'd been nothing pretend about the hangover he woke up with next day.

Over the past few years, mimes had started moving into center city Clowntown, renting apartments, restoring brownstones. Now they were a familiar sight every weekday morning, going off to their jobs wearing the tight jumpsuits of their class, striped jerseys, a white oval on the front of their faces, their hats decorated with a flower or a butterfly on a wire. And all of them, all, relentlessly walking against some wind that only they could feel. A lot of clowns resented the mimes, claiming they were stand-offish and wouldn't give you the time of day. Bozo knew that wasn't true. Mimes were kind, gentle folk, quick, at the slightest encouragement, with the big smile and the gift of an imaginary flower.

"Boy, Waco really got a charge out of watching those mimes go through their paces—like sitting on bar stools that weren't there or leaning on empty air like it was the most natural thing in the world," said the waitress. "'I've seen the future and it works,' he said as we walked out the door. Afterward we went around the corner to his place. He didn't try anything funny. We just had coffee and he showed me pictures of his kids."

"Where was this?" demanded Bozo.

"Corner of Pantaloon and Rigoletto," she said. "But don't waste your time. That was a couple of months ago. He said he was moving. He said the owner of his apartment building wanted to renovate and rent the place out for big bucks to the mimes. Hey, maybe he left his landlord a forwarding address."

She thought for a moment and said, "The only other guy I ever saw with Bunco was this big-jawed, big-chested clown in a red bowler and a tight orange suit."

Bozo drummed four fingers against his white cheek. "A tough-looking customer with a skull-and-crossbones on his left hand?" he asked. When she nodded, he had his clown. The only trouble was Mugo had been in jail for the last ten days on the charge of mime-bashing. But he had friends. Mugo could have arranged to have Bunco killed from there.

Mime-bashing was the crime of the moment among trendy clown criminals, a shameful business made all the more so by the victims' peaceful natures. Where clowns were incapable of harming another directly, mimes couldn't knowingly do harm to anyone, period. Except, of course, to themselves.

Unfortunately, a bad clown element had gotten wise to this. They would prowl the streets at night with their noses in their pockets so they couldn't later be identified in a police lineup. If they ran across a mime, they'd take a swing at him, being careful to miss by a good six inches. But mimes being what they were, they had to snap their heads around as though struck or hurl themselves backward into the nearest wall or down a flight of steps. Last month Mugo and a bunch of his friends had set upon four mimes, throwing punches at them until the mimes knocked themselves unconscious. Then the clowns had stripped them and left them naked and bloody in the street. Fortunately, two of the victims had been able to identify Mugo by his tattoo. Could Mugo be the murderer? Why would he want to kill Bunco?

"Hey," said the waitress, looking down at Bozo's empty plate. "It's fresh—how about a slice of custard pie?"

Bozo headed off for Pantaloon and Rigoletto. But in the next block he saw a sporting-goods store and decided to get his nose tended to.

The dark, old-fashioned shop smelled of leather and the rosin bag. Bozo's honk was answered by one from the back room and a moment later a dusty old clown with a burly grey moustache appeared, cleaning his wire-framed glasses on his striped apron. He spotted Bozo's problem at once and without a word ushered the Inspector into a small curtained alcove.

There Bozo handed over the nose and sat with a hand modestly covering his naked undernose. The old man put a jeweler's loupe in his eye and examined the inside of the rubber nose. He sighed and was about to start his sales pitch when he saw Bozo's name inscribed on the rim of the hole. "Inspector," he asked in a voice filled with awe, "was your father by any chance Big Bozo?"

Bozo nodded. His father had been a three-star general in the Clown Marines. Strutting out there at the head of his crack clown drill-team in his uniform of electric-blue with all the gold frogging and gold stripes on the sleeve and his shako with its immense pompom, he'd been the hit of every parade. The drill-team's trips and stumbles were all coordinated to perfection. When one marching clown slipped on a banana peel, a hundred did.

"Let me shake your hand," said the little old clown, doing just that. "The way I see it, Big Bozo and his drill-team set war back a hundred years. And isn't that what the military's supposed to be all about?" Then he returned to the matter at hand. "Inspector, this nose of yours has gone to the well once too often. I can fix it for now, but what you really need—"

"Is a new nose? Forget it," said Bozo. "Not on a police inspector's salary."

"I was thinking of maybe something nice in the second-hand line," said the nose-auger man.

Bozo frowned. Since the india-rubber cartel, there'd been a sharp rise in the theft of noses for resale. There were even stories of ghoulish clowns haunting midnight cemeteries to desecrate the graves of the recent dead.

The old man had produced a small box lined with white velvet. Inside was a smart red nose. "This has you written all over it," he said. "A match made in heaven. That undernose of yours is a real honker. This little honey belonged to one of your small-nosed rodeo clowns. It'll auger out real nice."

Bozo blinked and snatched the nose. The name *Waco* was inscribed around the rim. "How'd you come by this?"

"Last week this rodeo clown in chaps and cowboy hat walked in off the street," explained the old man. "He said he had this spare that was just collecting dust. He said he could use the cash. So we struck a deal. Trust me. Like I said, it'll auger out real nice."

The old man was clearly disappointed when Bozo told him he'd have to get back to him on that. He shrugged and set about repairing the old nose as best he could.

Bozo sat there patiently, considering this new development. Here was this rodeo clown, a friend of Bunco's who comes into some money and then drops out of sight. A couple of months later, Waco pops up again out of nowhere to sell a spare nose. A week later more or less and Bunco gets killed. What the hell did it all mean? Bozo didn't know. But as he paid for the repair job, he decided to flash Bunco's picture. "Seen this guy around?"

The old man looked at him like he was joking. "The outfit's all wrong, of course," he said, "but I swear that there's the Waco character I was just telling you about."

Bozo strode down the street puzzling out this new development. Then he heard an approaching siren and stopped to watch as a Clowntown Fire Department ladder truck, a caricature of a vehicle, rushed down the street with clown firefighters falling off

Suspicions?

What exactly is "this new development"? Can you help Inspector Bozo puzzle it out?

and chasing after it on all sides. Bozo smiled, knowing the bumble and ineptitude was part of the clown's art. That ladder truck would arrive at the fire as quickly if not quicker than any non-clown ladder truck. And, yes, the buckets of confetti they threw on the fire would extinguish it as effectively as any modern chemical mix. Clowns were proud of that.

As he resumed his walk, Bozo mused on why some clowns hated the mimes so much. He thought he knew the answer. It'd come to him a while back when he'd been eating his lunch on a park bench. Along came this mime, walking against the wind, and sat down across the path from him as though there was a bench there, which there wasn't. From an imaginary brown bag, he drew this imaginary napkin and tucked it under his chin. Next came an imaginary sandwich, which he unwrapped and smiled down at before eating with visible relish, scattering the crumbs for the real pigeons.

Then he peeled and ate an invisible banana while he watched the birds crowd around his feet. When he was through, he put the sandwich wrapper and banana peel into the paper bag, which he crushed into an imaginary ball and tossed at a wire trash-container twenty feet away. The mime's anxious face told Bozo about the flight of the ball. He knew it rimmed the target once, twice, three times before body English knocked it into the container. Delighted, the mime got up and strode happily back in the direction he'd come, still walking against the wind.

Sitting chewing on his baloney sandwich, which now tasted like ashes, Bozo decided clowns resented mimes not because the pigeons preferred their imaginary bread crumbs to a clown's substantial ones or because a mime's invisible tears seemed larger, his silent laughter louder than clown sorrow or joy. No, in the end he decided that the mimes made the clowns feel clumsy, coarse, material, and utterly earthbound.

Not that that justified mime-bashing.

The brick facade of Waco's old apartment building had been sandblasted. A spanking new canopy flapped over the front door with *Pierrot Plaza* written across it in cursive script. While Bozo stood there at the curb, a mime couple arrived, pushing their child in an imaginary stroller. As more mimes entered and left the building, Bozo noticed the fat clown in top hat, cutaway, and baggy striped trousers standing nearby watching them come and go with a big red smile and rubbing his gloved hands together vigorously. The man was the epitome of the old plutocrat clown so popular in the twenties and thirties. Here was clown avarice—greed carried to the point of laughter. Here was the Pierrot Plaza's landlord.

Honking his horn and wagging his badge with a thumb behind his lapel, Bozo stepped forward. "Bozo's the name, Homicide's the game," he said. "I'm trying to track down an old tenant of yours, a rodeo clown called Waco."

The landlord clown turned pale. Glancing quickly left and right, he led Bozo by the elbow down the sidewalk to the next apartment building. "If we're going to talk murder," he murmured, "let's do it here in front of my competitor's building. Violence makes mimes very nervous. But Waco didn't leave any forwarding address, if that's what you're after. I guess he's living somewhere in the high-rent district. Did you know he hit it big with the ponies a couple of months ago? He bet his bankroll. 'Play Animal Act in the fifth,' he told me. I wish I had. It paid a bundle."

Bozo frowned. Without a forwarding address, where did he go from here? "I don't suppose you caught the name of the people who moved his furniture?" he asked.

"That junk?" said the landlord. "He gave it all to the Poor Souls Rescue Mission. They fix up stuff like that for resale and use the money to help tramp and hobo clowns." He shook his head. "Boy, what a bunch of dodos they sent round to pick it up! Those clowns broke half the stuff on the way down, not counting what they did to the paint on the stairwell."

The landlord winced at the memory. Then he chuckled. "You want to hear something real funny? A month later when I'd fixed the place up for my new tenants, I was down in the lobby when this mime Pip, who I rented Waco's old apartment to, drives up in a truck with four mime buddies and they go through the rigmarole of unloading invisible furniture and carrying it up the stairs. Laugh, I thought I'd die. But here's what really got to me. Those mimes were a hell of a lot more careful moving furniture that only existed in their heads than those rescue-mission clowns were with the real McCoy.

"No, sir, I've got no complaints with the mimes," he continued, counting the reasons on his gloved fingers. "They're polite as hell. They're neat as pins. Maybe they're a bit emotional, but they don't talk your arm off. They don't trash the building. They pay their rent on time."

Warming to his subject, he added, "Look, I'm as big a clown booster as the next guy. But the circus doesn't stop here anymore. We've got to move with the times. Sure, Waco was a nice guy and he got lucky—good for him. But he never did a lick of work, nothing but mope around in his apartment all day or hang out at the track. Now take the mimes. Five mornings a week there they go, all heading for the financial district, all walking against the wind. And after work, here they all come back, still walking against the wind."

Bozo knew the mimes were highly favored by the financial community. The banks and brokerage houses liked them because of their honesty. As the saying goes, there are no pockets in mime jumpsuits.

The landlord barked a short laugh. "No, what I just said isn't quite right, come to think of it. They go and come back together, all except this

Pip I was telling you about. He works down in the financial district like the rest of them, but with him you never know what way he's going to go when he leaves for work or which way he'll come back. Strange, right?"

"Well, maybe not," said Bozo thoughtfully. "Wasn't it the great clown philosopher Plato who said that the only thing you could say for sure about the wind was that it didn't always blow from the same direction?"

He left the puzzled landlord scratching his head, went into the apartment building, and took the elevator to the fifth floor where the directory said this Pip character lived. Suppose the guy wasn't a mime? Suppose he couldn't fake the walking-against-the-wind bit? Suppose he actually had to be walking against the wind? That would mean sometimes he'd have to head off in a different direction from the others. But if the guy wasn't a mime, who was he? Bozo thought he knew.

 Suspicions?

What the landlord first said about all the mimes walking together against the wind on their way to and from work "isn't quite right" because with Pip, "you never know what way he's going to go when he leaves for work or which way he'll come back. Strange, right?" Can you make sense of what the landlord considers "strange"? Why, with Pip, might you "never know what way" he's going or coming?

The door to Pip's apartment was wide open. The place was quite empty of furniture. A pug-nosed man in the usual mime getup sat in midair in the middle of the room, seemingly engrossed in the play of his wrists and fingers along the keys of a baby grand that wasn't there. Bozo's polite horn-honk made the mime jump and look up quizzically.

"I'm Inspector Bozo of the Clowntown Police, Mr. Pip," said Bozo. I'm selling tickets for our annual Policeman's Ball."

Pip smiled broadly and nodded his head. Crossing the room, he seemed to sit down at an imaginary desk, pull out an imaginary drawer, take out an imaginary checkbook, and, with a visible flourish, make out an invisible check, which he handed over.

"You're very generous, Mr. Pip," said the police inspector. When the mime cocked his head modestly, Bozo continued, "You'll get your tickets in the mail, sir." Politeness made him add, "It's a nice place you've got here."

The mime beamed and, getting up, reached out his elbow and leaned with perfect ease on the precarious perch of a mantel Bozo could not see.

 Suspicions?

Can you make any connections between Mr. Pip's mime actions when Inspector Bozo visits him and other details in the story? Explain.

Back in the elevator, Bozo had to admit that Pip was one of the best mimes he'd ever seen. Boy, that mantel routine, that was really some—Bozo frowned and tugged thoughtfully at the ends of his bright bow tie. Reaching in his pocket, he pulled out the manila envelope of sales receipts and went through them until he came to the word he was looking for. When the elevator doors opened, he crossed to the lobby phone booth and skimmed through the classified ads, stopping to read in several places. Then he phoned for a police backup.

Rejoining the landlord out on the street, Bozo asked, "Did one of the mimes who helped Pip move in have a skull-and-crossbones tattoo on his hand?"

"Now that you mention it, one did. Strange. Mimes aren't much for tattoos. What's going on?"

"That's easy," said Bozo. "Those weren't mimes moving mock furniture. They were clowns in stolen mime outfits lugging real furniture up the stairs."

The landlord looked bewildered.

"Okay," said Bozo. "Do you know what the S-T in S-T Furniture Company stands for? See-Through, that's what. They make transparent home furnishings like fireplaces and mantels. And Crystal Palace Furniture only deals in glass tables and chairs and things like that. And surprise, surprise, PlexiGrandi Company makes Plexiglas pianos."

"So what're you telling me?"

"That your old tenant, Waco the clown, moved right back in again as Pip the mime. For him, clowning was a dead-end street. He dreamed of sending his kids to mime school to learn the basics—the tough stuff, like sitting on chairs and leaning on mantels that aren't really there. That meant passing himself off as a mime. Transparent furniture seemed the easiest way."

"So he wants his kids to have a better future than he did," said the landlord. "Since when was that a crime? Just between us and in case you hadn't noticed, being a clown isn't what it used to be. So big deal. Listen, you don't tell anybody about Waco, I won't either."

"I wish it was that simple," said Bozo. "You see, Waco paid a shady clown named Bunco to set up his operation, like getting the fake mime union card, the furnishings, and the bogus mime movers. It looks like Waco gave this Bunco his clown nose as payment for all his help. And his costume, too. After all, he wasn't going to need the stuff anymore. But Bunco had a little shakedown in mind. He calculated that Waco would end up in some mime job with a lot of money or insider-information lying around. Well, he was right. Where he made his mistake was thinking Waco would sit still for a lifetime of being blackmailed. Waco decided to have him killed with a custard pie."

As he spoke, a little fluorescent-yellow car with a big star on the door pulled up to the curb. Bozo's police backup had arrived. Fourteen uniformed officers got out and lined up in order of height, from a seven-foot beanpole to a dwarf no more than three feet tall. Back in the days before the cuts in the police budget, they could have gotten nineteen men out of the same car.

They were a smart-looking bunch of clowns, full of ginger and bicycle horns, eager to get the job done. Bozo divided them into two groups, one to take the stairs and his own assault group that would go up by elevator. At Bozo's signal, the policemen started tripping over themselves, bumping into each other, and trying to get through the apartment-building doorway at the same time. They were a crack unit. Even with a good dose of gaston-and-alphonsing on top of the obligatory clowning around, they were in position in record time.

The door to the false mime's apartment was closed. Signaling his men to keep clear, Bozo honked his bicycle horn at the keyhole and shouted, "Open up, Waco, it's the police! We're onto your game!"

From inside, a voice shouted, "There's nobody here named Waco! I'm Pip! I'm a—" Then, realizing he'd given himself away, Waco snarled a defiant, "Come and get me, coppers!"

Bozo heard the sound of a window opening. He signaled his men to break down the door, and followed in after them. Later he would remember the sorry dash of the Clowntown Police across a room filled with transparent furniture with a smile, but at the time the sight filled him with dismay. His men looked like a charge of stumblebums, barking their shins on the crystal coffee table and crashing into the Plexiglas piano and falling over the sofa and chairs.

Bozo rallied his men and, hot on Waco's trail, he led them out the window and up onto the roof. They got there just in time to see the fugitive clown cross over to the neighboring roof on a narrow plank. Sprinting as fast as his big shoes would allow, Bozo reached the edge just as Waco toppled the plank down between the two buildings. Bozo knew there'd be no catching him now.

Waco knew it, too. He lingered for a moment as Bozo's men came running up. "Doing things on too big a scale was my only mistake!" he called. "Next time I'll make do with a glass cardtable and folding chair, max! I'll sleep on the floor! I'll send the kids to mime boarding school! I won't tell them the truth about their daddy until they're old enough to understand! Then it'll be our little secret!"

"You'll never pull it off!" shouted Bozo earnestly. "Every time you sat down, it'd be a lie! And what kind of life would it be for your kids, always afraid to invite their friends home, always having to hide the dark secret that their dad was a clown?"

"I'm not a clown! I never was a clown! I'm a mime!" Waco cried in a fury. Then, as if he realized his anger belied his words, he forced himself to be calm. "All my life I've felt like an outsider," he said. "I told myself it was because I was a rodeo clown in a world where the rodeos are few and far between. But deep down in my bones, I always knew I was a mime. I think maybe the Gypsies stole me from a mime cradle and sold me to a nice childless couple of rodeo clowns. Okay, I can't recapture my mime heritage for myself, but I can damn well do it for my kids."

"You lost any chance of that when you killed Bunco," said Bozo.

"Bunco deserved what he got!" shouted Waco, turning away from the edge of the roof and starting toward the top of the metal ladder that would take him down to a fire escape and safety. "He would have sucked me dry! Then he'd have started on my kids! I don't regret what I did!"

It was cold on the roof. The sun poked through the dull winter sky like a nose of brass. A mere summer ago the same sun had set, a perfect fit, soft, warm, and red, down the slot of any Clowntown street. Bozo sighed to himself. He knew what he had to do. "I've got to take you in, Waco!" he called.

The murderer continued walking toward the ladder.

Bozo's men were lined up along the edge of the roof. They turned to him for instructions, honking their horns nervously. Bozo had hoped it wouldn't come to this, but police regulations were clear—he knew what he had to do. He drew his weapon. "Stop or I'll shoot, Waco!" he ordered.

The fugitive clown had reached the roof parapet now, his hands on the metal uprights of the ladder. He gave Bozo and the other policemen standing with their drawn weapons a pitying look and shook his head.

Bozo had no other choice. As humiliating as it would be, he pulled the trigger and the flag popped out of the end of the barrel. BANG! said the flag. In the next moment, all the clown policemen fired and all the flags at the ends of their pistol barrels said BANG! One policeman had a submachine gun. Its longer flag read RATATAT! What other kinds of weapons would be issued to clowns who by nature were unable to hurt anyone directly?

Waco knew that and he should have made his escape, but when the barrel flags appeared his body gave a sudden jump and spun as though hit with a fusillade of bullets. The horrified clowns watched Waco's grip on the ladder give way finger by finger until he fell back into that long emptiness that led to the street below.

Bozo watched in sad amazement. Could Waco's parents really have been mimes? Or was his desire to be a mime so strong that when the flag fire came he'd done what any real mime would have done even if it cost him his life?

Bozo sat on the edge of his unmade bed massaging his big bare left foot, which rested on his knobby right knee. He'd been thinking about the day's events. But now he turned his thoughts to Calliope hanging around circus winter quarters with clown stars in her eyes. It seemed to him that she'd been right to go and try. And he'd been right to stay, to see in his own small way that clowns got a fair shake and gave a fair shake. After all, wasn't justice as rare as stardom?

And when push came to shove, the mimes were right, too. They'd pared things down to the essentials—a jumpsuit, a hat, imaginary flowers and butterflies. It looked like the kind of act the world needed now. Maybe the doom-sayers were right. Maybe the clown days were numbered. Maybe they'd played the game with too heavy a hand.

Well, what the hell, clown or mime, hadn't they all sprung from the same crazy pair of ancestors, sitting arm in arm, fishing for the moon in a bucket?

Bozo reached for the bottle of Old Roustabout on the bedside table, drew out the stopper with his teeth, and looked around for his well-thumbprinted glass from the night before. When he couldn't find it, he grunted and spat out the stopper. Then he turned out the light, rolled over in bed, and fell quickly into clown slumber.

 How Clever?

1. Which specific acts of detection led Inspector Bozo first to conclude that Bunco's killer was a clown and that the clown was posing as the mime Mr. Pip?

2. Why did Waco create an elaborate scheme to appear to be a mime?

3. What motive did Waco have for killing Bunco? How did the fact that Inspector Bozo recognized the dead man as "a small-time confidence man and hustler" foreshadow later revelations in the story?

4. Of the possible explanations Inspector Bozo considers, what do you think was the reason that Waco mimed being hit with a fusillade of bullets and then fell to his very real death? Why did you choose that possibility?

5. Why did Inspector Bozo give the medical examiner a look of disbelief when the doctor said, "Strychnine. A massive dose in the birthday boy's custard pie"? What trade-secret among clowns made Inspector Bozo realize that Bunco's murderer had to be another clown who knew Bunco fairly well?

6. How did Inspector Bozo's stop at the sporting goods store lead to an important link between Waco and Bunco? What did Inspector Bozo realize after he showed the store's owner Bunco's picture and the owner said, "That there's the Waco character I was just telling you about"? How did Bunco wind up with Waco's clown nose and costume?

7. How did the sales receipts for furniture that Inspector Bozo found in Bunco's apartment function as an important clue in the story? Why had Bunco hidden them? What did Inspector Bozo later realize after he saw Mr. Pip both sit down "at an imaginary desk" and lean on "a mantel Bozo could not see"?

8. What particular act of detection led Inspector Bozo to think it important to visit Dinero's hamburger place? Did Inspector Bozo's recognizing the waitress's description of Mugo serve as a genuine clue or as a red herring in the story? Explain your reasoning.

9. If "clowns were totally incapable of causing direct physical harm to another person," how did Waco cause Bunco's death?

10. Explain how the bad clown element could seriously wound the mimes they picked on without ever laying a hand on them.

11. After Waco won a bit of money betting on the ponies, where did he move from and where did he move to? Why did Inspector Bozo ask Mr. Pip's landlord whether one of the mimes who had helped Pip move in had "a skull-and-crossbones tattoo on his hand"?

12. How did Waco give himself away when, after the police shouted, "Open up, Waco, it's the police! We're onto your game," Waco shouted back, "There's nobody here named Waco! I'm Pip. I'm a—"?

13. Explain why the policemen who fired at Waco used weapons that "shot" flags saying "BANG!" and "RATATAT!"

14. What conclusion did Inspector Bozo come to as to why clowns resented mimes?

15. Why do you think the author set his story in a fictional Clowntown populated by a variety of clowns and a minority of mimes?

16. How does the author use the format and structure of a detective story as the basis for social and philosophical commentary about ethnic groups, social class, stereotypes, prejudice, discrimination, and hate crimes? Give examples from the story of where the author makes clear his beliefs and attitudes about these issues.

17. The amount of humor in "A Dirge for Clowntown" is rather unusual for a mystery. What were some of your favorite instances of humor in the story's characters and in their actions, as well as in the author's use of language to describe them? How did these instances appeal to your sense of humor, wit, or social satire?

18. A "dirge" is a lament or a mournful or elegiac literary work. Explain why you think the author entitled his story "A Dirge for Clowntown."

DETECTWRITE: Characterization and Plot

1. How did you feel about Bozo the Clown as the crime-solving detective in "A Dirge for Clowntown"? Did the author make good use of particularly clown-like attributes as part of Inspector Bozo's detection

and reflection abilities? Did Bozo's being a clown interfere with his functioning as a crime-solver dedicated to the cause of justice?

2. Re-read the author's description of Inspector Bozo's outfit and physical appearance in the second, third, and fourth paragraphs of the story. How is it effective in introducing the major character of the story to you?

3. How does the author succeed in creating amusing images of the Keystone-cop-like antics of Clowntown's uniformed forces without undercutting the effectiveness of the men as law enforcement officers?

4. In a detective story you would write, would you create a police officer from a fantastical or unconventional background like Inspector Bozo? Explain why or why not.

DETECTWRITE: Plot

1. What do you lose from the dynamics of the plot's development if you substitute more traditional social groups and classes for the clowns and mimes?

2. How would such a substitution affect the various philosophical statements made directly and indirectly through the social commentary about class, ethnicity, stereotypes, prejudice, discrimination, and hate crimes?

3. Can you think of two groups—from the worlds of fantasy or science fiction—that, like the clowns and mimes, could be in social conflict within the larger framework of a detective story? Which groups would they be and what crime would you hinge your story on?

DETECTWRITE: Setting

Point out where you think the author did a particularly good job in establishing and conveying the setting of the story. In your opinion, is Clowntown successful as a real town that happens to be inhabited by clowns or as a special town because of its clownishness? Explain your opinion.

DETECTWRITE: Style

1. What do you feel the place of humor is in a detective story? Explain why you feel the way you do.

2. What are your favorite examples of word play used by the author in the story? Why did you respond positively to them?

3. What do you feel the place of fantasy or science fiction is in the detective story? Explain why you feel the way you do.

Part five

Celebrated Sleuths

The Adventure of the Six Napoleons

Sir Arthur Conan Doyle

It WAS NO VERY UNUSUAL THING FOR MR. LESTRADE, OF Scotland Yard, to look in upon us of an evening, and his visits were welcome to Sherlock Holmes, for they enabled him to keep in touch with all that was going on at the police headquarters. In return for the news which Lestrade would bring, Holmes was always ready to listen with attention to the details of any case upon which the detective was engaged, and was able occasionally, without any active interference, to give some hint or suggestion drawn from his own vast knowledge and experience.

On this particular evening, Lestrade had spoken of the weather and the newspapers. Then he had fallen silent, puffing thoughtfully at his cigar. Holmes looked keenly at him.

"Anything remarkable on hand?" he asked.

"Oh, no, Mr. Holmes—nothing very particular."

"Then tell me about it."

Lestrade laughed.

"Well, Mr. Holmes, there is no use denying that there is something on my mind. And yet it is such an absurd business, that I hesitated to bother you about it. On the other hand, although it is trivial, it is undoubtedly queer, and I know that you have a taste for all that is out of the common. But, in my opinion, it comes more in Dr. Watson's line than ours."

"Disease?" said I.

"Madness, anyhow. And a queer madness, too. You wouldn't think there was anyone living at this time of day who had such a hatred of Napoleon the First that he would break any image of him that he could see."

Holmes sank back in his chair.

"That's no business of mine," said he.

"Exactly. That's what I said. But then, when the man commits burglary in order to break images which are not his own, that brings it away from the doctor and on to the policeman."

Holmes sat up again.

"Burglary! This is more interesting. Let me hear the details."

Lestrade took out his official notebook and refreshed his memory from its pages.

"The first case reported was four days ago,' said he. "It was at the shop of Morse Hudson, who has a place for the sale of pictures and statues in the Kennington Road. The assistant had left the front shop for an instant, when he heard a crash, and hurrying in he found a plaster bust of Napoleon, which stood with several other works of art upon the counter, lying shivered into fragments. He rushed out into the road, but, although several passersby declared that they had noticed a man run out of the shop, he could neither see anyone nor could he find any means of identifying the rascal. It seemed to be one of those senseless acts of hooliganism which occur from time to time, and it was reported to the constable on the beat as such. The plaster cast was not worth more than a few shillings, and the whole affair appeared to be too childish for any particular investigation.

"The second case, however, was more serious, and also more singular. It occurred only last night.

"In Kennington Road, and within a few hundred yards of Morse Hudson's shop, there lives a well-known medical practitioner, named Dr. Barnicot, who has one of the largest practices upon the south side of the Thames. His residence and principal consulting-room is at Kennington Road, but he has a branch surgery and dispensary at Lower Brixton Road, two miles away. This Dr. Barnicot is an enthusiastic admirer of Napoleon, and his house is full of books, pictures, and relics of the French Emperor. Some little time ago he purchased from Morse Hudson two duplicate plaster casts of the famous head of Napoleon by the French sculptor, Devine. One of these he placed in his hall in the house at Kennington Road, and the other on the mantelpiece of the surgery at Lower Brixton. Well, when Dr. Barnicot came down this morning he was astonished to find that his house had been burgled during the night, but that nothing had been taken save the plaster head from the hall. It had been carried out and had been dashed savagely against the garden wall, under which its splintered fragments were discovered."

Holmes rubbed his hands.

"This is certainly very novel," said he.

"I thought it would please you. But I have not got to the end yet. Dr. Barnicot was due at his surgery at twelve o'clock, and you can imagine his amazement when, on arriving there, he found that the window had been opened in the night, and that the broken pieces of his second bust were strewn all over the room. It had been smashed to atoms where it stood. In neither case were there any signs which could give us a clue as to the criminal or lunatic who had done the mischief. Now, Mr. Holmes, you have got the facts."

"They are singular, not to say grotesque," said Holmes. "May I ask whether the two busts smashed in Dr. Barnicot's rooms were the exact duplicates of the one which was destroyed in Morse Hudson's shop?"

"They were taken from the same mould."

"Such a fact must tell against the theory that the man who breaks them is influenced by any general hatred of Napoleon. Considering how many hundreds of statues of the great Emperor must exist in London, it is too much to suppose such a coincidence as that a promiscuous iconoclast should chance to begin upon three specimens of the same bust."

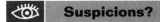

Suspicions?

Does the fact that the two busts that were smashed were made from the same mold help or hurt the theory that the person who broke them is so motivated by "a hatred of Napoleon the First that he would break any image of him that he could see"? Explain.

"Well, I thought as you do," said Lestrade. "On the other hand, this Morse Hudson is the purveyor of busts in that part of London, and these three were the only ones which had been in his shop for years. So, although, as you say, there are many hundreds of statues in London, it is very probable that these three were the only ones in that district. Therefore, a local fanatic would begin with them. What do you think, Dr. Watson?"

"There are no limits to the possibilities of monomania," I answered. "There is the condition which the modern French psychologists have called the *"idée fixe,"* which may be trifling in character, and accompanied by complete sanity in every other way. A man who had read deeply about Napoleon, or who had possibly received some hereditary family injury through the great war, might conceivably form such an *idée fixe* and under its influence be capable of any fantastic outrage."

"That won't do, my dear Watson," said Holmes, shaking his head, "for no amount of *idée fixe* would enable your interesting monomaniac to find out where these busts were situated."

"Well, how do *you* explain it?"

"I don't attempt to do so. I would only observe that there is a certain method in the gentleman's eccentric proceedings. For example, in Dr. Barnicot's hall, where a sound might arouse the family, the bust was taken outside before being broken, whereas in the surgery, where there was less danger of an alarm, it was smashed where it stood. The affair seems absurdly trifling, and yet I dare call nothing trivial when I reflect that some of my most classic cases have had the least promising commencement. You will remember, Watson, how the dreadful business of the Abernetty family was first brought to my notice by the depth which the parsley had sunk into the butter upon a hot day. I can't afford, therefore, to smile at your three broken busts, Lestrade, and I shall be very much obliged to you if you will let me hear of any fresh development of so singular a chain of events."

The development for which my friend had asked came in a quicker and an infinitely more tragic form than he could have imagined. I was still dressing in my bedroom next morning, when there was a tap at the door and Holmes entered, a telegram in his hand. He read it aloud:

"Come instantly, 131 Pitt Street, Kensington.
LESTRADE."

"What is it, then?" I asked.

"Don't know—may be anything. But I suspect it is the sequel of the story of the statues. In that case our friend the image-breaker has begun operations in another quarter of London. There's coffee on the table, Watson, and I have a cab at the door."

In half an hour we had reached Pitt Street, a quiet little backwater just beside one of the briskest currents of London life. No. 131 was one of a row, all flat-chested, respectable, and most unromantic dwellings. As we drove up, we found the railings in front of the house lined by a curious crowd. Holmes whistled.

"By George! it's attempted murder at the least. Nothing less will hold the London message-boy. There's a deed of violence indicated in that fellow's round shoulders and outstretched neck. What's this, Watson? The top steps swilled down and the other ones dry. Footsteps enough, anyhow! Well, well, there's Lestrade at the front window, and we shall soon know all about it."

The official received us with a very grave face and showed us into a sitting-room where an exceedingly unkempt and agitated elderly man, clad in a flannel dressing-gown, was pacing up and down. He was introduced to us as the owner of the house—Mr. Horace Harker, of the Central Press Syndicate.

"It's the Napoleon bust business again,' said Lestrade. "You seemed interested last night, Mr. Holmes, so I thought perhaps you would be glad to be present now that the affair has taken a very much graver turn."

"What has it turned to, then?"

"To murder. Mr. Harker, will you tell these gentlemen exactly what has occurred?"

The man in the dressing-gown turned upon us with a most melancholy face.

"It's an extraordinary thing," said he, "that all my life I have been collecting other people's news, and now that a real piece of news has come my own way I am so confused and bothered that I can't put two words together. If I had come in here as a journalist, I should have interviewed myself and had two columns in every evening paper. As it is, I am giving away valuable copy by telling my story over and over to a string of different people, and I can make no use of it myself. However, I've heard your name, Mr. Sherlock Holmes, and if you'll only explain this queer business, I shall be paid for my trouble in telling you the story."

Holmes sat down and listened.

"It all seems to centre round that bust of Napoleon which I bought for this very room about four months ago. I picked it up cheap from Harding Brothers, two doors from the High Street Station. A great deal of my journalistic work is done at night, and I often write until the early morning. So it was today. I was sitting in my den, which is at the back of the top of the house, about three o'clock, when I was convinced that I heard some sounds downstairs. I listened, but they were not repeated, and I concluded that they came from outside. Then suddenly, about five minutes later, there came a most horrible yell—the most dreadful sound, Mr. Holmes, that ever I heard. It will ring in my ears as long as I live. I sat frozen with horror for a minute or two. Then I seized the poker and went downstairs. When I entered this room I found the window wide open, and I at once observed that the bust was gone from the mantelpiece. Why any burglar should take such a thing passes my understanding, for it was only a plaster cast and of no real value whatever.

"You can see for yourself that anyone going out through that open window could reach the front doorstep by taking a long stride. This was clearly what the burglar had done, so I went round and opened the door.

Stepping out into the dark, I nearly fell over a dead man, who was lying there. I ran back for a light, and there was the poor fellow, a great gash in his throat and the whole place swimming in blood. He lay on his back, his knees drawn up, and his mouth horribly open. I shall see him in my dreams. I had just time to blow on my police-whistle, and then I must have fainted, for I knew nothing more until I found the policeman standing over me in the hall."

"Well, who was the murdered man?" asked Holmes.

"There's nothing to show who he was," said Lestrade. "You shall see the body at the mortuary, but we have made nothing of it up to now. He is a tall man, sunburned, very powerful, not more than thirty. He is poorly dressed, and yet does not appear to be a labourer. A horn-handled clasp knife was lying in a pool of blood beside him. Whether it was the weapon which did the deed, or whether it belonged to the dead man, I do not know. There was no name on his clothing, and nothing in his pockets save an apple, some string, a shilling map of London, and a photograph. Here it is."

It was evidently taken by a snapshot from a small camera. It represented an alert, sharp-featured simian man, with thick eyebrows and a very peculiar projection of the lower part of the face, like the muzzle of a baboon.

"And what became of the bust?" asked Holmes, after a careful study of this picture.

"We had news of it just before you came. It has been found in the front garden of an empty house in Campden House Road. It was broken into fragments. I am going round now to see it. Will you come?"

"Certainly. I must just take one look round." He examined the carpet and the window. "The fellow had either very long legs or was a most active man," said he. "With an area beneath, it was no mean feat to reach that window-ledge and open that window. Getting back was comparatively simple. Are you coming with us to see the remains of your bust, Mr. Harker?"

The disconsolate journalist had seated himself at a writing-table.

"I must try and make something of it," said he, "though I have no doubt that the first editions of the evening papers are out already with full details. It's like my luck! You remember when the stand fell at Doncaster? Well, I was the only journalist in the stand, and my journal the only one that had no account of it, for I was too shaken to write it. And now I'll be too late with a murder done on my own doorstep."

As we left the room, we heard his pen travelling shrilly over the foolscap.

The spot where the fragments of the bust had been found was only a few hundred yards away. For the first time our eyes rested upon this present-ment of the great emperor, which seemed to raise such frantic and destructive hatred in the mind of the unknown. It lay scattered, in splintered shards, upon the grass. Holmes picked up several of them and examined them carefully. I was convinced, from his intent face and his purposeful manner, that at last he was upon a clue.

"Well?" asked Lestrade.

Holmes shrugged his shoulders.

"We have a long way to go yet," said he. "And yet—and yet—well, we have some suggestive facts to act upon. The possession of this trifling bust was worth more, in the eyes of this strange criminal, than a human life. This is one point. Then there is the singular fact that he did not break it in the house, or immediately outside the house, if to break it was his sole object."

"He was rattled and bustled by meeting this other fellow. He hardly knew what he was doing."

"Well, that's likely enough. But I wish to call your attention very particularly to the position of this house, in the garden of which the bust was destroyed."

Lestrade looked about him.

"It was an empty house, and so he knew that he would not be disturbed in the garden."

"Yes, but there is another empty house farther up the street which he must have passed before he came to this one. Why did he not break it there, since it is evident that every yard that he carried it increased the risk of someone meeting him?"

"I give it up," said Lestrade.

Holmes pointed to the street lamp above our heads.

Suspicions?

How might the presence of the street lamp explain why the criminal chose to break the bust of Napoleon by the second empty house he passed instead of by the first?

"He could see what he was doing here, and he could not there. That was his reason."

"By Jove! that's true," said the detective. "Now that I come to think of it, Dr. Barnicot's bust was broken not far from his red lamp. Well, Mr. Holmes, what are we to do with that fact?"

"To remember it—to docket it. We may come on something later which will bear upon it. What steps do you propose to take now, Lestrade?"

"The most practical way of getting at it, in my opinion, is to identify the dead man. There should be no difficulty about that. When we have found who he is and who his associates are, we should have a good start in learning what he was doing in Pitt Street last night, and who it was who met him and killed him on the doorstep of Mr. Horace Harker. Don't you think so?"

"No doubt; and yet it is not quite the way in which I should approach the case."

"What would you do then?"

"Oh, you must not let me influence you in any way. I suggest that you go on your line and I on mine. We can compare notes afterwards, and each will supplement the other."

"Very good," said Lestrade.

"If you are going back to Pitt Street, you might see Mr. Horace Harker. Tell him for me that I have quite made up my mind, and that it is certain that a dangerous homicidal lunatic, with Napoleonic delusions, was in his house last night. It will be useful for his article."

Lestrade stared.

"You don't seriously believe that?"

Holmes smiled.

"Don't I? Well, perhaps I don't. But I am sure that it will interest Mr. Horace Harker and the subscribers of the Central Press Syndicate. Now, Watson, I think that we shall find that we have a long and rather complex day's work before us. I should be glad, Lestrade, if you could make it convenient to meet us at Baker Street at six o'clock this evening. Until then I should like to keep this photograph, found in the dead man's pocket. It is possible that I may have to ask your company and assistance upon a small expedition which will have to be undertaken tonight, if my chain of reasoning should prove to be correct. Until then goodbye and good luck!"

Sherlock Holmes and I walked together to the High Street, where we stopped at the shop of Harding Brothers, whence the bust had been purchased. A young assistant informed us that Mr. Harding would be absent until afternoon and that he was himself a newcomer, who could give us no information. Holmes's face showed his disappointment and annoyance.

"Well, well, we can't expect to have it all our own way, Watson," he said, at last. "We must come back in the afternoon, if Mr. Harding will not be here until then. I am, as you have no doubt surmised, endeavouring to trace these busts to their source in order to find if there is not something peculiar which

> **👁 Suspicions?**
>
> Holmes credits Dr. Watson with surmising that Holmes is "endeavouring to trace these busts to their source in order to find if there is not something peculiar which may account for their remarkable fate." You probably made the same surmise (guess or conjecture). What further surmises can you make about the source of the busts and about the nature of the "something peculiar"?

may account for their remarkable fate. Let us make for Mr. Morse Hudson of the Kennington Road and see if he can throw any light upon the problem."

A drive of an hour brought us to the picture-dealer's establishment. He was a small, stout man with a red face and a peppery manner.

"Yes, sir. On my very counter, sir," said he. "What we pay rates and taxes for I don't know, when any ruffian can come in and break one's goods. Yes, sir, it was I who sold Dr. Barnicot his two statues. Disgraceful, sir! A Nihilist plot—that's what I make it. No one but an anarchist would go about breaking statues. Red republicans—that's what I call 'em. Who did I get the statues from? I don't see what that has to do with it. Well, if you really want to know, I got them from Gelder & Co. in Church Street, Stepney. They are a well-known house in the trade and have been this twenty years. How many had I? Three—two and one are three—two of Dr. Barnicot's, and one smashed in broad daylight on my own counter. Do I know that photograph? No, I don't. Yes, I do, though. Why, it's Beppo. He was a kind of Italian piece-work man, who made himself useful in the shop. He could carve a bit, and gild and frame, and do odd jobs. The fellow left me last week, and I've heard nothing of him since. No, I don't know where he came from nor where he went to. I had nothing against him while he was here. He was gone two days before the bust was smashed."

"Well, that's all we could reasonably expect from Morse Hudson," said Holmes, as we emerged from the shop. "We have this Beppo as a common factor, both in Kennington and in Kensington, so that is worth a ten-mile drive. Now, Watson, let us make for Gelder & Co., of Stepney, the source and origin of the busts. I shall be surprised if we don't get some help down there."

In rapid succession we passed through the fringe of fashionable London, hotel London, theatrical London, literary London, commercial London, and, finally, maritime London, till we came to a riverside city of a hundred thousand souls, where the tenement houses swelter and reek with the outcasts of Europe. Here, in a broad thoroughfare, once the abode of wealthy City merchants, we found the sculpture works for which we searched. Outside was a considerable yard full of monumental masonry. Inside was a large room in which fifty workers were carving or moulding. The manager, a big blond German, received us civilly and gave a clear answer to all Holmes's questions. A reference to his books showed that hundreds of casts had been taken from a marble copy of Devine's head of Napoleon, but that the three which had been sent to Morse Hudson a year or so before had been half of a batch of six, the other three being sent to Harding Brothers, of Kensington. There was no reason why those six should be different from any of the other casts. He could suggest no possible cause why anyone should wish to destroy them—in fact, he laughed at the idea. Their wholesale price was six shillings, but the retailer would get twelve or more. The cast was taken into two moulds from each side of the face, and then these two profiles of plaster of Paris were joined together to make the complete bust. The work was usually done by Italians, in the room we were in. When finished, the busts were put on a table in the passage to dry, and afterwards stored. That was all he could tell us.

But the production of the photograph had a remarkable effect upon the manager. His face flushed with anger, and his brows knotted over his blue Teutonic eyes.

"Ah, the rascal!" he cried. "Yes, indeed, I know him very well. This has always been a respectable establishment, and the only time that we have ever had the police in it was over this very fellow. It was more than a year ago now. He knifed another Italian in the street, and then he came to the works with the police on his heels, and he was taken here. Beppo was his name—his second name I never knew. Serve me right for engaging a man with such a face. But he was a good workman—one of the best."

"What did he get?"

"The man lived and he got off with a year. I have no doubt he is out now, but he has not dared to show his nose here. We have a cousin of his here, and I daresay he could tell you where he is."

"No, no," cried Holmes, "not a word to the cousin—not a word, I beg of you. The matter is very important, and the farther I go with it, the more important it seems to grow. When you referred in your ledger to the sale of those casts I observed that the date was June 3rd of last year. Could you give me the date when Beppo was arrested?"

"I could tell you roughly by the pay-list," the manager answered. "Yes," he continued, after some turning over of pages, "he was paid last on May 20th."

"Thank you," said Holmes. "I don't think that I need intrude upon your time and patience any more." With a last word of caution that he should say nothing as to our researches, we turned our faces westwards once more.

The afternoon was far advanced before we were able to snatch a hasty luncheon at a restaurant. A news-bill at the entrance announced 'Kensington Outrage. Murder by a Madman,' and the contents of the paper showed that Mr. Horace Harker had got his account into print after all. Two columns were occupied with a highly sensational and flowery rendering of the whole incident. Holmes propped it against the cruet-stand and read it while he ate. Once or twice he chuckled.

"This is all right, Watson," said he. "Listen to this:

"It is satisfactory to know that there can be no difference of opinion upon this case, since Mr. Lestrade, one of the most experienced members of the official force and Mr. Sherlock Holmes, the well-known consulting expert, have each come to the conclusion that the grotesque series of incidents, which have ended in so tragic a fashion, arise from lunacy rather than from deliberate crime. No explanation save mental aberration can cover the facts."

"The Press, Watson, is a most valuable institution if you only know how to use it. And now, if you have quite finished, we will hark back to Kensington and see what the manager of Harding Brothers has to say on the matter."

The founder of that great emporium proved to be a brisk, crisp little person, very dapper and quick, with a clear head and a ready tongue.

"Yes, sir, I have already read the account in the evening papers. Mr. Horace Harker is a customer of ours. We supplied him with the bust some months ago. We ordered three busts of that sort from Gelder & Co., of Stepney. They are all sold now. To whom? Oh, I daresay by consulting our sales book we could very easily tell you. Yes, we have the entries here. One to Mr. Harker you see, and one to Mr. Josiah Brown, of Laburnum Lodge, Laburnum Vale, Chiswick, and one to Mr. Sandeford of Lower Grove Road, Reading. No, I have never seen this face which you show me in the photograph. You would hardly forget it, would you, sir, for I've seldom seen an uglier. Have we any Italians on the staff? Yes, sir, we have several among our workpeople and cleaners. I daresay they might get a peep at that sales book if they wanted to. There is no particular reason for keeping a watch upon that book. Well, well, it's a very strange business, and I hope that you will let me know if anything comes of your inquiries."

Holmes had taken several notes during Mr. Harding's evidence and I could see that he was thoroughly satisfied by the turn which affairs were taking. He made no remark, however, save that, unless we hurried, we should be late for our appointment with Lestrade. Sure enough, when we reached Baker Street the detective was already there, and we found him pacing up and down in a fever of impatience. His look of importance showed that his day's work had not been in vain.

"Well?" he asked. "What luck, Mr. Holmes?"

"We have had a very busy day and not entirely a wasted one," my friend explained. "We have seen both the retailers and also the wholesale manufacturers. I can trace each of the busts now from the beginning."

"The busts!" cried Lestrade. "Well, well, you have your own methods, Mr. Sherlock Holmes, and it is not for me to say a word against them, but I think I have done a better day's work than you. I have identified the dead man."

"You don't say so?"

"And found a cause for the crime."

"Splendid!"

"We have an inspector who makes a specialty of Saffron Hill and the Italian Quarter. Well, this dead man had some Catholic emblem round his neck, and that, along with his colour, made me think he was from the South. Inspector Hill knew him the moment he caught sight of him. His name is Pietro Venucci from Naples, and he is one of the greatest cut-throats in London. He is connected with the Mafia, which, as you know, is a secret political society, enforcing its decrees by murder. Now, you see how the affair begins to clear up. The other fellow is probably an Italian also, and a member of the Mafia. He has broken the rules in some fashion. Pietro is set upon his track. Probably the photograph we found in his pocket is the man himself, so that he may not knife the wrong person. He dogs the fellow, he sees him enter a house, he waits outside for him, and in the scuffle he receives his own death-wound. How is that, Mr. Sherlock Holmes?"

Holmes clapped his hands approvingly.

"Excellent, Lestrade, excellent!" he cried. "But I didn't quite follow your explanation of the destruction of the busts."

"The busts! You never can get those busts out of your head. After all, that is nothing; petty larceny, six months at the most. It is the murder that we are really investigating, and I tell you that I am gathering all the threads into my hands."

"And the next stage?"

"Is a very simple one. I shall go down with Hill to the Italian Quarter, find the man whose photograph we have got, and arrest him on the charge of murder. Will you come with us?"

"I think not. I fancy we can attain our end in a simpler way. I can't say for certain, because it all depends—well, it all depends upon a factor which is completely outside our control. But I have great hopes—in fact, the betting is exactly two to one—that if you will come with us tonight I shall be able to help you to lay him by the heels."

"In the Italian Quarter?"

"No, I fancy Chiswick is an address which is more likely to find him. If you will come with me to Chiswick tonight, Lestrade, I'll promise to go to the Italian Quarter with you tomorrow, and no harm will be done by the delay. And now I think that a few hours' sleep would do us all good, for I do not propose to leave before eleven o'clock, and it is unlikely that we shall be back before morning. You'll dine with us, Lestrade, and then you are welcome to the sofa until it is time for us to start. In the meantime, Watson, I should be glad if you would ring for an express messenger, for I have a letter to send and it is important that it should go at once."

Holmes spent the evening in rummaging among the files of the old daily papers with which one of our lumber-rooms was packed. When at last he descended, it was with triumph in his eyes, but he said nothing to either of us as to the result of his researches. For my own part, I had followed step by step the methods by which he had traced the various windings of this complex case, and, though I could not yet perceive the goal which we would reach, I understood clearly that Holmes expected this grotesque criminal to make an attempt upon the two remaining busts, one of which, I remembered, was at Chiswick. No doubt the object of our journey was to catch him in the very act, and I could not but admire the cunning with which my friend had inserted a wrong clue in the evening paper, so as to give the fellow the idea that he could continue his scheme with impunity. I was not surprised when Holmes suggested that I should take my revolver with me. He had himself picked up the loaded hunting-crop, which was his favourite weapon.

A four-wheeler was at the door at eleven, and in it we drove to a spot at the other side of Hammersmith Bridge. Here the cabman was directed to wait. A short walk brought us to a secluded road fringed with pleasant houses, each standing in its own grounds. In the light of a street lamp we read "Laburnum Villa" upon the gate-post of one of them. The occupants had evidently retired to rest, for all was dark save for a fanlight over the hall door, which shed a single blurred circle on to the garden path. The wooden fence which separated the grounds from the road threw a dense black shadow upon the inner side, and here it was that we crouched.

"I fear that we'll have a long wait," Holmes whispered. "We may thank our stars that it is not raining. I don't think we can even venture to smoke to pass the time. However, it's a two to one chance that we get something to pay us for our trouble."

It proved, however, that our vigil was not to be so long as Holmes had led us to fear, and it ended in a very sudden and singular fashion. In an instant, without the least sound to warn us of his coming, the garden gate swung open, and a lithe, dark figure, as swift and active as an ape, rushed up the garden path. We saw it whisk past the light thrown from over the door and disappear against the black shadow of the house. There was a long pause, during which we held our breath, and then a very gentle creaking sound came to our ears. The window was being opened. The noise ceased, and again there was a long silence. The fellow was making his way into the house. We saw the sudden flash of a dark lantern inside the room. What he sought was evidently not there, for again we saw the flash through another blind and then through another.

"Let us get to the open window. We will nab him as he climbs out," Lestrade whispered.

But before we could move, the man had emerged again. As he came out into the glimmering patch of light, we saw that he carried something white under his arm. He looked stealthily all around him. The silence of the deserted street reassured him. Turning his back upon us he laid down his burden, and the next instant there was the sound of a sharp tap, followed by a clatter and rattle. The man was so intent upon what he was doing that he never heard our steps as we stole across the grass plot. With the bound of a tiger Holmes was on his back, and an instant later Lestrade and I had him by either wrist, and the handcuffs had been fastened. As we turned him over I saw a hideous, sallow face, with writhing, furious features, glaring up at us, and I knew that it was indeed the man of the photograph whom we had secured.

But it was not our prisoner to whom Holmes was giving his attention. Squatted on the doorstep, he was engaged in most carefully examining that which the man had brought from the house. It was a bust of Napoleon, like the one which we had seen that morning, and it had been broken into similar fragments. Carefully Holmes held each separate shard to the light, but in no way did it differ from any other shattered piece of plaster. He had just completed his examination when the hall lights flew up, the door opened, and the owner of the house, a jovial, rotund figure in shirt and trousers, presented himself.

"Mr. Josiah Brown, I suppose?" said Holmes.

"Yes, sir; and you, no doubt, are Mr. Sherlock Holmes? I had the note which you sent by the express messenger, and I did exactly what you told me. We locked every door on the inside and awaited developments. Well, I'm very glad to see that you have got the rascal. I hope, gentlemen, that you will come in and have some refreshment."

However, Lestrade was anxious to get his man into safe quarters, so within a few minutes our cab had been summoned and we were all four upon our way to London. Not a word would our captive say, but he glared at us from the shadow of his matted hair, and once, when my hand seemed within his reach, he snapped at it like a hungry wolf. We stayed long enough at the police-station to learn that a search of his clothing revealed nothing save a few shillings and a long sheath knife, the handle of which bore copious traces of recent blood.

"That's all right," said Lestrade, as we parted. "Hill knows all these gentry, and he will give a name to him. You'll find that my theory of the Mafia will work out all right. But I'm sure I am exceedingly obliged to you, Mr. Holmes, for the workmanlike way in which you laid hands upon him. I don't quite understand it all yet."

"I fear it is rather too late an hour for explanations," said Holmes. "Besides, there are one or two details which are not finished off, and it is one of these cases which are worth working out to the very end. If you will come round once more to my rooms at six o'clock tomorrow, I think I shall be able to show you that even now you have not grasped the entire meaning of this business, which presents some features which make it absolutely original in the history of crime. If ever I permit you to chronicle any more of my little problems, Watson, I foresee that you will enliven your pages by an account of the singular adventure of the Napoleonic busts."

When we met again next evening, Lestrade was furnished with much information concerning our prisoner. His name, it appeared, was Beppo, second name unknown. He was a well-known ne'er-do-well among the Italian colony. He had once been a skillful sculptor and had earned an honest living, but he had taken to evil courses and had twice already been in jail—once for a petty theft, and once, as we had already heard, for stabbing a fellow-countryman. He could talk English perfectly well. His reasons for destroying the busts were still unknown, and he refused to answer any questions upon the subject, but the police had discovered that these same busts might very well have been made by his own hands, since he was engaged in this class of work at the establishment of Gelder & Co. To all this information, much of which we already knew, Holmes listened with polite attention, but I, who knew him so well, could clearly see that his thoughts were elsewhere, and I detected a mixture of mingled uneasiness and expectation beneath that mask which he was wont to assume. At last he started in his chair, and his eyes brightened. There had been a ring at the bell. A minute later we heard steps upon the stairs, and an elderly red-faced man with grizzled side-whiskers was ushered in. In his right hand he carried an old-fashioned carpet-bag, which he placed upon the table.

Suspicions?

What do you think Beppo's motive might have been for going about destroying the busts that the police now think he most likely made with his own hands? Explain your reasoning.

"Is Mr. Sherlock Holmes here?"

My friend bowed and smiled. "Mr. Sandeford of Reading, I suppose?" said he.

"Yes, sir. I fear that I am a little late, but the trains were awkward. You wrote to me about a bust that is in my possession."

"Exactly."

"I have your letter here. You said, "I desire to possess a copy of Devine's Napoleon and am prepared to pay you ten pounds for the one which is in your possession." Is that right?"

"Certainly."

"I was very much surprised at your letter, for I could not imagine how you knew that I owned such a thing."

"Of course you must have been surprised, but the explanation is very simple. Mr. Harding of Harding Brothers, said that they had sold you their last copy, and he gave me your address."

"Oh, that was it, was it? Did he tell you what I paid for it?"

"No, he did not."

"Well, I am an honest man, though not a very rich one. I only gave fifteen shillings for the bust, and I think you ought to know that before I take ten pounds from you."

"I am sure the scruple does you honour, Mr. Sandeford. But I have named that price, so I intend to stick to it."

"Well, it is very handsome of you, Mr. Holmes. I brought the bust up with me, as you asked me to do. Here it is!" He opened his bag, and at last we saw placed upon our table a complete specimen of that bust which we had already seen more than once in fragments.

Holmes took a paper from his pocket and laid a ten-pound note upon the table.

> **◁◉▷   Suspicions?**
>
> What possible reasons might Sherlock Holmes have for going to all the bother and expense of buying, unconditionally, the unbroken bust of Napoleon brought to him by Mr. Sandeford? Explain. Predict what you expect Sherlock Holmes will do next.

"You will kindly sign that paper, Mr. Sandeford, in the presence of these witnesses. It is simply to say that you transfer every possible right that you ever had in the bust to me. I am a methodical man, you see, and you never know what turn events might take afterwards. Thank you, Mr. Sandeford; here is your money, and I wish you a very good evening."

When our visitor had disappeared, Sherlock Holmes's movements were such as to rivet our attention. He began by taking a clean white cloth from a drawer and laying it over the table. Then he placed his newly acquired bust in the centre of the cloth. Finally, he picked up his hunting-crop and struck Napoleon a sharp blow on the top of the head. The figure broke into fragments, and Holmes bent eagerly over the shattered remains. Next instant, with a loud shout of triumph he held up one splinter, in which a round, dark object was fixed like a plum in a pudding.

"Gentlemen," he cried, "let me introduce you to the famous black pearl of the Borgias."

Lestrade and I sat silent for a moment, and then, with a spontaneous impulse, we both broke out clapping, as at the well-wrought crisis of a play. A flush of colour sprang to Holmes's pale cheeks, and he bowed to us like the master dramatist who receives the homage of his audience. It was at such moments that for an instant he ceased to be a reasoning machine, and betrayed his human love for admiration and applause. The same singularly proud and reserved nature which turned away with disdain from popular notoriety was capable of being moved to its depths by spontaneous wonder and praise from a friend.

"Yes, gentlemen," said he, "it is the most famous pearl now existing in the world, and it has been my good fortune, by a connected chain of inductive reasoning, to trace it from the Prince of Coronna's bedroom at the Dacre Hotel, where it was lost, to the interior of this, the last of the six busts of Napoleon which were manufactured by Gelder & Co. of Stepney. You will remember, Lestrade, the sensation caused by the disappearance of this valuable jewel, and the vain efforts of the London police to recover it. I was myself consulted upon the case, but I was unable to throw any light upon it. Suspicion fell upon the maid of the Princess who was an Italian, and it was proved that she had a brother in London, but we failed to trace any connection between them. The maid's name was Lucretia Venucci, and there is no doubt in my mind that this Pietro who was murdered two nights ago was the brother. I have been looking up the dates in the old files of the paper, and I find that the disappearance of the pearl was exactly two days before the arrest of Beppo, for some crime of violence—an event which took place in the factory of Gelder & Co. at the very moment when these busts were being made. Now you clearly see the sequence of events, though you see them, of course, in the inverse order to the way in which they presented themselves to me. Beppo had the pearl in his possession. He may have stolen it from Pietro, he may have been Pietro's confederate, he may have been the go-between of Pietro and his sister. It is of no consequence to us which is the correct solution.

"The main fact is that he *had* the pearl, and at that moment, when it was on his person, he was pursued by the police. He made for the factory in which he worked, and he knew that he had only a few minutes in which to conceal this enormously valuable prize, which would otherwise be found on him when he was searched. Six plaster casts of Napoleon were drying in the passage. One of them was still soft. In an instant Beppo, a skillful workman, made a small hole in the wet plaster, dropped in the pearl, and with a few touches covered over the aperture once more. It was an admirable hiding-place. No one could possibly find it. But Beppo was condemned to a year's imprisonment, and in the meanwhile his six busts were scattered over London. He could not tell which contained his treasure. Only by breaking them could he see. Even shaking would tell him nothing, for as the plaster was wet it was probable that the pearl would adhere to it—as, in fact, it had done. Beppo did not despair, and he conducted his search with considerable ingenuity and perseverance. Through a cousin who works with Gelder, he found out the retail firms who had bought the busts. He managed to find employment with Morse Hudson and in that way tracked down three of them. The pearl was not there. Then, with the help of some Italian employé, he succeeded in finding out where the other three busts had gone. The first was at Harker's. There he was dogged by his confederate, who held Beppo responsible for the loss of the pearl, and he stabbed him in the scuffle which followed."

"If he was his confederate, why should he carry his photograph?" I asked.

"As a means of tracing him, if he wished to inquire about him from any third person. That was the obvious reason. Well, after the murder I calculated that Beppo would probably hurry rather than delay his movements. He would fear that the police would read his secret, and so he hastened on before they should get ahead of him. Of course, I could not say that he had not found the pearl in Harker's bust. I had not even concluded for certain that it was the pearl, but it was evident to me that he was looking for something, since he carried the bust past the other houses in order to break it in the garden which had a lamp overlooking it. Since Harker's bust was one in three, the chances were exactly as I told you— two to one against the pearl being inside it. There remained two busts, and it was obvious that he would go for the London one first. I warned the inmates of the house, so as to avoid a second tragedy, and we went down, with the happiest results. By that time, of course, I knew for certain that it was the Borgia pearl that we were after. The name of the murdered man linked the one event with the other. There only remained a single bust—the Reading one—and the pearl must be there. I bought it in your presence from the owner—and there it lies."

We sat in silence for a moment.

"Well," said Lestrade, "I've seen you handle a good many cases, Mr. Holmes, but I don't know that I ever knew a more workmanlike one than that. We're not jealous of you at Scotland Yard. No, sir, we are very proud of you, and if you come down tomorrow, there's not a man, from the oldest inspector to the youngest constable, who wouldn't be glad to shake you by the hand."

"Thank you!" said Holmes. "Thank you!" and as he turned away, it seemed to me that he was more nearly moved by the softer human emotions than I had ever seen him. A moment later he was the cold and practical thinker once more. "Put the pearl in the safe, Watson," said he, "and get out the papers of the Conk-Singleton forgery case. Goodbye, Lestrade. If any little problem comes your way, I shall be happy, if I can, to give you a hint or two as to its solution."

 How Clever?

1. In the story, Dr. Watson refers to Holmes as being "a reasoning machine." What does Watson mean by both parts of this label? How did Holmes's solution of the case of the six broken Napoleons result from his functioning as "a reasoning machine"? Be specific.

2. Inspector Lestrade of Scotland Yard says of Holmes's solving of the case: "I've seen you handle a good many cases, Mr. Holmes, but I don't know that I ever knew a more workmanlike one than that." In what ways was Holmes's handling of the case "workmanlike"? What important specific observations (instances of detection) did Holmes make in the course of the story that formed the foundation for his inductive reasoning (reflection)? What was Holmes's "chain of reasoning"?

3. Although coincidence and chance may play a part in life (and in detective fiction), why does Holmes rule out coincidence and chance when he learns that the first three busts of Napoleon that were broken all came from the same mold? What explanation does Inspector Lestrade give for the probability that these three busts would be among the first broken?

4. Holmes tells Dr. Watson that "there is a certain method" in the "eccentric proceedings" of the man who broke the first three busts. What method did Holmes observe? Since "eccentric" literally means "off-center," how does Holmes's explanation of a method to the seeming madness re-establish a focused center to the criminal's actions?

5. Prior to Sherlock Holmes's explanation of "the sequence of events," the story provides no clues for the reader suggesting that the particular object molded inside one of the busts of Napoleon is the black pearl of the Borgias

("the most famous pearl now existing in the world," we later learn from Sherlock Holmes). What clues are provided to indicate that there might well be something concealed inside one of the busts and that the object is of considerable value and probably Italian in origin?

6. How does Inspector Lestrade's theory of the motive behind the smashed images of Napoleon function as a red herring in the story? Do Lestrade's methods of investigation strengthen or lessen the effect of this red herring on the reader? Explain.

7. From which particular observation did Sherlock Holmes conclude that it was "evident" to him that Beppo "was looking for something" inside the bust?

8. Why did Beppo's confederate, Pietro Venucci, carry a photograph of Beppo with him on his travels?

9. When Inspector Lestrade asks Holmes to go with him to the Italian Quarter to find Beppo, Holmes replies: "I think not. I fancy we can attain our end in a simpler way. I can't say for certain, because it all depends—well, it all depends upon a factor which is completely outside of our control. But I have great hopes—in fact, the betting is exactly two to one—that if you will come with us tonight I shall be able to help you to lay him by the heels." What is the factor that is completely outside Holmes's control, and why is the betting "exactly two to one" that Holmes will be successful? (You might also want to go back to your answers to question 3 and relate them to the thinking you're to do in connection with this question.)

10. How and where in the story does Inspector Lestrade function as a foil to Sherlock Holmes? (Notice that at one point Holmes tells Inspector Lestrade that the inspector's proposed next step is "not quite the way in which I should approach the case.")

11. Holmes reminds the reader that Dr. Watson is the fictional narrator of all the Sherlock Holmes stories when he says: "If ever I permit you to chronicle any more of my little problems, Watson, I foresee that you will enliven your pages by an account of the singular adventure of the Napoleonic busts." In addition to being his narrator and sidekick, how does Dr. Watson function as a foil to Sherlock Holmes?

DETECTWRITE: Characterization

1. Although he primarily comes across as the "cold and practical thinker," Sherlock Holmes does occasionally reveal, in this story and others, that he is capable of "the softer human emotions." Find examples of the more human and less machinelike Holmes in "The Adventure of the Six Napoleons." How do you feel about this aspect of the "reasoning machine's" personality? Which particular character traits would you empha-

size in the detective featured in a mystery story you would write? How human and how machinelike would you make your detective? Why?

2. Sherlock Holmes's name, although a proper noun, has become almost generic. To call someone "Sherlock" or to refer to someone as "a regular Sherlock Holmes" is the highest compliment to a person's powers of observation and reasoning. Which examples of detection and reflection in "The Adventure of the Six Napoleons" best defined Sherlock Holmes for you?

DETECTWRITE: Characterization and Plot

1. Dr. Watson is probably the most famous sidekick in detective fiction. What specific functions does he serve in "The Adventure of the Six Napoleons"? In a detective story you would write, would you use a sidekick? Explain why or why not.

2. Inspector Lestrade of Scotland Yard tell Holmes that "We're not jealous of you at Scotland Yard. No, sir, we are very proud of you." We can accept this statement at face value or wonder whether Lestrade and his men don't begin to feel as foolish as they are made to look whenever they match wits and techniques with the renowned Sherlock Holmes. In a detective story you would write, what part, if any, would the police play? How would you handle the relationship between your private detective and the police force? Will they compete or work closely together? Who will get or share the honors? What part will professional rivalry and jealously play?

3. Consider Dr. Watson's role as character and narrator. In a detective story you would write, who would your narrator be? Will it be the major character himself or herself (first-person narration), another character in the story (also first-person narration), or your voice—the voice of the author (third-person narration)? What are the advantages and disadvantages to these different approaches to telling the story? At what times would you favor one method or another?

The Phantom Pistol

Jack Adrian

ON THIS CHILL NOVEMBER NIGHT FOG ROLLED UP FROM THE River Thames, a shifting, eddying blanket that insinuated itself inexorably through the grimy streets of central London. It pulsed like a living thing, moved by its own remorseless momentum—for there was no wind—great banks of it surging across the metropolis, soot and smoke from a hundred thousand chimneys adding to its murk. Within an hour from the moment the faint tendrils of a river mist had heralded its approach, the fog, like a dirty-ochre shroud, had entombed the city.

Here, in the heart of the metropolis, in High Holborn, the rattle of hansom cab wheels, the raucous coughs of the newfangled petrol-driven taxis, were muffled, the rumble of the crawling traffic stifled as it edged and lurched its way along, the dim yellow light of street lamps serving to obscure rather than illuminate. On the pavements, slick with slimy dew, hunched figures, only dimly discerned, almost wraithlike, groped and shuffled along through the gloom, an army of the newly blind, snuffling and hawking at the harsh, choking reek of soot and coalsmoke.

Yet only fifty yards away from the main thoroughfare, down a narrow side street that had not changed appreciably since Dr. Johnson's day, sodium flares fizzed and roared, powerful electric globes thrust back the muddy haze. For only a few feet, to be sure, yet enough to reveal the tarnished gilt portico of the Empire Palace of Varieties, a large poster outside announcing in bold scarlet lettering, two inches high that here, and only here, were to be witnessed the dazzling deeds of the Great Golconda—illusionist *extraordinaire!*

Inside the theatre the atmosphere was just as miasmal, but here the fog was a blend of pungent penny cigars and the richer reeks of Larangas, Partagas, Corona-Coronas, and Hoyos de Monterrey, for the astonishing variety and ingenuity of the Great Golconda's baffling feats of prestidigitation fascinated the rich as well as the poor.

The Great Golconda was something of a democrat. He had consistently refused to perform in the gilded palaces that lined the Haymarket and Shaftesbury Avenue, preferring the smaller halls of the outer circuit. Thus whenever and wherever he appeared, rich men, dukes, earls, high-born ladies, and even (it was whispered) members of the Royal Family were forced to make the unaccustomed trek away from the gilt and glitter of London's West End to less salubrious haunts, there to mix with the lower orders—not to mention enjoy the unusual experience of paying half the price for twice the amount of entertainment. For certainly the Great Golconda was a magician and illusionist of quite extraordinary ability. It was even rumored that emissaries of Maskelyne and Devant—whose fame as illusionists was spread worldwide—had endeavored to lure his secrets away with fabulous amounts of money and, when these offers were spurned, had even gone so far as to try for them by less scrupulous methods.

Whether or not this was true, the Great Golconda stubbornly performed on the stages of the tattier music halls, and all kinds and conditions and classes of men and women flocked to see him and to cheer him.

But tonight was a special night. The Great Golconda was retiring from the stage. This was to be positively his final performance.

Unusually, the act started the show. Normally, the Great Golconda and his assistant Mephisto came on for the last half hour of the first house and the last half hour of the second. As an act, nothing could follow it.

Tonight, however, the audience—restless at the thought of having to sit through the somewhat dubious hors d'oeuvres of jugglers, low comedians, soubrettes, and "Come-into-the-garden-Maud" baritones before getting down to the main course—sat up in eager anticipation as the curtain rose at last to reveal a totally bare stage with a black backcloth, from the center of which stared two enormous eyes woven in green and gold.

For several seconds there was utter silence, a total absence of movement—on the stage and off. Then the lights dimmed and the glowing figure of the Great Golconda himself could be seen—in black silk hat, long flowing cloak, arms folded across his chest—descending slowly from the darkness above the stage, apparently floating on air. Simultaneously, two more Golcondas, dressed exactly alike, marched towards the center of the stage from both left and right wings. Just before they met, there was a flash of white light, a loud bang, a puff of red smoke, and all three figures seemed to merge.

And there, standing alone, smiling a mite maliciously, stood the Great Golconda. The audience roared.

From then on, for the next twenty minutes, wonders did not cease.

White horses cantered across the boards, to disappear in a dazzling firework display; doves, peacocks, birds-of-paradise soared and strutted, all, seemingly, appearing from a small Chinese lacquered cabinet on a rostrum; a girl in sequinned tights pirouetted in midair, had her head sawn off by the Great Golconda's assistant Mephisto, then, carrying her head beneath her arm, climbed a length of rope and slowly vanished, like the smile of the Cheshire Cat, about thirty feet above the ground.

Part of the performance was what appeared to be a running battle between the Great Golconda and his assistant Mephisto. Mephisto made it plain he wanted to do things his way but invariably, like the sorcerer's apprentice, failed, the Great Golconda smoothly but sensationally saving the trick—whatever trick it happened to be—at the very last moment. Penultimately, Mephisto became so incensed at the Great Golconda's successes that he knocked him down, crammed and locked him into a four-foot-high oak sherry cask, and then proceeded to batter and smash it to pieces with a long-handled axe.

Triumphantly, he turned to the audience, his chalk-white, clownlike face (its pallor accentuated by the skin-tight black costume he wore, leaving only his face, neck, and arms below the elbows bare) leering malevolently—to be greeted by gales of laughter as the Great Golconda himself suddenly appeared from the wings behind him to tap him on the shoulder.

At last the stage was cleared for the final act. Mephisto was to fire a revolver at the Great Golconda, who would catch the bullet between his teeth.

Members of the audience were invited up to the front of the stage to examine the .45 service revolver and six bullets and vouch for their authenticity. Among them was a stocky, moustachioed man in his late forties, in frock coat and bowler hat, who clearly, from the professional way he handled the gun—flicking open the chamber, extracting the bullets, testing them between his teeth—had more than a little knowledge of firearms. The Great Golconda noticed this.

"You sir!"

The stocky figure acknowledged this with an abrupt nod.

"You seem to know your way about a pistol, sir."

"I should do," admitted the man.

"May I enquire of your profession, sir?"

"You may. I'm a superintendent at Scotland Yard."

The Great Golconda was clearly delighted. Seen close up he was younger than the Scotland Yard man had supposed—perhaps in his mid-thirties. Something else he noted was the distinct resemblance between the Great Golconda and his assistant Mephisto, now standing to one side, his pasty white face impassive.

"And your name, sir?"

"Hopkins. Stanley Hopkins."

The Great Golconda bowed.

"A name that is not unknown to me from the newssheets, sir. Indeed, a name to be—ha-ha!—*conjured* with! And what is your professional opinion of the revolver, Superintendent?"

Still holding the bullets, Hopkins dry-fired the gun. The hammer fell with a loud 'click,' the chamber snapped round.

"Perfectly genuine."

"Pree-*cisely*!"

With a flourish of his cape, the Great Golconda handed the revolver to his assistant Mephisto and ushered the half dozen or so members of the audience off the stage.

The lights dimmed. Twin spots bathed the two men in two separate cones of light. They stood at the rear of the stage, against the black back-cloth, about ten yards apart. All around them was utter darkness. From his seat Hopkins watched intently.

Mephisto, wearing black gloves now and holding the gun two-handed, raised his arms slowly into the air, high above his head. Hopkins, following the movement could only just see the revolver, which was now above the circle of radiance surrounding Mephisto—then light glittered along the barrel as the assistant brought his hands back into the spotlight's glare and down, his arms held straight out. The revolver pointed directly at the Great Golconda.

It seemed to Hopkins that the Great Golconda's expression—up until then one of supercilious amusement—suddenly slipped. A look of mild puzzlement appeared on his face.

Hopkins glanced at the right-hand side of the stage but could see nothing but darkness. At that moment there was the oddly muted crack of a shot, and Hopkins, his eyes already turning back to the Great Golconda, saw the illusionist cry out and throw up his arms, then fall to the floor.

There was a stunned silence.

Even from where he was sitting, the Scotland Yard man could see plainly that around the Great Golconda's mouth were scarlet splashes, where none had been before.

Then the screaming started.

Mr. Robert Adey, the manager of the Empire Music Hall, looked as though he was on the verge of an apoplexy. His face was red, his mouth gaped, his mutton-chop whiskers quivered with emotion.

He stuttered, "It . . . it *couldn't* have happened!"

"But it did," Superintendent Stanley Hopkins said bluntly.

They were on the stage of the now-empty theatre. Even with all the stagelights up and the crystal chandeliers blazing over the auditorium, there was a desolate air about the place; shadows still gathered thickly in the wings, and above, beams and struts and spars could only just be glimpsed.

Since the shocking death of the Great Golconda—whose body now lay under a rug where it had fallen—nearly an hour had elapsed. During that time an extraordinary fact had emerged: although the Great Golconda had been shot, his assistant Mephisto (now detained in his dressing room) could not have shot him. Of that, there seemed not a doubt.

And yet neither could anyone else.

Adey—with a slight West Midlands twang to his voice—gabbled, "It . . . it's utterly inexplicable!"

"This is 1912," said a sharp voice behind him. "*Nothing* is inexplicable."

Adey turned. The man who had spoken—a tall, thin, almost gaunt individual of sixty or so, with a high forehead, dark hair shot with gray, an aquiline nose, and eyes that seemed to pierce and probe and dissect all that they looked upon—had accompanied Hopkins up to the stage when the theatre had been cleared. Adey had no idea who he was.

"A colleague?" he muttered to the Scotland Yard man.

 Suspicions?

1. Despite the fog outside and the cigar blend of fog inside, do you have a clear conception of who might have killed the illusionist the Great Golconda, why, and how it was done? Explain your suspicions.

2. Using detection and reflection, review each of the following statements for clues to the murder of the Great Golconda. What suspicions do you have now as to who did it? Connect your suspicions to specific clues.

   a. "Tonight was a special night. The Great Golconda was retiring from the stage. This was to be positively his final performance."

   b. "Unusually, the act started the show. Normally, the Great Golconda and his assistant Mephisto came on for the last half hour of the first house and the last half hour of the second. As an act, nothing could follow it."

"Just a friend," said Hopkins, "a very old friend. We're both interested in the impossible—why we're here tonight. The Great Golconda's illusions had certain . . ." he glanced at his friend ". . . points of interest."

"Although many, I fancy, were accomplished with the aid of certain kinematic devices," said the older man. "The girl in the sequinned tights, for example—a lifelike image only, I take it."

Adey nodded uneasily.

"Of course, I know very little about how he managed his tricks. Magicians are a close-mouthed bunch. This one in particular. He was adamant that during his act both wings should be blocked off, so no one—not even the stagehands—could see what he was doing. Always worried people were trying to pinch his tricks. Of course, he had to have some assistance in erecting certain items on stage, but all the preliminary construction work was done by him and his brother."

"Mephisto," said Hopkins.

"Yes. Their real name was Forbes-Sempill. Golconda was Rupert, Mephisto Ernest. They were twins—not identical. Rupert was the elder by fifteen minutes . . ." Adey's voice sank to a worried mumble. "That was half the trouble."

"The reason why the Great Golconda was retiring from the stage?" said the gaunt man. "The baronetcy, and the 200,000 pounds?"

Adey stared at him, open-mouthed.

"How the devil did you know that?"

Suspicions?

(continued)

c. "Part of the performance was what appeared to be a running battle between the Great Golconda and his assistant Mephisto."

d. "At last the stage was cleared for the final act. Mephisto was to fire a revolver at the Great Golconda, who would catch the bullet between his teeth."

e. "Something else he [Scotland Yard Superintendent Stanley Hopkins] noted was the distinct resemblance between the Great Golconda and his assistant Mephisto."

f. "The lights dimmed. Twin spots bathed the two men in two separate cones of light. They stood at the rear of the stage, against the black backcloth, about ten yards apart. All around them was utter darkness."

"Ah," Hopkins said waggishly, "my friend here keeps his finger on the pulse of great events—don't you, Mr. H.?"

The older man permitted himself a thin smile.

"Now *you* tell us about the baronetcy and all them sovs," said the Scotland Yard detective.

Adey shrugged his shoulders.

"Both Rupert and Ernest had a row with their family years ago. Left the ancestral home—somewhere in Scotland, I believe—never," he smiled faintly, "to darken its doors again. But their father's recently died, and Rupert succeeded to the title, estates, and money. It's as simple as that, although it wasn't generally known."

"I take it," said the gaunt old man, "that Ernest disliked his brother?"

"Ernest *hated* Rupert. Made no secret of the fact. One of the reasons their act went down so well—Ernest communicated that hatred to the audience. Rupert didn't object. Said it added spice to the performance. I don't see it myself, but it seemed to work."

"Doubtless the new Viennese school of mind analysis could explain that," said the older man dryly, "but for the time being I am far more interested in why Mephisto should for no apparent reason have donned black gloves to fire his revolver tonight."

"So he did," said Adey, in a surprised tone. "But how . . . ?"

"This is not the first time we have seen the Great Golconda perform. As Mr. Hopkins implied, his act was an unusual one, and I have always had an interest in the more sensational aspects of popular culture." The gaunt old man's eyes took on a faraway, introspective look. "On previous occasions Mephisto fired his revolver bare-handed. That he did not this time seems to me to be a matter of some significance."

"But the *weapon*, Mr. H.?" said Hopkins, almost violently. "We now know what ought to have happened. The real revolver is shown to the audience. It's stone-cold genuine. But when Golconda hands the gun to Mephisto—flourishing his cloak and all—he's already

Suspicions?

(continued)

g. "Mephisto, wearing black gloves now and holding the gun two-handed, raised his arms slowly into the air, high above his head. Hopkins, following the movement, could only just see the revolver, which was now above the circle of radiance surrounding Mephisto—then light glittered along the barrel as the assistant brought his hands back into the spotlight's glare and down, his arms held straight out. The revolver pointed directly at the Great Golconda."

h. "It seemed to Hopkins that the Great Golconda's expression —up until then one of supercilious amusement—suddenly slipped. A look of mild puzzlement appeared on his face."

i. "Hopkins glanced at the right-hand side of the stage but could see nothing but darkness. At that moment there was the oddly muted crack of a shot . . ."

substituted it for another gun—one that only fires blank shots. The real gun is now hidden in his cloak. Mephisto fires the fake gun at him and he pretends to catch the bullet, which is already in his mouth, between his teeth. Simple!"

"Except that this time he falls dead with a bullet in his head."

"From a phantom pistol!" exploded Hopkins. "The gun Mephisto held in his hands didn't fire that bullet—*couldn't* fire that bullet! The real gun was still in the folds of the Great Golconda's cloak—so that's out, too! He wasn't killed by someone firing from the wings, because the wings were blocked off! Nor through the backcloth, because there ain't no hole! Nor from above or from the audience, because the bullet went into his head in a straight line through his mouth!"

Here Adey broke in excitedly.

"It's as I said—inexplicable! Indeed, downright *impossible!*"

The gaunt old man shot him a darkly amused look.

> **Suspicions?**
>
> (continued)
>
> j. "They were on the stage of the now-empty theatre . . . ; shadows still gathered thickly in the wings, and above, beams and struts and spars could only just be glimpsed."
>
> k. "Nearly an hour had elapsed. During that time an extraordinary fact had emerged: although the Great Golconda had been shot, his assistant Mephisto (now detained in his dressing room) could not have shot him. Of that, there seemed not a doubt. And yet neither could anyone else."

"In my experience, Mr. Adey, the more bizarre and impossible the occurrence, the less mysterious it will in the end prove to be."

"That's all very well, sir," said the manager a mite snappishly, "but facts are facts! The entire audience was watching Mephisto. When Golconda fell dead, all Mephisto did was drop the revolver he was holding and stand there gaping. Let's say for the sake of argument he had another weapon. What did he do with it? Damm it, sir, he didn't move an inch from where he was standing, nor did he make any violent gesture, as though to throw it away from him. We've searched the entire stage. We've even searched him—not that that was at all necessary because his costume's so skin-tight you couldn't hide a button on him without it bulging."

"Perhaps," said the older man slowly, "he didn't need to throw it away."

"Didn't need?" Adey's voice rose to an outraged squeak. "You'll be telling me next he popped it into his mouth and ate it!"

"By no means as outrageous a suggestion as you might imagine," said the gaunt old man sternly. He turned to the Scotland Yard detective. "You

The Phantom Pistol 367

will recall, Hopkins, the case of the abominable Italian vendettist, Pronzini, who did just that."

Hopkins nodded sagely. The older man began to pace up and down the stage, gazing at the sable backcloth.

"Notice how black it is," he murmured, gesturing at the curtain. "How very black . . . " He swung around on Adey again. "Apart from the incident of the gloves, is there anything else to which you might wish to draw our attention?"

"Anything else?"

"Anything unusual."

Adey's honest face assumed a perplexed expression.

"Well . . . no, I don't believe so."

"The placing of the Great Golconda's act, for example?"

"Oh. Why, yes! Right at the beginning, you mean? That was unusual. They did have a bit of a barney about that. It was Mephisto's idea—begin the show and end it, he said. Golconda finally agreed."

"Nothing else?"

"Not that I can . . ."

Suspicions?

1. What motives might Mephisto have had for killing his brother?

2. Do you agree with Mr. H. that it is "a matter of some significance" that on this occasion Mephisto wore black gloves to fire his revolver when previously Mephisto fired his revolver bare-handed? Explain.

3. What conclusions can you draw from this change? Explain.

4. Is the Great Golconda's death, as Robert Adey, the theater manager of the Empire Music Hall, insists, "Inexplicable! Indeed, downright impossible!"? Explain. Why doesn't Mr. H. agree?

"I noticed that tonight they both stood at the rear of the stage. Did they not normally stand at the front?"

"Well, yes. Now you come to . . ."

"You will forgive my saying so, Mr. Adey," there was a touch of asperity in the old man's voice, "but your powers of observation are somewhat limited."

"You believe Mephisto killed Golconda?" said Hopkins.

"I am convinced of it."

"Then we'd better have a chat with him."

The older man smiled frostily.

"That will not be necessary. You have a stepladder?" he enquired of Adey. "Bring it on."

"Stepladder?" muttered Hopkins. "You think there's something up top?"

"Of course. There has to be. A second gun. Golconda was killed by a bullet. Bullets, for the most part, are shot from guns. Golconda's revolver was incapable of shooting anything, only of making a noise. Thus . . ."

The Scotland Yard man interrupted. "Ah. But. Wait on, Mr. H. These two were masters of illusion, am I correct?"

"Certainly."

"But when you get right down to it, their illusions, like all illusions, are fake. Created. Constructed."

"To be sure."

"So this here Mephisto needn't have used a gun at all. He was a clever fellow. Could've built some kind of weapon that fired a bullet, and . . ." He stopped as a thought struck him. "Here, remember the to-do you once had with that tiger-potting colonel. Now *he* had a special shooter."

"Indeed, an air-gun constructed by a German mechanic, who, though blind, had a genius for invention." The old man smiled a skeletal smile. "But you miss the point entirely, my dear Hopkins. It matters not *what* the weapon is, but *where* it is. That is the nub of the problem. We have searched everywhere, eliminated everything, on this level. As we must inevitably strike out from our enquiry any suggestion of magic, the inexorable conclusion we must come to is that the weapon—whatever it is—must be above us."

Hopkins struck the palm of his hand with a clenched fist. "But it can't be! Mephisto stood stock-still the whole time. We *know* he didn't chuck anything into the air."

"As I remarked before, perhaps he did not need to . . ."

By this time the heavy wheeled ladder had been trundled on and heaved to the center of the stage. A stagehand climbed into the darkness above.

"Merely look for anything that seems out of the ordinary," the old man directed.

In less than a minute the stagehand was calling out excitedly.

"Something here . . . wound round one of the spars on—why, it's elasticated cord!"

"Unwind it. Let it drop."

Seconds later a small object fell through the air, then bounced upwards again as the cord reached its nadir. The old man stretched up and caught it before it could fly out of reach. He turned to the watchers.

"What do you see?"

Hopkins frowned.

"Not a thing."

Suspicions?

1. Do you share Mr. H.'s conviction that Mephisto killed the Great Golconda? Why or why not?

2. Where do you think the murder weapon can be found? Why?

The old man opened his fingers.

"Come closer."

The Scotland Yard detective stepped forward, his expression turning to one of amazement. Gripped in the gaunt old man's hand—clearly seen against the white of his skin—was a miniature chamberless pistol, perhaps five inches long from grip to muzzle, painted entirely matt-black. The old man pressed at the bottom of the stock and the barrel slid forward, revealing a two-inch cavity.

"A Williamson derringer pistol, capable of firing one shot only—quite enough to kill a man," said the old man dryly. "Hand me the false pistol."

He held the blank-firing pistol in his left hand with the derringer gripped in his right, leveling both at an imaginary target. From the side all that could be seen was the massive bulk of the service revolver. Then he clicked the triggers of both guns and opened his right hand. The derringer, at the end of the taut elasticated cord—totally invisible against the black backcloth—flew upwards into the darkness above, whipping round and round the high spar to which it was attached.

Adey looked utterly at sea.

"But how did you . . . what made you . . . ?" he babbled.

"When three singular variations in a set routine—the black gloves, the change of position not only of the act itself but of the two principals on the stage in that act—take place," said the old man a trifle testily, "one is tempted, to use the vernacular, to smell a rat. After that, it is a matter of simple deduction. The gift of observation—sadly lacking in the general populace—allied to intuition. Believe me, there is really no combination of events—however inexplicable on the surface—for which the wit of man cannot conceive an elucidation."

He began to pace up and down the stage again, his hands clasped firmly behind his back.

"Mephisto tied the derringer to the spar, letting it hang down just within reach of his outstretched arm. It could not be seen because he had painted it black and hung it close to the black curtain. In any case, the lighting was subdued. Even so, there was the risk of someone spotting it, so he persuaded his brother that their act should start the show. Came the climax of the performance. The two spotlights only lit up the area within their twin beams. Mephisto raised his arms, holding the false revolver, until his hands were just above the spotlight's glare. He has positioned himself perfectly—no doubt he rehearsed the entire sequence thoroughly—and the hanging derringer was now within inches of his right hand. If his hands had been bare, one might possibly have noticed that he was holding something else, but he took the precaution of wearing black gloves, thereby making assurance double sure. Grasping the derringer, he pulled it down on its elasticated thread, pressing it to the side of the much larger weapon, as his arms dropped to the leveled-off position. He was now holding not one, but *two* guns—one hidden from the audience's view and in any case virtually invisible. Except to the man at whom he was pointing them."

"Yes!" snapped Hopkins. "That's what made Golconda look surprised. I thought he'd seen something *behind* Mephisto."

"Mephisto then fired the derringer, releasing his grip on the gun, which shot up into the air. All eyes were on Golconda falling to the floor. The derringer wound itself round the spar to which its cord was attached. In the confusion afterwards, doubtless, Mephisto meant to get rid of the evidence. What he did not reckon on was the presence of a Scotland Yard detective who would immediately take charge of the proceedings and confine him to his dressing room. But in the meantime there was absolutely nothing to show that he had just murdered his brother in cold blood. It was as though," the old man finished, shrugging, "the Great Golconda had indeed been shot with a phantom pistol."

"And being next in line," said Hopkins, "Mephisto would've stepped into the baronetcy and all them lovely golden sovs. Nice work, Mr. H. Nice work, indeed!"

 How Clever?

1. Explain in detail how Mr. H. used his powers of observation (detection) in solving the murder.

2. Explain in detail how Mr. H. used his reasoning powers (reflection) in solving the murder.

3. Which particular examples of Mr. H.'s powers of detection and reflection impressed you the most? Why?

4. Follow Mr. H.'s reasoning in his dialogue that begins with "Of course" and ends with "Thus" on page 367. Explain the logic of what he says. How does Mr. H.'s saying "bullets, for the most part, are shot from guns" give Superintendent Hopkins an idea?

5. Do you agree with Mr. H. that "it matters not *what* the weapon is, but *where* it is. That is the nub of the problem." Why or why not?

6. Using logic, where does Mr. H. conclude "the weapon—whatever it is" must be?

7. How did Mephisto make use of and then get rid of the murder weapon?

8. Why does the author of the story make a point of saying that when Superintendent Hopkins stepped closer to Mr. H., the miniature chamberless pistol was "clearly seen against the white of his skin"?

9. Which "three singular variations in a set routine" took place that caused Mr. H. to "smell a rat"? Explain.

10. Summarize Mr. H.'s detection (the observations he makes) and his reflection (the deductions he comes to) when he explains to Mr. Adey, the theater manager, and to Superintendent Hopkins how Mephisto killed the Great Golconda. What do you think Mr. H. means when he adds a third element—intuition?

11. Mr. Robert Adey, the theater manager, repeatedly comments during the story that the death of the Great Golconda is "inexplicable" and "impossible." The detective, Mr. H., puts down Mr. Adey with the comment, "You will forgive my saying so, Mr. Adey, but your powers of observation are somewhat limited." Why would Mr. Adey not have made a good detective?

12. Mr. H. makes two related points about making sense of something that seems to make no sense at all. He says that "the more bizarre and impossible the occurrence, the less mysterious it will in the end prove to be" and also that "there is really no combination of events—however inexplicable on the surface—for which the wit of man cannot conceive an elucidation." Also, in an exchange of dialogue between Superintendent Hopkins and Mr. H., Superintendent Hopkins says, "You believe Mephisto killed Golconda?" and Mr. H. replies, "I am convinced of it".

    How do these three comments of Mr. H.'s show that he has what it takes to be a good detective?

13. Mr. H. says of this case, "We must inevitably strike out from our enquiry any suggestion of magic," which had earlier been equated by Superintendent Hopkins to illusion, which is "fake. Created. Constructed." Why must it be true that what Mr. H. says about this particular case is true of all detective cases? Explain.

14. Do you agree with Superintendent Hopkins when he says of Mr. H.'s solving of the case of the phantom pistol, "Nice work, Mr. H. Nice work, indeed!"? Explain.

DETECTWRITE: Characterization

1. Compare Mr. H. with Scotland Yard Superintendent Stanley Hopkins in terms of their physical appearance, actions, and dialogue in the story.

2. At what point in the story would it be fairly safe for the reader to predict that it would be Mr. H., and not Superintendent Hopkins, who would solve the crime? Explain why you chose that point in the story.

3. The Great Golconda, illusionist extraordinaire, is characterized as "something of a democrat." What evidence does the story supply for this assertion?

4. How does the music hall manager, Robert Adey, serve as a foil to Mr. H.? Does Superintendent Hopkins also serve as a foil? Explain.

5. Illusionists like the Great Golconda and his brother Mephisto appear fairly frequently as characters in mystery and detective stories. Why do you think that is?

6. Based on your reading of this story and Sir Arthur Conan Doyle's "The Adventure of the Six Napoleons," compare and contrast Mr. H.'s personality and sleuthing techniques with the personality and sleuthing techniques of Sherlock Holmes.

7. Compare and contrast the men who represent the London police department and serve as foils in this story and in Conan Doyle's Sherlock Holmes series—Superintendent Stanley Hopkins vs. Inspector Lestrade.

DETECTWRITE: Plot

1. Although humor need not be absent from mystery and detective stories, it often is. Find some instances of humor or word play in "The Phantom Pistol." (One inside joke is that the name Pronzini, given to "the abominable Italian vendettist," is the last name of Bill Pronzini, author of many mystery and detective stories.)

2. Do you think the author gave too much away when he wrote that that night's performance by the Great Golconda "was to be positively his final performance"? Would most readers interpret that wording as a very strong hint or obvious foreshadowing that, more than retiring, the Great Golconda was going to die? Explain.

3. Would knowing that the Great Golconda was going to die during his act spoil the story for readers? Explain.

DETECTWRITE: Setting

1. Quote words, phrases, and sentences from the opening paragraphs of the story that help to set the scene and create an atmosphere. Overall, what feeling is established for the reader at the start of the story—before he or she is even introduced to the Great Golconda?

2. How does the feeling created by the atmospheric setting of London in 1912 contribute to both characterization and plot in this story of a magician and illusionist killed by what appears to be "a phantom pistol"?

The Dead Sleep Lightly

John Dickson Carr

THE CHARACTERS

Dr. Gideon Fell
Hoskins
George Pendleton
Pamela Bennett
Mrs. Tancred
Wilmot
Superintendent Hadley
Mary Ellen Kimball
Taxi Driver
Telephone Operator

Setting: London, 1933.

NARRATOR: It was dark that night too. Very dark. A gusty March evening ten years ago in London. There was peace; there was security; and no living thing could harm you. But a black wind whistled that night in the narrow streets off the Strand and flapped at the shutters and growled in the chimneys and penetrated even into the snug book-lined study up two flights of stairs. There in the great padded armchair before the fire, sat Dr. Gideon Fell. His face had grown even ruddier in the heat of the fire. His several chins folded out over his collar. Cigar ash was spilled down the mountainous ridges of his waistcoat. His eyeglasses, on the wide black ribbon, had become a trifle lopsided. Doubtless he was deep in thought over some difficult problem, since . . .

(*As the voice fades, there are several long and impressive snores. Door opens as* HOSKINS *approaches.*)

HOSKINS: Dr. Fell, sir! Wake up! Dr. Fell!

DR. FELL (*at end of a snore, starting*): Eh? What's that?

HOSKINS: Begging your pardon, sir, but *will* you wake up?

DR. FELL (*with dignity*): Yes, of course; I was merely concentrating. What is it?

HOSKINS: There's a lunatic downstairs, sir.

DR. FELL: A what? Then what's wrong, my good Hoskins? What ails you? Why don't you show him up?

HOSKINS: Are you sure you *want* to see him, sir?

DR. FELL: That depends. What sort of a lunatic is he?

HOSKINS: He's a big, fine-looking gent, about fifty. Got a limousine outside. But he's shaking all over and near purple in the face. I don't like the look of him.

DR. FELL: Did he give any name?

HOSKINS: Well, sir, he started to take out a card case. But his fingers shook so much that he spilled the cards all over the floor. Then he scooped up the lot and put 'em back in his pocket again. I think he said "Pendleton" or something like that.

DR. FELL (*ruminating*): Pendleton. That wouldn't be George Pendleton, the publisher?

HOSKINS: I dunno, sir.

DR. FELL: Mr. George Pendleton, Hoskins, is a very celebrated and successful man. What he should be doing at my humble door . . . Ask him to come up, will you?

HOSKINS (*rapidly, under his breath*): Cripes, sir, I don't need to. 'Ere 'e is.

(*Door opens.* PENDLETON *has an authoritative and pompous voice, the voice of a man used to getting his own way. Just now he has himself in hand, but he is badly frightened.*)

PENDLETON (*huskily*): I beg your pardon. Am I addressing Dr. Gideon Fell?

DR. FELL: At your service, sir. Mr. Pendleton?

PENDLETON: Yes. I followed your servant up. That dark hall downstairs . . . (*Correcting himself quickly*) I mean, I hope you'll excuse my intrusion at this time of the night. I mean . . .

DR. FELL: Steady, man! Don't trip over anything. Here, come up to the fire. It's a cold night.

PENDLETON (*fervently*): It is, it is!

DR. FELL: Hoskins, take Mr. Pendleton's hat and coat. Now draw up a chair.

PENDLETON: Tell me, Doctor, there's no clay in this house, there?

DR. FELL: Clay?

PENDLETON: Clay soil. And gravel. Of the sort you often find in . . . graveyards.

HOSKINS (*under his breath*): 'Ere! Stop a bit!

DR. FELL: That will be all, Hoskins. You may go.

HOSKINS (*unwillingly*): Very good, sir.

(*Door closes.*)

PENDLETON: I thought I stepped on some clay and gravel as I was coming upstairs. Perhaps a trick of the imagination.

DR. FELL: It certainly must have been, unless Hoskins is an even worse housekeeper than I think he is.

PENDLETON: You see, Doctor . . . I went to a funeral yesterday.

DR. FELL: You've lost someone?

PENDLETON: No, no, no! It was only a fellow club-member. A lot of us went to the funeral in a body, as a mark of respect. (*Pompously*) I'm a busy man, Doctor, but I find it pays to keep up the little social duties like that. Business, with the right personal touch: that's how I've got on in the world, if you don't mind my saying so.

DR. FELL: I see. And on this particular social occasion . . . ?

PENDLETON (*startled*): Social occasion? Who the devil said anything about social occasions?

DR. FELL: I thought you did. Please go on.

PENDLETON: It was a wet day in Kensal Green cemetery. There we were, a lot of middle-aged men, standing about an open grave in the rain. Feeling liverish; nothing right; you know how it is.

DR. FELL: Unfortunately, I do.

PENDLETON: I was arranging to get away next day for a long holiday in the south of France. After that I was giving up my house in St. John's Wood, and taking a flat closer to the West End. Light! Life! *Something!* I'd taken my secretary along to that infernal funeral in case I wanted to dictate any last letters. (*Suddenly struck by this*) Last letters! Never mind! (*Fade in sounds of rain*) As we were on our way out of the cemetery, we must have got confused, because . . .

(The voice fades into a long roll of thunder. The steady noise of rain backs the scene throughout. PAMELA BENNETT *speaks. She is young and keeps her voice, as a rule, at a colourless level.)*

PAMELA: Mr. Pendleton, are you sure we haven't taken the wrong turning? This isn't the way to the car.

PENDLETON *(irritably):* You said it was, Miss Bennett.

PAMELA: No, sir. I said . . .

PENDLETON: Anyway, how can you expect to see anything in this rain? And all this nightmare of tombstones?

PAMELA: It looks like an older part of the cemetery.

PENDLETON: It is. It's where they bury you when you haven't much money. Always remember that, Miss Bennett.

PAMELA: I'm sorry if I got the directions mixed, Mr. Pendleton. I thought . . .

PENDLETON *(magnanimously):* Please don't mention it, Miss Bennett. It's a small matter, in fact, compared to other things. I'll pay you the compliment of saying you're the best secretary I ever had. Yet you want to leave me?

PAMELA: I want to get married, yes.

PENDLETON: That's what Mr. Fraser was telling me. *(Spitefully)* And who is this paragon of yours? What does he do? Does he make any money?

PAMELA: Frank's a radio technician. He's not very well-off, I admit.

PENDLETON: Well-off? I'll bet he doesn't make as much as I pay you, yet you want to get married!

(Fade up rain.)

PAMELA *(bewildered):* Is there anything so very strange about that?

PENDLETON: Yes, if it interferes with your career. It . . .

(Peak and fade rain to background.)

PAMELA *(as though alarmed):* What's wrong?

PENDLETON *(in a low voice):* Good . . . *God!*

PAMELA: What is it? Don't lower your umbrella like that, or you'll get soaking wet. What's wrong?

PENDLETON: Do you see that grave?

PAMELA: Which one?

PENDLETON: On the end. The very-much-neglected grave with the little stone cross. The name's almost effaced. Can you read it?

PAMELA *(slowly):* "Sacred to the Memory of Mary . . . Ellen . . . Kimball."

PENDLETON *(astonished):* So it is; so it is!

PAMELA: "Born . . ." No, I can't read that part of it. What about her?

PENDLETON (*genuinely moved*): Poor Mary Ellen! (*He sighs*) Now I come to think of it, she did have an aunt or someone living at Kensal Rise. It's a girl I used to know twenty-five, thirty years ago.

PAMELA: Did you know her well?

PENDLETON (*brooding*): I'll tell you a deep secret, Miss Bennett. I would have married her . . . yes, so help me! . . . only . . .

PAMELA: Only . . . what?

PENDLETON: Do I have to explain these things? I came from small beginnings. I had my way to make in the world. And she wouldn't have helped me.

PAMELA: I still don't think I understand.

PENDLETON (*dogmatically*): A man of my sort owes it to himself to make a wealthy marriage or none at all. That's what I've always said, and that's what I believe. Anything else is sentimental rubbish. I was sorry to break with her, but I thought it was kinder to break cleanly. I was sorry to hear of her death . . . that was years afterwards . . . (*Fade in thunder*) But . . . well, I had other things to think about.

PAMELA (*under her breath*): You *poisonous* . . . (*The word is almost but not quite drowned out by a roll of thunder.*)

PENDLETON (*startled, not hearing*): What's that? Did you say something?

PAMELA (*colourless again*): No, Mr. Pendleton. Hadn't we better get on to the car?

PENDLETON: Yes, I suppose so. (*Wistfully*) Poor Mary Ellen, though.

PAMELA: I'm sorry, Mr. Pendleton, but I've got suede shoes on, and this clay is ruining them. Couldn't we go on?

PENDLETON: She was a pretty little thing, and absolutely devoted to me. (*Defensively*) I was sorry for her, you know.

PAMELA: If you really feel like that, Mr. Pendleton . . .

PENDLETON: Well?

PAMELA: You could have her grave tidied up, and some flowers put on it. Shall I attend to it for you?

PENDLETON (*eagerly*): By George, yes! That's a good idea. She'd have liked that. But . . . how are they going to identify her?

PAMELA: Identify her?

PENDLETON: There must be thousands of graves here. Look!

PAMELA: Yes. Didn't you ever have anything to do with cemeteries, Mr. Pendleton?

PENDLETON (*shuddering*): No! I hate the thought of death! I . . .

PAMELA: Each grave has a number cut into the stone at one side. This one is Kensal Green 1-9-3-3.

PENDLETON *(blankly):* Kensal Green 1-9-3-3.

PAMELA: Sounds like a telephone number, doesn't it?

PENDLETON *(quietly):* Yes. Doesn't it? Kensal Green 1-9-3-3. Kensal Green 1-9-3-3.

PAMELA *(pleading): Couldn't* we go on now, Mr. Pendleton?

PENDLETON *(unheeding):* Make a note of that, Miss Bennett. Attend to it first thing next week, and . . . *(Waking up)* Wait a minute! I forgot. You're leaving the office. Has it ever occurred to you, Miss Bennett, that you take the most impossible times for inconveniencing me with your personal affairs?

PAMELA *(helplessly):* I'm sorry, Mr. Pendleton. I can't seem to do anything to please you today.

PENDLETON: You could please me, at least, by staying on at the office.

PAMELA: I've told you before that . . .

PENDLETON *(significantly):* You're not a bad-looking girl. I could do a lot for you, you know, if I wanted to.

PAMELA *(unemotionally):* As you did for Mary Ellen Kimball?

PENDLETON: Confound your impertinence!

PAMELA: Were you speaking of impertinence, Mr. Pendleton?

PENDLETON *(stiffly):* Perhaps you're right. Yes, I'm quite sure you're right. Shall we forget I ever mentioned it?

PAMELA: If you please.

PENDLETON *(blankly):* Kensal Green 1-9-3-3. Kensal Green 1-9-3-3.

PAMELA: Why do you keep on repeating that number?

PENDLETON: Not because I regret anything, mind you!

PAMELA: I'm sure you don't.

PENDLETON: After all, you can't take a girl like that into society. Not when she's thrown her cap over the windmill for you and got herself talked about. It's just that her utter devotion touched me a good deal.

PAMELA: I'm sure it did.

PENDLETON: She always said she'd come back if I called her. And sometimes . . .

PAMELA: You felt like calling her?

PENDLETON: Years ago, maybe. But there she is with the worms and clay *(arrogantly),* and here *I* am where I've always wanted to be. It's too late now, isn't it?

PAMELA: Much too late, Mr. Pendleton. *Much too late.*

(*Swell thunder and then fade into* PENDLETON'S *voice.*)

PENDLETON: . . . and that, Dr. Fell, was all that happened at the cemetery. Little enough, you'd say. But it started preying on my mind. I couldn't forget that girl.

DR. FELL: You mean Miss Bennett?

PENDLETON (*impatiently*): Miss Bennett . . . No! I can't think what made me forget myself there. I mean Mary Ellen Kimball.

DR. FELL: You've made your mental state fairly clear, I think. And then?

PENDLETON: For some reason I began to get nervous. I lunched at my club, and couldn't eat. I went to my office, and couldn't work. That infernal number kept running through my head: Kensal Green 1-9-3-3. Then, when I went home in the evening . . . (*Abruptly*) Have you ever seen my house?

DR. FELL: I have not had that pleasure, sir. But I believe it's one of the showplaces of St. John's Wood.

PENDLETON (*bitterly*): Great ugly mausoleum of a place! I told you I was moving house into a flat that'd suit me better when I came back from Europe. I knew most of the servants would be gone, of course. But I thought Mrs. Tancred—that's my housekeeper—would still be there. (*Fade in rain*) It was still raining, with thunder about. Then, when I went up the path about half-past six . . .

Suspicions?

Based on characters' actions, dialogue, and tone of voice (as indicated in the stage directions), whom do you suspect at this point in the play is up to no good? Explain why.

(*Swell rain and fade down. Distant ringing of a doorbell. A heavy door is opened.* MRS. TANCRED *is elderly and well-spoken.*)

MRS. TANCRED (*surprised*): Bless me, sir; I didn't know it was you.

(*Door shuts out the rain.*)

PENDLETON: Sorry to trouble you, Mrs. Tancred. I seem to have mislaid my latchkey. And yet I could have sworn I had it on my key-ring this morning.

MRS. TANCRED: It's no trouble, Mr. Pendleton.

PENDLETON (*irritably*): Confound it, what are all these packing-cases doing in the hall?

MRS. TANCRED (*reproachfully*): I hope you haven't forgotten you're leaving here, sir?

PENDLETON (*waking up*): Oh, yes. Yes, of course. Have you got my bags packed?

MRS. TANCRED: All ready for you, sir. Your hat and coat? Will you be dining at home tonight?

PENDLETON *(still rather dazed):* Yes. Yes, I suppose I'd better. For the last time.

MRS. TANCRED: It does seem a pity, doesn't it?

PENDLETON *(quickly):* What seems a pity?

MRS. TANCRED: Leaving here, after all these years.

PENDLETON *(hurriedly):* Now you've been a very good housekeeper, Mrs. Tancred. I've always treated *you* generously, haven't I? I've got you a good position to follow this one, haven't I?

MRS. TANCRED *(offended):* I wasn't meaning that, sir.

PENDLETON: Then what did you mean?

MRS. TANCRED: Breaking up a lovely home like this.

PENDLETON: This? This infernal picture gallery? Where I feel like . . . like old Scrooge every time I come home!

MRS. TANCRED *(sympathetically):* It must have been a bit lonely at times, I daresay.

PENDLETON *(fiercely):* Lonely? I am never lonely!

MRS. TANCRED *(submissively):* No, sir.

PENDLETON: There are a lot of people who envy me, Mrs. Tancred. And, what's more, I deserve their envy.

MRS. TANCRED: Yes, sir.

PENDLETON: I ... *(giving it up)* ... never mind. They haven't taken the furniture out of the library, have they?

MRS. TANCRED: No, sir. Only the books off the shelves.

PENDLETON: I shall be in the library, then. Dinner at seven-thirty. And ... Mrs. Tancred!

MRS. TANCRED: Yes, sir?

PENDLETON: If I ever feel the need of any sympathy for my unhappy lot, I'll ask for it. Do I make myself quite clear?

MRS. TANCRED: Yes, sir. Just as you wish, sir.

(Door opens and closes heavily. Slight pause. PENDLETON *draws a deep breath.)*

PENDLETON *(muttering):* What's a library without books? Empty mortuary kind of place . . . Confound her; she's even taken the writing paper off my desk. Nothing's right. Nothing *has* ever been right! And where's my Venetian mirror? Have they gone and stolen my Ven . . . Oh, no. No. Here we are. *(Slight pause. He changes his tone.)* George Pendleton, my lad, you might as well face the fact that you can't stick dinner alone in this house tonight. Never mind *why* you can't do it. Never mind whether it's your health *(fade in rain)*, or what it is. Rain going on forever. It'll be wet in that cemetery. And is there any reason on earth why you shouldn't go out for dinner and enjoy yourself? That's it! Ring Bill Fraser, and go out to dinner. Ring Bill Fraser. Telephone . . . here we are.

(Noise of receiver lifted, and receiver-hook jiggled up and down.)

PENDLETON: Hello! Hello! Hello!

OPERATOR: Number, please?

PENDLETON: Hello? I want . . . *(Groping)* Bill's number. Now what's Bill's number? What the devil *is* Bill's number?

OPERATOR: Number, please?

PENDLETON: I want . . . I want . . . *(Blurting it out)* Kensal Green 1-9-3-3. *(Heavy crash of thunder)* Good God! What have I said?

OPERATOR *(unemotionally)*: Kensal Green 1-9-3-3.

PENDLETON *(in consternation)*: Operator, wait! There's some mistake! I said the wrong thing! I want . . .

OPERATOR: Kensal Green 1-9-3-3.

(Ringing tone. Then a woman's voice answers; it is a girlish voice, very faint and almost whispering.)

VOICE: Yes? Who is it?

PENDLETON *(wildly)*: There's been some mist . . .

VOICE *(with sudden eagerness)*: George dear, is that you?

PENDLETON *(alarmed)*: Who is that? Who's speaking?

VOICE: It's Mary Ellen, dear. Don't you recognize my voice?

PENDLETON: No! No! No!

VOICE: I knew you'd call me sooner or later, dear. But I've waited *ever* so long.

PENDLETON: I . . .

VOICE *(eagerly)*: And of course I'll come if you want me. I'll be there just as soon as I can.

PENDLETON: I tell you—!

VOICE: I'll be there by seven o'clock, truly I will. But you mustn't be frightened at how I look now.

PENDLETON: You're not Mary Ellen! This is a trick! *Mary Ellen is dead!*

VOICE: Yes, dear. But the dead sleep lightly. And they can be lonely too.

PENDLETON: Don't talk to me! You can't talk to me! I won't listen to you! I . . .

VOICE: I'll wear a veil, dear. Because I'm not very pretty now. But I won't hurt you, my darling. Truly I won't!

PENDLETON *(frantically):* Go away, do you hear? Go . . .

VOICE: Goodbye, dear. Remember, when the clock strikes seven.

(There is a click and a long pause.)

PENDLETON *(breathing hard):* Mrs. Tancred! *(Shouting)* Mrs. Tancred!

(Door opens.)

MRS. TANCRED *(flustered):* Lord 'a' mercy, sir, what's the matter?

(Door shuts.)

PENDLETON *(levelly but hoarsely):* Who's been playing tricks on me?

MRS. TANCRED: Tricks, sir?

PENDLETON: I want to know who's been playing the fool with this telephone.

MRS. TANCRED *(surprised):* Nobody, sir. It's only what you ordered. *(Nervously amused)* You haven't been trying to *use* the phone, have you?

PENDLETON: Use it? I rang up a friend of mine. A woman's voice answered and pretended to be somebody I used to know years ago . . .

> ### 👁 Suspicions?
>
> It is a convention of the detective genre that all explanations of the mysterious, including the solution to the crime, must be natural, not supernatural. Therefore, Pendleton must be correct when he says, "This is a trick! *Mary Ellen is dead!*" Whom do you suspect is behind the voice on the telephone and why?

MRS. TANCRED *(alarmed and offended):* Now, sir, stop your joking.

PENDLETON: You think I'm *joking*?

MRS. TANCRED *(commiseratingly):* You're all upset, that's what it is. Sit down by the desk. Hang up the receiver and put the phone down . . . There!

PENDLETON *(desperately):* Will you kindly tell me . . . ?

MRS. TANCRED: You didn't use that telephone, sir. Nobody could have used that phone.

PENDLETON: And why not?

MRS. TANCRED: Because it was disconnected this morning. *(After a pause, she continues patiently.)* You're giving up the house, sir. Don't you remember? You ordered the telephone to be removed. The man came this morning, and disconnected all the wires and took the metal box off the base-board of the wall.

PENDLETON *(not loudly):* Are you mad, or am I?

MRS. TANCRED: Just look for yourself, then. There's the flex of the phone hanging halfway down to the floor. It ends in mid-air; it's not connected with anything.

PENDLETON *(breathing in):* That's . . . true!

MRS. TANCRED: Of course it's true.

PENDLETON: The phone's *not* connected. It wasn't connected when I spoke to . . .

MRS. TANCRED: When I saw you there with the phone in your hand, and the receiver off the hook, and the cord not going anywhere, and looking as though you'd really been talking to somebody . . . *(Doubtfully)* You *were* just pretending, weren't you, sir?

PENDLETON: What if I said no?

MRS. TANCRED: Really, Mr. Pendleton! Please!

PENDLETON: I tell you, I was talking to a woman on this telephone just before you came in here!

MRS. TANCRED *(flatly):* Indeed, sir.

PENDLETON: You don't believe me, do you?

MRS. TANCRED: I must ask to be excused, if you don't mind. I'm the only person here, and I've got to see to your dinner, and . . .

(Door opens.)

PENDLETON *(hoarsely):* Mrs. Tancred! Wait a minute!

MRS. TANCRED: Yes, sir?

PENDLETON: Mrs. Tancred *(pause),* how long have you been my house-keeper?

MRS. TANCRED: Three years and eight months. Why, sir?

PENDLETON: Sometimes, in certain lights, I get the notion we'd met before you came here.

MRS. TANCRED: Indeed, sir.

PENDLETON *(sharply):* Had we met before?

MRS. TANCRED: If I'd ever met you, sir, it isn't likely I should have forgotten you. Now is it?

PENDLETON: Mrs. Tancred! Wait! Don't go away! You're not going to leave me here alone?

MRS. TANCRED: Leave you alone? A big, able-bodied man! Really, sir!

(Door closes.)

PENDLETON: Mrs. Tancred! *(Desperately)* Mrs. Tancred! What . . . time is it?

MRS. TANCRED (*coldly, through closed door*): There's a clock on the mantel in there, sir. It must be . . .

(*Clock slowly strikes seven. Music up.*)

DR. FELL: I see, Mr. Pendleton. I see. But surely the story doesn't end there?

PENDLETON (*huskily*): End there . . . how do you mean?

DR. FELL: The clock strikes. The mystic hour arrives. Well? Did the ghostly visitor appear?

PENDLETON: I don't know.

DR. FELL: You don't know?

PENDLETON: I lost my head and bolted out of that house as though the devil were after me. Maybe he was.

DR. FELL: And afterwards?

PENDLETON: I spent the night at a hotel. Going abroad today was out of the question. I'm a practical man; I had to *know*.

DR. FELL: You . . . investigated?

PENDLETON: I got in touch with the telephone people. That phone was disconnected yesterday morning. Besides, I could see that for myself. I can take my living oath there was no wire leading from that phone.

DR. FELL: Yet you heard a voice speaking from the receiver?

PENDLETON: I did.

DR. FELL: Mary Ellen Kimball's voice?

PENDLETON (*after a pause*): Yes.

DR. FELL: I see. Did you find out anything else in your investigations today?

PENDLETON: There's no doubt she's dead, if that's what you mean. I couldn't find her aunt at Kensal Rise . . . the aunt's gone away as a servant or something. But I found the doctor who attended Mary Ellen. She died of pneumonia brought on by . . . (*Hesitates*)

DR. FELL: Brought on by what?

PENDLETON: Well. Brought on by undernourishment. Anyway, she died. Called herself Mrs. Kimball.

DR. FELL (*quickly*): Why did she call herself Mrs. Kimball?

PENDLETON (*just as quickly*): I don't know.

DR. FELL: I must repeat the question, my good sir. It may be the most important thing in the whole affair. Why did she call herself Mrs. Kimball?

PENDLETON: I tell you, I don't know!

DR. FELL *(persuasively):* Mr. Pendleton, I am at the service of anyone with a problem in his head or a trouble on his back. But if you won't tell me the truth about this . . .

PENDLETON: You mean you won't help me?

DR. FELL: How can I?

PENDLETON: Look here, Dr. Fell. I've been through a lot already. I don't propose to be questioned and cross-questioned about something I don't think is important.

DR. FELL: Why not let *me* be the judge of that?

PENDLETON: If you think I'm afraid to go back to that house tonight, you're mistaken. *(Blustering)* I'm not without people I pay, and pay well, to look after me. There's Wilmot, for one.

DR. FELL *(sharply):* Wilmot? Who's Wilmot?

PENDLETON: My chauffeur. He's outside in the car now.

DR. FELL: Is Wilmot by any chance a young man?

PENDLETON: Yes, fairly young. Very *(mockingly)* superior sort of chap, but reliable. Why?

DR. FELL: It may not mean anything. It probably doesn't.

> **Suspicions?**
>
> What "truth" do you think Mr. Pendleton is withholding ("something I don't think is important") and Dr. Fell is trying to get at ("It may be the most important thing in the whole affair")? What do you base your conclusion on? Can you now predict who is behind the strange things that are going on in Mr. Pendleton's house?

PENDLETON: As a matter of fact, I'd already had a word about this with a friend of mine at Scotland Yard. Superintendent Hadley.

DR. FELL: Oh? You've mentioned this to Hadley?

PENDLETON: Unofficially, of course.

DR. FELL: And what did *he* say?

PENDLETON: He told me to see you. I came here, fair and square, to get advice. And do I get advice? No! I get a lot of wrangling and quibbling when I'm trying to tell my story. I can't go to the police; I can't go to you; where *can* I go?

DR. FELL: If I were less polite, sir, I should tell you.

PENDLETON: That's your last word?

DR. FELL: Until you say yours.

PENDLETON *(grimly):* All right! I'll take it as that. Where's that manservant of yours? *(Calling)* Hoy!

(Door opens.)

HOSKINS: Yes, sir?

PENDLETON: Get me my hat and coat, please.

HOSKINS: Got 'em right 'ere, sir. *(Conversationally)* Wind's rising tonight, gentlemen.

DR. FELL: Blowing hard, is it?

HOSKINS: Regular gale and black as your hat.

PENDLETON *(bursting out):* And you want me to go home alone?

DR. FELL: Look here, man; why not be sensible? Tell me the whole story.

PENDLETON: I've told just as much as I'm going to tell this side of eternity. If anything happens to me, it's on your own head. Good night, and I can find my own way out.

DR. FELL *(under his breath):* Hoskins!

HOSKINS: Yes, sir?

DR. FELL *(in a low voice):* When you've seen Mr. Pendleton out, bring my cloak and walking-stick . . .

HOSKINS: Stop a bit, sir! You're not . . .

DR. FELL: Quiet! He's on the stairs; he'll hear you. Close the door.

HOSKINS: Yes, sir.

(Door closes.)

DR. FELL *(querulously):* Now he's made me feel like a selfish hound. I suppose I've got to follow him.

HOSKINS: You're not going out of the house tonight, sir?

DR. FELL *(with dignity):* And why not, my good custodian?

HOSKINS: 'Cos you oughtn't to be out at any time, that's why. You haven't got the foggiest idea where you're going; you concentrate across the street against a red light; you walk off underground platforms onto trains that ain't there . . .

DR. FELL *(with still more dignity):* If you are implying, my good Hoskins, that I occasionally suffer from a slight . . . a very slight . . . absent-mindedness . . .

HOSKINS *(awed):* Absent-mindedness, sir?

DR. FELL: That was the word.

HOSKINS: So help me, sir, when you was solving that Vickerly case, you came home cold sober and stood for twenty minutes trying to open the front door with a corkscrew.

DR. FELL: Listen to me, Hoskins.

HOSKINS: Yes, sir?

DR. FELL: Our friend Pendleton is going to have a bad night. Probably the worst night of his life. He may be in real danger.

HOSKINS: If you've got to go out, sir, let me ring Superintendent Hadley and have him meet you.

DR. FELL: Oh, no, my lad. No. We don't want the police in this.

HOSKINS: The man's in danger, but you *don't* want the police?

DR. FELL: That's exactly what I mean. Wait till he's gone, and then get me a taxi. What is he going to see in that house tonight? *What* is he going to see in that house tonight?

(Music up and down. Sounds of wind and a motorcar, which approaches and stops.)

TAXI DRIVER: I'm sorry about the engine trouble, governor. But I couldn't make it any sooner.

(Car door opens. Grunt suggesting heavy body getting out. Door closes.)

DR. FELL *(grimly resigned):* That's all right. It can't be helped. You're sure this is where Mr. Pendleton lives?

DRIVER: Dead sure, governor. You can't mistake those funny towers and the fir trees growing up the path. *(Breaking off)* Hullo! There's somebody standing by the gate.

DR. FELL *(calling sharply):* Who's there? Who's there?

(SUPERINTENDENT HADLEY has a military voice and a no-nonsense manner.)

HADLEY: *I'm* here, Fell. And wishing to blazes I'd stayed at the pub.

DR. FELL: That's not Hadley? Superintendent Hadley?

HADLEY: Oh, yes, it is. Waiting for twenty minutes in the perishing cold, while . . .

DR. FELL: But how did *you* get here?

HADLEY *(surprised):* You sent for me, didn't you?

DR. FELL: *I* sent for you?

HADLEY: Hoskins did, anyway. He said it was an urgent matter for the police. He said . . .

DR. FELL: So the blighter's disobeyed my orders again. *(Breaking off)* That's all, driver. Good night.

DRIVER: Good night, governor.

(Taxi moves away.)

HADLEY: Let me get things straight, Fell. This is George Pendleton's house. I was here two years ago about a little matter of a burglary, and I know. You didn't drag me here at this hour to discuss that crazy yarn about a dead woman and a ghost telephone?

DR. FELL *(rather testily):* My good Hadley, I didn't drag you here to discuss anything. I gather, though, you didn't believe the yarn?

HADLEY *(past comment):* Believe it? For the love of . . . !

DR. FELL: There's no time to argue that. The point is, did Pendleton get home safely tonight?

HADLEY: *I* don't know. There's a light in the library, anyway. *(Wind up)* Look up the path, past the fir trees. Those two French windows to the left of the front door.

DR. FELL: And one of these French windows, you notice, is standing partway open.

HADLEY: Well? What about it?

DR. FELL: It's a fine night for that, isn't it?

HADLEY *(impatiently):* Maybe it blew open. Maybe Pendleton likes fresh air. Maybe . . .

(PAMELA'S *voice cries out as though startled.)*

HADLEY: I *beg* your pardon, miss. It's so dark here I didn't see you.

PAMELA *(tense but composed):* That's quite all right. But would you mind letting me through the gate, please?

DR. FELL: Do you by any chance want to go in and see Mr. Pendleton?

PAMELA *(surprised):* Yes, of course. I . . . why do you ask that?

DR. FELL: I ask because my friend here is Superintendent Hadley from Scotland Yard . . .

PAMELA *(startled):* Scotland Yard?

DR. FELL: And I am Dr. Gideon Fell, an old scatter-brain occasionally found where there's trouble.

PAMELA: I'm Pamela Bennett. Mr. Pendleton's secretary. I came here because of Mrs. Tancred. She phoned the office today. She said Mr. Pendleton had gone rushing out last night, leaving his suitcases and everything else in the house and hadn't been back since. He hasn't been in touch with the office, either. Mr. Fraser was worried. He asked me if I'd come round here, and . . . Mr. Pendleton *is* all right, isn't he?

DR. FELL: I very much fear he isn't.

HADLEY: Don't talk nonsense, Fell!

DR. FELL: It may *be* nonsense, of course. I've talked a lot of it in my time. But let's go in and see him, Hadley. Let's face the powers of darkness in their lair. Let's open the gate . . .

(Metallic creaking of the gate. Then WILMOT *speaks: a soft, insinuating, well-bred voice. He is in his middle twenties and speaks as one trying to be agreeable.)*

WILMOT: If I were you, gentlemen, *I* shouldn't touch that gate.

PAMELA *(crying out):* Who spoke then? *(No reply, except the whistling of the wind)* I heard somebody! Who was it?

WILMOT: You heard *me,* young lady. I'm inside the gate; you're outside. Let's leave it at that.

HADLEY *(exasperated):* Look here, young fellow, what's going on in this place? Who *are* you?

WILMOT: My name is Wilmot. I turn an electric torch round and . . . notice my chauffeur's uniform. Also notice the rifle in my other hand.

HADLEY: I'm a police officer, cocky. What's the idea of the rifle?

WILMOT: The governor's orders are to patrol these grounds and make sure nobody gets in. I'm doing it.

HADLEY: And has anybody got in?

WILMOT: No. Not a living soul.

DR. FELL: That's an interesting choice of phrase, young man. If you're Mr. Pendleton's chauffeur . . .

WILMOT: Such is my humble position, Dr. Fell.

DR. FELL *(sharply):* You know who I am?

WILMOT: As a matter of fact, I just recognized you. I drove the boss to your house tonight. *Is* this man here a police officer?

DR. FELL: Yes. And the young lady beside me is Mr. Pendleton's secretary.

WILMOT: Excuse me if I didn't recognize her. I haven't been on this job very long.

PAMELA: Mr. Pendleton is all right, isn't he?

WILMOT: He couldn't be in a happier state. I drove him to Dr. Fell's; I brought him back safely; I delivered him to the mercies of Mrs. Tancred; I went down the street to put the car away . . .

DR. FELL: If you went to put the car away, how can you be sure nobody's got in?

WILMOT *(sharply):* It's impossible!

DR. FELL: Why?

WILMOT: That was half an hour ago!

DR. FELL: He could have died half an hour ago.

PAMELA: Don't *say* that!

WILMOT *(quickly):* His nibs was upset about something; I'll give you that. He went lurching up the path talking to himself, and Mrs. Tancred couldn't do anything with him.

DR. FELL: What was he talking to himself about?

WILMOT: *I* don't know. Some woman or other. He said he was going to ring her up and dare her to come back again.

DR. FELL *(quietly)*: Look here, Hadley. We've *got* to go up there now.

HADLEY: But what in blazes do you think is wrong? He couldn't have been attacked without an outcry. And there hasn't been a sound. Look at this place. Only that little light from the library. Dark, silent, and peaceful as the gra— *(A woman's distant scream, very shrill)* What was that?

PAMELA: It sounded like a woman's voice!

DR. FELL *(grimly)*: Would anybody like to bet it isn't Mrs. Tancred?

PAMELA: Look! It *is* Mrs. Tancred! She's coming out of that open French window, and she looks . . .

MRS. TANCRED *(calling)*: Wilmot! Wilmot! Wilmot!

WILMOT *(calling)*: I'm here, Mrs. Tancred! Out by the gate!

(MRS. TANCRED *is almost hysterically frightened, but trying to be steady.*)

MRS. TANCRED: He said he didn't want any sympathy. All right! He won't *get* any sympathy. Just as though a body didn't try to do the best she could every single day of her life, and . . . and . . . for God's sake, get a doctor!

WILMOT: You don't mean it's the governor?

MRS. TANCRED: "If ever I need any sympathy for my unhappy lot" . . . that's just what he said . . . "I'll ask for it." All right! Let him try to ask for it *now*, and see if anybody cares!

HADLEY: What is it, ma'am? What's wrong?

MRS. TANCRED: It's murder, that's what it is! He's lying on the floor in the library with the telephone beside him. His face is an awful colour, and I don't think he's breathing.

WILMOT: There hasn't been a sound out of that house. I swear there hasn't!

MRS. TANCRED: No, of course there wasn't a sound. All I did was go in and ask him if he wanted some coffee. And there he was in a dim little ugly light, with his face as blue as though he'd had a stroke . . .

HADLEY: As though he'd had a stroke, eh? Then what's all this about murder?

MRS. TANCRED: I tell you, his face . . . ! And then there's the clay tracked across the floor from the window to where he's lying. There's even wet clay on Mr. Pendleton, as though . . .

HADLEY: As though . . . what?

MRS. TANCRED *(slowly)*: As though somebody covered with clay had tried to hold him.

(Music up and down. A door opens.)

DR. FELL *(musing):* And this, apparently, is the famous library. This is the place where bogies walk and a telephone talks of its own accord.

PAMELA *(urgently):* Dr. Fell! Please!

DR. FELL: "From the hag and the hungry goblin

That into rags would rend ye:

And the spirit that stands by the evil lands

In the book of moons . . . defend ye!"

(Waking up) Er . . . I beg your pardon. What's that?

PAMELA: Dr. Fell, you've got to tell me. Is he . . . dead?

DR. FELL: No, Miss Bennett. He's not dead. Hadley and Wilmot have carried him upstairs. He's had a bad heart attack. But I'm afraid he'll pull through.

PAMELA *(surprised):* You're *afraid* he'll pull through?

DR. FELL: If Mr. George Pendleton has got a soul, it must be a pretty shabby one. *(Casually)* Don't you think so?

PAMELA *(hesitating):* I didn't exactly like him, no. But you get *used* to a person, I suppose. I shouldn't like to think he was . . .

DR. FELL: Haunted to death?

(Gust of wind rises strongly. Wooden noise suggesting flapping of window.)

DR. FELL: Don't be frightened, Miss Bennett. It's only the French window banging.

PAMELA: I'm not frightened. At least . . . not much. What did you mean by "haunted to death"?

DR. FELL *(unheeding):* There's the claw-footed desk. There's the Venetian mirror where his own reflection scared him. There's the famous telephone. There's the line of clay marks. There's the whole show-piece of death and terror, my dear.

PAMELA *(more loudly):* What did you mean by "haunted to death"?

DR. FELL: Just that, my dear. Literally that.

PAMELA: You mean he's been haunted by—by a dead person?

DR. FELL: Oh, no. Not at all. I mean he's been haunted by a very much living person.

PAMELA: Dr. Fell!

DR. FELL *(musingly):* What's your opinion of Mrs. Tancred, by the way? With her demure grey hair and her great devotion?

PAMELA: What on earth has Mrs. Tancred got to do with this? Or Wilmot or anybody here?

DR. FELL *(with lordly effect):* "I can call spirits from the vasty deep." "Ay, but will they come, if you do call them?" *(Changing his tone, distressed)* Especially by telephone. Oh, my eye! Surely it's plain that some person . . . one single person . . . has been trying to scare that man out of his wits? Don't you see now what happened here tonight?

PAMELA: No, I don't think I do.

DR. FELL: As Pendleton sat here in the dim little ugly light, a ghostly figure appeared at that French window. It wore long old-fashioned skirts and a heavy black veil. It walked towards him, tracking graveyard clay. It stretched out its arms to him, like this . . .

 **Suspicions?**

What do you think has happened, and whom do you suspect to be behind it all and why?

PAMELA: Dr. Fell, please keep away from me! You look . . .

DR. FELL: Forgive me. I was *(clearing his throat)* carried away. *(Pause)* Would you care to hear how the whole trick was worked?

PAMELA: Trick! What trick?

DR. FELL: Has anyone told you about the ghost-voice on the disconnected telephone?

PAMELA: Yes, Mrs. Tancred was gabbling something about it. But ...

DR. FELL: Suppose you ask, as Pendleton did, to have a telephone disconnected. They disconnect it at the Central Exchange. If you're leaving the house, they come round and collect it later. But, my dear Miss Bennett, I'll tell you what they *don't* do.

PAMELA: Well?

DR. FELL: They don't send a man round to yank the whole apparatus off the wall, put it on the desk, and say he'll be back for it next day. That's obvious nonsense.

PAMELA: You mean Mrs. Tancred wasn't telling the truth when she said that?

DR. FELL: Oh, no. She was telling the truth. But this "man from the telephone company" was an imposter.

PAMELA: The man from the telephone company . . . who was he?

DR. FELL: Can't you guess?

PAMELA: No, I don't think so. What did he do?

DR. FELL: He took away the real phone and substituted a "spirit telephone." You don't know what a "spirit telephone" is?

PAMELA: No, of course not.

DR. FELL: It's an old device used by fake spiritualists. You see a telephone, without wires, standing on a desk. Like that one on the floor now. You lift the receiver and talk to the dead. Of course, you never really talk into the phone at all.

PAMELA: But if you don't really talk into the phone, then how . . . ?

DR. FELL: Fixed underneath the desk is a tiny two-button microphone, with hidden wires leading to another room in the same house. The microphone under the desk picks up every word you think you're saying to that telephone. Am I clear?

PAMELA: Yes, I think so.

DR. FELL: The dummy telephone contains a low-power radio receiving unit. Somebody in another room can talk back to you, with every possible ghostly effect . . . Would you mind picking up the telephone now?

PAMELA: You don't mean it works now?

DR. FELL: Oh, no. It's been changed. Just pick it up.

PAMELA: All right. There you are.

DR. FELL: If Pendleton hadn't rung Kensal Green 1-9-3-3, then rest assured that same number would have rung *him*.

PAMELA: The scheme couldn't fail either way?

DR. FELL: Correct.

PAMELA *(tensely):* The ghost-voice, you said, came from a room in this house?

DR. FELL: Yes. I can't tell you which one, because the mechanism's been removed.

PAMELA: Then the person responsible for it must *live* in this house.

DR. FELL: Not necessarily. You see, there's one thing I guess . . . I firmly believe . . . but I can't prove.

PAMELA: Oh? And what's that?

DR. FELL: Tell me, Miss Bennett, just *why* did you work this whole trick? Why did you try to scare your father to death? *(Crash of an object dropped on the floor;* DR. FELL *continues mildly.)* Don't drop the telephone, my dear. Pendleton surely *is* your father, isn't he? And the late Mary Ellen Kimball was your mother?

PAMELA *(through her teeth):* I do not like you, Doctor Fell. The reason why I cannot tell . . .

DR. FELL *(heartily):* Now I, on the other hand, admire you tremendously. *(Deprecating)* But my dear girl, hang it all, I knew you must be behind this when I heard your fiancé is a radio technician.

PAMELA: You leave Frank out of this!

DR. FELL: This fiancé, I imagine, installed the ghost-mechanism and took it away today. He probably thought it was only a joke.

PAMELA: He did! I swear he did!

DR. FELL: There was surely a reason, you see, why Mary Ellen Kimball called herself Mrs. Kimball. *You* led Pendleton to the wrong gate in the cemetery, past that neglected grave. *You* put it into his mind. *You* suggested the telephone number. *You* stole his latchkey to this house, since he had it at the office that morning. You needed that key to come and go as you liked and impersonate the two voices on the phone. Then when you were ready for your last appearance tonight . . .

PAMELA *(fiercely):* Is there any need to go on with this? He killed her.

DR. FELL *(startled):* You mean Pendleton killed your mother?

PAMELA: Oh, not cleanly. Not with a knife or a bullet or poison. All he did was break her heart and leave her to starve.

DR. FELL: Did he know about you?

PAMELA: He knew there *was* a child; that's all.

DR. FELL: Yes, I thought he knew it.

PAMELA: But she was too proud to ask for anything. And he *(mimicking)* "had other things to think about." I think I've dreamed all my life of getting close to him, one day, when he didn't know who I was.

DR. FELL: For the love of Mike, go easy! If somebody should come in here now . . .

PAMELA: I've done what I wanted to do. I've torn his whole rotten life in pieces; and there he is gasping for breath upstairs; and I'm glad! I'm . . . *(Breaking down)* Oh, God, I can't go on with this! Call your superintendent and give the game away. *I'm* not sorry!

DR. FELL *(amazed):* Just one moment. Hey! You don't think *I'm* going to tell Hadley anything?

PAMELA *(taken aback):* Aren't you? Isn't that why you're here?

DR. FELL: On the contrary, I've been trying to keep the police away from this house all evening.

PAMELA: What's the good of trying to hide it, even if I wanted to? *They'll* find out!

DR. FELL: Are you quite sure they'll find out?

PAMELA: Look at the clay marks on the floor.

DR. FELL: Those footprints can't be identified, you know. They're only smudges.

PAMELA: I think I can hear somebody outside in the hall. If it's Superintendent Hadley . . .

DR. FELL *(grimly):* If it is, my dear, and you dare to say one word about this . . .

PAMELA: Then who made the footprints?

DR. FELL *(blandly):* Didn't you know? Why, Pendleton made them himself.

PAMELA: What on earth are you talking about?

DR. FELL: Hadley thinks the esteemed gentleman is mad. Obviously, of course, he is mad. He kept dashing to that window on the lookout for a pursuing ghost. So he tracked in clay soil from the garden, and collapsed here when he heard an imaginary noise.

PAMELA: But his shoes! There'll be no clay on his shoes!

DR. FELL: Oh, yes, there will. Please remember that the gentleman didn't come home last night or take a suitcase with him. His shoes, if I'm not mistaken, will still bear excellent traces of the clay he really did get yesterday in Kensal Green cemetery. *(Complacently)* I often think that I should have made an admirable criminal myself.

HADLEY *(from a distance):* Dr. Fell! Dr. Fell! Where are you?

DR. FELL *(galvanized):* There's Hadley now! If you don't keep your head and brace up, I'll come and haunt you myself. Don't turn on the tears now, when you've come through all the rest of it with a poker face. Just keep repeating after me, "I do not like you, Doctor Fell . . . "

(Door opens.)

HADLEY: Look here, my fat detective; there's been no crime committed in this place. Pendleton's own shoes . . .

DR. FELL *(loudly):* Oh, Miss Bennett, what were you saying?

PAMELA *(hysterically):* Nothing! Nothing at . . .

DR. FELL *(reciting, still more loudly):* I do not like you, Doctor Fell, the reason why I cannot tell . . .

PAMELA *(almost crying):* But this I know, and know full well . . . I think *I like you,* Dr. Fell!

(Music up.)

 How Clever?

1. Find the earliest indication in the play that George Pendleton's mental condition has been seriously affected by his experience in Kensal Green cemetery.

2. Explain how the stage direction for the actress portraying Pamela Bennett on p. 378 is an important one if the audience is to later suspect Pamela. Compare this stage direction with the one for Pamela's tone of voice on p. 389. What is the significance of the change?

3. How is the exchange of dialogue between Pendleton and Pamela (beginning with "Mr. Pendleton, are you sure . . . ?" and ending with "No, sir. I said") a clue to how Pamela has manipulated Pendleton's actions and his mental state?

4. What significance is there to Pendleton's mentioning to Mrs. Tancred (and indirectly to the audience) that it seems he has mislaid his latchkey?

5. How does the exchange of dialogue between Mrs. Tancred and Mr. Pendleton on p. 380–381 serve as a red herring (false clue)? Another convention of the mystery genre is that whenever an author makes use of a red herring, he or she must play fair with the reader. Explain why you think the author is or is not playing fair with the reader in his use of this particular red herring.

6. Do you consider the exchange of dialogue between Dr. Fell and Mr. Pendleton about Pendleton's chauffeur to be a red herring? Explain why or why not. If you believe the details of the conversation to be a red herring, was this red herring a fair one? Explain.

7. Explain why Pamela tried to haunt her father to death.

8. Why did Dr. Fell think that Mr. Pendleton had known about Mary Ellen Kimball's child?

9. Why does Dr. Fell want Pamela to keep repeating "I do not like you, Dr. Fell"? Why does the play end with Pamela's saying "I think *I like you*, Dr. Fell"?

10. How do you feel about the fact that the criminal in this story gets away with her crime? Explain why you feel the way you do.

DETECTWRITE: Dialogue and Setting

1. Re-read Mrs. Tancred's dialogue that explains why and how Mr. Pendleton's telephone was disconnected. Do you feel that in this piece of dialogue the playwright tells the audience just enough to serve as a real clue without telling so much as to make it too obvious? Explain why.

2. Did you feel in your reading of the play that John Dickson Carr presented a particular red herring in a way that was unfair to the reader trying to solve the case? If so, rewrite the dialogue so that it still contains the same red herring and yet is expressed in a fair way.

3. Create an exchange of dialogue between two characters for a projected detective story of your own in which you make use of a red herring. Then, in a separate paragraph, explain the red herring and tell why you think it is both effective and fair to the reader.

4. Choose a scene from the play and rewrite the dialogue (staying true to the plot of the story) so that the play sounds like the scene is set in contemporary America rather than in London in 1933.

DETECTWRITE: Characterization

1. Compare the characterization of the somewhat absent-minded Dr. Fell with other detectives that you have met in this collection. (In addition to Dr. Fell's actions and dialogue throughout the play, review the narrator's dialogue at the very beginning of the play.) To indirectly meet Dr. Fell in another story, read "The Man Who Read John Dickson Carr" in the "You, Sherlock" section of this text.

2. Do Dr. Fell's traits strike you as less likely to be those of an American detective and more likely to be those of a British one? Explain why you do or do not think so.

3. Compare and contrast Dr. Gideon Fell with the most renowned British detective, Sherlock Holmes. Which of the two seems more "heart and brain" than just "brain"? Explain.

DETECTWRITE: Creating a Title for Your Story

1. The title of this story appears in the voice's dialogue on p. 382. Explain how it fits both the plot and characterization of the story.

2. Make up a title for a projected detective story of your own and explain what it is you like about your title. Get feedback from others on their opinion of the appeal of your title.

The Bearded Lady

Ellery Queen

$\mathbf{M}$R. PHINEAS MASON, ATTORNEY-AT-LAW—OF THE RICHLY, almost indigestibly respectable firm of Dowling, Mason & Coolidge, 40 Park Row—was a very un-Phineaslike gentleman with a chunky nose and wrinkle-bedded eyes which had seen thirty years of harassing American litigation and looked as if they had seen a hundred. He sat stiffly in the lap of a chauffeur-driven limousine, his mouth making interesting sounds.

"And now," he said in an angry voice, "there's actually been murder done. I can't imagine what the world is coming to."

Mr. Ellery Queen, watching the world rush by in a glaring Long Island sunlight, mused that life was like a Spanish wench: full of surprises, none of them delicate and all of them stimulating. Since he was a monastic who led a riotous mental existence, he liked life that way; and since he was also a detective—an appellation he cordially detested—he got life that way. Nevertheless, he did not vocalize his reflections: Mr. Phineas Mason did not appear the sort who would appreciate fleshy metaphor.

He drawled: "The world's all right; the trouble is the people in it. Suppose you tell me what you can about these curious Shaws. After all, you know, I shan't be too heartily received by your local Long Island constabulary; and since I foresee difficulties, I should like to be forearmed as well."

Mason frowned. "But McC. assured me—"

"Oh, bother J.J.! He has vicarious delusions of grandeur. Let me warn you now, Mr. Mason, that I shall probably be a dismal flop. I don't go about pulling murderers out of my hat. And with your Cossacks trampling the evidence—"

"I warned them," said Mason fretfully. "I spoke to Captain Murch myself when he telephoned this morning to inform me of the crime." He made a sour face. "They won't even move the body, Mr. Queen. I wield—ah—a little local influence, you see."

"Indeed," said Ellery, adjusting his *pince-nez;* and he sighed. "Very well, Mr. Mason. Proceed with the dreary details."

"It was my partner, Coolidge," began the attorney in a pained voice, "who originally handled Shaw's affairs. John A. Shaw, the millionaire. Before your time, I daresay. Shaw's first wife died in childbirth in 1895. The child—Agatha; she's a divorcee now, with a son of eight—of course survived her mother; and there was one previous child, named after his father. John's forty-five now . . . At any rate, old John Shaw remarried soon after his first wife's death, and then shortly after his second marriage died himself. This second wife, Maria Paine Shaw, survived her husband by a little more than thirty years. She died only a month ago."

"A plethora of mortalities," murmured Ellery, lighting a cigarette. "So far, Mr. Mason, a prosaic tale. And what has the Shaw history to do—"

"Patience," sighed Mason. "Now old John Shaw bequeathed his entire fortune to this second wife, Maria. The two children, John and Agatha, got nothing, not even trusts; I suppose old Shaw trusted Maria to take care of them."

"I scent the usual story," yawned Ellery. "She didn't? No go between stepmother and acquired progeny?"

The lawyer wiped his brow. "It was horrible. They fought for thirty years like—like savages. I will say, in extenuation of Mrs. Shaw's conduct, that she had provocation. John's always been a shiftless, unreliable beggar: disrespectful, profligate, quite vicious. Nevertheless she's treated him well in money matters. As I said, he's forty-five now; and he hasn't done a lick of work in his life. He's a drunkard, too."

"Sounds charming. And Sister Agatha, the divorcee?"

"A feminine edition of her brother. She married a fortune-hunter as worthless as herself; when he found out she was penniless he deserted her and Mrs. Shaw managed to get her a quiet divorce. She took Agatha and her boy, Peter, into her house and they've been living there ever since, at daggers' points. Please forgive the—ah—brutality of the characterizations; I want you to know these people as they are."

"We're almost intimate already," chuckled Ellery.

"John and Agatha," continued Mason, biting the head of his cane, "have been living for only one event—their stepmother's death. So that they might inherit, of course. Until a certain occurrence a few months ago Mrs. Shaw's will provided generously for them. But when that happened—"

Mr. Ellery Queen narrowed his gray eyes. "You mean—?"

"It's complicated," sighed the lawyer. "Three months ago there was an attempt on the part of someone in the household to poison the old lady!"

"Ah!"

"The attempt was unsuccessful only because Dr. Arlen—Dr. Terence Arlen is the full name—had suspected such a possibility for years and had kept his eyes open. The cyanide—it was put in her tea—didn't reach Mrs. Shaw but killed a house-cat. None of us, of course, knew who had made the poisoning attempt. But after that Mrs. Shaw changed her will."

"Now," muttered Ellery, "I *am* enthralled. Arlen, eh? That creates a fascinating mess. Tell me about Arlen, please."

"Rather mysterious old man with two passions: devotion to Mrs. Shaw and a hobby of painting. Quite an artist, too, though I know little about such things. He lived in the Shaw house about twenty years. Medico Mrs. Shaw picked up somewhere; I think only she knew his story, and he's always been silent about his past. She put him on a generous salary to live in the house and act as the family physician; I suspect it was rather because she anticipated what her stepchildren might attempt. And then too it's always seemed to me that Arlen accepted this unusual arrangement so tractably in order to pass out of—ah—circulation."

They were silent for some time. The chauffeur swung the car off the main artery into a narrow macadam road. Mason breathed heavily.

"I suppose you're satisfied," murmured Ellery at last through a fat smoke-ring, "that Mrs. Shaw died a month ago of natural causes?"

"Heavens, yes!" cried Mason. "Dr. Arlen wouldn't trust his own judgment, we were so careful; he had several specialists in, before and after her death. But she died of the last of a series of heart-attacks; she was an old woman, you know. Something-thrombosis, they called it." Mason looked gloomy. "Well, you can understand Mrs. Shaw's natural reaction to the poisoning episode. 'If they're so depraved,' she told me shortly after, 'that they'd attempt my *life*, they don't deserve any consideration at my *hands*.' And she had me draw up a new will, cutting both of them off without a cent."

"There's an epigram," chuckled Ellery, "worthy of a better cause."

Mason tapped on the glass. "Faster, Burroughs." The car jolted ahead. "In looking about for a beneficiary, Mrs. Shaw finally remembered that there was someone to whom she could leave the Shaw fortune without feeling that she was casting it to the winds. Old John Shaw had had an elder brother, Morton, a widower with two grown children. The brothers quarrelled violently and Morton moved to England. He lost most of his money there; his two children, Edith and Percy, were left to shift for themselves when he committed suicide."

"These Shaws seem to have a penchant for violence."

"I suppose it's in the blood. Well, Edith and Percy both had talent of a sort, I understand, and they went on the London stage in a brother-and-sister music-hall act, managing well enough. Mrs. Shaw decided to leave her money to this Edith, her niece. I made inquiries by correspondence and discovered that Edith Shaw was now Mrs. Edythe Royce, a childless widow of many years' standing. On Mrs. Shaw's decease I cabled her and she crossed by the next boat. According to Mrs. Royce, Percy—her brother—was killed in an automobile accident on the Continent a few months before; so she had no ties whatever."

"And the will—specifically?"

"It's rather queer," sighed Mason. "The Shaw estate was enormous at one time, but the depression whittled it down to about three hundred thousand dollars. Mrs. Shaw left her niece two hundred thousand outright. The remainder, to his astonishment," and Mason paused and eyed his tall young companion with a curious fixity, "was put in trust for Dr. Arlen."

"Arlen!"

"He was not to touch the principal, but was to receive the income from it for the remainder of his life. Interesting, eh?"

"That's putting it mildly. By the way, Mr. Mason, I'm a suspicious bird. This Mrs. Royce—you're satisfied she *is* a Shaw?"

The lawyer started; then he shook his head. "No, no, Queen, that's the wrong tack. There can be absolutely no question about it. In the first place she possesses the marked facial characteristics of the Shaws; you'll see for yourself; although I will say that she's rather—well, rather a character, rather a character! She came armed with intimate possessions of her father, Morton Shaw; and I myself, in company with Coolidge, questioned her closely on her arrival. She convinced us utterly, from her knowledge of *minutiae* about her father's life and Edith Shaw's childhood in America—knowledge impossible for an outsider to have acquired—that she is Edith Shaw. We were more than cautious, I assure you; especially since neither John nor Agatha had seen her since childhood."

"Just a thought." Ellery leaned forward. "And what was to be the disposition of Arlen's hundred-thousand-dollar trust on Arlen's death?"

The lawyer gazed grimly at the two rows of prim poplars flanking a manicured driveway on which the limousine was now noiselessly treading. "It was to be equally divided between John and Agatha," he said in a careful voice. The car rolled to a stop under a coldly white *porte-cochère*.

"I see," said Ellery. For it was Dr. Terence Arlen who had been murdered.

A county trooper escorted them through high Colonial halls into a remote and silent wing of the ample old house, up a staircase to a dim cool corridor patrolled by a nervous man with a bull neck.

"Oh, Mr. Mason," he said eagerly, coming forward. "We've been waiting for you. This is Mr. Queen?" His tone changed from unguent haste to abrasive suspicion.

"Yes, yes. Murch of the county detectives, Mr. Queen. You've left everything intact, Murch?"

The detective grunted and stepped aside. Ellery found himself in the study of what appeared to be a two-room suite; beyond an open door he could see the white counterpane of a bird's-eye-maple four-poster. A hole at some remote period had been hacked through the ceiling and covered with glass, admitting sunlight and converting the room into a sky-light studio. The trivia of a painter's paraphernalia lay in confusion about the room, overpowering the few medical implements. There were easels, paintboxes, a small dais, carelessly draped smocks, a profusion of daubs in oils and watercolors on the walls.

A little man was kneeling beside the outstretched figure of the dead doctor—a long brittle figure frozen in death, capped with curiously lambent silver hair. The wound was frank and deep: the delicately chased haft of a stiletto protruded from the man's heart. There was very little blood.

Murch snapped: "Well, Doc, anything else?"

The little man rose and put his instruments away. "Died instantly from the stab-wound. Frontal blow, as you see. He tried to dodge at the last instant, I should say, but wasn't quick enough." He nodded and reached for his hat and quietly went out.

Ellery shivered a little. The studio was silent, and the corridor was silent, and the wing was silent; the whole house was crushed under the weight of a terrific silence that was almost uncanny. There was something indescribably evil in the air . . . He shook his shoulders impatiently. "The stiletto, Captain Murch. Have you identified it?"

"Belonged to Arlen. Always right here on this table."

"No possibility of suicide, I suppose."

"Not a chance, Doc said."

Mr. Phineas Mason made a retching sound. "If you want me, Queen—" He stumbled from the room, awakening dismal echoes.

The corpse was swathed in a paint-smudged smock above pajamas; in the stiff right hand a paint-brush, its hairs stained jet-black, was still clutched. A color-splashed palette had fallen face down on the floor near him . . . Ellery did not raise his eyes from the stiletto. "Florentine, I suppose. Tell me what you've learned so far, Captain," he said absently. "I mean about the crime itself."

"Damned little," growled the detective. "Doc says he was killed about two in the morning—about eight hours ago. His body was found at seven this a.m. by a woman named Krutch, a nurse in the house here for a couple of years. Nice wench, by God! Nobody's got an alibi for the time of the murder, because according to their yarns they were all sleeping, and they all sleep separately. That's about the size of it."

"Precious little, to be sure," murmured Ellery. "By the way, Captain, was it Dr. Arlen's custom to paint in the wee hours?"

"Seems so. I thought of that, too. But he was a queer old cuss and when he was hot on something he'd work for twenty-four hours at a clip."

"Do the others sleep in this wing?"

"Nope. Not even the servants. Seems Arlen liked privacy, and whatever he liked the old dame—Mrs. Shaw, who kicked off a month ago—said 'jake' to." Murch went to the doorway and snapped: "Miss Krutch."

She came slowly out of Dr. Arlen's bedroom—a tall fair young woman who had been weeping. She was in nurse's uniform and there was nothing in common between her name and her appearance. In fact, as Ellery observed with appreciation, she was a distinctly attractive young woman with curves in precisely the right places. Miss Krutch, despite her tears, was the first ray of sunshine he had encountered in the big old house.

"Tell Mr. Queen what you told me," directed Murch curtly.

"But there's so little," she quavered. "I was up before seven, as usual. My room's in the main wing, but there's a storeroom here for linen and things . . . As I passed I—I saw Dr. Arlen lying on the floor, with the knife sticking up— The door was open and the light was on. I screamed. No one heard me. This is so far away . . . I screamed and screamed and then Mr. Shaw came running, and Miss Shaw. Th-that's all."

"Did any of you touch the body, Miss Krutch?"

"Oh, no, sir!" She shivered.

"I see," said Ellery, and raised his eyes from the dead man to the easel above, casually, and looked away. And then instantly he looked back, his nerves tingling. Murch watched him with a sneer.

"How," jeered Murch, "d'ye like that, *Mr.* Queen?"

Ellery sprang forward. A smaller easel near the large one supported a picture. It was a cheap "processed" oil painting, a commercial copy of Rembrandt's famous self-portrait group, *The Artist and His Wife.* Rembrandt himself sat in the foreground, and his wife stood in the background. The canvas on the large easel was a half-finished replica of this painting. Both figures had been completely sketched in by Dr. Arlen and brushwork begun: the lusty smiling mustached artist in his gayly plumed hat, his left arm about the waist of his Dutch-garbed wife.

👁 Suspicions?

What do you think county detective Murch's notion is? What would your notion be at this point in the story and why?

And on the woman's chin there was painted a beard.

Ellery gaped from the processed picture to Dr. Arlen's copy. But the one showed a woman's smooth chin, and the other—the doctor's—a squarish, expertly stroked black beard. And yet it had been daubed in hastily, as if the old painter had been working against time.

"Good heavens!" exclaimed Ellery, glaring. "That's insane!"

"Think so?" said Murch blandly. "Me, I don't know. I've got a notion about it." He growled at Miss Krutch: "Beat it," and she fled from the studio, her long legs twinkling.

Ellery shook his head dazedly and sank into a chair, fumbling for a cigarette. "That's a new wrinkle to me, Captain. First time I've ever encountered in a homicide an example of the beard-and-mustache school of art—you've seen the pencilled hair on the faces of men and women in billboard advertisements? It's—" and then his eyes narrowed as something leaped into them and he said abruptly: "Is Miss Agatha Shaw's boy—that Peter—in the house?"

Murch, smiling secretly as if he were enjoying a huge jest, went to the hallway door and roared something. Ellery got out of the chair and ran across the room and returned with one of the smocks, which he flung over the dead man's body.

A small boy with frightened yet inquisitive eyes came slowly into the room, followed by one of the most remarkable creatures Ellery had ever seen. This apparition was a large stout woman of perhaps sixty, with lined rugged features—so heavy they were almost wattled—painted, bedaubed, and varnished with an astounding cosmetic technique. Her lips, gross as they were, were shaped by rouge into a perfect and obscene cupid's-bow; her eyebrows had been tweezed to incredible thinness; round rosy spots punctuated her sagging cheeks; and the whole rough heavy skin was floury with white powder.

But her costume was even more amazing than her face. For she was rigged out in Victorian style—a tight-waisted garment, almost bustle-hipped, full wide shirts that reached to her thick ankles, a deep and shiny bosom, and an elaborate boned lace choker-collar . . . And then Ellery remembered that, since this must be Edythe Shaw Royce, there was at least a partial explanation for her eccentric appearance: she was an old woman, she came from England, and she was no doubt still basking in the vanished glow of her girlhood theatrical days.

"Mrs. Royce," said Murch mockingly, "*and* Peter."

"How d'ye do," muttered Ellery, tearing his eyes away. "Uh—Peter."

The boy, a sharp-featured and skinny little creature, sucked his dirty forefinger and stared.

"Peter!" said Mrs. Royce severely. Her voice was quite in tune with her appearance: deep and husky and slightly cracked. Even her hair, Ellery noted with a wince, was nostalgic—a precise deep brown, frankly dyed. Here was one female, at least, who did not mean to yield to old age without a determined struggle, he thought. "He's frightened. Peter!"

"Ma'am," mumbled Peter, still staring.

"Peter," said Ellery, "look at that picture." Peter did so, reluctantly. "Did you put that beard on the face of the lady in the picture, Peter?"

Peter shrank against Mrs. Royce's voluminous skirts. "N-no!"

"Curious, isn't it?" said Mrs. Royce cheerfully. "I was remarking about that to Captain Burch—Murch only this morning. I'm sure Peter would-n't have drawn the beard on *that* one. He'd learned his lesson, hadn't you, Peter?" Ellery remarked with alarm that the extraordinary woman kept screwing her right eyebrow up and drawing it deeply down, as if there were something in her eye that bothered her.

"Ah," said Ellery. "Lesson?"

"You see," went on Mrs. Royce, continuing her ocular gymnastics with unconscious vigor, "it was only yesterday that Peter's mother caught him drawing a beard with chalk on one of Dr. Arlen's paintings in Peter's bedroom. Dr. Arlen gave him a round hiding, I'm afraid, and himself removed the chalk-marks. Dear Agatha was *so* angry with poor Dr. Arlen. So you didn't do it, did you, Peter?"

"Naw," said Peter, who had become fascinated by the bulging smock on the floor.

"Dr. Arlen, eh?" muttered Ellery. "Thank you," and he began to pace up and down as Mrs. Royce took Peter by the arm and firmly removed him from the studio. A formidable lady, he thought, with her vigorous room-shaking tread. And he recalled that she wore flat-heeled shoes and had, from the ugly swelling of the leather, great bunions.

"Come on," said Murch suddenly, going to the door.

"Where?"

"Downstairs." The detective signalled a trooper to guard the studio and led the way. "I want to show you," he said as they made for the main part of the house, "the reason for the beard on that dame-in-the-picture's jaw."

"Indeed?" murmured Ellery, and said nothing more. Murch paused in the doorway of a pale Colonial livingroom and jerked his head.

Ellery looked in. A hollow-chested, cadaverous man in baggy tweeds sat slumped in a Cogswell chair staring at an empty glass in his hand, which was shaking. His eyes were yellow-balled and shot with blood, and his loose skin was a web of red veins.

"That," said Murch contempuously and yet with a certain triumph, "is Mr. John Shaw."

Ellery noted that Shaw possessed the same heavy features, the same fat lips and rock-hewn nose, as the wonderful Mrs. Royce, his cousin; and for that matter, as the dour and annoyed-looking old pirate in the portrait over the fireplace who was presumably his father.

And Ellery also noted that on Mr. John Shaw's unsteady chin there was a bedraggled, pointed beard.

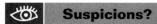 **Suspicions?**

Do you suspect Mr. John Shaw, Jr. in the death of Dr. Arlen because on Shaw's chin "there was a bedraggled, pointed beard"? Why or why not?

Mr. Mason, a bit greenish about the jowls, was waiting for them in a sombre reception-room. "Well?" he asked in a whisper, like a supplicant before the Cumæan Sibyl.

"Captain Murch," murmured Ellery, "has a theory."

The detective scowled. "Plain as day. It's John Shaw. It's my hunch Dr. Arlen painted that beard as a clue to his killer. The only one around here with a beard is Shaw. It ain't evidence, I admit, but it's something to work on. And believe you me," he said with a snap of his brown teeth, "I'm going to work on it!"

"John," said Mason slowly. "He certainly has motive. And yet I find it difficult to . . ." His shrewd eyes flickered. "Beard? What beard?"

"There's a beard painted on the chin of a female face upstairs," drawled Ellery, "the face being on a Rembrandt Arlen was copying at the time he was murdered. That the good doctor painted the beard himself is quite evident. It's expertly stroked, done in black oils, and in his dead hand there's still the brush tipped with black oils. There isn't any one else in the house who paints, is there?"

"No," said Mason uncomfortably.

"*Voila.*"

"But even if Arlen did such a—a mad thing," objected the lawyer, "how do you know it was just before he was attacked?"

"Aw," growled Murch, "when the hell else would it be?"

"Now, now, Captain," murmured Ellery, "let's be scientific. There's a perfectly good answer to your question, Mr. Mason. First, we all agree that Dr. Arlen couldn't have painted the beard after he was attacked; he died instantly. Therefore, he must have painted it before he was attacked. The question is: How long before? Well, why did Arlen paint the beard at all?"

"Murch says as a clue to his murderer," muttered Mason. "But such a—a fantastic legacy to the police! It looks deucedly odd."

"What's odd about it?"

"Well, for heaven's sake," exploded Mason, "if he wanted to leave a clue to his murderer, why didn't he write the murderer's name on the canvas? He had the brush in his hand . . ."

"Precisely," murmured Ellery. "A very good question, Mr. Mason. Well, why didn't he? If he was alone—that is, if he was *anticipating* his murder—he certainly would have left us a written record of his concrete suspicions. The fact that he left no such record shows that he didn't anticipate his murder before the appearance of his murderer. Therefore, he painted the beard *while his murderer was present.* But now we find an explanation for the painted beard as a clue. With his murderer present, he *couldn't* paint the name; the murderer would have noticed it and destroyed it. Arlen was forced, then, to adopt a subtle means: leave a clue that would escape his killer's attention. Since he was painting at the time, he used a painter's means. Even if his murderer noticed it, he probably ascribed it to Arlen's nervousness; although the chances are he didn't notice it."

Murch stirred. "Say, listen—"

"But a beard on a woman's face," groaned the lawyer. "I tell you—"

"Oh," said Ellery dreamily, "Dr. Arlen had a precedent."

"Precedent?"

"Yes; we've found, Captain Murch and I, that young Peter in his divine innocence had chalked a beard and mustache on one of Dr. Arlen's daubs which hangs in Peter's bedroom. This was only yesterday. Dr. Arlen whaled the tar out of him for this horrible crime *vers l'art*, no doubt justifiably. But Peter's beard-scrawl must have stuck in the doctor's mind; threshing about wildly in his mind while his murderer talked to him, or threatened him, the beard business popped out at him. Apparently he felt that it told a story, because he used it. And there, of course, is the rub."

"I still say it's all perfectly asinine," grunted Mason.

"Not asinine," said Ellery. "Interesting. He painted a beard on the chin of Rembrandt's wife. Why Rembrandt's wife, in the name of all that's wonderful?—a woman dead more than two centuries! These Shaws aren't remote descendants . . ."

"Nuts," said Murch distinctly.

"Nuts," said Ellery, "is a satisfactory word under the circumstances, Captain. Then a grim jest? Hardly. But if it wasn't Dr. Arlen's grisly notion of a joke, what under heaven was it? What did Arlen mean to convey?"

"If it wasn't so ridiculous," muttered the lawyer, "I'd say he was pointing to—Peter."

"Nuts and double-nuts," said Murch, "begging your pardon, Mr. Mason. The kid's the only one, I guess, that's got a real alibi. It seems his mother's nervous about him and she always keeps his door locked from the outside. I found it that way myself this morning. And he couldn't have got out through the window."

"Well, well," sighed Mason, "I'm sure I'm all at sea. John, eh . . . What do *you* think, Mr. Queen?"

> **Suspicions?**
>
> 1. What is your reaction to the reasoning employed by Ellery Queen and to the reasoning of police captain Murch? Whose side in this argument do you find yourself on—and why?
>
> 2. "Apparently," Ellery Queen says, Arlen must have felt that painting the beard on Rembrandt's wife "told a story, because he used it." What story do you think it tells—and why?

"Much as I loathe argument," said Ellery, "I can't agree with Brother Murch."

"Oh, yeah?" jeered Murch. "I suppose you've got reasons?"

"I suppose," said Ellery, "I have; not the least impressive of which is the dissimilar shapes of the real and painted beards."

The detective glowered. "Well, if he didn't mean John Shaw by it, what the hell did he mean?"

Ellery shrugged. "If we knew that, my dear Captain, we should know everything."

"Well," snarled Murch, "I think it's spinach, and I'm going to haul Mr. John Shaw down to county headquarters and pump the old bastard till I *find* it's spinach."

"I shouldn't do that, Murch," said Ellery quickly. "If only for—"

"I know my duty," said the detective with a black look, and he stamped out of the reception-room.

John Shaw, who was quietly drunk, did not even protest when Murch shoved him into the squad car. Followed by the county morgue-truck bearing Dr. Arlen's body, Murch vanished with his prey.

Ellery took a hungry turn about the room, frowning. The lawyer sat in a crouch, gnawing his fingernails. And again the room, and the house, and the very air were charged with silence, an ominous silence.

"Look here," said Ellery sharply, "there's something in this business you haven't told me yet, Mr. Mason."

The lawyer jumped, and then sank back biting his lips. "He's such a worrisome creature," said a cheerful voice from the doorway and they both turned, startled, to find Mrs. Royce beaming in at them. She came in with the stride of a grenadier, her bosom joggling. And she sat down by Mason's side and with daintiness lifted her capacious skirts with both hands a bit above each fat knee. "I know what's troubling you, Mr. Mason!"

The lawyer cleared his throat hastily. "I assure you—"

"Nonsense! I've excellent eyes. Mason, you haven't introduced this nice young man." Mason mumbled something placative. "Queen, is it? Charmed, Mr. Queen. First sample of a reasonably attractive American I've seen since my arrival. I can appreciate a handsome man; I was on the London stage for many years. And really," she thundered in her formidable baritone, "I wasn't so ill-looking myself!"

"I'm sure of that," murmured Ellery. "But what—"

"Mason's afraid for me," said Mrs. Royce with a girlish simper. "A most conscientious barrister! He's simply petrified with fear that whoever did for poor Dr. Arlen will select me as his next victim. And I tell him now, as I told him a few moments ago when you were upstairs with that dreadful Murch person, that for one thing I shan't be such an easy victim—" Ellery could well believe *that*—and for another I don't believe either John or Agatha, which is what's in Mason's mind—don't deny it, Mason!—was responsible for Dr. Arlen's death."

"I never—" began the lawyer feebly.

"Hmm," said Ellery. "What's *your* theory, Mrs. Royce?"

"Some one out of Arlen's past," boomed the lady with a click of her jaws as a punctuation mark. "I understand he came here twenty years ago under most mysterious circumstances. He may have murdered somebody, and that somebody's brother or some one has returned to avenge—"

"Ingenious," grinned Ellery. "As tenable as Murch's, Mr. Mason."

The lady sniffed. "He'll release Cousin John soon enough," she said complacently. "John's stupid enough under ordinary circumstances, you know, but when he's drunk—! There's no evidence, is there? A cigarette if you please, Mr. Queen."

Ellery hastened to offer his case. Mrs. Royce selected a cigarette with a vast paw, smiled roguishly as Ellery held a match, and then withdrew the cigarette and blew smoke, crossing her legs as she did so. She smoked almost in the Russian fashion, cupping her hand about the cigarette instead of holding it between two fingers. A remarkable woman! "Why are you so afraid for Mrs. Royce?" he drawled.

"Well—" Mason hesitated, torn between discretion and desire. "There may have been a double motive for killing Dr. Arlen, you see. That is," he added hurriedly, "*if* Agatha or John had anything to do—"

"Double motive?"

"One, of course, is the conversion of the hundred thousand to Mrs. Shaw's stepchildren, as I told you. The other . . . Well, there is a proviso in connection with the bequest to Dr. Arlen. In return for offering him a home and income for the rest of his life, he was to continue to attend to the medical needs of the family, you see, with *special* attention to Mrs. Royce."

"Poor Aunt Maria," said Mrs. Royce with a tidal sigh. "She must have been a dear, dear person."

"I'm afraid I don't quite follow, Mr. Mason."

"I've a copy of the will in my pocket." The lawyer fished for a crackling document. "Here it is. 'And in particular to conduct monthly medical examinations of my niece, Edith Shaw—or more frequently if Dr. Arlen should deem it necessary—to insure her continued good health; a provision' (mark this, Queen!) '*a provision I am sure my stepchildren will appreciate.*'"

"A cynical addendum," nodded Ellery, blinking a little. "Mrs. Shaw placed on her trusted leech the responsibility for keeping you healthy, Mrs. Royce, suspecting that her dearly beloved stepchildren might be tempted to—er—tamper with your life. But why should they?"

For the first time something like terror invaded Mrs. Royce's massive face. She set her jaw and said, a trifle tremulously: "N-nonsense. I can't believe— Do you think it's possible they've already tr—"

"You don't feel ill, Mrs. Royce?" cried Mason, alarmed.

Suspicions?

Do Mr. Mason's revelations about a possible "double motive" based on "the proviso in connection with the bequest to Dr. Arlen" make you more or less suspicious of Agatha and John? Explain.

Under the heavy coating of powder her coarse skin was muddily pale. "No, I—Dr. Arlen was supposed to examine me for the first time tomorrow. Oh, if it's . . . The food—"

"Poison was tried three months ago," quavered the lawyer. "On Mrs. Shaw, Queen, as I told you. Good God, Mrs. Royce, you'll have to be careful!"

"Come, come," snapped Ellery. "What's the point? Why should the Shaws want to poison Mrs. Royce, Mason?"

"Because," said Mason in a trembling voice, "in the event of Mrs. Royce's demise her estate is to revert to the original estate: which would automatically mean to John and Agatha." He mopped his brow.

Ellery heaved himself out of the chair and took another hungry turn about the somber room. Mrs. Royce's right eyebrow suddenly began to go up and down with nervousness.

"This needs thinking over," he said abruptly; and there was something queer in his eyes that made both of them stare at him with uneasiness. "I'll stay the night, Mr. Mason, if Mrs. Royce has no objection."

"Do," whispered Mrs. Royce in a tremble; and this time she was afraid, very plainly afraid. And over the rooms settled an impalpable dust, like a distant sign of approaching villainy. "Do you think they'll actually *try* . . . ?"

"It is entirely," said Ellery dryly, "within the realm of possibility."

The day passed in a timeless haze. Un-accountably, no one came; the telephone was silent; and there was no word from Murch, so that John Shaw's fate remained obscure. Mason sat in a miserable heap on the front porch, a cigar cold in his mouth, rocking himself like a wizened old doll. Mrs. Royce retired, subdued, to her quarters. Peter was off somewhere in the gardens tormenting a dog; occasionally Miss Krutch's tearful voice reprimanded him ineffectually.

To Mr. Ellery Queen it was a painful, puzzling, and irritatingly evil time. He prowled the rambling mansion, a lost soul, smoking tasteless cigarettes and thinking . . . That a blanket of menace hung over this house his nerves convinced him. It took all his willpower to keep his body from springing about at unheard sounds; moreover, his mind was distracted and he could not think clearly. A murderer was abroad; and this was a house of violent people.

He shivered and darted a look over his shoulder and shrugged and bent his mind fiercely to the problem at hand . . . And after hours his thoughts grew calmer and began to range themselves in orderly rows, until it was evident that there was a beginning and an end. He grew quiet.

He smiled a little as he stopped a tiptoeing maid and inquired the location of Miss Agatha Shaw's room. Miss Shaw had wrapped herself thus far in a mantle of invisibility. It was most curious. A sense of rising drama excited him a little . . .

A tinny female voice responded to his knock, and he opened the door to find a feminine Shaw as bony and unlovely as the masculine edition curled in a hard knot on a *chaise-longue,* staring balefully out the window. Her *négligé* was adorned with boa feathers and there were varicose veins on her swollen naked legs.

"Well," she said acidly, without turning. "What do you want?"

"My name," murmured Ellery, "is Queen, and Mr. Mason has called me in to help settle your—ah—difficulties."

She twisted her skinny neck slowly. "I've heard all about you. What do you want me to do, kiss you? I suppose it was you who instigated John's arrest. You're fools, the pack of you!"

"To the contrary, it was your worthy Captain Murch's exclusive idea to take your brother in custody, Miss Shaw. He's not formally arrested, you know. Even so, I advised strongly against it."

She sniffed, but she uncoiled the knot and drew her shapeless legs beneath her wrapper in a sudden consciousness of femininity. "Then sit down, Mr. Queen. I'll help all I can."

"On the other hand," smiled Ellery, seating himself in a gilt and Gallic atrocity, "don't blame Murch overly, Miss Shaw. There's a powerful case against your brother, you know."

"And me!"

"And," said Ellery regretfully, "you."

She raised her thin arms and cried: "Oh, how I hate this damned, damned house, that damned woman! She's the cause of all our trouble. Some day she's likely to get—"

"I suppose you're referring to Mrs. Royce. But aren't you being unfair? From Mason's story it's quite evident that there was no ghost of coercion when your stepmother willed your father's fortune to Mrs. Royce. They had never met, never corresponded, and your cousin was three thousand miles away. It's awkward for you, no doubt, but scarcely Mrs. Royce's fault."

"Fair! Who cares about fairness? She's taken our money away from us. And now we've got to stay here and—and be *fed* by her. It's intolerable, I tell you! She'll be here at least two years—trust her for that, the painted old hussy!—and all that time . . ."

"I'm afraid I don't understand. Two years?"

"That *woman's* will," snarled Miss Shaw, "provided that this precious cousin of ours come to live here and preside as mistress for a minimum of two years. That was her revenge, the despicable old witch! Whatever father saw in her . . . To 'provide a home for John and Agatha,' she said in the will, 'until they find a permanent solution of their problems.' How d'ye like that? I'll never forget those words. Our 'problems'! Oh, every time I think—" She bit her lip, eyeing him sidewise with a sudden caution.

Ellery sighed and went to the door. "Indeed? And if something should—er—drive Mrs. Royce from the house before the expiration of the required period?"

"We'd get the money, of course," she flashed with bitter triumph; her thin dark skin was greenish. "If something should happen—"

"I trust," said Ellery dryly, "that nothing will." He closed the door and stood for a moment gnawing his fingers, and then he smiled rather grimly and went downstairs to a telephone.

John Shaw returned with his escort at ten that night. His chest was hollower, his fingers shakier, his eyes bloodier; and he was sober. Murch looked like a thundercloud. The cadaverous man went into the living room and made for a full decanter. He drank alone, with steady mechanical determination. No one disturbed him.

"Nothing," growled Murch to Ellery and Mason.

At twelve the house was asleep.

The first alarm was sounded by Miss Krutch. It was almost one when she ran down the upper corridor screaming at the top of her voice: "Fire! Fire! Fire!" Thick smoke was curling about her slender ankles and the moonlight shining through the corridor-window behind her silhouetted her long plump trembling shanks through the thin nightgown.

The corridor erupted, boiled over. Doors crashed open, dishevelled heads protruded, questions were shrieked, dry throats choked over the bitter smoke. Mr. Phineas Mason, looking a thousand years old without his teeth, fled in a cotton nightshirt toward the staircase. Murch came pounding up the stairs, followed by a bleary, bewildered John Shaw. Scrawny Agatha in silk pajamas staggered down the hall with Peter, howling at the top of his lusty voice, in her arms. Two servants scuttled downstairs like frantic rats.

But Mr. Ellery Queen stood still outside the door of his room and looked quietly about, as if searching for someone.

"Murch," he said in a calm, penetrating voice.

The detective ran up. "The fire!" he cried wildly. "Where the hell's the fire?"

"Have you seen Mrs. Royce?"

"Mrs. Royce? Hell, no!" He ran back up the hall, and Ellery followed on his heels, thoughtfully. Murch tried the knob of a door; the door was locked. "God, she may be asleep, or overcome by—"

"Well, then," said Ellery through his teeth as he stepped back, "stop yowling and help me break this door down. We don't want her frying in her own lard, you know."

In the darkness, in the evil smoke, they hurled themselves at the door . . . At the fourth assault it splintered off its hinges and Ellery sprang through. An electric torch in his hand flung its powerful beam about the room, wavered . . . Something struck it from Ellery's hand, and it splintered on the floor. The next moment Ellery was fighting for his life.

His adversary was a brawny, panting demon with muscular fingers that sought his throat. He wriggled about, coolly, seeking an armhold. Behind him Murch was yelling: "Mrs. Royce! It's only us!"

Something sharp and cold flicked over

> ### 👁 Suspicions?
>
> 1. Who do you think started the fire and why?
>
> 2. Ellery Queen "bent his mind fiercely to the problem . . . And after hours his thoughts grew calmer and began to arrange themselves in orderly rows." Before Ellery Queen provides the solution to the murder of Dr. Arlen, try to arrange your thoughts about clues "in orderly rows." Who do you think is the killer and why?

Ellery's cheek and left a burning line. Ellery found a naked arm. He twisted, hard, and there was a clatter as steel fell to the floor. Then Murch came to his senses and jumped in. A county trooper blundered in, fumbling with his electric torch . . . Ellery's fist drove in, hard, to a fat stomach. Fingers relaxed from his throat. The trooper found the electric switch . . .

Mrs. Royce, trembling violently, lay on the floor beneath the two men. On a chair nearby lay, in a mountain of Victorian clothing, a very odd and solid-looking contraption that might have been a rubber *brassière*. And something was wrong with her hair; she seemed to have been partially scalped.

Ellery cursed softly and yanked. Her scalp came away in a piece, revealing a pink gray-fringed skull.

"She's a man!" screamed Murch.

"Thus," said Ellery grimly, holding Mrs. Royce's throat firmly with one hand and with the other dabbing at his bloody cheek, "vindicating the powers of thought."

"I still don't understand," complained Mason the next morning, as his chauffeur drove him and Ellery back to the city, "how you guessed, Queen."

Ellery raised his eyebrows. "Guessed? My dear Mason, that's considered an insult at the Queen hearth. There was no guesswork whatever involved. Matter of pure reasoning. And a neat job, too," he added reflectively, touching the thin scar on his cheek.

"Come, come, Queen," smiled the lawyer, "I've never really believed McC.'s panegyrics on what he calls your uncanny ability to put two and two together; and though I'm not unintelligent and my legal training gives me a mental advantage over the layman and I've just been treated presumably to a demonstration of your—er—powers, I'll be blessed if I yet believe."

"A sceptic, eh?" said Ellery, wincing at the pain in his cheek. "Well, then, let's start where I started—with the beard Dr. Arlen painted on the face of Rembrandt's wife just before he was attacked. We've agreed that he deliberately painted in the beard to leave a clue to his murderer. What could he have meant? He was not pointing to a *specific* woman, using the beard just as an attention-getter; for the woman in the painting was the wife of Rembrandt, a historical figure and as far as our *personæ* went an utter unknown. Nor could Arlen have meant to point to a woman with a beard *literally*, for this would have meant a freak, and there were no freaks involved. Nor was he pointing to a bearded man, for there was a *man's face* on the painting which he left untouched; had he meant to point to a bearded man as his murderer—that is, to John Shaw—he would have painted the beard on Rembrandt's beardless face. Besides, Shaw's is a vandyke, a pointed beard, and the beard Arlen painted was squarish in shape . . . You see how exhaustive it is possible to be, Mason."

"Go on," said the lawyer intently.

"The only possible conclusion, then, all others having been eliminated, was that Arlen meant the beard *merely to indicate masculinity,* since facial hair is one of the few exclusively masculine characteristics left to our sex by dear, dear Woman. In other words, by painting a beard on a woman's face—any woman's face, mark—Dr. Arlen was virtually saying: 'My murderer is a person who seems to be a woman but is really a man.'"

"Well, I'll be damned!" gasped Mason.

"No doubt," nodded Ellery. "Now, 'a person who seems to be a woman but is really a man' suggests, surely, impersonation. The only actual stranger at the house was Mrs. Royce. Neither John nor Agatha could be impersonators, since they were both well-known to Dr. Arlen as well as to you; Arlen had examined them periodically, in fact, for years as the personal physician of the household. As for Miss Krutch, aside from her unquestionable femininity—a ravishing young woman, my dear Mason—she could not possibly have had motive to be an impersonator.

"Now, since Mrs. Royce seemed the likeliest possibility, I thought over the infinitesimal phenomena I had observed connected with her person— that is, appearance and movements. I was amazed to find a vast number of remarkable confirmations!"

"Confirmations?" echoed Mason, frowning.

"Ah, Mason, that's the trouble with sceptics; they're so easily confounded. Of course! Lips constitute a strong difference between the sexes: Mrs. Royce's were shaped meticulously into a perfect Cupid's-bow with lipstick. Suspicious in an old woman. The general overuse of cosmetics, particularly the heavy application of face powder: *very* suspicious, when you consider that overpowdering is not common among genteel old ladies and also that a man's skin, no matter how closely and frequently shaved, is undisguisably coarser.

"Clothes? Really potent confirmation. Why on earth that outlandish Victorian get-up? Here was presumably a woman who had been on the stage, presumably a woman of the world, a sophisticate. And yet she wore those horrible doodads of the '90s. Why? Obviously, to swathe and disguise a padded figure—impossible with women's thin, scanty, and clinging modern garments. And the collar—ah, the collar! That was his inspiration. A choker, you'll recall, concealing the entire neck? But since a prominent Adam's-apple is an inescapable heritage of the male, a choker-collar becomes virtually a necessity in a female impersonation. Then the baritone voice, the vigorous movements, the mannish stride, the flat shoes . . . The shoes were especially illuminating. Not only were they flat, but they showed signs of great bunions—and a man wearing woman's shoes, no matter how large, might well be expected to grow those painful excrescences."

"Even if I grant all that," objected Mason, "still they're generalities at best, might even be coincidences when you're arguing from a conclusion. Is that all?" He seemed disappointed.

"By no means," drawled Ellery. "These were, as you say, the generalities. But your cunning Mrs. Royce was addicted to three habits which are exclusively masculine, without argument. For one thing, when she sat down on my second sight of her she elevated her skirts at the knees with both hands; that is, one to each knee. Now that's precisely what a man does when he sits down: raises his trousers; to prevent, I suppose, their bagging at the knees."

 Suspicions?

Now that Ellery Queen has demonstrated that Mrs. Royce is a man, speculate on which particular man he might be. Keep in mind what you know about "Mrs. Royce's" background, and consider a motive, a means, and an opportunity for a certain man to impersonate Mrs. Royce.

"But—"

"Wait. Did you notice the way she screwed up her right eyebrow constantly, raising it far up and then drawing it far down? What could this have been motivated by except the lifelong use of a monocle? And a monocle is masculine . . . And finally, her peculiar habit, in removing a cigarette from her lips, of cupping her hand about it rather than withdrawing it between the forefinger and middle finger, as most cigarette smokers do. But the cupping gesture is precisely the result of *pipe smoking,* for a man cups his hands about the bowl of a pipe in taking it out of his mouth. Man again. When I balanced these three specific factors on the same side of the scale as those generalities, I felt certain Mrs. Royce was a male.

"What male? Well, that was simplest of all. You had told me, for one thing, that when you and your partner Coolidge quizzed her she had shown a minute knowledge of Shaw history and specifically of Edith Shaw's history. On top of that, it took histrionic ability to carry off this female impersonation. Then there was the monocle deduction—England, surely? And the strong family resemblance. So I knew that 'Mrs. Royce,' being a Shaw undoubtedly, and an English Shaw to boot, was the other Shaw of the Morton side of the family—that is, Edith Shaw's brother Percy!"

"But she—he, I mean," cried Mason, "had told me Percy Shaw died a few months ago in Europe in an automobile accident!"

"Dear, dear," said Ellery sadly, "and a lawyer, too. She lied, that's all!—I mean 'he,' confound it. Your legal letter was addressed to Edith Shaw, and Percy received it, since they probably shared the same establishment. If he received it, it was rather obvious, wasn't it, that it was Edith Shaw who must have died shortly before; and that Percy had seized the opportunity to gain a fortune for himself by impersonating her?"

"But why," demanded Mason, puzzled, "did he kill Dr. Arlen? He had nothing to gain—Arlen's money was destined for Shaw's cousins, not for Percy Shaw. Do you mean there was some past connection—"

"Not at all," murmured Ellery. "Why look for past connections when the motive's slick and shiny at hand? If Mrs. Royce was a man, the motive was at once apparent. Under the terms of Mrs. Shaw's will Arlen was periodically to examine the family, with particular attention to Mrs. Royce. And Agatha Shaw told me yesterday that Mrs. Royce was constrained by will to remain in the house for two years. Obviously, then, the only way Percy Shaw could avert the cataclysm of being examined by Dr. Arlen and his disguise penetrated—for a doctor would have seen the truth instantly on examination, of course—was to kill Arlen. Simple, *nein?*"

"But the beard Arlen drew—that meant he *had* seen through it?"

"Not unaided. What probably happened was that the imposter, knowing the first physical examination impended, went to Dr. Arlen the other night to strike a bargain, revealing himself as a man. Arlen, an honest man, refused to be bribed. He must have been painting at the time and, thinking fast, unable to rouse the house because he was so far away from the others, unable to paint his assailant's name because 'Mrs. Royce' would see it and destroy it, thought of Peter's beard, made the lightning connection, and calmly painted it while 'Mrs. Royce' talked to him. Then he was stabbed."

"And the previous poisoning attempt on Mrs. Shaw?"

"That," said Ellery, "undoubtedly lies between John and Agatha."

Mason was silent, and for some time they rode in peace. Then the lawyer stirred, and sighed, and said: "Well, all things considered, I suppose you should thank Providence. Without concrete evidence—your reasoning was unsupported by legal evidence, you realize that, of course, Queen—you could scarcely have accused Mrs. Royce of being a man, could you? Had you been wrong, what a beautiful suit she could have brought against you! That fire last night was an act of God."

"I am," said Ellery calmly, "above all, my dear Mason, a man of free will. I appreciate acts of God when they occur, but I don't sit around waiting for them. Consequently . . ."

"You mean—" gasped Mason, opening his mouth wide.

"A telephone call, a hurried trip by Sergeant Velie, and smoke-bombs were the material for breaking into Mrs. Royce's room in the dead of night," said Ellery comfortably. "By the way, you don't by any chance know the permanent address of—ah—Miss Krutch?"

 How Clever?

1. Find what you consider to be the earliest clue in the story that Mrs. Edythe Royce (formerly Miss Edith Shaw, daughter of John Shaw's brother Morton) is in all probability a man. Explain.

2. Find at least seven clues to Mrs. Royce's actual gender from the story's description of her "appearance and movements" before the second *Suspicions?* break in the story.

3. Ellery Queen characterizes Mrs. Royce as "a remarkable woman," which literally means that there are things about her that causes others to remark, comment, or otherwise take notice. Find at least five additional clues to Mrs. Royce's actual gender from the story's description of the "remarkable" Mrs. Royce before the fourth *Suspicions?* break.

4. What was Mrs. Shaw's reason for including in her will the provision that Dr. Arlen give Mrs. Royce "special attention," that he "'conduct monthly medical examinations of my niece, Edith Shaw"? How does this provision give Mrs. Royce a motive for killing Dr. Arlen? How does the story give a clue to that motive when the author has Mrs. Royce reveal that Dr. Arlen "was supposed to examine me for the first time tomorrow." Explain.

5. Find at least two additional clues to Mrs. Royce's actual gender from the story's description of her "appearance and movements" before the third *Suspicions?* break in the story.

6. Ellery Queen concludes near the end of the story that the poisoning attempt on the life of Mrs. Shaw "undoubtedly lies between John and Agatha." If you, too, suspected them as you read the story, did that cause you to think they had killed Dr. Arlen? If so, how were you a victim of a red herring (misleading clue)?

7. Ellery Queen asks Mrs. Shaw's attorney, Phineas Mason, "This Mrs. Royce—you're satisfied she *is* a Shaw?" Mason responds: "No, no, Queen, that's the wrong tack. There can be absolutely no question about it." Later Mason adds: "She convinced us utterly, from her knowledge of *minutiae* about her father's life and Edith Shaw's childhood in America—knowledge impossible for an outsider to have acquired—that she is Edith Shaw."

On first glance, Mason's facts and reasoning appear so solid that the reader can be blinded from seeing another possible interpretation of the same set of facts. What has happened between Ellery Queen's asking "you're satisfied she is a Shaw?" and Mason's concluding "she is Edith Shaw"? Using lateral thinking, explain how Mason's conclusion "she is Edith Shaw" can be wrong—despite Mason's being right both about the fact that "an outsider" could not have had such intimate family knowledge and his belief that Ellery Queen is taking the wrong approach when he questions whether Mrs. Royce is a member of the Shaw family.

8. What observations—scientific and otherwise—did Ellery Queen make that led him to conclude that Dr. Arlen "had told a story," had himself painted in haste the beard on the chin of Rembrandt's wife as "a subtle means" for providing "a clue to his killer"?

9. Do you think that at the time of the murder Mrs. Royce noticed that Dr. Arlen had painted the beard? Ellery Queen speculates that "even if his murderer noticed it, he probably ascribed it to Arlen's nervousness, although the chances are he didn't notice it." Which of these two possible explanations do you consider more likely in Mrs. Royce's case? Why?

10. Ellery Queen wonders "Why Rembrandt's wife, in the name of all that's wonderful?" Ask that same question aloud twice—first with a stress on the word "Rembrandt's" and then a stress on the word "wife." How do these two different ways of saying the same sentence provide a clue to the question "What did Arlen mean to convey?"

11. Summarize how in this case Ellery Queen demonstrated an "uncanny ability to put two and two together." Where do you find his "powers of thought" and his "reasoning" particularly impressive or "exhaustive"? Why?

12. Where and how does Ellery Queen use the technique of "process of elimination" in his reasoning?

13. Which observations that Ellery Queen made about the "remarkable" Mrs. Royce struck you as the most impressive? Why?

14. Why did Percy Shaw decide to impersonate his sister, and why did he decide to kill Dr. Arlen when he did?

15. What do you think of the explanation Ellery Queen offers about "what probably happened" just before Percy Shaw killed Dr. Arlen? Why?

16. Mason tries to have the last word with Ellery Queen by telling Queen he was lucky that the fire broke out; otherwise, "without concrete evidence—your reasoning was unsupported by legal evidence, you realize that, of course, Queen—you could scarcely have accused Mrs. Royce of being a man, could you? . . . That fire last night was an act of God."

How does Ellery Queen have the last word? How did he make certain that the conclusions he had come to based on his observations of Mrs. Royce's appearance and movements would be accepted as irrefutable facts in the eyes of others?

DETECTWRITE: Characterization

1. How does the fact that Ellery Queen wears a pince-nez fit the kind of man and detective he is—"a monastic who led a riotous mental existence"? In your opinion, has the link between high intelligence and the wearing of spectacles (eyeglasses) crossed over from "type" to "stereotype" so that you would avoid using a glasses-wearing detective in any mystery story you would write? Explain.

2. Early in the story, Ellery Queen muses that "life was like a Spanish wench: full of surprises, none of them delicate and all of them stimulating." How is this true of Ellery's life as a detective as the plot of "The Bearded Lady" unfolds? Explain why you would or would not want the detective for a mystery story you would write to share Ellery Queen's philosophy of life.

3. What philosophy of life is also revealed for Ellery Queen when he tells Phineas Mason near the start of the story that "the world's all right; the trouble is the people in it"? Should this attitude be true of detectives in general? Explain.

4. What other attitudes did you detect Ellery Queen has based on your careful reading of his dialogue and actions in the story? Where specifically, in the story, did you infer these attitudes from?

5. Why is Ellery Queen insulted when Mason says to him, "I still don't understand how you guessed"?

6. When it comes to "detection" and "reflection," how do you rate Ellery Queen among the detectives you have met in this collection? Explain.

7. Why do you think Ellery "detested" the appellation "detective"? Based on your understanding of his character, what title, label, or name do you think Ellery would have preferred? Explain.

8. "Ellery Queen" is both the name of the detective in the story and the name of the author of the stories featuring that detective. Actually, "Ellery Queen" is the pen name for two men who wrote the entire series of Ellery Queen detective stories together: Frederic Dannay and Manfred B. Lee. What do you like or dislike about the name "Ellery Queen" for the detective?

9. What name might you give to the detective in a story you would create and why? If you were to use a pen name for your mystery story writing, what would it be? Why?

DETECTWRITE: Detailing the Plot

1. Which facts from the story about Mrs. Royce's "appearance and movements" did you not find helpful in solving the mystery because of your own lack of knowledge or experience? Explain.

2. How would you take care to make certain that the readers of a detective story that you would create would not be unfamiliar with certain "realities" that refer to key clues in your story?

3. Did you feel that the number and the nature of the clues pointing to the probability that Mrs. Royce was a man were too much or too obvious? Why or why not? How would you guard against this potential problem in a detective story you might write?

4. What is your opinion of the number and the nature of the red herrings used by the author of "The Bearded Lady" to throw the reader off the scent of the true killer? Explain. As a writer of detective stories, what is your authorial position on the use of red herrings? Explain.

DETECTWRITE: Characterization and Plot

Having the featured detective in a story match wits with another less competent character who is also trying to solve the crime (or is the detective's "sidekick" or assistant) is a fairly common plot technique among mystery story writers. How is this device used in "The Bearded Lady"? How is it used in other stories in this collection? In which story do you feel it is most successfully used? Explain.

Part six

You, Sherlock

The Man Who Read
John Dickson Carr

William Brittain

ALTHOUGH HE DID NOT REALIZE IT AT THE TIME, EDGAR Gault's life first gained purpose and direction when, at the age of twelve, he idly picked up a copy of John Dickson Carr's *The Problem of the Wire Cage* at his neighborhood lending library. That evening after supper he sat down with the book and read until bedtime. Then, smuggling the book into his room, he finished it by flashlight under the sheets.

He returned to the library the following day for another of Carr's books, *The Arabian Nights Murder,* which took him two days to finish—Edgar's governess had confiscated the flashlight. Within a week he read every John Dickson Carr mystery the library had on its shelves. His gloom on the day he finished reading the last one turned to elation when he learned that his favorite author also wrote under the pseudonym of Carter Dickson.

In the course of the next ten years Edgar accompanied Dr. Gideon Fell, Sir Henry Merrivale, et al. through every locked room in the Carr-Dickson repertoire. He was exultant the day his knowledge of an elusive point in high school physics allowed him to solve the mystery of *The Man Who Could Not Shudder* before the author saw fit to give his explanation. It was probably then that Edgar made his momentous decision.

One day he, Edgar Gault, would commit a locked-room murder which would mystify the master himself.

An orphan, Edgar lived with his uncle in a huge rambling house in a remote section of Vermont. The house was not only equipped with a library—that boon to mystery writers, but something few modern houses possess—but the library had barred windows and a two-inch-thick oak door which, opening into the room, could be locked only by placing a ponderous wooden bar into iron carriers bolted solidly to the wall on both sides of the door. There were no secret passages. The room, in short, would have pleased any of Carr's detectives, and it suited Edgar perfectly.

The victim, of course, would be Edgar's Uncle Daniel. Not only was he readily available, but he was a believer in Ralph Waldo Emerson's philosophy of self-reliance, and in order to help Edgar achieve that happy condition, Uncle Daniel had decided to cut the youth out of his will in the near future.

Since Edgar was perfectly prepared to wallow in his uncle's filthy lucre all the days of his life, it was up to him to do the old man in before the will could be changed.

All of which serves only to explain why Edgar, one bright day in early spring, was standing inside the library fireplace, covered with soot and scrubbing the inside of the chimney until it gleamed.

The chimney, of course, was Edgar's means of escape from his locked room. It was just large enough to accommodate his slim body and had an iron ladder which ran up the inside for the convenience of a chimney sweep. The necessity of escape by chimney somewhat disappointed Edgar, since Dr. Gideon Fell had ruled it out during his famous locked-room lecture in *The Three Coffins*. But it was the only exit available, and Edgar had devised a scheme to make use of it that he was sure even John Dickson Carr would approve of. Maybe Edgar would even get a book written about his crime—like Carr's *The Murder of Sir Edmund Godfrey*.

It didn't worry Edgar that he would be immediately suspected of the crime. Nobody saw his preparations—Uncle Daniel was away on business, and the cook and gardener were on vacation. And at the time the crime would actually be committed, Edgar would have two unimpeachable witnesses to testify that neither he—nor, for that matter, any other human being—could possibly have been the murderer.

Finishing his scrubbing, Edgar carried the pail of water to the kitchen and emptied it down the drain. Then, after a thorough shower to rid his body of soot, he went to the linen closet, took out a newly washed bedsheet, and returned to the library. Wrapping the sheet around him, he got back into the fireplace and began to climb the iron ladder. Reaching the top, he came down again, purposely rubbing the sheet against the stones at frequent intervals.

Stepping back into the library, he walked to a window, removed the sheet, and held it up to the sunlight. Although wrinkled, it had remained gleamingly white. Edgar smiled as he put the sheet into a hamper. Then, going upstairs, he unlocked the window of a storeroom beside which the chimney rose. After that, in his own room, he dressed in clothing chosen especially for the crime—white shirt, white trousers, and white tennis shoes. Finally, he removed a long cavalry saber from the wall, took it to the library, and stood it in a shadowy corner.

His preparations were nearly complete.

Early that evening, from his chair in the music room, Edgar heard his uncle's return. "Edgar? You home?" The nasal New England twang of Uncle Daniel's voice bespoke two hundred years of unbroken Vermont ancestry.

"I'm in here, Uncle Daniel—in the music room."

"Ayah," said Daniel, looking in through the door. "That's the trouble with you, young fella. You think more o' strummin' that guitar than you do about gettin' ahead in the world. Business first, boy—that's the only ticket for success."

"Why, Uncle, I've been working on a business arrangement most of the day. I just finished about an hour ago."

"Well, I meant what I said about my will, Edgar," Uncle Daniel continued. "In fact, I'm going to talk to Stoper about it tonight when he comes over for cards."

Even the weekly game of bridge, in which Edgar was usually a reluctant fourth to Uncle Daniel, Lemuel Stoper, and Dr. Harold Crowley, was a part of The Plan. Even the perfect crime needs witnesses to its perfection.

Later, as Edgar arranged the last of three armloads of wood in the library fireplace—and added to the kindling a small jar from his pocket—he heard the heavy knocker of the front door bang three times. He took the opportunity to set his watch. Exactly seven o'clock.

"Take the gentlemen to the music room and make them comfortable," said Uncle Daniel. "Give 'em a drink and get the card table ready. I'll be in presently."

"Why must they always wait for you, Uncle?" asked Edgar, his assumed frown almost a smirk.

"They'll wait forever for me and like it, if that's what I want. They know where the biggest part of their earnings comes from, all right." And still another part of Edgar's plan dropped neatly into place.

Entering the old house, Lemuel Stoper displayed, as always, an attitude of disdain toward everything not directly involved with Uncle Daniel's considerable fortune. "White, white, and more white," he sneered, looking at Edgar's clothing. "You look like a waiter in a restaurant."

"Don't let him get to you, boy," said a voice from outside. "You look fine. Been playin' tennis?" Dr. Crowley, who reminded Edgar of a huge lump of clear gelatine, waddled in and smiled benignly.

"No need to butter the boy up any more," said Stoper. "Dan'l's changin' his will tonight."

"Oh," said Crowley, surprised. "That's too bad, boy—uh—Edgar."

"Yes, Uncle has already spoken to me about his decision," said Edgar. "I'm in complete agreement with it." No sense in providing *too* much in the way of a motive.

In a small but important change from the usual routine Edgar led the men to the door of the library on the way to the music room. "Uncle," he called. "Dr. Crowley and Mr. Stoper are here."

"I know they're here," growled Daniel. "Wait in the music room. I'll be along in a few minutes."

The two men had seen Uncle Daniel alive and well. Everything was now ready.

In the music room Edgar poured drinks and set up the card table. Then he snapped his fingers and raised his eyebrows—the perfect picture of a man who has just remembered something.

"I must have left the cards upstairs," he said. "I'll go and find them." And before his guests could answer, he left the room.

Once through the door, Edgar's pace quickened. He reached the door of the library eight seconds later. Ignoring his uncle's surprised expression, Edgar took the saber from its corner and strode to the desk where Daniel sat, a newspaper still in his hand.

"Edgar, what in—" Without a word Edgar thrust the sword violently at his uncle. The point entered Daniel's wattled neck just below the chin and penetrated the neck to the back of the chair, pinning the old man to his place. Edgar chuckled, recalling a similar scene in Carr's *The Bride of Newgate*.

He held the sword in place for several seconds. Then he felt carefully for a pulse. None. The murder had been carried off exactly as planned—in seventy seconds.

Hurrying to the fireplace, Edgar picked up the small jar he had placed there earlier. Then, shuffling his feet through the generous supply of paper among the kindling and wood, he pulled the tall fire screen into place and began to climb up the chimney. Reaching the top, he glanced at his watch. Two minutes had gone by since he had left Stoper and Crowley.

Standing on the roof beside the chimney, Edgar removed several small pieces of blank paper from the jar. He had prepared the paper himself from a formula in a book on World War II sabotage operations. These "calling cards" were designed to burst into flame shortly after being exposed to the air. During the war they had been dropped from planes to start fires in fields of enemy grain. Edgar, who had shortened the time needed to make them ignite, knew the pieces of paper would start a fire in the library fireplace.

Dropping the papers down the chimney, he waited a few seconds, and finally was rewarded with a blast of warm air coming up through the opening. Three minutes and ten seconds. Right on schedule.

Edgar moved along the slanted roof to a large decorative gable in which was set the storeroom window. Carefully inching along the edge of the roof, he raised the window and scrambled inside, taking care not to get dust or dirt on his clothing. He went to his own room, took a fresh deck of cards he had left there earlier, then trotted loudly down the stairs to the music room. He re-joined the two guests a little less than five minutes after he had left them—again exactly as planned.

Edgar apologized for his short absence, privately gloating over the unsullied whiteness of his clothing. Surely he could not just have climbed up the inside of a chimney from which smoke was now issuing.

Soon Stoper became restless. "I wonder what's keepin' Dan'l?" he grumbled.

"Mebbe we'd better fetch him," said Crowley.

As they rose, Edgar attempted a yawn while his heart pounded wildly. "I believe I'll wait here," he said, trying to act nonchalant.

John Dickson Carr would be proud of me, thought Edgar as Stoper and Crowley left the room. He hoped that the investigation of his crime would not include any theories involving the supernatural. He remembered his disappointment at the ending in *The Burning Court* with its overtones of witchcraft.

Odd, he thought, that there was no shouting, no crashing sounds as the two old men tried to batter down the heavy library door. But there was no need to worry. The plan was perfect, foolproof. It was—

 Suspicions?

The author ends the story in just six more paragraphs. Before you read any further, consider how you would conclude the story. Then finish the story yourself in your writer's journal, using your skills of detection and reflection and ending the story in a way that most satisfies you. (Keep in mind the conventions of locked room mystery stories and what has gone before in this particular story's plot, setting, and characterization). However, use as many scenes, characters, and as much dialogue as you like. Then continue your reading of William Brittain's story until the next break.

In the doorway of the music room appeared the figure of Lemuel Stoper, looking tired and beaten. In his hand he held a revolver from Uncle Daniel's desk.

"Did his money mean that much to you, boy?" Stoper asked, his voice trembling with shock and rage. "Is that why you did it?"

For only a moment Edgar wondered how Mr. Stoper had got into the library so fast. And then suddenly he knew. For a fleeting instant he wondered if a plea of insanity would help. But then nobody would appreciate the perfect crime he had advised. What would Dr. Fell think of him now? What would H. M. think? What would John Dickson Carr himself think?

What could anyone think of a locked-room murder in which the murderer had forgotten to lock the door?

 Suspicions?

1. Edgar wonders what two famous literary detectives (Dr. Gideon Fell and Sir Henry Merrivale) and their creator, John Dickson Carr, would "think of him now." What else does Edgar wonder about that provides a clue as to why Edgar realized that he had failed to commit the perfect locked room crime?

2. What error do you think Edgar made and what clues do you base your conclusion on?

 How Clever?

1. Recall for a moment that the major question the traditional, conventional locked room mystery poses is: How did the criminal get out of the room in which the crime was committed when all the means of escape are either locked or sealed from the inside?

   What, then, is ironic about the one detail that Edgar forgot among all his preparations when he made his "momentous decision" to "commit a locked-room murder which would mystify the master [John Dickson Carr] himself"?

2. Review the preparations Edgar made as part of "The Plan," and explain what the purpose was behind each of the following:
   a. scrubbing the inside of the chimney and testing it with an all-white sheet wrapped around himself?
   b. unlocking the window of a storeroom alongside the chimney?
   c. dressing completely in white?
   d. killing his uncle when the cook and gardener were on vacation?
   e. standing the long cavalry saber in a shadowy corner of the library?
   f. killing his uncle on the night of the weekly game of bridge?

> g. adding a small jar from his pocket to the fireplace kindling?
>
> h. noting that his uncle's guests always had to wait for him?
>
> i. in a break from the usual routine, leading his uncle's guests past the door of the library on their way to the music room?
>
> j. "forgetting" to bring the cards to the music room when he set up the card table?

3. How clever do these careful preparations make Edgar appear to be? Explain.

4. Sometimes a clue involves not what is there to be seen but what should be there and is missing (the *noticeable absence* of something that should be present). How does "The Man Who Read John Dickson Carr" prove the truth of this statement about detective stories?

5. Based on your reading of the stories in "Inside a Locked Room," Section III of this text, how well does this story work in all respects as a locked-room mystery up until its final paragraph? Explain your position.

6. Is it possible for a reader to understand and appreciate the appeal of "The Man Who Read John Dickson Carr" without being familiar with a locked-room mystery's special requirements? Explain.

7. At what point in the story did you get the feeling that Edgar Gault, so careful in all other respects, had forgotten the one thing that made all his other precautions superfluous? What gave you the feeling at that point?

8. How does Edgar show his understanding of the nature of the detective story when he hopes that "the investigation of his crime would not include any theories involving the supernatural"?

9. Why would nobody appreciate "the perfect crime" Edgar had devised if he pleaded insanity?

10. Compare and contrast your ending for this story with the one William Brittain wrote. In your writer's journal, discuss how you feel about the two endings.

DETECTWRITE: Creating Plot Details

1. As this story makes painfully clear, it's all in the details. Do you recall the important detail that the murderer in "Kim's Game," the opening story in this collection, failed to notice? How did the path of the congealed blood prevent her from getting away with murder?

Write an extended paragraph of fiction for a detective story in which you intentionally mishandle a plot detail that is crucial to your criminal's plan to get away with a crime.

Then try the paragraph out on others to see whether they can discover the bungled detail. If they cannot, explain your planned mistake to them and see whether they understand and agree with your explanation.

2. Compare and contrast the bungled detail in this story with the bungled detail Nora observes when she plays Kim's Game for real in the story "Kim's Game" by M. D. Lake.

3. It can be said that this story has a trick ending. Explain why you liked or did not like the trick ending of this particular story. Then explain why you would favor or avoid trick endings in a detective story you might write.

DETECTWRITE: Setting

1. The story states that Uncle Daniel's house was equipped with a library and adds, "that boon to mystery writers." Explain why you would agree that having a library in a private home as part of your story's setting is a boon to mystery writers, particularly writers of that type of detective story known as a locked-room mystery?

2. Edgar regrets having to use the chimney as his means of escape from the library because he has read a lecture by John Dickson Carr's fictional detective Dr. Gideon Fell (Dr. Fell is featured in "The Dead Sleep Lightly" in the "Celebrated Sleuths" section of this collection). In his lecture, Dr. Fell categorically ruled out an author's using a chimney as the means of escape in a locked-room mystery story. Thinking like an author of locked-room mysteries, explain in a paragraph why you think Dr. Fell did not allow escape by chimney. Then explain why you agree or disagree with what you believe to be Dr. Fell's reasons.

3. Compare the setting for this locked-room mystery with the settings for the stories in Part III of this text, "Inside a Locked Room." What generalizations can you make about the settings for locked room mysteries?

4. If you have not already done so, complete the writing of the locked-room mystery story you began after reading "The Locked Tomb Mystery" in Part III.

The Witness for the Prosecution

Agatha Christie

MR. MAYHERNE ADJUSTED HIS PINCE-NEZ AND CLEARED HIS throat with a little dry as dust cough that was wholly typical of him. Then he looked again at the man opposite him, the man charged with wilful murder.

Mr. Mayherne was a small man, precise in manner, neatly, not to say foppishly dressed, with a pair of very shrewd and piercing grey eyes. By no means a fool. Indeed, as a solicitor, Mr. Mayherne's reputation stood very high. His voice, when he spoke to his client, was dry but not unsympathetic.

"I must impress upon you again that you are in very grave danger, and the utmost frankness is necessary."

Leonard Vole, who had been staring in a dazed fashion at the blank wall in front of him, transferred his glance to the solicitor.

"I know," he said hopelessly. "You keep telling me so. But I can't seem to realize yet that I'm charged with murder—*murder.* And such a dastardly crime too."

Mr. Mayherne was practical, not emotional. He coughed again, took off his pince-nez, polished them carefully, and replaced them on his nose. Then he said:

"Yes, yes, yes. Now, my dear Mr. Vole, we're going to make a determined effort to get you off—and we shall succeed—we shall succeed. But

I must have all the facts. I must know just how damaging the case against you is likely to be. Then we can fix upon the best line of defence."

Still the young man looked at him in the same dazed, hopeless fashion. To Mr. Mayherne the case had seemed black enough, and the guilt of the prisoner assured. Now, for the first time, he felt a doubt.

"You think I'm guilty," said Leonard Vole, in a low voice. "But, by God, I swear I'm not! It looks pretty black against me, I know that. I'm like a man caught in a net—the meshes of it all round me, entangling me whichever way I turn. But I didn't do it, Mr. Mayherne, I didn't do it!"

In such a position a man was bound to protest his innocence. Mr. Mayherne knew that. Yet, in spite of himself, he was impressed. It might be, after all, that Leonard Vole was innocent.

"You are right, Mr. Vole," he said gravely. "The case does look very black against you. Nevertheless, I accept your assurance. Now, let us get to facts. I want you to tell me in your own words exactly how you came to make the acquaintance of Miss Emily French."

"It was one day in Oxford Street. I saw an elderly lady crossing the road. She was carrying a lot of parcels. In the middle of the street she dropped them, tried to recover them, found a 'bus was almost on top of her and just managed to reach the curb safely, dazed and bewildered by people having shouted at her. I recovered her parcels, wiped the mud off them as best I could, retied the string of one, and returned them to her."

"There was no question of your having saved her life?"

"Oh! dear me, no. All I did was to perform a common act of courtesy. She was extremely grateful, thanked me warmly, and said something about my manners not being those of most of the younger generation—I can't remember the exact words. Then I lifted my hat and went on. I never expected to see her again. But life is full of coincidences. That very evening I came across her at a party at a friend's house. She recognized me at once and asked that I should be introduced to her. I then found out that she was a Miss Emily French and that she lived at Cricklewood. I talked to her for some time. She was, I imagined, an old lady who took sudden and violent fancies to people. She took one to me on the strength of a perfectly simple action which anyone might have performed. On leaving, she shook me warmly by the hand, and asked me to come and see her. I replied, of course, that I should be very pleased to do so, and she then urged me to name a day. I did not want particularly to go, but it would have seemed churlish to refuse, so I fixed on the following Saturday. After she had gone, I learned something about her from my friends. That she was rich, eccentric, lived alone with one maid and owned no less than eight cats."

"I see," said Mr. Mayherne. "The question of her being well off came up as early as that?"

"If you mean that I inquired——" began Leonard Vole hotly, but Mr. Mayherne stilled him with a gesture.

"I have to look at the case as it will be presented by the other side. An ordinary observer would not have supposed Miss French to be a lady of means. She lived poorly, almost humbly. Unless you had been told the contrary, you would in all probability have considered her to be in poor circumstances—at any rate to begin with. Who was it exactly who told you that she was well off?"

"My friend, George Harvey, at whose house the party took place."

"Is he likely to remember having done so?"

"I really don't know. Of course it is some time ago now."

"Quite so, Mr. Vole. You see, the first aim of the prosecution will be to establish that you were in low water financially—that is true, is it not?"

Leonard Vole flushed.

"Yes," he said, in a low voice. "I'd been having a run of infernal bad luck just then."

"Quite so," said Mr. Mayherne again. "That being, as I say, in low water financially, you met this rich old lady and cultivated her acquaintance assiduously. Now if we are in a position to say that you had no idea she was well off and that you visited her out of pure kindness of heart——"

"Which is the case."

"I dare say. I am not disputing the point. I am looking at it from the outside point of view. A great deal depends on the memory of Mr. Harvey. Is he likely to remember that conversation or is he not? Could he be confused by counsel into believing that it took place later?"

Leonard Vole reflected for some minutes. Then he said steadily enough, but with a rather paler face:

"I do not think that that line would be successful, Mr. Mayherne. Several of those present heard his remark, and one or two of them chaffed me about my conquest of a rich old lady."

The solicitor endeavoured to hide his disappointment with a wave of the hand.

"Unfortunate," he said. "But I congratulate you upon your plain speaking, Mr. Vole. It is to you I look to guide me. Your judgement is quite right. To persist in the line I spoke of would have been disastrous. We must leave that point. You made the acquaintance of Miss French, you called upon her, the acquaintanceship progressed. We want a clear reason for all this. Why did you, a young man of thirty-three, good-looking, fond of sport, popular with your friends, devote so much of your time to an elderly woman with whom you could hardly have anything in common?"

Leonard Vole flung out his hands in a nervous gesture.

"I can't tell you—I really can't tell you. After the first visit, she pressed me to come again, spoke of being lonely and unhappy. She made it difficult for me to refuse. She showed so plainly her fondness and affection for me that I was placed in an awkward position. You see, Mr. Mayherne, I've got a weak nature—I drift—I'm one of those people who can't say "No." And believe me or not, as you like, after the third or fourth visit I paid her I found myself getting genuinely fond of the old thing. My mother died when I was young, an aunt brought me up, and she too died before I was fifteen. If I told you that I genuinely enjoyed being mothered and pampered, I dare say you'd only laugh."

Mr. Mayherne did not laugh. Instead he took off his pince-nez again and polished them, always a sign with him that he was thinking deeply.

"I accept your explanation, Mr. Vole," he said at last. "I believe it to be psychologically probable. Whether a jury would take that view of it is another matter. Please continue your narrative. When was it that Miss French first asked you to look into her business affairs?"

"After my third or fourth visit to her. She understood very little of money matters, and was worried about some investments."

Mr. Mayherne looked up sharply.

"Be careful, Mr. Vole. The maid, Janet Mackenzie, declares that her mistress was a good woman of business and transacted all her own affairs, and this is borne out by the testimony of her bankers."

"I can't help that," said Vole earnestly. "That's what she said to me."

Mr. Mayherne looked at him for a moment or two in silence. Though he had no intention of saying so, his belief in Leonard Vole's innocence was at that moment strengthened. He knew something of the mentality of elderly ladies. He saw Miss French, infatuated with the good-looking young man, hunting about for pretexts that should bring him to the house. What more likely than that she should plead ignorance of business, and beg him to help her with her money affairs? She was enough of a woman of the world to realize that any man is slightly flattered by such an admission of his superiority. Leonard Vole had been flattered. Perhaps, too, she had not been averse to letting this young man know that she was wealthy. Emily French had been a strong-willed old woman, willing to pay her price for what she wanted. All this passed rapidly through Mr. Mayherne's mind, but he gave no indication of it, and asked instead a further question.

"And you did handle her affairs for her at her request?"

"I did."

"Mr. Vole," said the solicitor. "I am going to ask you a very serious question, and one to which it is vital I should have a truthful answer. You were in low water financially. You had the handling of an old lady's affairs—an old lady who, according to her own statement, knew little or nothing of business. Did you at any time, or in any manner, convert to your own use the securities which you handled? Did you engage in any transaction for your own pecuniary advantage which will not bear the light of day?" He quelled the other's response. "Wait a minute before you answer. There are two courses open to us. Either we can make a feature of your probity and honesty in conducting her affairs whilst pointing out how unlikely it is that you would commit murder to obtain money which you might have obtained by such infinitely easier means. If, on the other hand, there is anything in your dealings which the prosecution will get hold of—if, to put it baldly, it can be proved that you swindled the old lady in any way, we must take the line that you had no motive for the murder, since she was already a profitable source of income to you. You perceive the distinction. Now, I beg of you, take your time before you reply."

But Leonard Vole took no time at all.

"My dealings with Miss French's affairs are all perfectly fair and above board. I acted for her interests to the very best of my ability, as anyone will find who looks into the matter."

"Thank you," said Mr. Mayherne. "You relieve my mind very much. I pay you the compliment of believing that you are far too clever to lie to me over such an important matter."

"Surely," said Vole eagerly, "the strongest point in my favour is the lack of motive. Granted that I cultivated the acquaintanceship of a rich old lady in the hopes of getting money out of her—that, I gather, is the substance of what you have been saying—surely her death frustrates all my hopes?"

The solicitor looked at him steadily. Then, very deliberately, he repeated his unconscious trick with his pince-nez. It was not until they were firmly replaced on his nose that he spoke.

"Are you not aware, Mr. Vole, that Miss French left a will under which you are the principal beneficiary?"

"What?" The prisoner sprang to his feet. His dismay was obvious and unforced. "My God! What are you saying? She left her money to me?"

Mr. Mayherne nodded slowly. Vole sank down again, his head in his hands.

"You pretend to know nothing of this will?"

"Pretend? There's no pretence about it. I knew nothing about it."

"What would you say if I told you that the maid, Janet Mackenzie, swears that you *did* know? That her mistress told her distinctly that she had consulted you in the matter and told you of her intentions?"

"Say? That she's lying! No, I go too fast. Janet is an elderly woman. She was a faithful watchdog to her mistress, and she didn't like me. She was jealous and suspicious. I should say that Miss French confided her intentions to Janet and that Janet either mistook something she said, or else was convinced in her own mind that Miss French actually told her so."

"You don't think she dislikes you enough to lie deliberately about the matter?"

Leonard Vole looked shocked and startled.

"No, indeed! Why should she?"

"I don't know," said Mr. Mayherne thoughtfully. "But she's very bitter against you."

The wretched young man groaned again.

"I'm beginning to see," he muttered. "It's frightful. I made up to her, that's what they'll say; I got her to make a will leaving her money to me, and then I go there that night, and there's nobody in the house—they find her the next day—oh! my God, it's awful!"

"You are wrong about there being nobody in the house," said Mr. Mayherne. 'Janet, as you remember, was to go out for the evening. She went, but about half-past nine she returned to fetch the pattern of a blouse sleeve which she had promised to a friend. She let herself in by the back door, went upstairs and fetched it, and went out again. She heard voices in the sitting-room, though she could not distinguish what they said, but she will swear that one of them was Miss French's and one was a man's."

"At half-past nine," said Leonard Vole. "At half-past nine . . ." He sprang to his feet. "But then I'm saved—saved——"

"What do you mean, saved?" cried Mr. Mayherne, astonished.

"By half-past nine I was at home again! My wife can prove that. I left Miss French about five minutes to nine. I arrived home about twenty past nine. My wife was there waiting for me. Oh! Thank God—thank God! And bless Janet Mackenzie's sleeve pattern."

In his exuberance, he hardly noticed that the grave expression of the solicitor's face had not altered. But the latter's words brought him down to earth with a bump.

"Who, then, in your opinion, murdered Miss French?"

"Why, a burglar, of course, as was thought at first. The window was forced, you remember. She was killed with a heavy blow from a crowbar, and the crowbar was found lying on the floor beside the body. And several articles were missing. But for Janet's absurd suspicions and dislike of me, the police would never have swerved from the right track."

"That will hardly do, Mr. Vole,' said the solicitor. "The things that were missing were mere trifles of no value, taken as a blind. And the marks on the window were not at all conclusive. Besides, think for yourself. You say you were no longer in the house by half-past nine. Who, then, was the man Janet heard talking to Miss French in the sitting-room? She would hardly be having an amicable conversation with a burglar?"

"No," said Vole. "No——" He looked puzzled and discouraged. "But anyway," he added with reviving spirit, "it lets me out. I've got an alibi. You must see Romaine—my wife—at once."

"Certainly," acquiesced the lawyer. "I should already have seen Mrs. Vole but for her being absent when you were arrested. I wired to Scotland at once, and I understand that she arrives back tonight. I am going to call upon her immediately I leave here."

Vole nodded, a great expression of satisfaction settling down over his face.

"Yes, Romaine will tell you. My God! it's a lucky chance that."

"Excuse me, Mr. Vole, but you are very fond of your wife?"

"Of course."

"And she of you?"

"Romaine is devoted to me. She'd do anything in the world for me."

He spoke enthusiastically, but the solicitor's heart sank a little lower. The testimony of a devoted wife—would it gain credence?

"Was there anyone else who saw you return at nine-twenty? A maid, for instance?"

"We have no maid."

"Did you meet anyone in the street on the way back?"

"Nobody I knew. I rode part of the way in a 'bus. The conductor might remember."

Mr. Mayherne shook his head doubtfully.

"There is no one, then, who can confirm your wife's testimony?"

"No. But it isn't necessary, surely?"

"I dare say not. I dare say not," said Mr. Mayherne hastily. "Now there's just one thing more. Did Miss French know that you were a married man?"

"Oh, yes."

"Yet you never took your wife to see her. Why was that?"

For the first time, Leonard Vole's answer came halting and uncertain. "Well—I don't know."

"Are you aware that Janet Mackenzie says her mistress believed you to be single, and contemplated marrying you in the future?"

Vole laughed.

"Absurd! There was forty years difference in age between us."

"It has been done," said the solicitor drily. "The fact remains. Your wife never met Miss French?"

"No——" Again the constraint.

"You will permit me to say," said the lawyer, "that I hardly understand your attitude in the matter."

Vole flushed, hesitated, and then spoke.

"I'll make a clean breast of it. I was hard up, as you know. I hoped that Miss French might lend me some money. She was fond of me, but she wasn't at all interested in the struggles of a young couple. Early on, I found that she had taken it for granted that my wife and I didn't get on— were living apart. Mr. Mayherne—I wanted the money—for Romaine's sake. I said nothing, and allowed the old lady to think what she chose. She spoke of my being an adopted son to her. There was never any question of marriage—that must be just Janet's imagination."

"And that is all?"

"Yes—that is all."

Was there just a shade of hesitation in the words? The lawyer fancied so. He rose and held out his hand.

"Goodbye, Mr. Vole." He looked into the haggard young face and spoke with an unusual impulse. "I believe in your innocence in spite of the multitude of facts arrayed against you. I hope to prove it and vindicate you completely."

Vole smiled back at him.

"You'll find the alibi is all right," he said cheerfully.

Again he hardly noticed that the other did not respond.

"The whole thing hinges a good deal on the testimony of Janet Mackenzie," said Mr. Mayherne. "She hates you. That much is clear."

"She can hardly hate me," protested the young man.

The solicitor shook his head as he went out.

"Now for Mrs. Vole," he said to himself.

He was seriously disturbed by the way the thing was shaping.

Suspicions?

1. The solicitor, or lawyer, Mr. Mayherne, tells Leonard Vole, "I believe in your innocence in spite of the multitude of facts arrayed against you. I hope to prove it and vindicate you completely." Review all the facts presented so far— those that make a case for Leonard Vole and those that make a case against him. Do you agree with Mr. Mayherne that the preponderance of facts points to Mr. Vole's guilt? Explain.

2. Do you, like Mr. Mayherne, believe in Mr. Vole's innocence? Explain.

The Voles lived in a small shabby house near Paddington Green. It was to this house that Mr. Mayherne went.

In answer to his ring, a big slatternly woman, obviously a charwoman, answered the door.

"Mrs. Vole? Has she returned yet?"

"Got back an hour ago. But I dunno if you can see her."

"If you will take my card to her," said Mr. Mayherne quietly. "I am quite sure that she will do so."

The woman looked at him doubtfully, wiped her hand on her apron and took the card. Then she closed the door in his face and left him on the step outside.

In a few minutes, however, she returned with a slightly altered manner. "Come inside, please."

She ushered him into a tiny drawing room. Mr. Mayherne, examining a drawing on the wall, started up suddenly to face a tall pale woman who had entered so quietly that he had not heard her.

"Mr. Mayherne? You are my husband's solicitor, are you not? You have come from him? Will you please sit down?"

Until she spoke he had not realized that she was not English. Now, observing her more closely, he noticed the high cheekbones, the dense blue-black of the hair, and an occasional very slight movement of the hands that was distinctly foreign. A strange woman, very quiet. So quiet as to make one uneasy. From the very first Mr. Mayherne was conscious that he was up against something that he did not understand.

"Now, my dear Mrs. Vole," he began, "you must not give way——"

He stopped. It was so very obvious that Romaine Vole had not the slightest intention of giving way. She was perfectly calm and composed.

"Will you please tell me all about it?" she said. "I must know everything. Do not think to spare me. I want to know the worst." She hesitated, then repeated in a lower tone, with a curious emphasis which the lawyer did not understand: "I want to know the worst."

Mr. Mayherne went over his interview with Leonard Vole. She listened attentively, nodding her head now and then.

"I see," she said, when he had finished. "He wants me to say that he came in at twenty minutes past nine that night?"

"He did come in at that time?" said Mr. Mayherne sharply.

"That is not the point," she said coldly. "Will my saying so acquit him? Will they believe me?"

Mr. Mayherne was taken aback. She had gone so quickly to the core of the matter.

"That is what I want to know," she said. "Will it be enought? Is there anyone else who can support my evidence?"

There was a suppressed eagerness in her manner that made him vaguely uneasy.

"So far there is no one else," he said reluctantly.

"I see," said Romaine Vole.

She sat for a minute or two perfectly still. A little smile played over her lips. The lawyer's feeling of alarm grew stronger and stronger.

"Mrs. Vole——" he began. "I know what you must feel——"

"Do you?" she said. "I wonder."

"In the circumstances——"

"In the circumstances—I intend to play a lone hand."

He looked at her in dismay.

"But, my dear Mrs. Vole—you are overwrought. Being so devoted to your husband——"

"I beg your pardon?"

The sharpness of her voice made him start. He repeated in a hesitating manner:

"Being so devoted to your husband——"

Romaine Vole nodded slowly, the same strange smile on her lips.

"Did he tell you that I was devoted to him?" she asked softly. "Ah! yes, I can see he did. How stupid men are! Stupid—stupid—stupid——"

She rose suddenly to her feet. All the intense emotion that the lawyer had been conscious of in the atmosphere was now concentrated in her tone.

"I hate him, I tell you! I hate him. I hate him. I hate him! I would like to see him hanged by the neck till he is dead."

The lawyer recoiled before her and the smouldering passion in her eyes.

She advanced a step nearer, and continued vehemently:

"Perhaps I *shall* see it. Supposing I tell you that he did not come in that night at twenty past nine, but at twenty past *ten*? You say that he tells you he knew nothing about the money coming to him. Supposing I tell you he knew all about it, and counted on it, and committed murder to get it? Supposing I tell you that he admitted to me that night when he came in what he had done? That there was blood on his coat? What then? Supposing that I stand up in court and say all these things?"

Her eyes seemed to challenge him. With an effort, he concealed his growing dismay, and endeavoured to speak in a rational tone.

"You cannot be asked to give evidence against your husband——"

"He is not my husband!"

The words came out so quickly that he fancied he had misunderstood her.

"I beg your pardon? I——"

"He is not my husband."

The silence was so intense that you could have heard a pin drop.

"I was an actress in Vienna. My husband is alive but in a madhouse. So we could not marry. I am glad now."

She nodded defiantly.

"I should like you to tell me one thing," said Mr. Mayherne. He contrived to appear as cool and unemotional as ever. "Why are you so bitter against Leonard Vole?"

She shook her head, smiling a little.

"Yes, you would like to know. But I shall not tell you. I will keep my secret . . ."

Mr. Mayherne gave his dry little cough and rose.

"There seems no point in prolonging this interview," he remarked. "You will hear from me again after I have communicated with my client."

She came closer to him, looking into his eyes with her own wonderful dark ones.

"Tell me," she said, "did you believe—honestly—that he was innocent when you came here today?"

"I did," said Mr. Mayherne.

"You poor little man," she laughed.

"And I believe so still," finished the lawyer. "Good evening, madam."

He went out of the room, taking with him the memory of her startled face.

"This is going to be the devil of a business," said Mr. Mayherne to himself as he strode along the street.

Extraordinary, the whole thing. An extraordinary woman. A very dangerous woman. Women were the devil when they got their knife into you.

What was to be done? That wretched young man hadn't a leg to stand upon. Of course, possibly he did commit the crime . . .

"No," said Mr. Mayherne to himself. "No—there's almost too much evidence against him. I don't believe this woman. She was trumping up the whole story. But she'll never bring it into court."

He wished he felt more conviction on the point.

The police court proceedings were brief and dramatic. The principal witnesses for the prosecution were Janet Mackenzie, maid to the dead woman, and Romaine Heilger, Austrian subject, the mistress of the prisoner.

Mr. Mayherne sat in court and listened to the damning story that the latter told. It was on the lines she had indicated to him in their interview.

The prisoner reserved his defence and was committed for trial.

Mr. Mayherne was at his wits' end. The case against Leonard Vole was black beyond words. Even the famous KC who was engaged for the defence held out little hope.

"If we can shake the Austrian woman's testimony, we might do something," he said dubiously. "But it's a bad business."

Mr. Mayherne had concentrated his energies on one single point. Assuming Leonard Vole to be speaking the truth, and to have left the murdered woman's house at nine o'clock, who was the man whom Janet heard talking to Miss French at half-past nine?

The only ray of light was in the shape of a scapegrace nephew who had in bygone days cajoled and threatened his aunt out of various sums of money. Janet Mackenzie, the solicitor learned, had always been attached to this young man and had never ceased urging his claims upon her mistress. It certainly seemed possible that it was this nephew who had been with Miss French after Leonard Vole left, especially as he was not to be found in any of his old haunts.

In all other directions, the lawyer's researches had been negative in their result. No one had seen Leonard Vole entering his own house, or leaving that of Miss French. No one had seen any other man enter or leave the house in Cricklewood. All inquiries drew blank.

It was the eve of the trial when Mr. Mayherne received the letter which was to lead his thoughts in an entirely new direction.

It came by the six o'clock post. An illiterate scrawl, written on common paper and enclosed in a dirty envelope with the stamp stuck on crooked.

Mr. Mayherne read it through once or twice before he grasped its meaning.

DEAR MISTER:

You're the lawyer chap wot acks for the young feller. If you want that painted foreign hussy showd up for wot she is an her pack of lies you come to 16 Shaw's Rents Stepney tonight It ull cawst you 2 hundred quid Arsk for Missis Mogson.

Suspicions?

1. Now that you've met and heard Romaine Vole, how do you feel about the case for and against Leonard Vole at this point in the story? Explain.

2. How do you react to Mr. Mayherne's feeling that "there's almost too much evidence" against Leonard Vole? Why?

3. Mr. Mayherne says to himself about Romaine Vole and her remarks to him, "I don't believe this woman. She was trumping up the whole story. But she'll never bring it into court." Do you believe Romaine Vole and her story? Explain. Do you think she will testify against Leonard Vole? Why or why not?

The solicitor read and re-read this strange epistle. It might, of course, be a hoax, but when he thought it over, he became increasingly convinced that it was genuine, and also convinced that it was the one hope for the prisoner. The evidence of Romaine Heilger damned him completely, and the line the defence meant to pursue, the line that the evidence of a woman who had admittedly lived an immoral life was not to be trusted, was at best a weak one.

Mr. Mayherne's mind was made up. It was his duty to save his client at all costs. He must go to Shaw's Rents.

He had some difficulty in finding the place, a ramshackle building in an evil-smelling slum, but at last he did so, and on inquiry for Mrs. Mogson was sent up to a room on the third floor. On this door he knocked, and getting no answer, knocked again.

At this second knock, he heard a shuffling sound inside, and presently the door was opened cautiously half an inch and a bent figure peered out.

Suddenly the woman, for it was a woman, gave a chuckle and opened the door wider.

"So it's you, dearie," she said, in a wheezy voice. "Nobody with you, is there? No playing tricks? That's right. You can come in—you can come in."

With some reluctance the lawyer stepped across the threshold into the small dirty room, with its flickering gas jet. There was an untidy unmade bed in a corner, a plain deal table and two rickety chairs. For the first time Mr. Mayherne had a full view of the tenant of this unsavoury apartment. She was a woman of middle age, bent in figure, with a mass of untidy grey hair and a scarf wound tightly round her face. She saw him looking at this and laughed again, the same curious toneless chuckle.

"Wondering why I hide my beauty, dear? He, he, he. Afraid it may tempt you, eh? But you shall see—you shall see."

She drew aside the scarf and the lawyer recoiled involuntarily before the almost formless blur of scarlet. She replaced the scarf again.

"So you're not wanting to kiss me, dearie? He, he, I don't wonder. And yet I was a pretty girl once—not so long ago as you'd think, either. Vitriol, dearie, vitriol—that's what did that. Ah! but I'll be even with 'em——"

She burst into a hideous torrent of profanity which Mr. Mayherne tried vainly to quell. She fell silent at last, her hands clenching and unclenching themselves nervously.

"Enough of that," said the lawyer sternly. "I've come here because I have reason to believe you can give me information which will clear my client, Leonard Vole. Is that the case?"

Her eyes leered at him cunningly.

"What about the money, dearie?" she wheezed. "Two hundred quid, you remember."

"It is your duty to give evidence, and you can be called upon to do so."

"That won't do, dearie. I'm an old woman, and I know nothing. But you give me two hundred quid, and perhaps I can give you a hint or two. See?"

"What kind of hint?"

"What should you say to a letter? A letter from *her.* Never mind how I got hold of it. That's my business. It'll do the trick. But I want my two hundred quid."

Mr. Mayherne looked at her coldly, and made up his mind.

"I'll give you ten pounds, nothing more. And only that if this letter is what you say it is."

"Ten pounds?" She screamed and raved at him.

"Twenty," said Mr. Mayherne, "and that's my last word."

He rose as if to go. Then, watching her closely, he drew out a pocketbook, and counted out twenty one-pound notes.

"You see," he said. "That is all I have with me. You can take it or leave it."

But already he knew that the sight of the money was too much for her. She cursed and raved impotently, but at last she gave in. Going over to the bed, she drew something out from beneath the tattered mattress.

"Here you are, damn you!" she snarled. "It's the top one you want."

It was a bundle of letters that she threw to him, and Mr. Mayherne untied them and scanned them in his usual cool, methodical manner. The woman, watching him eagerly, could gain no clue from his impassive face.

He read each letter through, then returned again to the top one and read it a second time. Then he tied the whole bundle up again carefully.

They were love letters, written by Romaine Heilger, and the man they were written to was not Leonard Vole. The top letter was dated the day of the latter's arrest.

"I spoke true, dearie, didn't I?" whined the woman. "It'll do for her, that letter?"

Mr. Mayherne put the letters in his pocket, then he asked a question.

"How did you get hold of this correspondence?"

"That's telling," she said with a leer. "But I know something more. I heard in court what that hussy said. Find out where *she* was at twenty past ten, the time she says she was at home. Ask at the Lion Road Cinema. They'll remember—a fine upstanding girl like that—curse her!"

"Who is the man?" asked Mr. Mayherne. "There's only a Christian name here."

The other's voice grew thick and hoarse, her hands clenched and unclenched. Finally she lifted one to her face.

"He's the man that did this to me. Many years ago now. She took him away from me—a chit of a girl she was then. And when I went after him—

and went for him too—he threw the cursed stuff at me! And she laughed—damn her! I've had it in for her for years. Followed her, I have, spied upon her. And now I've got her! She'll suffer for this, won't she, Mr. Lawyer? She'll suffer?"

"She will probably be sentenced to a term of imprisonment for perjury," said Mr. Mayherne quietly.

"Shut away—that's what I want. You're going, are you? Where's my money? Where's that good money?"

Without a word, Mr. Mayherne put down the notes on the table. Then, drawing a deep breath, he turned and left the squalid room. Looking back, he saw the old woman crooning over the money.

He wasted no time. He found the cinema in Lion Road easily enough, and, shown a photograph of Romaine Heilger, the commissionaire recognized her at once. She had arrived at the cinema with a man some time after ten o'clock on the evening in question. He had not noticed her escort particularly, but he remembered the lady who had spoken to him about the picture that was showing. They stayed until the end, about an hour later.

Mr. Mayherne was satisfied. Romaine Heilger's evidence was a tissue of lies from beginning to end. She had evolved it out of her passionate hatred. The lawyer wondered whether he would ever know what lay behind that hatred. What had Leonard Vole done to her? He had seemed dumbfounded when the solicitor had reported her attitude to him. He had declared earnestly that such a thing was incredible—yet it had seemed to Mr. Mayherne that after the first astonishment his protests had lacked sincerity.

He *did* know. Mr. Mayherne was convinced of it. He knew, but he had no intention of revealing the fact. The secret between those two remained a secret. Mr. Mayherne wondered if some day he should come to learn what it was.

The solicitor glanced at his watch. It was late, but time was everything. He hailed a taxi and gave an address.

"Sir Charles must know of this at once,' he murmured to himself as he got in.

The trial of Leonard Vole for the murder of Emily French aroused widespread interest. In the first place the prisoner was young and good-looking, then he was accused of a

👁 **Suspicions?**

1. How has the introduction of the character of Mrs. Mogson affected your feelings about Leonard Vole's guilt or innocence? Explain.

2. Compare and contrast Romaine Vole and Mrs. Mogson. How are they similar? How are they different? Which one do you think will have the greater effect on Leonard Vole's fate? Why?

particularly dastardly crime, and there was the further interest of Romaine Heilger, the principal witness for the prosecution. There had been pictures of her in many papers and several fictitious stories as to her origin and history.

The proceedings opened quietly enough. Various technical evidence came first. Then Janet Mackenzie was called. She told substantially the same story as before. In cross-examination counsel for the defence succeeded in getting her to contradict herself once or twice over her account of Vole's association with Miss French, he emphasized the fact that though she had heard a man's voice in the sitting-room that night, there was nothing to show that it was Vole who was there, and he managed to drive home a feeling that jealousy and dislike of the prisoner were at the bottom of a good deal of her evidence.

Then the next witness was called.

"Your name is Romaine Heilger?"

"Yes."

"You are an Austrian subject?"

"Yes."

"For the last three years you have lived with the prisoner and passed yourself off as his wife?"

Just for a moment Romaine Heilger's eyes met those of the man in the dock. Her expression held something curious and unfathomable.

"Yes."

The questions went on. Word by word the damning facts came out. On the night in question the prisoner had taken out a crowbar with him. He had returned at twenty minutes past ten and had confessed to having killed the old lady. His cuffs had been stained with blood, and he had burned them in the kitchen stove. He had terrorized her into silence by means of threats.

As the story proceeded, the feeling of the court which had, to begin with, been slightly favourable to the prisoner, now set dead against him. He himself sat with downcast head and moody air, as though he knew he were doomed.

Yet it might have been noted that her own counsel sought to restrain Romaine's animosity. He would have preferred her to be a more unbiased witness.

Formidable and ponderous, counsel for the defence arose.

He put it to her that her story was a malicious fabrication from start to finish, that she had not even been in her own house at the time in question, that she was in love with another man and was deliberately seeking to send Vole to his death for a crime he did not commit.

Romaine denied these allegations with superb insolence.

Then came the surprising denouement, the production of the letter. It was read aloud in court in the midst of a breathless stillness.

Max, beloved, the Fates have delivered him into our hands! He has been arrested for murder—but, yes, the murder of an old lady! Leonard who would not hurt a fly! At last I shall have my revenge. The poor chicken! I shall say that he came in that night with blood upon him—that he confessed to me. I shall hang him, Max—and when he hangs he will know and realize that it was Romaine who sent him to his death. And then—happiness, Beloved! Happiness at last!

There were experts present ready to swear that the handwriting was that of Romaine Heilger, but they were not needed. Confronted with the letter, Romaine broke down utterly and confessed everything. Leonard Vole had returned to the house at the time he said, twenty past nine. She had invented the whole story to ruin him.

With the collapse of Romaine Heilger, the case for the Crown collapsed also. Sir Charles called his few witnesses, the prisoner himself went into the box and told his story in a manly straightforward manner, unshaken by cross-examination.

The prosecution endeavoured to rally, but without great success. The judge's summing up was not wholly favourable to the prisoner, but a reaction had set in and the jury needed little time to consider their verdict.

"We find the prisoner not guilty."

Leonard Vole was free!

Little Mr. Mayherne hurried from his seat. He must congratulate his client.

He found himself polishing his pince-nez vigorously, and checked himself. His wife had told him only the night before that he was getting a habit of it. Curious things, habits. People themselves never knew they had them.

An interesting case—a very interesting case. That woman, now, Romaine Heilger.

The case was dominated for him still by the exotic figure of Romaine Heilger. She had seemed a pale quiet woman in the house at Paddington, but in court she had flamed out against the sober background. She had flaunted herself like a tropical flower.

If he closed his eyes he could see her now, tall and vehement, her exquisite body bent forward a little, her right hand clenching and unclenching itself unconsciously all the time.

Curious things, habits. That gesture of hers with the hand was her habit, he supposed. Yet he had seen someone else do it quite lately. Who was it now? Quite lately—

He drew in his breath with a gasp as it came back to him. *The woman in Shaw's Rents . . .*

He stood still, his head whirling. It was impossible—impossible——Yet, Romaine Heilger was an actress.

The KC came up behind him and clapped him on the shoulder.

"Congratulated our man yet? He's had a narrow shave, you know. Come along and see him."

But the little lawyer shook off the other's hand.

He wanted one thing only—to see Romaine Heilger face to face.

He did not see her until some time later, and the place of their meeting is not relevant.

"So you guessed," she said, when he had told her all that was in his mind. "The face? Oh! that was easy enough, and the light of that gas jet was too bad for you to see the make-up."

"But why—why——"

"Why did I play a lone hand?" She smiled a little, remembering the last time she had used the words.

"Such an elaborate comedy!"

"My friend—I had to save him. The evidence of a woman devoted to him would not have been enough—you hinted as much yourself. But I know something of the psychology of crowds. Let my evidence be wrung from me, as an admission, damning me in the eyes of the law, and a reaction in favour of the prisoner would immediately set in."

"And the bundle of letters?"

"One alone, the vital one, might have seemed like a—what do you call it?—put-up job."

"Then the man called Max?"

"Never existed, my friend."

"I still think," said little Mr. Mayherne, in an aggrieved manner, "that we could have got him off by the—er—normal procedure."

"I dared not risk it. You see, you *thought* he was innocent——"

Suspicions?

1. What is your reaction to Romaine Vole's testimony against her husband? Why?

2. What is the significance of Mr. Mayherne's thoughts on the habits that people never know they have?

3. Who had Mr. Mayherne seen recently with the same habit as Romaine Vole's of continually but unconsciously "clenching and unclenching" the right hand? What might be the significance of Mr. Mayherne's remembering this similarity at the point in the story at which Leonard Vole has been found not guilty of the murder of Miss Emily French? Explain.

"And you knew it? I see," said little Mr. Mayherne.

"My dear Mr. Mayherne," said Romaine, "you do not see at all. I knew—he was guilty!"

 ## How Clever?

1. Leonard Vole's lawyer, Mr. Mayherne, says to his client in the opening dialogue of the story: "I must impress upon you again that you are in very grave danger, and the utmost frankness is necessary." Leonard responds: "I know. You keep telling me so." Why, then, does Leonard Vole lie to Mr. Mayherne?

2. Mr. Mayherne tells Leonard Vole that he must have "all the facts," and adds, "I must know just how damaging the case against you is likely to be. Then we can fix upon the best line of defense." Putting aside for the moment what you know about Leonard's guilt, how damaging is the prosecution's case against him as it is presented in the opening section of the story? Explain.

3. Explain "the distinction" Mr. Mayherne makes for Leonard Vole between "the two courses open to us."

4. How do Miss Emily French's will and Janet Mackenzie's hearing a man's voice in the sitting-room affect Leonard Vole's contention that "'the strongest point in my favour is the lack of motive'"?

5. Leonard Vole tells Mr. Mayherne that "'Romaine is devoted to me. She'd do anything in the world for me.'" Why does this remark cause Mr. Mayherne's heart to sink? How is Mr. Mayherne's reaction a foreshadowing of how Romaine will respond when Mr. Mayherne goes to interview her?

6. How does what Romaine Vole intends to testify about for the prosecution make the prosecution's case against Leonard Vole stronger?

7. Explain what Romaine Vole understood about the difference between being "a witness for the defense" and being "the witness for the prosecution." To prove that Romaine understood this difference psychologically from the jury's point of view, quote from Romaine's dialogue in the scene in which Mr. Mayherne first visits and interviews her.

8. At what point do you think Romaine Vole conceived of her plan to be the prosecution's star witness—and how does this prove that it was not something she and Leonard Vole had decided on together?

9. Explain the key details of the complete plan Romaine Vole put together—including the incriminating letters in her own handwriting—in order to get her husband to be found "not guilty"? Why did the plan work?

10. Ironically, it turns out that despite Romaine's becoming "the witness for the prosecution," Leonard Vole was right when he told Mr. Mayherne that "'Romaine is devoted to me. She'd do anything in the world for me.'" Explain the irony.

11. How does the introduction of Miss French's nephew and Janet Mackenzie's fondness for him serve as a red herring (misleading clue) in the story? In your opinion, how effective was it as a red herring—in other words, did it help you to think of Leonard Vole as being innocent?

12. Why did Mrs. Mogson make a point of drawing aside her scarf to show Mr. Mayherne "the almost formless blur of scarlet" caused by someone's throwing vitriol (acid) at her?

13. When Mr. Mayherne visits Mrs. Mogson, where does the author plant a clue that will connect with Romaine Vole's habit noticed by Mr. Mayherne at the end of the story?

14. Find references in different parts of the story to Mr. Mayherne's habit of constantly taking off and polishing his pince-nez (French for eyeglasses "pinched" or clipped to the bridge of the nose). How did this minor habit of the story's detective, one recently commented on by his wife, trigger the solution to the mystery for Mr. Mayherne?

15. How do you feel about Romaine Vole's "devotion" to Leonard Vole to the point of saving him from being convicted of a murder she knew he committed? Why?

16. How do you feel about the twist ending captured in the dialogue between Mr. Mayherne and Romaine Vole at the conclusion of the story? Explain why you feel the way you do. How much of what you feel comes from a general fondness for or a general dislike of twist endings in mystery stories?

DETECTWRITE: Characterization

1. In the opening two paragraphs of the story, how does Agatha Christie paint a verbal portrait of her "detective," who is actually a defense lawyer? What is it that we learn about this "practical, not emotional" man that makes him no match for Romaine Vole's skills?

2. Retrace the changes of heart and mind Mr. Mayherne goes through in the opening two scenes of the story (his interview with Leonard Vole followed by his interview with Romaine Vole) as he wonders whether Leonard Vole is guilty or innocent of the death of Miss Emily French. How do these changes help to reveal Mr. Mayherne's character and the way he sees and goes about doing his job as a defense attorney?

3. How did Agatha Christie succeed in painting a portrait of Leonard Vole that made the reader think he was innocent of the murder? Find specific descriptions, actions, and lines of dialogue.

4. How did Agatha Christie succeed in painting a portrait of Romaine Vole that made the reader think she hated her husband and wanted to see him "hanged by the neck till he is dead"? Find specific descriptions, actions, and lines of dialogue.

5. Do you think that the Mr. Mayherne that you meet in this short story would or would not be a good choice as the featured lawyer detective in a series of mystery stories? Explain.

6. What particular habit—and remember that according to Agatha Christie, "People themselves never knew they had them"—would you give to a detective in a mystery story you might write? Explain why you chose that habit or why you would make certain not to give your detective an identifying habit.

DETECTWRITE: Plot

1. Explain why, as an author, you would or would not consider writing a mystery short story in which the detective is outwitted and the criminal gets away with the crime.

2. Explain why, as an author, you would or would not make use of a twist ending in a mystery story you might write.

DETECTWRITE: Characterization and Dialogue

1. We are told in the story that when Romaine Vole was called to the witness stand that after some initial questions about her identity, "the questions went on. Word by word the damning facts came out."

   On your own or with a writing partner, write the scene in which Romaine Vole both testifies for the prosecution and responds to questions put to her by Mr. Mayherne, the counsel for the defense. In writing Romaine's testimony, be certain to be true to the facts of the story and to suit her dialogue (what she says and how she says it) to her character, her motive at that point in the story, her emotional state (we are told that "her own counsel sought to restrain Romaine's animosity," preferring her to be "a more unbiased witness"), and to her skills as an actress.

DETECTWRITE: Title

From an author's point of view, consider the differences in meaning in the following alternate titles and explain why you think one of them is the best title for Agatha Christie's story: A Witness for the Prosecution, The Witness for the Prosecution, Witness for the Prosecution.

DETECTWRITE: Characterization and Plot

In 1954, Agatha Christie reworked her very popular 1924 short story "The Witness for the Prosecution" into a full-length play, which was later made into a very successful film. The major difference between the short story and the play is that in the play (and film) the story continues beyond the twist ending long enough for a second twist. Although Agatha Christie was a master of the twist ending, in the play version she literally does herself one better.

See whether you can have some Agatha Christie–type fun by continuing the story of "The Witness for the Prosecution" to include as many scenes, characters and as much dialogue as you like. Try to remain faithful to what has come before, but put a twist on it. Then read the ending from the play, "Witness for the Prosecution," which follows, and compare and contrast your second twist ending with Christie's.

Witness for the Prosecution

SIR WILFRID: I've got him off—in spite of you.

ROMAINE: In *spite*—of me.

SIR WILFRID: You don't deny, do you, that you did your best to hang him?

ROMAINE: Would they have believed me if I had said that he was at home with me that night and did not go out? Would they?

SIR WILFRID: *(Slightly uncomfortable)* Why not?

ROMAINE: Because they would have said to themselves: this woman loves this man—she would say or do anything for him. They would have had sympathy with me, yes. But they would not have *believed* me.

SIR WILFRID: If you'd been speaking the truth they would.

ROMAINE: I wonder. *(She pauses.)* I did not want their sympathy—I wanted them to dislike me, to mistrust me, to be convinced that I was a liar. And then, when my lies were broken down—then they believed . . . *(In the Cockney accent of the* WOMAN *who visited* SIR WILFRID *at his office.)* So now you know the whole story, mister—like to kiss me?

SIR WILFRID: *(Thunderstruck.)* My God!

ROMAINE: *(As herself)* Yes, the woman with the letters. I wrote those letters. I brought them to you. I was that woman. It wasn't *you* who won freedom for Leonard. It was *I*. And because of it I shall go to prison. *(Her eyes close.)* But at the end of it Leonard and I will be together again. Happy—loving each other.

SIR WILFRID: *(Moved.)* My dear . . . But couldn't you trust me? We believe, you know, that our British system of justice upholds the truth. We'd have got him off.

ROMAINE: I couldn't risk it. *(Slowly.)* You see, you *thought* he was innocent . . .

SIR WILFRID: *(With quick appreciation.)* And you *knew* he was innocent. I understand.

ROMAINE: But you do not understand at all. *I* knew he was *guilty*.

SIR WILFRID: *(Thunderstruck.)* But aren't you afraid?

ROMAINE: Afraid?

SIR WILFRID: Of linking your life with a murderer's.

ROMAINE: You don't understand—we love each other.

SIR WILFRID: The first time I met you I said you were a very remarkable woman—I see no reason to change my opinion. (*Crosses and exits up C.*)

WARDER: (*Off up L.*) It's no good going in there, miss. It's all over.

(*There is a* COMMOTION *off up L. and then a* GIRL *comes running on up L. She is a very young strawberry blonde with a crude, obvious appeal. She rushes to* LEONARD *through the* Q.C.'s *bench and meets him down* R.C.)

GIRL: Len, darling, you're free. (*She embraces him.*) Isn't it wonderful? They're trying to keep me out. Darling, it's been awful. I've been nearly crazy.

ROMAINE: (*With sudden violent harshness.*) Leonard—who—is—this girl!

GIRL: (*To* ROMAINE *defiantly.*) I'm Len's girl. I know all about *you.* You're not his wife. Never have been. (*She crosses to* R. *of* ROMAINE.) You're years older than him, and you just got hold of him—and you've done your best to hang him. But that's all over now. (*She turns to* LEONARD.) We'll go abroad like you said on one of your cruises—to all those grand places. We'll have a wonderful time.

ROMAINE: Is—this—true? Is she your girl, Leonard?

LEONARD: (*Hesitates, then decides that the situation must be accepted.*) Yes, she is.

(*The* GIRL *crosses above* LEONARD *to* R. *of him.*)

ROMAINE: After all I've done for you . . . What can *she* do for you that can compare with that?

LEONARD: (*Flinging off all disguise of manner and showing coarse brutality.*) She's fifteen years younger than you are. (*He laughs.*)

(ROMAINE *flinches as though struck.*)

(*He crosses to* R. *of* ROMAINE. *Menacingly.*) I've got the money. I've been acquitted, and I can't be tried again, so don't go shooting off your mouth, or you'll just get *yourself* hanged as an accessory after the fact. (*He turns to the* GIRL *and embraces her.*)

ROMAINE: (*Picks up the knife from the table. Throwing her head back in sudden dignity.*) No, that will not happen. I shall not be tried as an accessory after the fact. I shall not be tried for perjury. I shall be tried for murder— (*She stabs* LEONARD *in the back.*) the murder of the only man I ever loved.

(LEONARD *drops. The* GIRL *screams.* MAYHEW *bends over* LEONARD, *feels his pulse, and shakes his head.*)

(*She looks up at the* JUDGE'S *seat.*) Guilty, my lord.

CURTAIN

Paper Trail

Joan Hess

Wellington House
#1 Wellington Road
Hampser, NC 27444
November 13, 1972

The Hampser Hero
c/o Hampser High School
Hampser, NC 27444

 Suspicions?

For your reading of "Paper Trail," keep a separate "Suspicions?" journal in which you note your suspicions and the clues they're based on. "Paper Trail" takes the form of a series of letters.

To the faculty adviser:

Congratulations on your ranking in the national contest for high school journals. How exceedingly proud of your young men and women you must be! All I can say is "Bravo!" These days so many young people are obsessed with athletics, politics, and other less admirable pursuits. To have such a dedicated and talented group must bring you vast satisfaction.

I shall assume that you are aware of my novels published under the pseudonyms of Alisha Wells and Alexandra Worthington. I would be delighted to speak to your classes. Wellington House can be rather lonely at times, and I truly look forward to each and every opportunity to visit with my fans and discuss my work. I cannot begin to count the number of times I've presented talks at luncheons—and loved every bite of it!

Perhaps I take advantage of my position in the literary community when I make this modest proposal, but I think you will agree it offers a splendid opportunity for one of your students. My filing has simply gotten away from me, as if it were a freight train barreling through the door each and every day. I put away one paper, and three more arrive in the post! If it weren't so aggravating, it would be amusing. But what with my editors calling, the publicity demands, and the necessity of responding to an increasing amount of fan mail, I can hardly find the time to write.

I would be so deeply grateful if you could recommend a student to come in for an hour or two a week and help me conquer this quagmire of paperwork. I regret that I can pay only minimum wage, but I hope one of your students who aspires to become an author might find it interesting to deal with my busy work. I would prefer a young woman, especially one who needs financial help and will appreciate any guidance I can give her in her future career. Please call me at your convenience.

Yours truly,
Aurora Wellington

T'was the night before Christmas
or the week before, anyway

Dear Heather,

You are going to die when I tell you this! I mean, you'd better sit down before you read one more word! I am working for Aurora Wellington, who just happens to be Alisha Wells and Alexandra Worthington. Are you dead??? I was so excited when you sent me *The Willow Lake Legacy* for my birthday that I finished it that very night. Then last month Miss Hayes gets this letter from her, and she wants somebody to file papers for her, and Miss Hayes asks me if I want to, and I just about faint! Do I want to work for Aurora Wellington? That's like asking me if I wanna marry Paul McCartney—right?

Hayes is waiting, so I say I might if the hours are right, and she says well, if you're not interested I'll speak to Rebecca Lawson, and I say maybe I'll ask my mother and it might be okay (Ma's the same and no, Dad hasn't written, but I figure it's hard to find stamps in prison). Anyway, I say yeah, and she gives me a letter that's *actually* from Aurora Wellington and tells me to go to her house (!!!) Saturday morning at ten.

I put on my blue jumper and the super shirt you gave me for Christmas last year, but I'm about to wet my pants when I ring the bell. She's written—what? forty books?—and I'm standing on her porch, ringing her bell like I'm a Girl Scout selling cookies. Finally, she answers the door, and is she beautiful! Think about it—how would you expect her to look? She's old, sure, but she has ash blond hair to her shoulders, deep lavender eyes like Elizabeth Taylor, and she's wearing—get this—a peignoir that's the exact same shade as her eyes. She's got to be at least fifty, but her complexion's right off the cover of *Seventeen*. She wouldn't make cheerleader—but who wants to be a dumb cheerleader when you can make zillions of dollars writing steamy novels?

My knees are knocking, but I manage to stammer my name and before I know it, we're sitting in the "parlor," as she calls it, me with a Coke and her with gin, and she's telling me (your humble second cousin!) her problems. Since I doubt Paul McCartney's going to call (for the record, Charlie and I broke up, so he's not calling either), I figure I've been snatched straight up to heaven. She tells me how she cannot concentrate on her "work" with all the paperwork lying around to depress her, and she wants me to come in for three hours on Saturday mornings and help out.

So for the last three Saturdays your cousin, the one and only greatest soon-to-be world-famous novelist, drops by the home of Aurora Wellington and reads her mail. Officially, I'm getting paid for three hours, but she comes in to chat and somehow it turns into four or five. Last week she had me do her grocery shopping on top of everything else, and I was so hungry I ate one of her apples on the way back from the store. If you'd like further details, you owe me a letter.

Eat your heart out,
Kristy

Wellington House
#1 Wellington Road
Hampser, NC 27444
March 15, 1973

Friends of the Barport Library
101 Swinton Lane
Barport, NC 27031

Dear Miss Chart,

Miss Wellington is dreadfully sorry that she will be unable to speak at your luncheon next month and has asked me to pass along her regrets. As you know, Miss Wellington has always felt nothing but the deepest respect for the public library system's dedication to literacy. Only her frantic writing schedule could deter her from the opportunity to express her gratitude for your good works in the community. She dearly hopes you will forgive her when you read *Devilish Delights* (by Alexandra Worthington) a year from now.

Yours truly,
Kristen Childers

March 23, 1973

Dear Miss Hayes,

I'm really sorry that I didn't have time to do the interview with the head of the creative writing department at the college. I know it's too late for excuses, but Miss Wellington is having me work all day on Saturdays and sometimes on Sundays, and my mother's in the hospital again. I promise that I'll do better and won't miss any deadlines.

Sorry,
Kristy C.

Wellington House
#1 Wellington Road
Hampser, NC 27444
May 3, 1973

Dear Tommie,

Your idea was absolutely brilliant! The girl isn't especially brilliant, but she is ever so diligent and such a perfectionist that at times I want to throw my hands in the air and give up the ghost. The child can be dictatorial, if you can believe it—I'm almost afraid to open my mail, read it, and lay it down somewhere in my office, because along will come grim little Kristy, the incriminating evidence clutched in her sweaty hand, demanding to know if I've lost the envelope with the return address or gone completely batty and responded without consulting her! Consulting her, mind you! I'm old enough to be . . . her big sister, not to mention being a best-selling author (did you see the divine review in *Heartbeat Digest* last week?), and I'm being ordered about by a sweet young snippet who's not yet graduated from high school.

I know, I'm being utterly absurd. Now that I've trained her, why shouldn't I allow her to take complete control of the tedium so that I can take advantage of all the lovely free time to write, write, write—and meet the next nasty deadline? Yes, Tommie darling, I'm well aware that the book's due in less than a month and that daft young adolescent in publicity is putting together the tour. If you were more of a friend and less of a slave driver, you'd absolutely insist they put me up at the Plaza this year.

Huggies,
Aurora Borealis

A midsummer night's eve (maybe)

Dear Cuz,

I am absolutely pea green jealous about you going to Chapel Hill! There'll be so many gorgeous men that you won't have time to study, much less to "pursue a degree in political history." Try to think fondly of me as you take a toke (just joking!!!).

The junior college will have to do until I find a bag of money on the street. Ma's back at the butterfly farm (aka the rehab center), as I'm sure Aunt Sissie has told you, and her health insurance has run out. Miss W. is letting me work every day for a few hours, but I'm barely scraping by. I'd ask Dad, but I think he earns about ten cents an hour making license plates. He sent me a box of stationery for graduation. I hear you got a car, you lucky dog. Want a personalized plate? I know where to get one—ha ha.

Yeah, I'd like to hit up Miss W. for a raise, but writers don't make as much money as you'd think and she has a pretty quiet life. Nobody ever comes by, as far as I can tell, and she doesn't do anything except write all day and brood all night. She got mad at her agent because of some silly thing and changed her telephone number, so now it's unlisted. I may be the only person on the planet who can call her. And, boy, did I learn my lesson last week! On the way to her house, I had a flat tire, and by the time I got it changed, I was two hours late. She about had a kitten and made me promise to call whenever I'm going to be five minutes late. Remember that crazy lady who lived next door to us the summer you came? Miss W. makes *her* look like a Junior League president!!!

Okay, I'm exaggerating—Miss W. doesn't own three dozen cats. Just one, and it's a mangy, motheaten old thing named Lady Amberline after the heroine in *Sweet Surrender* (or vice versa). I wish the darn thing would surrender itself to a garbage truck! Every time I look at her, I get itchy, and I spray myself for fleas once a week.

Charlie joined the army and shipped out to some base in Texas. The night before he left, we went out to dinner at a fancy restaurant and had this really serious talk, but basically he wants me to stay home and knit socks for two years. I would have laughed in his face—had I not been so tired that it sounded like a super idea.

To answer your nosy questions: I snooped through Miss W.'s papers and she is fifty-seven years old! Can you believe it? In person she looks every bit as sleek as she does on her cover shot, even if it was taken at least twenty years ago. She's never been married, although she does drop dark hints about a lost love, and her only relative is some cousin in Tallahassee who occasionally calls or writes. No, she doesn't read anyone else's books, but she absolutely despises Veronica St. James and is forever making hysterically funny comments about her. The house is about a hundred years old and not in great shape, but it's "the ancestral home" that she inherited from dear departed "Papa" back in the days of the dinosaurs. The living room's a shrine to her awards (lots of them!) and yes, her bed has pink satin sheets and a ruffly canopy.

So, days with Miss W. and nights without Charlie. Life's a bowl of cherries, and I'm in the pits!!

Love,
Kristy

Wellington House
#1 Wellington Road
Hampser, NC 27444
February 27, 1974

Darling Tommie,

I shall arrive at the Plaza around five in the afternoon on Friday. I would adore to allow you to take me to dinner, but the train does take quite a long time and I'm afraid I'll be utterly exhausted. Tell Natalie that I shall call upon her at eleven the next morning to discuss this latest travesty of a cover. No reader in her right mind would give it a second glance—much less buy it!

Kristy will stay at the house during my tour to feed Lady Amberline, collect the mail, water the plants, and fend off burglars. The girl is a dear thing and ever so courageous about her family situation, which has all the makings of a gothic horror story. I've told you about her mother, a pathetic alcoholic, and her father, a contemporary blackguard if ever there were one. He's currently in prison for burglary, assault, attempted homicide, and a host of other barbaric charges.

Several weeks ago I drove by her house, simply out of curiosity, and it's one of those quaint tract houses with a weedy yellow lawn, at least one broken window, a cluttered carport, a roof within minutes of collapsing, and located in a development called, of all things, Clover Creek.

Dandelion Dump would be more fitting!

Kristy dropped out of college this semester, saying she was unable to pay her tuition. She mentioned that she'd applied at a local restaurant for the night shift, but I told her in no uncertain terms that I should not be comfortable employing someone who, if I may lapse into colloquialisms, slings hash. No greasy fingers on my correspondence, thank you! Although my budget is already stretched to its meager limit, I told her to plan to put in a full day's work five days a week until she is able to return to school.

I must tell you this, Tommie dear, but never ever breathe a word of it to her! She's been dating a local boy for several months, and with her mother unavailable, I felt that someone should take a maternal interest in the matter and assess the boy. She arranged for him to come to the house to pick her up one evening last week and brought him into the parlor to meet me. For the occasion, he chose blue jeans, white socks, sneakers, and the sort of blue cotton shirt one associates with factory workers (and why not? It seems he works at a poultry processing establishment!). I said nothing, of course, but the next day I did tell Kristy that he seemed curiously inarticulate, unintelligent, and we laughed until we cried as I painted a vivid picture of his dreary, beery future as a line foreman of a merry little band of chicken pluckers. I do believe we'll see no more of that young man, thank God. Kristy's indispensable, and I'm not about to allow her to elope with a moon-faced factory worker!

Anyway, darling, lunch at the Russian Tea Room on Saturday!

Your obedient servant,
Aurora

Wellington House
#1 Wellington Road
Hampser, NC 27444
March 15, 1974

Dear Mrs. Cathwright,

I regret to inform you that your services are no longer desired at Wellington House. I have reviewed the household accounts, and was tempted to bring to Miss Wellington's attention numerous questionable purchases from Maclay's Market, an establishment owned, I understand, by your brother-in-law.

However, I feel it best not to disturb Miss Wellington. Should you desire references, please contact me directly. Miss Wellington is much too preoccupied with her work to speak to you in person or to communicate with you in any fashion whatsoever, but if you insist, I cannot promise that she will not file charges. Enclosed is severance pay of two weeks.

Yours truly,
Kristen Childers

From the desk of Aurora Wellington
March 28, 1974

Dear Mrs. C.,

Kristy has told me of your sudden decision to retire and move to Earlsville to be near your son and grandchildren. Although I am devastated by the loss of your invaluable services after all these years, I do understand your feelings. I don't know how I shall survive without your chicken salad and flaky, sinfully rich cream pies. You've spoiled me rotten for twenty years, you wicked woman! Lady Amberline sends her fondest regards, and does hope you'll send photographs of those darling babies.

Warmly,
Miss W.

Wellington House
#1 Wellington Road
Hampser, NC 27444
September 2, 1975

Dear Mrs. Harold Maron,

I still giggle every time I think of you being married! Doesn't it feel totally weird to have a new name after all these years? Harold looks divine in the photographs, you are radiant, and even our bratty little cousin Wendy is sweet (did she put thistles in the flower basket?). I'm sick I missed the wedding.

Miss W. still hasn't recovered completely and is doing most of her writing in bed these days. You'd think the doctors could figure out what's wrong after all those tests, but no one has any ideas and poor Miss W. often feels faint if she ventures downstairs. I helped her out to the garden yesterday and we sat in the gazebo all afternoon, her dictating (and drinking gin, of course) and me scribbling until I thought my fingers would bleed. *The Scarlet Sand,* for your information, a Worthington book. It's going to be super—and after the disappointing sales figures for *The Passages of Pleasure,* it'd better be.

Did Mrs. Harold Maron come out of her honeymoon daze long enough to notice the return address? After the funeral, I went back to the house and found the sheriff howling on the doorstep. It seems my mother forgot to pay property taxes, and with the cost of the funeral and all the bills from the butterfly farm, there was no way I could catch up on the taxes and at the same time have electricity! Apparently, someone's already offered to buy it for back taxes.

I rented an okay apartment, but when Miss W. discovered it was on the wrong side of the tracks—in every sense of the word—she insisted that I move into the house. I figured I might as well, since she was keeping me until eight or nine o'clock every night, although my paycheck sure hasn't been reflecting the extra hours. Now at least I get room and board out of the deal. No satin sheets, alas. Just cat hairs on my pillow, Lady Amberline's cute way of reminding me of my allergies.

Love,
Sneezy

Wellington House
#1 Wellington Road
Hampser, NC 27444
May 29, 1976

Penman Publishing, Inc.
375 Hudson Street
New York, NY 10014
Miss Natalie Burlitzer, editor

Dear Miss Burlitzer,

Miss W. asked me to let you know that the manuscript of *Lady Amberline's Revenge* is within a few days of completion and should reach you by the end of next week. She's been working on it around the clock and is sure you will be as delighted with it as she is.

Should you wish to discuss the manuscript, we will be at the lake house for the summer. There is no telephone, but the proprietor of the general store will convey messages, and I've been told you have his number. I look forward to meeting you this fall when we're in New York for the release of *The Sins of the Whittiers*.

Yours truly,
Kristen Childers

Banbury Cottage
RFD 1, Box 18
Willow Lake, NC 27019
July 25, 1976

Veronica, my dearest cohort,

I was so incredibly pleased for you when I saw that effervescent review in *Romantic Times*! If only the gal could have gotten the plot synopsis a bit less muddled—but we old hacks know how clumsy reviewers can be. I'm sure you laughed at that banal and ever so tacky line in paragraph four about "St. James's passion for convoluted prose," and also at the "stale predictability of the story." Then again, she did get the title right, and what else matters?

Although I'd intended to stay here until the end of August, we're heading back home tomorrow. Usually I can rely on total solitude at this end of the lake, but this year the cabin just down the road was rented to a trio of college boys . . . from Yale, I believe. There's certainly nothing Ivy League about them, let me tell you! They're forever thrashing and bellowing in the lake as if they were ungainly bears and playing loud music until all hours of the night. One of them has cozied up to Kristy and lured her to their squalid parties, which no doubt degenerate into orgies of the most primitive and repulsive sort.

So I'm virtually getting no work done. Yesterday afternoon I ran out of typewriter paper, but Kristy was out in a battered rowboat with "her beau" and failed to return until after sunset. The beer on her breath was enough to make me quite ill to my stomach. She apologized as best she could, but I told her to start packing at that very hour and not to leave the house under any circumstances. I can only hope they've failed to exchange addresses. What on earth will I do if he begins showing up at Wellington House?

Your number-one fan,
Aurora

Wellington House
#1 Wellington Road
Hampser, NC 27444
October 1, 1976

Wee Care Animal Clinic
454 Pathway Road
Hampser, NC 27444

Dear Dr. Wallsby,

Miss Wellington has asked me to express her gratitude for all the loving care you and your staff bestowed on Lady Amberline on that tragic day. We have searched the house from top to bottom and can only conclude that Lady Amberline must have slipped out and chanced upon the poison in a neighbor's garden shed. After some consideration, Miss Wellington has decided that a new kitten would only cause her to grieve more deeply over Lady Amberline's untimely demise.

Sincerely,
Kristy Childers

Wellington House
#1 Wellington Road
Hampser, NC 27444
September 16, 1977

Dearest Tommie,

Kristy and I had a lovely summer at the lake house. This year there was no one to disturb us, and I was able to sit on the porch all day while Kristy tended to the chores and brought me trays at mealtime, always with a little vase of wildflowers. Once a tendril of poison ivy crept in, but I spotted it and Kristy nearly cried when she apologized, and so of course I forgave her. I know you think it's appallingly bucolic, but I get more writing done there in three months than I do the rest of the year. Whenever I need inspiration, I gaze out at the rippling azure water—and *voilà!* "Monica turned her azure eyes toward Dr. Bodley and the faintest hint of a smile rippled across her pale, worried face."

The visit was timely, I must admit. I had Kristy volunteer at the hospital last spring in order to glean some insights into the dynamics of the place. She became quite adept at sneaking into the emergency room to observe the gory casualties, and came home each evening with stories both charmingly lurid and screechingly funny. All I can say is I do not intend to be placed in one—ever.

The problems began with some shaggy young intern whom she took to meeting for coffee after his shift and occasionally on his free days. One night she came home well after midnight, and it was obvious they had behaved indiscreetly. I said nothing, of course, but took it upon myself to have a word with the head of the program, one of Papa's old friends who should have retired decades ago! He was quite stuffy in his refusal to take action until I mentioned the possibility of an endowment for cancer research. Our young "Dr. Kildare" has decided to complete his internship at a hospital in California.

Don't think for an instant that I deserve to be scolded for interfering in Kristy's personal life. For one thing, the poor girl is technically an orphan and someone really and truly must watch out for her. If I allowed her to roam the streets when we're in New York, I have no doubt whatsoever she'd come back with someone sleazier than that convict father of hers. Her taste in men is atrocious, and without my constant supervision, she might well become the proverbial good time that was had by all!

I've encouraged her to attempt some writing of her own, but I fear it was an egregious error on my part. Only last week, she showed me the first chapter of a novel. I did my best not to laugh as I pointed out the weaknesses in her little story and the shallow characterizations.

I'm sending a snapshot of Pittypat, who simply appeared at the back door of the lake house one morning and refused to leave. I took one look at those big blue eyes and silky whiskers, and told Kristy to fetch a saucer of milk!

Your silly, softhearted author,
Aurora

Wellington House
#1 Wellington Road
Hampser, NC 27444
November 2, 1977

Wee Care Animal Clinic
454 Pathway Road
Hampser, NC 27444

Dear Dr. Wallsby,

Once again Miss Wellington has asked me to express her gratitude for your concern during the tragedy. I'm sure all of us are horrified that anyone could be so vicious as to strangle an innocent kitten and leave its poor little body in the gazebo. Miss Wellington was overwhelmed with shock when she found it, but she has finally recovered and is able to work.

Yours truly,
Kristen Childers

From the desk of Aurora Wellington
12-13-77

Dearest Veronica,

Yes, I think I will accept your kind invitation to spend a few days in Atlanta. The weather's as dreary as my thoughts (I did tell you about Pittypat, didn't I?), but I cherish the supposition that elegant luncheons, lavish dinner parties, and dedicated late night bouts of drinking and gossip will be my salvation.

It's so kind of you to consider Kristy. I must offer her regrets, alas. The deadline for the next Wells manuscript is coming up, and I've made so many revisions that she'll have to retype all six hundred pages during the holiday season.

See you in a week!

Wellington House
#1 Wellington Road
Hampser, NC 27444
January 6, 1978

Mrs. Janice O'Leod
1477 Lakeside Road
Tallahassee, FL 32304

Dear Mrs. O'Leod,

Miss Wellington apologizes for not writing herself, but the holiday season has thrown her off schedule and she is working frantically on her newest book. She asked me to let you know that she was delighted with the gloves and umbrella you sent her for Christmas, and hopes you enjoy the autographed copy of *The Sins of the Whittiers.*

I regret that I cannot give you our new unlisted telephone number, as per your request, but once it's been given to someone, it seems to spread like a virus until we're literally inundated with calls. I am under order to guard it as if it were a Vatican treasure.

As much as Miss Wellington would love to see you this spring, her dubious health dictates that she must decline your invitation to meet at your hotel for lunch. Due to time restraints, she is unable to entertain guests here at Wellington House.

Yours truly,
Kristen Childers

Wellington House
#1 Wellington Road
Hampser, NC 27444
September 18, 1983

Dear Traci,

I was thrilled to get your letter after all these years. I would have sold my soul to go to our tenth reunion, but Miss W. was so sick that there was no way to leave her for even an hour. She's had this problem for years, on and off, and it flares up at the most inopportune times. Did you hear why I wasn't at the fifth reunion? While I was getting dressed, I heard a noise and discovered Miss W. lying at the bottom of the stairs. It wasn't until the next day that I finally persuaded her to go to the emergency room for X-rays. Nothing broken, thank God, but she hobbled around with a cane for months.

My glamorous life? Get real—your carpools and babysitting crises and burned pot roasts sound a lot more exciting than what I do. You would not believe the amount of paperwork involved in being an author. It takes me all morning to sort through requests for personal appearances, send photographs to fans, respond to queries from the editorial and publicity departments, answer sweet little letters from junior high girls, and fend off supplications from "wannabee" writers who'd like Miss W. to critique their thousand-page manuscripts. Miss W. ordered me to fire the cook after an heirloom ring vanished, so I fix lunch and when the weather is nice, we eat in the gazebo. She dictates until it's too dark for me to see, and after I fix dinner, we spend our really "glamorous" evenings in the parlor. Miss W. can be somewhat funny when she's talking about some of her rivals, especially after she's been cooing on the telephone with them for hours.

I'm glad Heather saved the postcard from the Plaza, but the inside of the room's about all I see when we're there. Miss W. insists that I bring the portable typewriter and do revisions or work on the newsletter. Want to be on the mailing list so you'll know what Miss W. has for breakfast and what inspired her to write *Vanessa's Folly?**

Enough of this dazzling lifestyle. So Charlie's getting bald, and his wife resembles a tugboat? Three children can do that. I almost threw up when I heard Sam Longspur's a dentist—I went out with him our junior year, and he spent so much time poking his tongue down my throat that I still get queasy just thinking about it. I knew Heather was pregnant, but I agree that I wouldn't have dared put on a bathing suit if I were such a blimp (don't you dare repeat that!).

I must stop. Miss W. wants me to pack for our annual jaunt to New York, where she will wine and dine with her editor and agent, and I will merely whine. Thanks so much for all the luscious gossip from the reunion. Maybe I'll make the next one and Charlie will be as bald as a persimmon.

Love,
Kristy

*An English muffin and tea, and have you ever read *The Roses in Eden* by Veronica St. James?

Wellington House
#1 Wellington Road
Hampser, NC 27444
November 10, 1984

Thomas Domingo Literary Agency
188 W. 79th Street
New York, NY 10122

Dear Mr. Domingo,

I have reviewed the royalty statements of 10/31/84 and have found serious discrepancies either in the publisher's computations or in yours. Please note return figures for *Summer of the Shadows* and the lack of information regarding foreign sales of the same. Also, in that *Cape Serenity* has gone into a third printing, I find it curious that no sales are reported for the six-month period prior to the statement.

    I am hesitant to bring this to Miss W.'s attention. For the last five years she has relied on me to handle all of her business affair, and trusts me to do so with meticulous care. Frankly, she is unable to work more than three or four hours a day as it is. I cannot allow her to lose that precious time by concerning herself with financial matters.

    Please respond to this within ten days.

Yours truly,
Kristen Childers

From the desk of Aurora Wellington

Tommie, dearest:

I am at a loss for words—after having written millions of them over the last twenty years! Apparently you are, too, in that you've failed to answer my last two letters. But if what Kristy has shown me proves to be true, then I can never forgive you. How many years have I trusted you? Now Kristy has told me that you have systematically stolen thousands and thousands of dollars from me. Tommie, dear Tommie, you must come down immediately after the holidays and review all this over a civilized glass of gin, not in the gazebo at this time of year, but surely in the parlor.

Yours in bewilderment,
Aurora

Wellington House
#1 Wellington Road
Hampser, NC 27444
December 10, 1984

NC State Correctional Facility
Raleigh, NC 27603
#1987-431-1

Dear Dad,

So they're letting you out after all these years, are they? I'm sure their rehabilitation efforts have taken effect and you will enter society determined to lead a blameless life. It must be hard to imagine yourself living on the outside, but let's hope you've had enough vocational training to find a job—even in these economically depressed days. I realize there's still a lot of discrimination against convicted felons, and it's really not fair to send you out onto the streets with only a few dollars and a new suit. Anyway, good luck job hunting and don't faint when you see how expensive everything is out here!

As you know, I live with an incredibly rich old woman who's written best-selling novels for thirty years. I hate to say it, but she'd be utterly helpless without me. She's small and frail and her hearing seems to get worse every year, but thank God her mind is quite sharp and she has a fantastic memory for details. She never forgets a face and can describe it with astonishing preciseness—as can all writers. On the other hand, she can't remember to put away her jewelry in the box on the dresser in her bedroom, and last week on her way to bed, she left the kitchen door ajar and the house was freezing by morning. We're lucky that she's too miserly to install decent locks; she's misplaced the keys so often that I've become quite adept with a hairpin. I guess that's one talent I inherited from you—ha, ha.

Anyway, I think I would like to see you, if only for old time's sake. The only two days I will not be available are December 24 and 25, when I'm visiting Cousin Heather for the first time in years. She has four kids now, and Harold is some kind of manager at his office. This time I've warned Miss W. that I am definitely going, even if she objects or claims to be sick. I'm hoping to be at Heather's by dark and will be home the next evening. I feel terribly guilty about leaving Miss W. all alone in the house for two days, but our cleaning woman insists on being with her own family and no one else ever comes by to see Miss W. I don't really blame them; the house is so isolated at the end of the road, and you can't have neighbors if you own all the land for several miles. It's the only drawback I can think of to being rich!

Write me a note once you're settled. I'd tell you to call, but the squirrels have been gnawing on the telephone lines again, and it usually takes several weeks for a repairman to come.

Your daughter,
Kristy

Wellington House
#1 Wellington Road
Hampser, NC 27444
April 11, 1985

Shady Oaks Realty, Inc.
3168 Katherine Avenue
Hampser, NC 27444

Dear Ms. Rowan,

Please address all future correspondence concerning the sale of Wellington House and the adjoining property to me, c/o Thomas Domingo Literary Agency, 188 West Seventy-ninth Street, New York, NY 10122. I'm sure you're aware of how lengthy a process probate can be, but I believe that we can entertain offers and perhaps work out a lease-purchase agreement until a sale can be finalized.

As for the house Miss Wellington owned in the Clover Creek addition, I have rented it to a distant member of my family and will allow him to occupy it at least until the estate is settled.

Should an emergency arise, I am staying at the Plaza and you may leave a message at the desk. If the remodeling proceeds on schedule, as of the first of June I will be in permanent residence at the house on Willow Lake.

Yours truly,
Kristen Childers

Dear Suzanne,

I'm sorry it's taken so long for me to respond to your charming letter, but I must say I'm impressed with the dedication you've shown in discovering my real name and tracking me down at this address. I'm delighted that you enjoyed *Lady Amberline's Fortune,* and I agree that she's a feisty young woman with a strong sense of ambition. You might watch for *Shadows and Smoke,* a more contemporary novel about a girl just a few years older than you!

As for your generous offer, I fear I must demur. Although there are days that I feel as if I'm drowning in papers, I simply wouldn't be comfortable having someone come in to assist with the filing and correspondence. You sound like a sensible girl, perhaps as ambitious as Amberline, and I'm confident that you'll find a way to have a successful career in literature, just as I did.

Warm wishes,
Kristy Childers

 How Clever?

1. How many years are covered by the various correspondence that makes up the story? In other words, how long did it take for Kristy to become "the one and only greatest soon-to-be world-famous novelist"? How many different people write the letters?

2. What might be ironic about Kristen Childers first and last names? Explain, in detail, how the "paper trail" of the title leads to Kristy.

3. In the opening letter of the story, Aurora Wellington states that she believes her offer is "a splendid opportunity" for one of Miss Hayes's students on the high school journal, "The Hampster Hero," who "aspires to become an author." Explain how this prediction turned out to be true.

4. Explain why in the last letter that makes up the story, Kristen Childers tells Suzanne that she "wouldn't be comfortable having someone in to assist with the filing and correspondence." Isn't she "drowning in papers" just the way Aurora Wellington was? Do you see a possible attempt at "poetic justice" in Suzanne's "charming letter"? Explain.

5. In the last lines of her letter to the faculty adviser of the Hampster High School newspaper, Aurora Wellington mentions that she will provide guidance in her future career to the young woman who takes the job. How did the fate of Aurora Wellington in effect serve Kristy Childers as a kind of "guidance" in her future career?

6. From what evidence—direct, indirect, or circumstantial—did you conclude that Kristy Childers slowly but surely took over Aurora Wellington's life and caused her death a dozen years after she went to work for her? Other than evidence of one kind or another, what did you base your belief on?

7. Explain the irony in Aurora Wellington's "modest proposal" of November 13, 1972 and in her behind-the-scenes attempts to take complete control over Kristy's life.

8. Did Kristy's father play a part in Aurora Wellington's death? Justify your opinion.

9. What other crimes do you believe Kristy was responsible for during the twelve years she worked for Aurora Wellington? What evidence—direct, indirect, or circumstantial—do you have? Other than evidence of one kind or another, what do you base your belief on?

10. In your opinion, which letter contains what you would consider to be the key turning point for Kristy on her road to "a successful career in literature"? Explain why you think so.

11. Explain how the letter of March 15, 1974 foreshadows the letter of November 10, 1984. Do you think both letters were actually sent? Explain your reasoning for each letter.

12. In your opinion, why isn't it clearly stated in the story how Aurora Wellington died? Did anyone get away with murder? Was there no justice—legal, moral, poetic? Explain.

13. Do the twenty-three letters of the story constitute a "paper trail" of evidence? In other words, do the letters contain sufficient incriminating evidence for charges to be brought?

14. Who does the detection and reflection in the story "Paper Trail"? What do you find interesting about your answer?

DetectWrite: Characterization and Plot

1. How effective did you find the author's decision to tell the story through a series of letters sent by two characters to a number of different people? Explain.

2. Try rewriting any letter of the story in a more conventional narrative form, being certain to place the two characters involved together in the scene. How does your version compare with Joan Hess's approach?

3. In a mystery story you would write, would you consider using a correspondence structure similar to the one used by Hess? Why or why not?

4. Consider writing a mystery story like "Paper Trail" in which there is no detective except for the reader of the story. What do you believe to be the advantages and disadvantages to this approach?

DETECTWRITE: Dialogue

In "Paper Trail," since no two characters are ever together and all the words in the story are in the form of written correspondence, technically, there is no dialogue. However, each letter could be considered a kind of monologue, with the understanding that no monologue of one character is ever heard by the other. Read (or share the reading of) "Paper Trail" aloud to hear what this kind of story sounds like—and if you like the sound of it, try writing one of your own.

Sorry, Wrong Number

Lucille Fletcher

The Characters

Mrs. Stevenson
1st Operator
1st Man
2nd Man
Chief Operator
2nd Operator
3rd Operator
4th Operator
5th Operator
Information
Hospital Receptionist
Western Union
Sergeant Duffy
A Lunch Room Counter Attendant

 Suspicions?

As you read this play, ask and answer your own questions in your writing journal or notebook.

SCENE: *As curtain rises, we see a divided stage, only the center part of which is lighted and furnished as Mrs. Stevenson's bedroom. Expensive, rather fussy furnishings. A large bed, on which Mrs. Stevenson, clad in bed-jacket, is lying. A night-table close by, with phone, lighted lamp, and pill bottles. A mantel, with clock, right. A closed door, right. A window, with curtains closed, rear. The set is lit by one lamp on night-table. It is enclosed by three flats. Beyond this central set, the stage, on either side, is in darkness.*

Mrs. Stevenson is dialing a number on phone, as curtain rises. She listens to phone, slams down receiver in irritation. As she does so, we hear sound of a train roaring by in the distance. She reaches for her pill bottle, pours herself a glass of water, shakes out pill, swallows it, then reaches for phone again, dials number nervously. SOUND: *Number being dialed on phone: Busy signal.*

MRS. STEVENSON: *(A querulous, self-centered neurotic)* Oh—dear! *(Slams down receiver. Dials Operator) (Scene: A spotlight, left of side flat, picks up, out of peripheral darkness, figure of 1st Operator, sitting with headphones at small table. If spotlight not available, use flashlight, clicked on by 1st Operator, illumining her face.)*

OPERATOR: Your call, please?

MRS. STEVENSON: Operator? I have been dialing Murray Hill 4-0098 now for the last three-quarters of an hour, and the line is always busy. But I don't see how it could be busy that long. Will you try it for me, please?

OPERATOR: Murray Hill 4-0098? One moment, please.

(Scene: She makes gesture of plugging in call through a switchboard.)

MRS. STEVENSON: I don't see how it could be busy all this time. It's my husband's office. He's working late tonight, and I'm all alone here in the house. My health is very poor—and I've been feeling so nervous all day . . .

OPERATOR: Ringing Murray Hill 4-0098 . . . *(Sound: Phone buzz. It rings three times. Receiver is picked up at other end.) (Scene: Spotlight picks up figure of a heavy-set man, seated at desk with phone on right side of dark periphery of stage. He is wearing a hat. Picks up phone, which rings three times.)*

MAN: Hello.

MRS. STEVENSON: Hello . . . ? *(A little puzzled)* Hello. Is Mr. Stevenson there?

MAN: *(Into phone, as though he had not heard)* Hello . . . *(Louder)* Hello. *(Scene: Spotlight on left now moves from Operator to another man, George. A killer type, also wearing hat, but standing as in a phone booth. A three-sided screen may be used to suggest this.)*

2ND MAN: *(Slow heavy quality, faint foreign accent)* Hello.

1ST MAN: Hello, George?

GEORGE: Yes, sir.

MRS. STEVENSON: *(Louder and more imperious, to phone)* Hello. Who's this? What number am I calling, please?

1ST MAN: We have heard from our client. He says the coast is clear for tonight.

GEORGE: Yes, sir.

1ST MAN: Where are you now?

GEORGE: In a phone booth.

1ST MAN: Okay. You know the address. At eleven o'clock the private patrolman goes around to the bar on Second Avenue for a beer. Be sure that all the lights downstairs are out. There should be only one light visible from the street. At eleven-fifteen a subway train crosses the bridge. It makes a noise in case her window is open, and she should scream.

MRS. STEVENSON: *(Shocked)* Oh—HELLO! What number is this, please?

GEORGE: Okay. I understand.

1ST MAN: Make it quick. As little blood as possible. Our client does not wish to make her suffer long.

GEORGE: A knife okay, sir?

1ST MAN: Yes. A knife will be okay. And remember—remove the rings and bracelet and the jewelry in the bureau drawer. Our client wishes it to look like simple robbery.

GEORGE: Okay—I get— *(Scene: Spotlight suddenly goes out on George.)* *(Scene: A bland buzzing signal) (Scene: Spotlight goes off on 1st Man.)*

MRS. STEVENSON: *(Clicking phone)* Oh . . . ! *(Bland buzzing signal continues. She hangs up.)* How awful! How unspeakably . . . *(Scene: She lies back on her pillows, overcome for a few seconds, then suddenly pulls herself together, reaches for phone.) (Sound: Dialing. Phone buzz) (Scene: Spotlight goes on at 1st Operator's switchboard. 1st and 2nd Man exit as unobtrusively as possible, in darkness.)*

OPERATOR: Your call, please?

MRS. STEVENSON: *(Unnerved and breathless, into phone)* Operator. I—I've just been cut off.

OPERATOR: I'm sorry, madam. What number were you calling?

MRS. STEVENSON: Why—it was supposed to be Murray Hill 4-0098, but it wasn't. Some wires must have crossed—I was cut into a wrong number—and—I've just heard the most dreadful thing—a—a murder—and —*(imperiously)* Operator, you'll simply have to retrace that call at once.

OPERATOR: I beg your pardon, madam—I don't quite—

MRS. STEVENSON: Oh—I know it was a wrong number, and I had no business listening—but these two men—they were cold-blooded fiends—and they were going to murder somebody—some poor innocent woman—who was all alone—in a house near a bridge. And we've got to stop them—we've got to—

OPERATOR: *(Patiently)* What number were you calling, madam?

MRS. STEVENSON: That doesn't matter. This was a *wrong* number. And *you* dialed it. And we've got to find out what it was—immediately!

OPERATOR: But—madam—

MRS. STEVENSON: Oh—why are you so stupid? Look—it was obviously a case of some little slip of the finger. I told you to try Murray Hill 4-0098 for me—you dialed it but your finger must have slipped—and I was connected with some other number—and I could hear them, but they couldn't hear me. Now, I simply fail to see why you couldn't make that same mistake again—on purpose—why you couldn't *try* to dial Murray Hill 4-0098 in the same careless sort of way. . .

OPERATOR: *(Quickly)* Murray Hill 4-0098? I will try to get it for you, madam.

MRS. STEVENSON: *(Sarcastically)* Thank you. *(Scene: She bridles, adjusts herself on her pillows, reaches for handkerchief, wipes forehead, glancing uneasily for a moment toward window, while still holding phone.) (Sound of ringing: Busy signal)*

OPERATOR: I am sorry. Murray Hill 4-0098 is busy.

MRS. STEVENSON: *(Frantically clicking receiver)* Operator. Operator.

OPERATOR: Yes, madam.

MRS. STEVENSON: *(Angrily)* You *didn't* try to get that wrong number at all. I asked explicitly. And all you did was dial correctly.

OPERATOR: I am sorry. What number were you calling?

MRS. STEVENSON: Can't you, for once, forget what number I was calling and do something specific? Now I want to trace that call. It's my civic duty—it's *your* civic duty—to trace that call . . . and to apprehend those dangerous killers—and if *you* won't . . .

OPERATOR: *(Glancing around wearily)* I will connect you with the Chief Operator.

MRS. STEVENSON: *Please! (Sound of ringing)* Scene: *Operator puts hand over mouthpiece of phone, gestures into darkness. A half whisper:*

OPERATOR: Miss Curtis. Will you pick up on 17, please? *(Miss Curtis, Chief Operator, enters. Middle-aged, efficient type, pleasant. Wearing headphones.)*

MISS CURTIS: Yes, dear. What's the trouble?

OPERATOR: Somebody wanting a call traced. I can't make head nor tail of it. . . .

MISS CURTIS: *(Sitting down at desk, as Operator gets up)* Sure, dear. 17? *(She makes gesture of plugging in her headphone, coolly and professionally.)* This is the Chief Operator.

MRS. STEVENSON: Chief Operator? I want you to trace a call. A telephone call. Immediately. I don't know where it came from or who was making it, but it's absolutely necessary that it be tracked down. Because it was about a murder. Yes, a terrible, cold-blooded murder of a poor innocent woman—tonight—at eleven-fifteen.

CHIEF OPERATOR: I see.

MRS. STEVENSON: *(High-strung, demanding)* Can you trace it for me? Can you track down those men?

CHIEF OPERATOR: It depends, madam.

MRS. STEVENSON: Depends on what?

CHIEF OPERATOR: If the parties have stopped talking to each other.

MRS. STEVENSON: Oh—but—but of course they must have stopped talking to each other by *now*. That was at least five minutes ago—and they didn't sound like the type who would make a long call.

CHIEF OPERATOR: Well, I can try tracing it. *(Scene: She takes pencil out of her hair-do.)* Now—what is your name, madam?

MRS. STEVENSON: Mrs. Stevenson. Mrs. Elbert Stevenson. But—listen—

CHIEF OPERATOR: *(Writing it down)* And your telephone number?

MRS. STEVENSON: *(More irritated)* Plaza 4-2295. But if you go on wasting all this time— *(Scene: She glances at clock on mantel.)*

CHIEF OPERATOR: And what is your reason for wanting this call traced?

MRS. STEVENSON: My reason? Well—for heaven's sake—isn't it obvious? I overhear two men—they're killers—they're planning to murder this woman—it's a matter for the police.

CHIEF OPERATOR: Have you told the police?

MRS. STEVENSON: No. How could I?

CHIEF OPERATOR: Well, Mrs. Stevenson—I seriously doubt whether we could make this check for you at this time just on your say-so as a private individual. We'd have to have something more official.

MRS. STEVENSON: Oh—for heaven's sake! You mean to tell me I can't report a murder without getting tied up in all this red tape? Why—it's perfectly idiotic. All right, then. I *will* call the police. *(She slams down receiver.)* *(Scene: Spotlight goes off on two Operators.)* Ridiculous! *(Sound of dialling)* *(Scene: Mrs. Stevenson dials numbers on phone, as two Operators exit unobtrusively in darkness.)* *(On right of stage, spotlight picks up a 2nd Operator, seated like first, with headphones at table [same one vacated by 1st Man]).*

2ND OPERATOR: Your call, please?

MRS. STEVENSON: *(Very annoyed)* The Police Department—*please.*

2ND OPERATOR: Ringing the Police Department. *(Ring twice. Phone is picked up.) (Scene: Left stage, at table vacated by 1st and Chief Operator, spotlight now picks up Sergeant Duffy, seated in a relaxed position. Just entering beside him is a young man in cap and apron, carrying a large brown paper parcel, delivery boy for a local lunch counter. Phone is ringing.)*

YOUNG MAN: Here's your lunch, Sarge. They didn't have no jelly doughnuts, so I give you French crullers. Okay, Sarge?

S. DUFFY: French crullers. I got ulcers. Whyn't you make it apple pie? *(Picks up phone, which has rung twice)* Police department Precinct 43. Duffy speaking. *(Scene: Lunch Room Attendant, anxiously.)* We don't have no apple pie, either, Sarge—

MRS. STEVENSON: Police Department? Oh. This is Mrs. Stevenson—Mrs. Elbert Smythe Stevenson of 53 North Sutton Place. I'm calling up to report a murder. *(Scene: Duffy has been examining lunch, but double-takes suddenly on above.)*

DUFFY: Eh?

MRS. STEVENSON: I mean—the murder hasn't been committed yet. I just overheard plans for it over the telephone . . . over a wrong number that the operator gave me. *(Scene: Duffy relaxes, sighs, starts taking lunch from bag.)* I've been trying to trace down the call myself, but everybody is so stupid— and I guess in the end you're the only people who could *do* anything.

DUFFY: *(Not too impressed) (Scene: Attendant, who exits)* Yes, ma'am.

MRS. STEVENSON: *(Trying to impress him)* It was a perfectly *definite* murder. I heard their plans distinctly. *(Scene: Duffy begins to eat sandwich, phone at his ear.)* Two men were talking, and they were going to murder some woman at eleven-fifteen tonight—she lived in a house near a bridge.

DUFFY: Yes, ma'am.

MRS. STEVENSON: And there was a private patrolman on the street. He was going to go around for a beer on Second Avenue. And there was some third man—a client, who was paying to have this poor woman murdered—they were going to take her rings and bracelets—and use a knife . . . well, it's unnerved me dreadfully—and I'm not well. . . .

DUFFY: I see. *(Scene: Having finished sandwich, he wipes mouth with paper napkin.)* When was all this, ma'am?

MRS. STEVENSON: About eight minutes ago. Oh . . . *(Relieved)* Then you *can* do something? You *do* understand—

DUFFY: And what is your name, ma'am? *(Scene: He reaches for pad.)*

MRS. STEVENSON: *(Impatiently)* Mrs. Stevenson. Mrs. Elbert Stevenson.

DUFFY: And your address?

MRS. STEVENSON: 53 North Sutton Place. *That's* near a bridge. The Queensboro Bridge, you know—and *we* have a private patrolman on *our* street—and Second Avenue—

DUFFY: And what was that number you were calling?

MRS. STEVENSON: Murray Hill 4-0098. *(Scene: Duffy writes it down.)* But—that wasn't the number I overheard. I mean Murray Hill 4-0098 is my husband's office. *(Scene: Duffy, in exasperation, holds pencil poised.)* He's working late tonight, and I was trying to reach him to ask him to come home. I'm an invalid, you know—and it's the maid's night off—and I *hate* to be alone—even though he says I'm perfectly safe as long as I have the telephone right beside my bed.

DUFFY: *(Stolidly)* *(Scene: He has put pencil down, pushes pad away.)* Well—we'll look into it, Mrs. Stevenson—and see if we can check it with the telephone company.

MRS. STEVENSON: *(Getting impatient)* But the telephone company said they couldn't check the call if the parties had stopped talking. I've already taken care of *that*.

DUFFY: Oh—yes? *(Scene: He yawns slightly.)*

MRS. STEVENSON: *(High-handed)* Personally I feel you ought to do something far more immediate and drastic than just check the call. What good does checking the call do, if they've stopped talking? By the time you track it down, they'll already have committed the murder.

DUFFY: *(Scene: He reaches for paper cup of coffee.)* Well—we'll take care of it, lady. Don't worry. *(Scene: He begins to take off paper top of coffee container.)*

MRS. STEVENSON: I'd say the whole thing calls for a search—a complete and thorough search of the whole city. *(Scene: Duffy puts down phone for a moment, to work on cup, as her voice continues.)* I'm very near a bridge, and I'm not far from Second Avenue. And I know *I'd* feel a whole lot better if you sent around a radio car to *this* neighborhood at once.

DUFFY: *(Scene: Picks up phone again, drinks coffee.)* And what makes you think the murder's going to be committed in your neighborhood, ma'am?

MRS. STEVENSON: Oh—I don't know. The coincidence is so horrible. Second Avenue—the patrolman—the bridge. . . .

DUFFY: *(Scene: He sips coffee.)* Second Avenue is a very long street, ma'am. And do you happen to know how many bridges there are in the city of New York alone? Not to mention Brooklyn, Staten Island, Queens, and the Bronx?

And how do you know there isn't some little house out on Staten Island—on some little Second Avenue you never heard about? *(Scene: A long gulp of coffee)* How do you know they were even talking about New York at all?

MRS. STEVENSON: But I heard the call on the New York dialling system.

DUFFY: How do you know it wasn't a long distance call you overheard? Telephones are funny things. *(Scene: He sets down coffee.)* Look, lady, why don't you look at it this way? Supposing you hadn't broken in on that telephone call? Supposing you'd got your husband the way you always do? Would this murder have made any difference to you then?

MRS. STEVENSON: I suppose not. But it's so inhuman—so cold-blooded. . . .

DUFFY: A lot of murders are committed in this city every day, ma'am. If we could do something to stop 'em, we would. But a clue of this kind that's so vague isn't much more use to us than no clue at all.

MRS. STEVENSON: But, surely—

DUFFY: Unless, of course, you have some reason for thinking this call is phoney—and that someone may be planning to murder *you*?

MRS. STEVENSON: *Me?* Oh—no—I hardly think so. I—I mean—why should anybody? I'm alone all day and night—I see nobody except my maid Eloise—she's a big two-hundred-pounder—she's too lazy to bring up my breakfast tray—and the only other person is my husband Elbert—he's crazy about me—adores me—waits on me hand and foot—he's scarcely left my side since I took sick twelve years ago—

DUFFY: Well—then—there's nothing for you to worry about, is there? *(Scene: Lunch Counter Attendant has entered. He is carrying a piece of apple pie on a plate. Points it out to Duffy triumphantly.)* And now—if you'll just leave the rest of this to us—

MRS. STEVENSON: But what will you *do*? It's so late—it's nearly eleven o'clock.

DUFFY: *(Firmly)* *(Scene: He nods to Attendant, pleased)* We'll take care of it, lady.

MRS. STEVENSON: Will you broadcast it all over the city? And send out squads? And warn your radio cars to watch out—especially in suspicious neighborhoods like mine? *(Scene: Attendant, in triumph, has put pie down in front of Duffy. Takes fork out of his pocket, stands at attention, waiting.)*

DUFFY: *(More firmly)* Lady, I *said* we'd take care of it. *(Scene: Glances at pie.)* Just now I've got a couple of other matters here on my desk that require my immediate—

MRS. STEVENSON: Oh! *(She slams down receiver.)* Idiot. *(Scene: Duffy, listening at phone, hangs up. Shrugs. Winks at Attendant as though to say, "What a crazy character!" Attacks his pie as spotlight fades out.) (Mrs. Stevenson, in bed, looking at phone nervously)* Now—why did I do that? Now—he'll think I *am* a fool. *(Scene: She sits there tensely, then throws herself back against pillows, lies there a moment, whimpering with self-pity.)* Oh—why doesn't Elbert come home? *Why* doesn't he? *(Scene: We hear sound of train roaring by in the distance. She sits up reaching for phone.) (Sound of dialling operator) (Scene: Spotlight picks up 2nd Operator, seated right.)*

OPERATOR: Your call, please?

MRS. STEVENSON: Operator—for Heaven's sake—will you ring that Murray Hill 4-0098 number again? I can't think what's keeping him so long.

OPERATOR: Ringing Murray Hill 4-0098. *(Rings; busy signal)* The line is busy. Shall I—

MRS. STEVENSON: *(Nastily)* I can hear it. You don't have to tell me. I know it's busy. *(Slams down receiver) (Scene: Spotlight fades off on 2nd Operator.) (Scene: Mrs. Stevenson sinks back against pillows again, whimpering to herself fretfully. She glances at clock, then turning, punches her pillows up, trying to make herself comfortable. But she isn't. Whimpers to herself as she squirms restlessly in bed.)* If I could only get out of this bed for a little while. If I could get a breath of fresh air—or just lean out the window—and see the street. . . . *(Scene: She sighs, reaches for pill bottle, shakes out a pill. As she does so, the phone rings. She darts for it instantly.)* Hello, Elbert? Hello. Hello. Hello. Oh—what's the *matter* with this phone? HELLO? HELLO? *(Slams down the receiver) (Scene: She stares at it, tensely.) (The phone rings again. Once. She picks it up.)* Hello? Hello. . . . Oh—for Heaven's sake—who *is* this? Hello. HELLO. *(Slams down receiver. Dials operator.) (Scene: Spotlight comes on left, showing 3rd Operator, at spot vacated by Duffy.)*

3RD OPERATOR: Your call, please?

MRS. STEVENSON: *(Very annoyed and imperious)* Hello. Operator. I don't know what's the matter with this telephone tonight, but it's positively driving me crazy. I've never seen such inefficient, miserable service. Now, look. I'm an invalid, and I'm very nervous, and I'm *not* supposed to be annoyed. But if this keeps on much longer. . . .

3RD OPERATOR: *(A young sweet type)* What seems to be the trouble, madam?

MRS. STEVENSON: Well—everything's wrong. The whole world could be murdered, for all you people care. And now—my phone keeps ringing. . . .

OPERATOR: Yes, madam?

MRS. STEVENSON: Ringing and ringing and ringing every five seconds or so, and when I pick it up, there's no one there.

OPERATOR: I am sorry, madam. If you will hang up, I will test it for you.

MRS. STEVENSON: I don't want you to test it for me. I want you to put through that call—whatever it is—at once.

OPERATOR: *(Gently)* I am afraid that is not possible, madam.

MRS. STEVENSON: *(Storming)* Not possible? And why—may I ask?

OPERATOR: The system is automatic, madam. If someone is trying to dial your number, there is no way to check whether the call is coming through the system or not—unless the person who is trying to reach you complains to his particular operator—

MRS. STEVENSON: Well, of all the stupid, complicated . . . ! And meanwhile *I've* got to sit here in my bed, *suffering* every time that phone rings—imagining everything. . . .

OPERATOR: I will try to check it for you, madam.

MRS. STEVENSON: Check it! Check it! That's all anybody can do. Of all the stupid, idiotic . . . ! *(She hangs up.)* Oh—what's the use. . . . *(Scene: 3rd Operator fades out of spotlight, as instantly Mrs. Stevenson's phone rings again. She picks up receiver. Wildly.)* Hello. HELLO. Stop ringing, do you hear me? Answer me? What do you want? Do you realize you're driving me crazy? *(Scene: Spotlight goes on right. We see a man in eyeshade and shirt-sleeves, at desk with phone and telegrams.)* Stark, staring . . . .

MAN: *(Dull flat voice)* Hello. Is this Plaza 4-2295?

MRS. STEVENSON: *(Catching her breath)* Yes. Yes. This is Plaza 4-2295.

WESTERN UNION: This is Western Union. I have a telegram here for Mrs. Elbert Stevenson. Is there anyone there to receive the message?

MRS. STEVENSON: *(Trying to calm herself)* I am Mrs. Stevenson.

WESTERN UNION: *(Reading flatly)* The telegram is as follows: "Mrs. Elbert Stevenson. 53 North Sutton Place, New York, New York. Darling. Terribly sorry. Tried to get you for last hour, but line busy. Leaving for Boston eleven P.M. tonight on urgent business. Back tomorrow afternoon. Keep happy. Love. Signed. Elbert."

MRS. STEVENSON: *(Breathlessly, aghast, to herself)* Oh . . . no. . . .

WESTERN UNION: That is all, madam. Do you wish us to deliver a copy of the message?

MRS. STEVENSON: No—no, thank you.

WESTERN UNION: Thank you, madam. Good night. *(He hangs up phone.)* *(Scene: Spotlight on Western Union immediately out)*

MRS. STEVENSON: *(Mechanically, to phone)* Good night. *(She hangs up slowly. Suddenly bursting into)* No—no—it isn't true! He couldn't do it! Not when he knows I'll be all alone. It's some trick—some fiendish. . . . *(Scene: We hear sound of train roaring by outside. She half rises in bed, in panic, glaring toward curtains. Her movements are frenzied. She beats with her knuckles on bed, then suddenly stops, and reaches for phone.) (She dials operator.) (Scene: Spotlight picks up 4th Operator, seated left.)*

OPERATOR: *(Coolly)* Your call, please?

MRS. STEVENSON: Operator—try that Murray Hill 4-0098 number for me just once more, please.

OPERATOR: Ringing Murray Hill 4-0098. *(Call goes through. We hear ringing at other end. Ring after ring.) (Scene: If telephone noises are not used audibly, have Operator say after a brief pause: "They do not answer.")*

MRS. STEVENSON: He's gone. Oh—Elbert, how could you? How could you . . . ? *(She hangs up phone, sobbing pityingly to herself, turning restlessly.) (Scene: Spotlight goes out on 4th Operator.)* But I can't be alone tonight. I can't. If I'm alone one more second . . . *(Scene: She runs hands wildly through hair.)* I don't care what he says—or what the expense is—I'm a sick woman—I'm entitled . . . *(Scene: With trembling fingers she picks up receiver again.) (She dials Information.) (Scene: The spotlight picks up Information Operator, seated right.)*

INFORMATION: This is Information.

MRS. STEVENSON: I want the telephone number of Henchley Hospital.

INFORMATION: Henchley Hospital? Do you have the address, madam?

MRS. STEVENSON: No. It's somewhere in the 70's though. It's a very small, private and exclusive hospital where I had my appendix out two years ago. Henchley. H-E-N-C—

INFORMATION: One moment, please.

MRS. STEVENSON: Please—hurry. And please—what *is* the time?

INFORMATION: I do not know, madam. You may find out the time by dialling Meridian 7-1212.

MRS. STEVENSON: *(Irritated)* Oh—for heaven's sake! Couldn't you—?

INFORMATION: The number of Henchley Hospital is Butterfield 7-0105, madam.

MRS. STEVENSON: Butterfield 7-0105. *(She hangs up before she finishes speaking, and immediately dials number as she repeats it.) (Scene: Spotlight goes out on Information.) (Phone rings.) (Scene: Spotlight picks up woman in nurse's uniform, seated at desk, left.)*

WOMAN: *(Middle-aged, solid, firm, practical)* Henchley Hospital, good evening.

MRS. STEVENSON: Nurses' Registry.

WOMAN: Who was it you wished to speak to, please?

MRS. STEVENSON: *(High-handed)* I want the Nurses' Registry at once. I want a trained nurse. I want to hire her immediately. For the night.

WOMAN: I see. And what is the nature of the case, madam?

MRS. STEVENSON: Nerves. I'm very nervous. I need soothing—and companionship. My husband is away—and I'm—

WOMAN: Have you been recommended to us by any doctor in particular, madam?

MRS. STEVENSON: No. But I really don't see why all this catechizing is necessary. I want a trained nurse. I was a patient in your hospital two years ago. And after all, I *do expect to pay* this person—

WOMAN: We quite understand that, madam. But registered nurses are very scarce just now—and our superintendent has asked us to send people out only on cases where the physician in charge feels it is absolutely necessary.

MRS. STEVENSON: *(Growing hysterical)* Well—it *is* absolutely necessary. I'm a sick woman. I—I'm very upset. Very. I'm alone in this house—and I'm an invalid—and tonight I overheard a telephone conversation that upset me dreadfully. About a murder—a poor woman who was going to be murdered at eleven-fifteen tonight—in fact, if someone doesn't come at once—I'm afraid I'll go out of my mind. . . . *(Almost off handle by now)*

WOMAN: *(Calmly)* I see. Well—I'll speak to Miss Philips as soon as she comes in. And what is your name, madam?

MRS. STEVENSON: Miss Phillips. And when do you expect her in?

WOMAN: I really don't know, madam. She went out to supper at eleven o'clock.

MRS. STEVENSON: Eleven o'clock. But it's not eleven yet. *(She cries out.)* Oh, my clock *has* stopped. I thought it was running down. What time is it? *(Scene: Woman glances at wristwatch.)*

WOMAN: Just fourteen minutes past eleven. . . . *(Sound of phone receiver being lifted on same line as Mrs. Stevenson's. A click.)*

MRS. STEVENSON: *(Crying out)* What's *that*?

WOMAN: What was what, madam?

MRS. STEVENSON: That—that click just now—in my own telephone? As though someone had lifted the receiver off the hook of the extension phone downstairs. . . .

WOMAN: I didn't hear it, madam. Now—about this . . .

MRS. STEVENSON: *(Scared)* But I *did.* There's someone in this house. Someone downstairs in the kitchen. And they're listening to me now. They're. . . . *(Scene: She puts hand over her mouth, hangs up phone.) (Scene: She sits there, in terror, frozen, listening.) (In a suffocated voice)* I won't pick it up, I won't let them hear me. I'll be quiet—and they'll think . . . *(With growing terror)* But if I don't call someone now—while they're still down there— there'll be no time. . . . *(She picks up receiver. Bland buzzing signal. She dials operator. Ring twice.) (Scene: On second ring, spotlight goes on right. We see 5th Operator.)*

OPERATOR: *(Fat and lethargic)* Your call, please?

MRS. STEVENSON: *(A desperate whisper)* Operator—I—I'm in desperate trouble . . . I—

OPERATOR: I cannot hear you, madam. Please speak louder.

MRS. STEVENSON: *(Still whispering)* I don't dare. I—there's someone listening. Can you hear me now?

OPERATOR: Your call, please? What number are you calling, madam?

MRS. STEVENSON: *(Desperately)* You've got to hear me. Oh—please. You've got to help me. There's someone in this house. Someone who's going to murder me. And you've got to get in touch with the . . . *(Click of receiver being put down on Mrs. Stevenson's line. Bursting out wildly)* Oh— there it is . . . he's put it down . . . he's coming . . . *(She screams.)* he's coming up the stairs . . . *(Scene: She thrashes in bed, phone cord catching in lamp wire, lamp topples, goes out. Darkness.) (Hoarsely)* Give me the Police Department . . . *(Scene: We see on the dark center stage, the shadow of door opening.) (Screaming)* The police! . . . *(Scene: On stage, swift rush of a shadow, advancing to bed—sound of her voice is choked out, as)*

OPERATOR: Ringing the Police Department. *(Phone is rung. We hear sound of a train beginning to fade in. On second ring, Mrs. Stevenson screams again, but roaring of train drowns out her voice. For a few seconds we hear nothing but roaring of train, then dying away, phone at police headquarters ringing.) (Scene: Spotlight goes on Duffy, left stage.)*

DUFFY: Police Department. Precinct 43. Duffy speaking. *(Pause) (Scene: Nothing visible but darkness on center stage.)* Police Department. Duffy speaking. *(Scene: A flashlight goes on, illuminating open phone to one side of Mrs. Stevenson's bed. Nearby, hanging down, is her lifeless hand. We see the second man, George, in black gloves, reach down and pick up phone. He is breathing hard.)*

GEORGE: Sorry. Wrong number. *(Hangs up) (Scene: He replaces receiver on hook quietly, exits, as Duffy hangs up with a shrug, and Curtain Falls.)*

How Clever?

1. Who contracted for Mrs. Stevenson to be murdered? When did you first suspect this individual?

2. As the detective outside the story, what observations and connections did you make that led you to conclude that it was Mrs. Stevenson who was going to be murdered at 11:15?

3. As the detective outside the story, what observations and connections did you make that led you to your conclusion about who "the client" was who arranged the murder? What do you think the client's motive was for arranging to have Mrs. Stevenson murdered? Why do you think so?

4. How early—exactly where—in the play did you form the correct hypothesis, the one that was confirmed at the end of the play?

5. What are the first three sounds the audience hears in the play? How does each serve as an example of foreshadowing?

6. In your opinion, does the fact that the play opens with Mrs. Stevenson's complaining that she has been dialing Murray Hill 4-0098 for three-quarters of an hour and that the line is always busy serve as an example of foreshadowing? Explain your reasoning.

7. As Mrs. Stevenson overhears the telephone conversation of the two men, how do we know that the first man is not her husband?

8. Did the clicks Mrs. Stevenson heard on the phone line mean that it was definite, possible, or probable that someone had entered her house to murder her? Explain.

9. At what point in the play did you become fairly certain that Mrs. Stevenson's fears were not the hysteria of a lonely and nervous woman with an active imagination? Why at that point?

DETECTWRITE: Setting and Stage Directions

1. Review those stage directions that determine how the stage on which the play is to be performed is divided up and sectioned off, how the stage is populated, and how it is lighted and darkened. After your review, explain why you agree or disagree with the idea that "Sorry, Wrong Number" could work as a film.

2. Based on your review of these same stage directions, explain why "Sorry, Wrong Number," which was originally created as a play for radio, would work well in that medium.

3. How important to the plot is its setting in a large city—in particular, New York City? Consider whether the plot would be effective or believable if a

small town setting were to be substituted for its urban one. How is it ironic that Mrs. Stevenson's desperate attempts to get help from others take place in a city of eight million people?

DETECTWRITE: Plot

1. Which emotions and feelings does the playwright intend for the audience to experience as the plot unfolds?

2. Is the murder more or less horrible because of the fact that it was contracted rather than directly committed? Explain why you feel the way you do.

3. How do we know that Mrs. Stevenson goes to her death never suspecting the reason she was killed?

4. Which details of the plot would have to be revised if this 1948 one-act play were to be updated? Explain. Given the many changes in telephone technology, are there aspects of the plot that would have to be extensively rewritten so that the story remains believable? Explain.

5. Mrs. Stevenson says to Sergeant Duffy that "the coincidence is so horrible." In your opinion, how realistic and believable is the coincidence, the fact that the telephone wires' crossing has enabled Mrs. Stevenson to overhear this particular conversation? Can the playwright count on the audience to "suspend disbelief" so that the story being triggered can be told? Or is Sergeant Duffy on to something when he says to Mrs. Stevenson, "Unless, of course, you have some reason for thinking this call is phony—and that someone may be planning to murder *you*"? Explain your position.

6. How essential is it to the plot that Mrs. Stevenson's wind-up clock has run down and stopped? Explain. In a modern version of the play, what would you as the playwright have done differently to achieve the same effect?

7. When a member of the audience for a play or movie knows or understands something that a character in the show doesn't but really needs to, this situation is known as "dramatic irony." How does "dramatic irony" play an important part in the play "Sorry, Wrong Number"?

8. Sergeant Duffy says to Mrs. Stevenson that "a clue of this kind that's so vague isn't much more use to us than no clue at all." Based on your reading of detective stories, do you agree or disagree with Sergeant Duffy? Explain your position.

DETECTWRITE: Characterization

1. How does Mrs. Stevenson's initial response to the details of the telephone call she overhears put the audience on her side? What else in the play makes her a sympathetic character? In what ways is she an unsympathetic character? Explain.

2. How realistic and believable are the actions and reactions of the various supporting characters in the play that Mrs. Stevenson comes into contact with over the telephone: the six telephone operators, information, the hospital receptionist, Sergeant Duffy? Support your position.

3. Argue in support of the point of view that all of the above minor characters are basically one single major character—one generic or stereotyped "Big City Attitude Person."

4. What actions does Mrs. Stevenson take that work against her getting the help she so desperately wants? Are these actions "in character"? Are they believable to an audience?

5. What other actions might Mrs. Stevenson have taken that would have increased the probability of her life being saved? If some of these more rational actions had been included by the playwright—but Mrs. Stevenson still failed to save herself—would the inclusion of these actions have helped or hurt the impact of the play? Explain why you think the way you do.

DETECTWRITE: Characterization and Stage Directions

1. Review the stage directions that cue the actress who plays the part of Mrs. Stevenson. What is the range of emotion for this character? Which different, yet related, emotions must the actress get into her voice if she is to be convincing in the role? Explain why.

2. Why are Mrs. Stevenson and Sergeant Duffy the only characters to have been given names by the playwright?

3. Write stage directions for the character we have called "Big City Attitude Person." Be certain that these stage directions could be used accurately for all of the minor characters in the play.

DETECTWRITE: Dialogue

Instead of ending with the sound of Mrs. Stevenson's screaming followed and drowned out by the roaring of the train, the play ends with a simple exchange of rather ordinary dialogue. In this context, what do you find particularly effective about the last line of the play? How much of this effectiveness carries over into its use as the play's title? Explain.